The Author...

JOSEPH ALTMAN received his Ph.D. from New York University in 1959. He was a Research Fellow from 1959 to 1960, serving at the College of Physicians and Surgeons, Columbia University. From 1960 to 1961 the author worked as Research Associate at Bellevue Medical Center. During this time he also taught at New York University. Currently, Professor Altman is a member of the Psychology Department at Massachusetts Institute of Technology. He has published several studies relating to the visual system, and to protein and nucleic acid metabolism of the brain under a variety of experimental conditions. A number of papers by Professor Altman have appeared in professional journals.

# ORGANIC
# FOUNDATIONS
# OF
# ANIMAL
# BEHAVIOR

# ORGANIC
# FOUNDATIONS
# OF
# ANIMAL
# BEHAVIOR

**Joseph Altman**
*Massachusetts Institute of Technology*

*HOLT, RINEHART and WINSTON, INC.*

*New York    Chicago    San Francisco    Toronto    London*

*In the wide ocean upon which we venture the possible*
*ways and directions are many; and the same studies*
*which have served for this work might easily, in other*
*hands, not only receive a wholly different treatment*
*and application, but lead also to essentially different*
*conclusions. Such, indeed, is the importance of the*
*subject that it still calls for fresh investigation, and may*
*be studied with advantage from the most varied points*
*of view. Meanwhile we are content if a patient hearing*
*be granted us, and if this book be taken and judged*
*as a whole.*

FROM THE INTRODUCTION, "THE CIVILIZATION
OF THE RENAISSANCE IN ITALY," BY JACOB
BURCKHARDT, TRANSLATED BY
S. G. C. MIDDLEMORE

# Preface

Until the beginning of this century, psychology was generally defined as the science of the mind, that is, of subjective or conscious phenomena, such as feeling, knowing, and willing. So defined, psychology justly occupied a unique and isolated position among the sciences, a mental science (*Geisteswissenschaft*) fundamentally different from the natural sciences (*Naturwissenschaften*). As an aftermath of the Darwinian revolution, this mentalistic conception of psychology gradually gave way to a more objective one, redefined as the science of behavior. A new era for psychology was heralded, as it was now to become a discipline belonging with the other natural sciences.

In the ensuing years, the adoption of rigorous scientific methods and sophisticated techniques of investigation made possible the accumulation of a large body of important facts. However, as a result of a restrictive definition of the subject matter of psychology as the externally observable or peripheral aspects of the organism's interaction with the environment (the so-called stimulus-response approach), psychologists tended to neglect the diverse internal processes which underlie behavior. That behavior is essentially an organic process, serving organic needs and carried out by organic mechanisms, was not sufficiently appreciated, and for a long time psychology remained isolated from the other life sciences.

As a consequence of great discoveries made recently by neurophysiologists and physiological psychologists bearing on the problem of the interrelation of brain and behavior, there has been a great resurgence of interest in the biological approach to psychology. The isolated position of psychology is now fast disappearing, and psychologists more and more collaborate with or adopt the techniques of biochemists, electrophysiologists, neuroanatomists, and endocrinologists in their investigations of the organic bases of behavior.

In agreement with this emerging trend, our view is that psychology, specifically animal psychology, is not an independent scientific discipline but an integral part of the life sciences. If this biologically oriented view of psychology is a correct one, it follows that an understanding of behavioral phenomena presupposes an acquaintance with the facts and theories of biology. But, more important, it obligates us to describe, analyze, and if possible systematize psychological findings in terms of biological concepts and categories, rather than in terms of philosophical ones (which is the traditional approach) or in terms of unrelated physical or mechanical ones (which is a common modern trend).

The book, which is divided into five parts, is organized loosely in a hierarchical manner. The initial sections are concerned with the elementary properties of living matter in general and the behaving organism in particular, and the last sections deal with some of the most complex functional categories of behavior.

Part I is entitled Biological Fundamentals. In it we are concerned, first, with the organizational or system properties of organisms. Following that, the biochemical composition and morphological structure of organisms are briefly reviewed. Finally, an account is given of the basic "vegetative" processes and "animative" activities displayed by plants and animals.

The second part is called Elementary Mechanisms of Animative Action. It deals with the basic properties of receptors, nerves, and muscle, the triad of organs utilized in all types of animal behavior. Then the anatomical organization of the vertebrate nervous system is described in some detail. Finally, as a supplement, a brief description is offered of the various techniques (neuroanatomical, neurophysiological, neurochemical, and pharmacological) used in psychobiological investigations.

In the third part, entitled Neural Control of Animative Action, we present our view of the functional organization of the nervous system. The argument is made, and supported by evidence, that the mammalian nervous system consists of three functional components, acquired in succession during phylogeny, each of which controls a separate class of animal functions. As separate components of the mammalian nervous system we distinguish a (1) spinomedullary, (2) paleocephalic, and (3) neencephalic system of structures. The functions controlled by these three systems are distinguished, respectively, as (1) apsychic maintenance activities, (2) affective catering activities, and (3) cognitive instrumental activities.

The fourth part of the book is called Organization of Interaction with the Environment. Interaction with the environment is dependent, first, on the presence of organized neural schemata of behavior. This is called "central programing," and three types of neural programing of behavior are distinguished: morphogenetic (innate), transactional (acquired), and an intermediate type called epigenetic (imprinted). Second, the adaptive execution of activities is dependent on peripheral, sensory or "afferent steering" mechanisms, which modulate and regulate the various programs of behavior with respect to the prevailing conditions of the environment. Afferent steering makes possible the opportunistic triggering of action programs and the modification of old, and the acquisition of new, action schemata. Finally, useful interaction with the environment necessitates the engagement of the mechanisms of action in the service of the changing needs of the organism. This topic is discussed under the category of "internal motivation" of activities.

In the final, fifth part of the book, called A Functional System of Behavior, four major categories of behavior are distinguished and discussed briefly. These are the economic, reproductive, social, and educational types of behavior. The category of "economic behavior" includes such unitary activities as feeding, drinking, hoarding, sheltering, homing, sleeping, hibernating, and migration. "Reproductive behavior" includes such activities as courtship, nest building, mating, parental-filial interaction, and the like. "Social behavior" includes such agonistic activities as intraspecies defensive or aggressive acts, and various affiliative manifestations. Finally, the term "educational behavior" is used to include such activities as juvenile playing and autochthonous exploratory and manipulatory activities displayed by all higher animals.

This book is not a textbook in the conventional sense of the term, as it attempts to do more than merely provide the student with the facts and theories of modern physiological psychology. In writing this book I attempted to accomplish two things. In addition to providing the reader with an account of the endeavors and accomplishments of modern physiological psychology, I also tried to present an integrated system of animal psychology employing the biological way of thinking and utilizing, wherever possible, biological principles of explanation. This mode of presentation has its advantages and disadvantages. The obvious advantage is that the student is not asked merely to memorize a large body of apparently unrelated facts, culled from a variety of disciplines, but is also provided with unifying principles and a framework to aid him in the organization of the material. The most obvious disadvantage of such an approach is the unavoidable bias in selecting data that support the theses presented, and of interpreting experimental findings in terms of set systematic preconceptions and categories.

The writing of this book, in its various versions, has taken me over a decade. Throughout this period I had the enthusiastic support of my wife, Elizabeth Conklin Altman, to whom I am most deeply indebted. In addition to her domestic role, she has been for years actively collaborating in various aspects of our research efforts.

I wish to thank also Dr. Hans-Lukas Teuber and Dr. Gopal Das for a long academic association, and Drs. Ronald Melzack, Patrick Wall, and Wayne Wickelgren for reading parts of an earlier version of this book and offering helpful suggestions. I am particularly indebted to Dr. F. Nowell Jones, who meticulously scrutinized the entire manuscript and brought to my notice many errors of fact and interpretation. Finally, I wish to express my thanks for editorial assistance to Mrs. Ruth Evans, Mrs. Virginia Hanson, and Mrs. Renate Stebbins. During preparation of this manuscript aid was received from a grant of The Commonwealth Fund to Dr. H.-L. Teuber, Department of Psychology, Massachusetts Institute of Technology.

JOSEPH ALTMAN

*Cambridge, Massachusetts*
*January 1966*

# Contents

## V  A FUNCTIONAL SYSTEM OF BEHAVIOR

PART I

# BIOLOGICAL
# FUNDAMENTALS

# 1

# Organization in
# the Living World

As complex material systems, organisms may be subdivided into component elements of descending complexity. Multicellular organisms can be articulated into organ systems, organs, tissues and cells; cells (or acellular organisms) can be further decomposed into subcellular organelles, biotic macromolecules, organic and inorganic compounds, and, finally, into atoms. This approach, which is referred to as the analytic or reductionistic method, can provide us with information about the structure and material constitution of organisms. The accumulation of data by means of this indispensable scientific procedure is not, however, by itself, sufficient for the understanding of the nature of organisms, because organisms represent more, and are different from, mere aggregates of their elementary constituents. Just as we cannot form an adequate picture of the nature of a complex machine from an inventory of the screws, gears, rods, plates, buttons, and the like used in its construction but must, in addition, have a blueprint of its design and know the function it was built for, so also, in studying the organism, it is essential that we determine the mode of interaction and system of organization of the constituent elements in the organism as a whole. Moreover, organisms display organizational properties not seen in inanimate constructions. First, organisms, unlike man-made machines, are not formed by an additive process, in which the components are linked with one another by such static agents as hooks, screws, or cement. Instead, organisms unfold and grow in a unique manner seldom if ever seen in the inorganic world. Second, even cursory observation of organic existence reveals several novel characteristics that are not seen in the inorganic world and that cannot be interpreted as simple functions of its composing elements.

We are, of course, referring here to the phenomena usually subsumed under the word "living." For the present, we may define as fundamental living phenomena the following three manifestations of organisms: self-maintenance, self-reproduction, and adaptive self-regulation. Briefly, *self-maintenance* refers to the ability of organisms to acquire matter and energy from their surroundings for building, energizing, and repairing their systems. *Self-reproduction* refers to the ability of organisms to reproduce their systems by a unique duplicative process. Finally, *adaptive self-regulation* connotes the ability of organisms to adjust themselves (to varying degrees) to diverse and changing external conditions.

Obviously, organisms represent something new and different from their constituting elements, and the place of living things in the general order of nature has been a fundamental problem of ancient and modern philosophy, and also of modern natural science. Is the relation between nonliving and living matter of a continuous nature, in the sense that the differences between them are attributable merely to a gradual growth in the complexity of organization of the same fundamental particles or forces? Or is there a discontinuity between these two realms of nature, in the sense that additional supernatural principles, such as a "soul" or "spirit," need to be postulated to explain life and organic phenomena? Or is the relation one of partial continuity and discontinuity, in the sense that new "emergent" phenomena appear when we pass from one level of organization to the other? Further, are biological phenomena determined strictly in accordance with the principle of causality, or are the organizing forces of living systems of a goal-seeking or teleologic nature?

In the following pages of this chapter we shall discuss these and several other related questions in an effort to present a picture, though clearly a tentative one, of the place of living things in the order of nature, and of some of the essential characteristics of the organization of living systems. We shall first briefly discuss some of the older philosophical attempts concerned with these problems, the formulations of *mechanism* and *vitalism*. These will be followed by a description of a more recent attempt, known under the name of *organismic* theory. As an elaboration of the latter concept, we shall then deal with some modern ideas developed by the *cybernetic* schools concerning the organization of artificial and natural systems. These latter attempts are aimed at describing the logical and mathematical properties of dynamic self-regulating systems, systems which manifest self-stabilizing and goal-seeking properties in many respects similar to those seen in living organisms. In this connection we shall try to point out some of the similarities as well as differences among natural inorganic systems, self-regulating machines, and living organisms, and shall briefly discuss the theoretical implications of the conception of living organisms that is presented.

**The Mechanistic Viewpoint**  The simplest and most parsimonious explanation of the nature of living things would be through derivation from the principles of inanimate matter. Because basically organisms are composed of inorganic substances and after a shorter or longer period of existence become decomposed into inanimate matter, should we not explain the intermediate living "episode" in terms of physicochemical principles? The attempt to do so may be associated with the mechanistic viewpoint, which presupposes that only physical matter has real existence and that all natural phenomena, from the simplest to the most complex, can or should be explained by the laws of matter, specifically the laws of mechanics.

The mechanistic philosophy of nature, which had its antecedents in the speculative atomic theory of Democritos, became particularly popular in the seventeenth century as a consequence of the development of Newtonian mechanics, and it remained largely the philosophical foundation of modern natural science until the beginning of this century. Newton's law of inertia and law of force (which state that a body will remain at rest or move at a constant speed in a straight line unless acted on by an external force, a condition in which its acceleration or deflection will be inversely proportional to its mass) permitted exact mathematical quantification of a great variety of natural phenomena. These included such macrocosmic events as the movements of planets around the sun and such earthly events as the motion of falling bodies; the laws could also be applied, as was demonstrated later, to microcosmic processes, such as the behavior of atoms and molecules in a gas. These mechanical laws also found wide and successful applications in modern engineering. Thus Newtonian mechanics provided natural scientists with a set of principles that apparently had universal validity. The hypothesis was therefore developed that nature is a material system whose constituents, whether stars or atoms, behave entirely in accordance with the principles of classical mechanics. Indeed, Laplace later suggested that an omniscient spirit (one who would know the mass, position, and velocity of all objects at a given time, and would be endowed with the ability to perform all the necessary calculations) could predict and determine all future events.

If all events in nature are determined strictly in accordance with the causal laws of mechanics, mechanical principles, by implication, should apply not only to inanimate processes but also to living phenomena. But can the quantitative principles of mechanics account for the various, qualitatively new phenomena that one observes in the living world? That quantitative variations in the mechanical interaction of particles can lead to qualitative changes is well established. An example is the kinetic theory of the gaseous, liquid, and solid phases of all matter. These three states are, to all appearances, qualitatively different from one another, because new mechanical, electrical, chemical, thermal, and other properties arise as matter passes from one phase to another. But these phenomena found a relatively simple explanation with the assumption that the cohesive forces which tend to tie atoms and molecules to one another can be counteracted by quantitative variations in their random motion or kinetic energy. In the gaseous phase molecules move about with such high velocities that their momentum is not sufficiently counteracted by the cohesive forces; the dissociated molecules therefore travel afar, and the gas expands and occupies all available space. The transition to the liquid phase is marked by a decrease in the kinetic energy of molecules, which can still move about with relation to one another (a liquid easily changes its shape) but cannot leave the aggregate altogether. If the kinetic energy of the material is further reduced, the cohesive forces become prepotent, and the atoms or molecules arrange themselves to form regular crystalline lattices, with the result that the substance assumes a stable, solid state.

Thus, in principle, qualitative transformations (the emergence of new physical and chemical properties) are possible as a consequence of quantitative variations of some parameters. Could the radical transformation from the inanimate to the living state be similarly explained in mechanistic terms? The idea that the properties of living things can, or at least should, be derived from physicochemical principles was widely held among biologists toward the end of the nineteenth century. However, owing to new developments at the beginning of the twentieth century in two diverse areas, atomic physics and the emerging self-conscious modern biology, the mechanistic philosophy in general, and its application to biological phenomena in particular, have largely been abandoned.

CRITICISMS OF THE MECHANISTIC VIEWPOINT. For a long time scientists have been aware of various physical phenomena that do not behave strictly in accordance with the laws of mechanics. In gravity, for instance, we have a force that acts over great distances in space, a mode of action that is not easy to reconcile with the mechanical conception of transfer of energy from one body to another through contact. (The assumption was made later that the effects of gravity are transmitted by a hypothetical medium, called ether, which was thought to fill all spaces not occupied by matter. But all attempts to demonstrate the existence of such a medium were negative, and it is generally accepted now that this medium, as originally conceived, cannot exist.) A similar difficulty arose with the interpretation of the nature of light. Originally, Newton conceived light to be composed of fine particles (referred to as the corpuscular theory), and he sought to explain various optical phenomena in mechanical terms. The wave theory of his contemporary, Huyghens, was neglected for a long time, until experiments with light interference brought clear evidence of the undulatory character of light. Then investigations of electrical and magnetic phenomena led to the development by Maxwell of the electromagnetic theory, which implied that a large class of physical phenomena can be conceived of as dynamic field events rather than static mechanical events.

These were the early signs of the inadequacy of the mechanistic conception as an explanation of *all* physical phenomena. Then further complications arose at the beginning of the twentieth century. Planck showed that light also has particulate characteristics, because electromagnetic energy is delivered in a discontinuous fashion in quantal units. Einstein proposed the equivalence of matter and energy, and Einstein's hypothesis that light is subject to the effects of gravitation was later confirmed. Rutherford's quasi-mechanistic model of atoms, in which electrons rotate around the nucleus in a manner resembling the rotation of the planets around the sun, was replaced by Bohr's model, in which electrons are restricted to rotate in selective quantal orbits. Then de Broglie proposed that the existence of selected quantal orbits can be explained if it is assumed that electrons also have wave properties, a suggestion soon confirmed experimentally and elaborated on mathematically by Schrödinger, Born, and others. Thus a new conception arose in which electromagnetic waves acquired material properties and matter could be characterized as packets or condensation of energy. In modern nuclear physics the concept of the equivalence of matter and energy is taken for granted, and the original idea of atoms behaving like billiard balls according to the laws of mechanics has been abandoned. Admittedly, no clear picture has so far emerged about the ultimate nature of matter and energy, but the inaccuracy of the old mechanistic world-picture is clearly established.

Another attack on mechanistic philosophy came from a different source, namely, biology. This criticism was not concerned with the validity of mechanistic interpretations of physical phenomena, but rather with the feasibility of explaining certain biological processes in terms of mechanistic principles. An important aspect of the mechanistic interpretation of natural events, which we have not considered so far, is the negation of the operation of teleological or purposive forces in nature. In opposition to the animistic or anthropomorphic mode of thinking, which attributes the occurrence of various natural events to desires, aims, or plans (which was prevalent in medieval science and philosophy), a basic axiom of mechanistic philosophy and of modern science is that present events are always determined by antecedent events and that they cannot be determined by goals or future end-states. The consideration of present events as means toward future ends or goals is considered a "teleological fallacy." Many biologists, however, came to doubt whether various, apparently future-oriented and goal-seeking organic processes could be determined exclusively by antecedent causal events.

The everyday conception of causality is based on the regularity of association between two events. If an event C is repeatedly followed by another event E, then E is considered to be caused by, or to be the effect of, C. Causal association is usually considered to be asymmetrical: the subsequent event E cannot be the cause of antecedent event C. If the association between two events is random, the connection between them is attributed to chance. The principle of causality implies that when a causal relation has been established, the presence of the cause makes the

subsequent occurrence of the effect imperative or probable and that therefore one can predict future events from past or present events. This of
course is the foundation of modern predictive sciences, which have sought
to identify such regular relations in nature in order to forecast events
(some sciences are reconstructive, for example, paleontology and arche-
ology).

The biological criticism we referred to took issue with the possibility of
conceiving of such end-directed activities as self-maintenance or adaptive
self-regulation, and such future-oriented processes as reproduction and
development, in terms of past-determined causal principles. Strict ad-
herence to the principle of causality would imply that the teleological
appearance of these phenomena is an illusion and that therefore, when an
organism, for instance, feeds itself, the "goal" of replenishing its losses
cannot be considered a variable that enters into the process.

**The Vitalistic Viewpoint**   The inadequacy of mechanistic explanations of life phenomena was
stressed by Aristotle, who proposed a vitalistic philosophy. According to
the Aristotelian viewpoint, the organism as a structure is machinelike, and
as such it resembles other material objects, but its construction and operation are attributable to the intervention of an immaterial force or purposive
agent, the soul. This dualistic solution (the separation of mind and body)
was very popular during the Middle Ages, but beginning with the
seventeenth century the monistic, mechanistic viewpoint became more
and more dominant. The difference in these two philosophies is exemplified by the embryological controversy between the preformationists and
epigeneticists. The *preformationists* asserted that all the properties of the
organism are present in the germ cell, and that development consists
merely of the growth and unfolding of preformed traits. This explanation
was essentially a mechanistic one, which saw little more than physicochemical growth in embryogenesis. The *epigeneticists*, in contrast, viewed
embryonic development as a "creative" process in which living structures
are produced from unlike inorganic components.

With the discovery of chromosomes as particulate genetic determinants,
the weight of evidence appeared to favor a modified preformationist theory
(as exemplified by Weismann's and Roux's *Entwicklungsmechanik*).
Then, at the beginning of the twentieth century, the embryologist Driesch
claimed to have produced incontrovertible evidence that the deterministic,
preformationist explanation of embryological processes is incorrect. Driesch
found that if he cut a sea-urchin egg into two, or fused two eggs into one,
the half or double egg could produce a normal embryo, indicating that the
egg had self-organizing properties transcending the effects of the particulate
determinants in the egg. That is, a normal end-state (whole embryo) was
achieved irrespective of what the initial material conditions (half or

double egg) were. A movement arose under the name of vitalism, which claimed that life processes cannot be explained without postulating the operation of supernatural organizing forces such as the soul, *entelechy*, *élan vital*, and the like.

CRITICISM OF THE VITALISTIC VIEWPOINT. That the vitalists had an argument cannot be denied. Self-organization and the pursuance of end-states are obviously the most characteristic and important properties of living organisms. To conceive, as did most mechanists in the nineteenth century, of organisms as random aggregates or machines that have accidentally acquired such properties is naive. On the other hand, Driesch's conclusion that evidence of self-organization in organic processes proves the involvement of supernatural organizing forces does not necessarily follow. Driesch failed to provide evidence of the existence or mode of operation of these animistic agents in embryonic development; it is entirely nebulous how these forces are generated and how they can affect material events. Moreover, the history of modern science has taught us that explanations in terms of supernatural forces have no heuristic value; such explanations compete with the scientific endeavor of assiduous seeking for empirically established relations among natural phenomena. It is therefore justifiable to conclude that the type of "explanation" offered by vitalists has no valid place in the natural sciences and has to be relegated to the domain of metaphysics.

**The Organismic and Cybernetic Viewpoints** If neither the mechanistic nor the vitalistic explanations of life processes can be considered valid, what other explanations are possible? In reaction to both mechanism (which tried to deny the goal-pursuing character of organic processes) and vitalism (which resorted to supernatural explanation), at the beginning of this century a new movement arose that became known under various names, such as emergent evolution, holism, and, more generally, the organismic approach (Haldane, 1935; Goldstein, 1939; Russell, 1945; von Bertalanffy, 1951; and others). The purpose of this movement was to stress the teleological or directive character of organic activities and to try to explain it, without resort to supernatural or psychic causation, in naturalistic terms. As Russell stated, "We must regard directiveness as an attribute not of mind but of life" (1945, p. 179). The attempt of organismic biologists, which remained largely a program rather than an accomplishment, has been further advanced recently by advocates of the cybernetic viewpoint introduced by Wiener (1948).

The *organismic* conception is allied with the dynamic world view developed by modern physics in this century. Physical and chemical associations are no longer considered to be products of random aggregation of static elementary particles, but rather the results of dynamic interactions among electromagnetically charged constituents. The corollary of this viewpoint is that, in order to understand the properties of atoms or molecules it is not sufficient to study their elementary properties; we must also investigate the mode of organization of their constituent elements within the integrated system of the whole. Correspondingly, in the investigation of living processes it becomes essential that the analytic procedure be supplemented by investigations of the system character of the organism and its processes. The organism, in this view, is a superordinate system in which the various constituents (atoms, molecules, macromolecules, and subcellular organelles) are in a process of complex, mutual interaction and therefore in a state of interdependence. What the elements contribute to the whole depends not only on their individual properties but also on the role they assume within the organized whole.

**Artificial and Natural Systems**   In attempting to describe the organizational characteristics of organisms, let us briefly consider the properties of some familiar artificial and natural systems. Perhaps the simplest example of a system is a house, in which various elements (bricks, cement, timber, glass, and the like) are put together according to a plan to form a unified structure. Chairs, tables, bridges, dams, and the like, would be other examples. Such constructions may be characterized as *passive and closed static systems:* "passive" because they are designed to remain in a resting state, "static" because their component elements are inert substances tied together with the aid of static forces. From another point of view, such static systems may also be described as "closed systems," because they are "complete" and can exist, without exchange of matter and energy, in their environments. Related to such static systems is another class of constructions, namely, machines. Machines, such as steam engines, may be characterized as *work-producing and open static systems.* They are considered static systems because their component elements (steam vessel, pistons, levers) are composed of inert materials and united by static forces, and they are characterized as "open systems" because they cannot function in isolation, that is, perform work without being provided from the outside with kinetic energy, fuel, raw materials, and the like. As another important characteristic, both passive and working static systems or constructions may be identified as *externally organized systems,* insofar as they are designed, assembled, and directed by external agents (architects, engineers, workers).

Such artificial systems differ from natural units, such as atoms, molecules, or the organism, because the latter are formed of active or charged components and are organized by intrinsic forces. These natural systems may therefore be distinguished from the man-made static systems and classified as *dynamic systems.* In atoms, for instance, negatively charged electrons are attracted by, and rotate around, positively charged atomic nuclei, and the lasting dynamic equilibrium is maintained through interaction among the component charged elements. Dynamic systems represent integrated wholes in which the attractive and repulsive forces of the participating constituents attain a state of equilibrium. Accordingly, the organization of dynamic systems or integrates is largely dependent on intrinsic forces rather than on external agents (as is true of constructions), and they may therefore be described as *self-organizing systems*. Dynamic systems may also be distinguished either as closed or open systems. Atoms may be considered *closed dynamic systems*, for the reason that the maintenance of their equilibrium does not require energy input from the outside. By definition, closed equilibric systems cannot perform work, because energy input or output will alter their state of equilibrium; indeed, their integrity is best maintained by isolation from their environment. In contrast, the maintenance of equilibrium in *open dynamic systems* depends on exchange of matter and energy with the surrounding medium. It will be obvious that the best example of an open dynamic system is the *living organism*, which can produce work at the expense of matter and energy obtained from its environment. The maintenance of the integrity of open systems requires continual adjustments in the material composition and energy level of the system; the adjustments are accomplished with the aid of *feedback devices* that have become familiar recently as components of modern self-regulating machines.

Accordingly, organisms have dual properties: they resemble natural systems, such as atoms, insofar as they are dynamic entities, but they also resemble machines, because they are work-producing open systems and are equipped with self-regulatory devices. To clarify the machinelike properties of organisms let us, for a moment, consider the system character of various machines. Machines are constructed to perform work, that is, transform energy or matter of one form (say, thermal or electric energy, or raw materials) into energy or matter of another, predetermined form. The simplest machine is one that we may describe as an *unregulated machine*. The output of an unregulated machine is dependent on the level of input; it therefore cannot produce a stabilized output. An example would be a primitive steam engine, the steam output of which is a function of the amount of wood or coal burned. A more useful machine is one that, within limits, can provide a constant output. This goal is achieved by the addition of controls, such as chokes or valves, with which the rate of burning or steam output can be controlled. Such a machine may be described as a manually or *externally regulated machine*, because output is dependent on the control operations of an external agent. A machine of even better design may be equipped with a feedback loop in such a way that some of the energy of the output is fed back to a control device to regulate the input, with the result that the machine itself controls its own output. A classical example of such a *self-regulating machine* is the steam engine designed by Watts, which was equipped with a "governor" to control steam output.

Self-regulating machines can deliver stabilized output as a consequence of negative feedback. The term *negative feedback* implies that the return loop is connected in such a fashion that when the level of output increases, the input is proportionally decreased, and *vice versa.* (Positive feedback would produce either continual acceleration or deceleration, making the machine run away with itself or come to a standstill.) A common example of a modern feedback system is a thermostat, which, set at a fixed value, opens or closes the steam valve when the ambient temperature falls or rises above the set level. In simpler feedback mechanisms energy from the output has to be diverted into the feedback loop, whereas in modern electrical and electronic feedback devices (which employ rectifiers, amplifiers, and relays) the original feedback energy may be negligible, it has only to meet the requirement of transmitting the necessary information from the output end to the regulating servomechanisms.

Mechanisms employing negative feedback represent *self-stabilizing systems*, because their accomplishment is the maintenance of steady-state and stabilized output. Recently more complicated servomechanisms have been devised (composed of scanning and receptor mechanisms, coding and encoding devices, memory units, and computers) that make it possible for a machine to pursue an object or end. Such a mechanism may be considered a *goal-guided system*, because it is set in motion by the appearance of a target and its behavior is adaptively controlled by the movements of the goal object. Theoretically, an even more complex mechanism could be devised, one that would start on a scouting mission by randomly moving about, begin to pursue the target object as soon as its "image" is projected on its receptors, pursue the object for a set period of time or a set distance, then retrace its movements, as determined by its memory device, and return to its home base. Such an apparatus could justifiably be described as a *goal-seeking system*, resembling in many ways the goal-seeking behavior manifested by organisms, as when a hungry animal sets out foraging for food and begins its pursuit action when the prey is located.

**System Properties of the Organism**    Insofar as organisms have machine-like properties, they are best characterized as self-regulating mechanisms that are endowed with all the control properties described, namely, homeostatic self-stabilization, and the manifestation of goal-guided and goal-seeking behavior. But organisms are in other respects unlike machines, because they are not static constructions but dynamic integrates. Among the many differential characteristics of machines and organisms we may consider the following.

1. Machines are composed of stable, permanent, and static constituents (metal shafts, levers, gears, wheels, and the like), as opposed to organisms, which are composed of unstable, transient and dynamic constituents (tissues and cells that, like the subcellular elements they are composed of, are in a continual state of change and turnover).

2. Machines are formed, assembled and repaired by extrinsic agents (engineers and workers), whereas organisms are produced and serviced by intrinsic forces (morphogenetic growth and self-regeneration).

3. Finally, in machines structure and functioning are separable insofar as the latter requires energization from an external source (addition of fuel, electric connections, and so on), in contrast to organisms in which structure and function are inseparable.

The important common denominator of these differences is that machines, whether or not they are equipped with self-regulating devices, are ultimately externally organized systems, whereas organisms, like other natural integrates, are strictly self-organizing systems. But the self-organization of organisms implies much more than the self-organization of simpler closed dynamic systems, such as atoms and molecules, in that complex feedback and servomechanisms are required to maintain their flux steady-state. The dynamic self-maintenance of organisms implies a continual self-regenerative process, which, as we shall see later, may be attributed to the presence of coded "programs" or "blueprints" in the form of various self-duplicating macromolecules in every cell of the body.

Is it possible to explain these unique organic properties in naturalistic terms? Ever since various inanimate self-regulating devices have become familiar, the vitalists have lost the argument that the self-regulatory properties of organisms indicate the operation of a supernatural organizing force. We can similarly reject the other vitalist argument, namely, that the existence of such organic mechanisms at least implies an original designer or constructor, because we no longer look on the organism as a construction (that is, a static system built by an external agent) but rather as a self-organizing dynamic system. However, the problem still remains: How could such complex self-organizing systems come about "spontaneously" through the operation of natural forces? We cannot at present answer the question in definitive terms; we may say, though, that a promising picture has begun to emerge in vague outlines. The emerging view of the origin of living systems lay emphasis on at least three considerations. First, it stresses the role of two complex groups of chemicals, nucleic acids and proteins, in the organization of basic life processes.

Second, it attaches great importance to the evolutionary origin, or historicity, of the development of genetic "programs" for the execution of life processes. Finally, it views the evolution of adaptive life processes, including behavior, as a function of the acquisition of ever-improving homeostatic and teleological servomechanisms within the organism.

**Reconciliation of**   The historical character of organ-
**Causality and Teleology**   isms is of great importance for the
understanding of the teleological aspects of organic existence and functioning. Mechanists in the last century embraced Darwin's theory of evolution as a basis for the causal explanation of the apparently teleological character of organic structure and function. The theory of evolution states that, owing to ecological limitations, organisms have to "struggle for existence," a circumstance that leads to "natural selection" and "survival of the fittest." Random variations have thus led to the creation of adaptive structures and functions. However, opponents of this interpretation have pointed out that the theory, as formulated by Darwin, already recognizes the teleological character of organisms by postulating that they struggle for their existence. This argument, we believe, no longer holds if we accept the viewpoint that all dynamic systems, organic and inorganic, "struggle for their existence." As we stated earlier, dynamic systems are assembled and maintained by the operation of complementary, intrinsic forces; therefore, by virtue of the operation of such forces, they resist interference with their state of equilibrium and "struggle" to reinstate it when it is disturbed.

The historicity of organisms implies, from the phylogenetic point of view, that ample time was at the disposal of organisms to assume multitudinous forms as a result of genetic variations and mutations (which are now attributed to minor or major rearrangements in the nucleic acid codes). As a consequence, organic forms came into existence in the course of time, with better and better adapted self-regulatory devices. The concept of historicity also implies, from the ontogenetic point of view, that the teleological character of organisms (which develop adaptive organs before they have an opportunity to function, and pursue ends that they have never before encountered) can be attributed to the possession of inherited, coded blueprints in the germ cells, which guide the growth and many of the mature activities of the organism without conscious planning or foresight.

The preadaptations of the organism and the adaptive guidance of many of its operations are made possible by information collected and stored in the germ cell throughout millions and billions of years of prior existence. Accordingly, the modern concept of teleology no longer connotes the intervention of conscious, purposive agents or forces in the goal-guided and goal-seeking activites of organisms; it merely presupposes the operation of genetically transmitted, built-in programs of action, in individuals of surviving and therefore well-adapted organic species. The future-oriented activities of organisms are causal products of antecedent events, namely, of "programs" or "blueprints" stored in coded form in the constituent cells. It was only at the latest stages of organic evolution, as in higher animals, that additional teleological devices have evolved, and individual experience and conscious planning have become auxiliary teleological guides of organic behavior.

**Hierarchic Levels and Types of Explanation** The dynamic viewpoint presented here is associated with the concept of *hierarchic levels* in Nature and with the notion of *emergence* of new qualitative properties as we pass from one level to another. Although all objects in Nature are composed of the same ultimate particles and forces, qualitatively distinct levels and properties emerge as we proceed from subatomic elements to atoms, from atoms to molecules, from molecules to organic macromolecules, from macromolecules to subcellular units, from subcellular units to organisms, and, at a still higher level, from individual organisms to social groups. The emergence of new properties with ever-increasing complexity may be attributed to the fact that whenever mutually attractive or equilibrium-seeking, electromagnetically charged elements become organized into balanced wholes of a higher level, the organizational transformations involved produce qualitatively new phenomena. There is nothing mystical or unnatural about these emergent transformations, we have only to remember that the integrative organization of dynamic systems differs from the mechanical, additive organization of constructions by representing interactive and therefore transfigurative processes. To quote a recent exponent of this view:

The concept of integrative levels of organization is a general description of the evolution of matter through successive and higher orders of complexity and integration. It views the development of matter, from the cosmological changes resulting in the formation of the earth to the social changes in society, as continuous because it is never-ending, and as discontinuous because it passes through a series of different levels of organization—physical, chemical, biological and sociological.

   In the continual evolution of matter new levels of complexity are superimposed on the individual units by the organization and integration of these units into a single system. What were wholes on one level become parts on a higher one. Each level of organization possesses unique properties of structure and behavior which, though dependent on the properties of the constituent elements, appear only when these elements are combined in the new system. (Novikoff, 1945, p. 209)

The concept of emergent, hierarchic levels has important methodological consequences. Logically, three major methods of scientific investigations are possible: (1) the analytical or reductionistic (lower level); (2) the correlative or comparative (same level); and (3) the teleological or functional (higher level). These three methods represent attempts to explain or answer the questions on (1) what things are made of, (2) what their characteristic properties are, and (3) what ends they serve.

The most successful experimental procedure employed in the natural sciences is the *analytical* or *reductionist method*, which articulates objects or events into their component elements and, this accomplished, "explains" their nature in terms of the properties of the elements composing them. The explanation of the properties of chemical compounds in terms of the properties of constituent atoms is an example from the physical sciences. The analysis of organic phenomena as atomic or molecular processes by means of biophysical and biochemical techniques is an example from the biological sciences. The attempt to explain complex behavioral phenomena in terms of neural circuits (reflexes) and modifications in these circuits (conditioned reflexes) are examples of the reductionist method in psychology. The analytical method of lower-level articulation has been very successful and will no doubt continue to provide important data concerning the elementary properties of natural phenomena. However, if we accept the proposition that as a result of dynamic integrative organization various hierarchic levels exist in nature (as Novikoff expressed it, "What are wholes on one level become parts on a higher one"), then, in order to achieve complete understanding of transfigurative dynamic phenomena, we cannot pursue exclusively the analytical or reductionist technique.

The *correlative* or *comparative method* is the attempt to describe, catalogue, and establish relations among same-level phenomena without recourse to analytic procedures. In all fields of inquiry there are facts, problems, techniques and concepts that can be dealt with profitably without relating them to other phenomena. If we are studying, for instance, the properties of chemical compounds, we may gather useful information by comparing their characteristics in terms of shared attributes, such as the chemical reactions they undergo, their melting and boiling points, their solubility, and so forth, without actually inquiring into the nature of these properties. Or we may study the problems of hereditary transmission in various species and establish the laws of heredity without simultaneously inquiring into the physicochemical basis of genetic transmisson. Or we may investigate the interrelation of various behavioral phenomena, such as the effects of different "schedules of reinforcement" on the acquisition of new behavior patterns without reference to circuits in the nervous system; in fact, without reference altogether to the physio-

logical properties of the organism. Historically, this method has been very successful in the early phases of the development of the various sciences because it is well suited to providing raw data unencumbered by considerations borrowed from other sciences.

But in terms of the preceding considerations the analytic and correlative methods are not sufficient for the complete elucidation of natural phenomena. We must also practice the *teleological* or *functional method*, which is concerned with the system properties of organized units, that is, the mode of transformation of simpler elements into more complex wholes. The important consequence of this consideration with respect to our investigation is that we cannot satisfy ourselves by merely analyzing organic and behavioral events with biophysical and biochemical techniques (this is the conventional approach of physiology and physiological psychology). Nor can we content ourselves with establishing behavioral and psychological laws by studying such phenomena in isolation from the organism and its teleological endeavors (the approach of behaviorism and traditional structural psychology). The organism with its behavioral repertoire represents a unique set of phenomena that is more than proteins and nucleic acids, neurons and reflex arcs, sensation and learning. Explanations of organic and behavioral phenomena in terms of "nothing more than" some other more elementary or simpler phenomena must remain inadequate and may, in many cases, be patently false. Such questions as the goal and function of organic processes not only are legitimate scientific problems but are, in fact, indispensable in biological investigations.

Accordingly, we shall try to deal in this study, first, with the elementary structure and properties of organisms, as established by analytical biophysical and biochemical investigations. We shall also pay due attention to various unique phenomena manifested by living organisms in general and animals in particular, as established by biological and behavioral methods of inquiry. Finally, we shall attempt to present a systematic picture of the organization of behavior, to the extent that such a task is possible at the present stage of the development of the behavioral sciences.

### SELECTED READINGS

Bertalanffy, L. von. *Problems of life*. New York: Wiley, 1952.

Blum, H. F. *Time's arrow and evolution*. Princeton, N.J.: Princeton University Press, 1951.

Bohm, D. *Causality and chance in modern physics*. Princeton, N.J.: Van Nostrand, 1957.

Driesch, H. *Science and philosophy of the organism*. London: A. & C. Black, 1908.

Frank, P. Philosophy of science. Englewood Cliffs, N.J.: Prentice-Hall, 1957.
Oparin, A. I. The origin of life. (3d ed.) New York: Academic Press, Inc.,
    1957.
Reichenbach, H. The rise of scientific philosophy. Berkeley: University of Cali-
    fornia Press, 1951.
Russell, E. S. The directiveness of organic activities. London: Cambridge, 1945.
Sommerhoff, G. Analytical biology. New York: Oxford, 1950.
Wiener, N. Cybernetics. New York: Wiley, 1948.

# 2

# Elementary Constituents of Organisms

Organisms are composed of organ systems, organs, tissues, cells, and subcellular organelles, and these living components can be articulated into macromolecules, organic and inorganic molecules, and, finally, into atoms. The properties of organisms are, to a certain extent, products of the properties of their organic constituents, which in turn are undoubtedly dependent on the properties of their physical and chemical components. It is not our task to deal here in detail with the great wealth of biophysical, biochemical, and biological studies that are relevant to an understanding of organic structure and function, though familiarity with these findings is an absolute prerequisite to an understanding of the organic foundations of behavior. In the following pages we shall provide merely a brief outline of the most essential findings regarding the elementary composition of organisms.

**Inorganic Constituents** The total atomic decomposition of organic substance reveals the presence of several dozen elements in both plant and animal tissue. Some of these atomic elements are present in large proportions; others can be detected in traces only. In the human body, which is rather typical in composition if compared with other higher animals, the distribution of these elements by percentage is as follows: oxygen 65, carbon 18.5, hydrogen 9.5, and nitrogen 3.3. The other elements present in comparatively large amounts are calcium 1.5, phosphorus 1, potassium 0.35, sulphur 0.25, chlorine 0.2, sodium 0.15, and magnesium 0.05. Iron, iodine, zinc, fluorine, and some other elements are found in traces only. Of these elements, four compose the bulk of all organic systems: oxygen, hydrogen, carbon, and nitrogen. What do these atomic constituents contribute to the structure and functions of the living system?

It is quite possible, as Henderson (1913) suggested some time ago, that the origin and existence of organisms are at least to some extent attributable

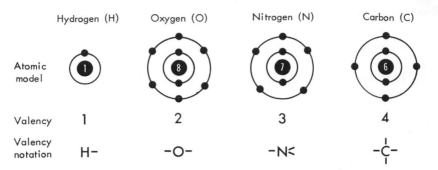

The four most abundant elements of organic matter. The atomic numbers of the elements, corresponding to the positive charge of the nucleus, are indicated inside the larger circle in the center. Smaller circles around the nucleus represent the extranuclear electrons of the atoms.

to the fortuitous "fitness" of these four elements for organic functions. These elements are all present in great abundance on the surface of the earth in atomic or compounded form, both in the atmosphere and the hydrosphere. The first two, hydrogen and oxygen, are essential components both as independent atoms and as the elements of that essential chemical compound, water. In atomic form, hydrogen and oxygen are important, as we shall see later, in all metabolic functions as the main mediators of oxidative-reductive processes in organic energy exchanges. The inorganic product of hydrogen and oxygen, water, is the most abundant of all the compounds within organisms. In temporarily inactive organisms, as in dormant seeds or dry spores, the water concentration may be very low. Also in inactive parts of the body, such as the bark of trees or in the feather, hair, or teeth of animals, the amount of water present may not be high. In functioning tissues, however, the water concentration is considerable, and the activation of dormant organic systems usually starts with the absorption of great amounts of water. Part of the water found in organisms is bound in chemical form; the rest serves as a dissolving or dispersing medium in which the various chemical transformations of the organism take place.

The suitability of water as a medium for organic processes is based on several properties. First, it is a liquid with the highest solvent capacity, making possible the enormous variety of chemical reactions on which life depends. Second, the particularly high heat capacity of water (water can absorb large quantities of heat without its own temperature rising considerably) makes the organism more independent of the temperature changes of its environment. Third, the high heat of vaporization of water further adds to the comparative thermal stability of the organism, because the body can dispose of great amounts of heat by vaporizing relatively small amounts of its water supply. Fourth, as a relatively neutral liquid (because of its high dielectric constant) water is a good dispersing and transporting medium of electrolytes and of other important substances of the body. And, last but not least, water is a good medium because, by means of hydrogen bonds, it can participate directly in many biochemical processes. Oxidation and reduction (page 40) are often dependent on water, and so are also the various hydrolytic processes by means of which various organic molecules are broken down or synthesized.

**Organic Constituents**    Water and some dissolved minerals and salts are the only inorganic compounds in the body of organisms. (The importance of some of these minerals and salts will be discussed later in conjunction with their paramount role in signal transmission in the nervous system, in Chapter 7.) The next three classes of chemical compounds to be considered, carbohydrates, lipoids, and proteins, are distinguished as "organic" compounds—carbon-containing substances that, under natural conditions, owe their existence to biosynthesis. Like hydrogen and oxygen, carbon is present in all organisms. It is a comparatively small atom with 4 valence electrons which may be lent to, completed by, or shared with others. That is, carbon can combine with metallic as well as nonmetallic substances and, in addition, with other carbon atoms. These bonds are comparatively strong; as a consequence, carbon may serve as a structural framework for very large and often very complex molecules. The molecular or chemical analysis of organisms has been carried out in a great variety of species. Apart from 66 percent water, the mammalian body is composed of about 16 percent

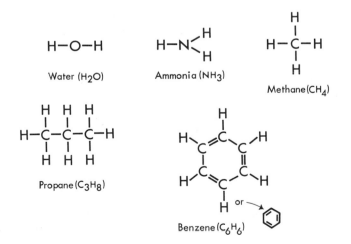

Some inorganic molecules formed by H, O, N, and C. Propane illustrates the formation of carbon chains; benzene, of carbon rings. Carbon chains and rings serve as skeletons of large and complex organic molecules.

protein, 13 percent fat and lipoid, and 0.6 percent carbohydrates; the remainder, about 5 percent ash, contains various minerals. In other organic forms the distribution of chemical constituents may be quite different: in certain marine invertebrates the water contents may exceed nine tenths of the body weight, and in plants the carbohydrate concentration is much higher than in animals.

**Carbohydrates** Simple carbohydrates consist of carbon, hydrogen, and oxygen, in which there are 6 or the multiple of 6 carbon atoms, and hydrogen and oxygen in the proportion of two to one, as in water. This is the composition of various hexose sugars. The least complex of these are the 6-carbon monosaccharides (examples of these are glucose or fructose); their empirical formula is $C_6H_{12}O_6$. Sucrose is a more complex carbohydrate, called a disaccharide; its formula is $C_{12}H_{22}O_{11}$, and it is considered to be the product of 1 glucose and 1 fructose molecule with the elimination of 1 unit of water ($H_2O$). The most complex of the carbohydrates are the polysaccharides. Their formula is $(C_6H_{10}O_5)n$; of these, starch, glycogen, and cellulose are the best known. The functions of carbohydrates in the body are various. Above all, as energy-rich compounds they are the most important sources of organic energy. Glucose is used directly by cells for the energization of a variety of functions, including neural activity, whereas starch represents the storage fuel of plants, and glycogen the storage fuel of animals. Cellulose is an inert material; it is found in plants as structural support or protective coating.

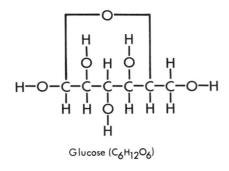

Glucose ($C_6H_{12}O_6$)

**Lipoids** The lipoids are a diverse group; various kinds of organic compounds are classed under this heading, including some which share only one common property with true lipids, namely, that they are insoluble in water but soluble in ether, chloroform, or benzene. The three main classes of compounds belonging to this group are the true fats, the phospho-lipids, and steroids. True fats, or lipids, are esters (salts) of the alcohol glycerol and various fatty acids. The organism tends to form fat whenever it is supplied with an excess of carbohydrates and proteins. Because fat is stored in a practically dry state, and because its caloric value is about twice as high as that of carbohydrates and proteins, the economy of this method of fuel storage is evident. Fat, possibly because of its hydrophobic nature (it is immiscible with water), is also thought to be important as a protective coating of some labile compounds, such as proteins, against the action of hydrolyzing enzymes. Lipids are also important as components of the cell membrane, and, in the nervous system, a lipid-containing material forms the insulating myelin sheath of nerve fibers.

Also of great importance are the phospholipids and phosphatides. They are closely related to true fats but contain, in addition to fatty acids, phosphoric acid and nitrogen. They are present in all organisms and are especially abundant in active cells and tissues. The other group of chemicals classified with lipoids, namely, the steroids and sterols, are complex alcohols with varied composition and properties. Cholesterol is one of the best known of this group; also, some hormones (such as the sex hormones) are steroids.

**Proteins** The most important of all organic compounds are proteins. Proteins belong to the most complex of all organic chemicals—a fact that may be related to their structural and functional importance. No organism has ever been found that does not contain proteins, and proteins appear to participate in all the essential functions of the organism. These very large organic compounds exist in endless variety, differing in structure according to the function they serve, but also differing from species to species even when performing similar functions. Although carbohydrates and lipoids taken from one organism may be directly used by another, because they are in all essentials alike, this property does not apply to proteins. Each species has its own self-made proteins, and when organisms acquire proteins from outside sources they first break these down into their components (amino acids) and then rebuild them in accordance with their own standards. There is basis for the assumption that, on the "molecular" level, the distinguishing characteristics of organic species are

**TABLE 1**

| Amino acid | Abbr. | Amino acid | Abbr. |
|---|---|---|---|
| Alanine | Ala | Leucine | Leu |
| Arginine | Arg | Lysine | Lys |
| Aspartic acid | Asp | Methionine | Met |
| Asparagine | An | Phenylalanine | Phe |
| Cysteine | Cys | Proline | Pro |
| Glutamic acid | Glu | Serine | Ser |
| Glutamine | Gn | Threonine | Thr |
| Glycine | Gly | Tryptophan | Try |
| Histidine | His | Tyrosine | Tyr |
| Isoleucine | Ileu | Valine | Val |

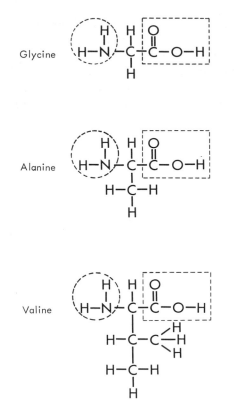

Formulas of some smaller amino acids with their amino groups and carboxyl groups. In each formula the amino group (-NH$_2$) is encased in a circle; the carboxyl group (-COOH), in a rectangle.

primarily the products of their specific proteins. Similarly, the differential properties of different cells and tissues within the same organism are to a large extent attributable to the specific proteins they are composed of.

In addition to carbon, hydrogen and oxygen, proteins also contain nitrogen and sulphur. The immediate building materials of proteins are amino acids, of which about 20 are commonly found incorporated into proteins. Out of these, through various combinations, the organism can synthesize an endless variety of proteins. All amino acids contain two distinctive chemical components, the amino group (–NH$_2$) and the carboxyl group (–COOH). The amino group is basic (that is, has the property of acquiring protons or hydrogen ions), whereas the carboxyl group is acidic (can make available protons). It is because of this fact that amino acids can behave as both acids and bases, depending on the electrolytic properties (the pH, or hydrogen-ion concentration) of the solution in which they are dissolved or dispersed. This dual ionic property is also the basis of the peptide linkage of proteins, where, after elimination of a water molecule, the amino group of one amino acid holds onto the carboxyl group of the other (–CO–NH–). In addition to the peptide bonds, which form the

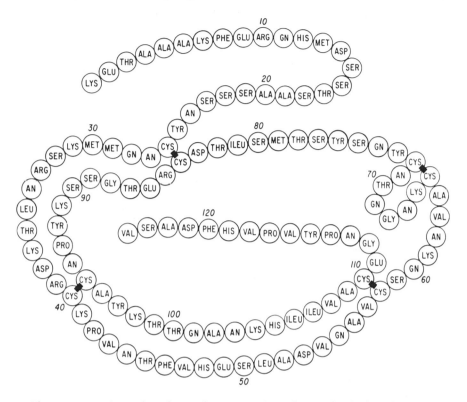

The structure of a relatively small protein, ribonuclease. The bridges between the sulphur-containing cysteine molecules are disulfide bonds. (From Anfinsen, *The molecular basis of evolution*, John Wiley & Sons, 1959)

backbone chain of proteins, disulfide bonds (–S–S–), ionic bonds, and hydrogen bonds are considered of great significance in folding the peptide chains into complex helical configurations characteristic of proteins. The weakest of these bonds is the hydrogen bond, and the destructive denaturation of proteins upon agitation, heating, and the like is thought to be caused by the breaking of the hydrogen bonds, which results in unfolding of the protein molecule.

Proteins have been classified in various ways. For our purposes their grouping into two main classes, structural and functional proteins, will be most useful. Inert proteins, like fibroin (found in silk), keratin (a constituent of hair), and collagen (present in connective tissue), are examples of structural proteins. The majority of proteins belong to the second class, and these functional proteins may be further subdivided into (1) globular proteins concerned with the control of organic chemical transformations; (2) fibrous proteins concerned with the transformation of chem-

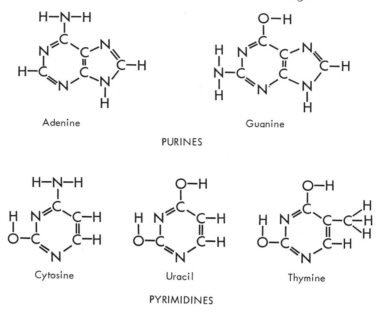

Adenine                                    Guanine

PURINES

Cytosine                    Uracil                    Thymine

PYRIMIDINES

The purine and pyrimidine bases of RNA and DNA.

ical energy into mechanical work; and (3) conjugated nucleoproteins concerned with the synthesis of proteins and reproductive autosynthesis.

Among the globular or corpuscular proteins are enzymes that guide chemical transformations in the body, hemoglobin, chlorophyll, certain hormones, antibodies, and a variety of other substances that play vital roles in organic processes. The best-known functional fibrous proteins are actin and myosin of muscle, which make possible, through their ability to contract and relax, the transformation of chemical energy into overt mechanical work. The third class of proteins, nucleoproteins, are complex compounds formed through conjugation of proteins and nucleic acids (RNA or DNA). Because of the great importance of nucleoproteins in vital organic functions, we shall review here briefly some of their characteristics. A discussion of the properties of the other functional proteins mentioned will be presented in the following chapters as we deal with the various organic processes in which they play a role. We may mention here that proteins are particularly abundant in nervous tissue and that nerve cells are characterized by an unusually high rate of protein metabolism.

**Nucleic Acids**   Nucleic   acids   are   polymers   of nucleotides; nucleotides consist of purine (adenine and guanine) and pyrimidine (cytosine, uracil, thymine) bases, phosphoric acids, and sugar (D-ribose or deoxy-D-ribose). Ribose nucleic acid (RNA) contains adenine (A), guanine (G), cytosine (C), uracil (U), phosphoric acid and D-ribose; deoxyribose nucleic acid (DNA) has the same composition, except that its pyrimidine base is thymine (T) instead of uracil and its sugar is deoxy-D-ribose. In the intact cell, nucleic acids are combined with proteins to form nucleo-proteins. Evidence has been accumulated recently which suggests that DNA, which is concentrated in the chromosomes of the cell nucleus, is the chemical substrate responsible for the genetic transmission of the hereditary properties of organisms, whereas RNA, which is present in the nucleolus and the cytoplasm, is concerned with the everyday synthesis of proteins.

Among the various lines of evidence suggesting the genetic role of DNA are the following:

1. DNA is localized mainly (though not exclusively) in the chromosomes, the classically accepted material substrate of heredity.

2. The concentration of DNA per chromosome set is approximately constant: haploid cells (cells with one set of chromosomes) contain half of the amount of DNA found in diploid cells (cells with the normal duplicate set of chromosomes). The duplication of chromosomes prior to cell division is preceded by approximate doubling of the DNA content of the cell.

3. Radioactive tracer experiments have shown that DNA, unlike other components of cells, is quite stable, a characteristic that would make it a suitable substance for the preservation and transmission of hereditary "information."

4. Viruses containing few or no other substances but nucleoproteins (in plant viruses these may be RNA) can reproduce themselves.

5. Finally, several investigators have shown that DNA from a donor administered to a host organism will produce in the latter genetically transmittable changes resembling those of the donor.

The exact nature of the self-reproductive power of DNA nucleoprotein is not known. According to a popular theory (Watson and Crick, 1953), the DNA macromolecule is made up of a double helix or two complementary spiral threads that are wound around and linked to each other by means of hydrogen bonds between purines of one strand and pyrimidines of the other (adenine being linked to thymine, and guanine to cytosine). These two threads separate before reproduction, and each assembles on its surface or template a complementary thread from material available in the protoplasmic medium.

DNA may thus serve as a hereditary link in transmitting genetic information from one generation to the next. However, there is no evidence that DNA is directly involved in the everyday synthesis of proteins, the compounds that control the chemical activities of the organism. Enuclea-

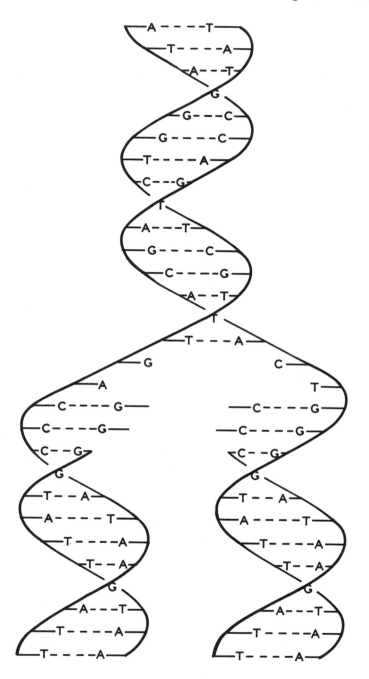

A simple model of a helical DNA molecule and its replication. A, adenine; G, guanine; C, cytosine; T, thymine. (From Sutton, *Genes, enzymes, and inherited diseases.* Holt, Rinehart and Winston, 1962)

tion of a cell, for instance, or destruction of DNA by means of x-ray irradiation does not interfere with continued protein synthesis for a period of time (such cells eventually die). As it is generally assumed, DNA is concerned with the synthesis of RNA; the synthesis of proteins, in turn, is mediated by RNA. The significance of RNA in protein synthesis is supported by the following evidence:

1. The concentration of RNA is greatest in cells with high protein turnover, such as enzyme-secreting glandular cells and nerve cells. Tissues with high metabolic rate but little protein production, such as muscle or kidney, show low RNA concentration.

2. Increase in the protein production of any given cell is preceded by an increase in RNA concentration.

3. The concentration of RNA is highest in the nucleolus and microsomes, regions which show the highest rate of amino acid incorporation. In fact, RNA-rich granules isolated from microsomes show a higher amino acid turnover than the microsomes themselves.

4. Removal of RNA from a cell, as by means of the enzyme ribonuclease, brings protein synthesis to a halt.

How do nucleic acids code the amino acid composition and amino acid sequence of specific proteins, and how are the appropriate amino acids assembled on the surface of nucleic acid "templates?" The sequence of bases in the polynucleotide chains of nucleic acids can be variable, and it was postulated that the order of bases serves as a code for the proper sequence of amino acids. But as there are only four bases (A, G, U, C) to the 20 amino acids (that is, the code consists of four symbols, but the language it stands for is made up of twenty symbols or "letters"), it was further assumed that multiples of bases (presumably triplets, because a combination of two bases could code only 16 amino acids) make up the code. Recently several laboratories have accumulated evidence that suggests the validity of such a coding mechanism. Thus it was found that RNA composed of uracil base only (polyuridylic acid) produces a peptide composed of phenylalanine, suggesting that the U sequence codes this amino acid. RNA composed of cytosine base only (polycytidylic acid) produces proline, indicating that the C sequence codes another amino acid. If the synthetic RNA contains cytosine or guanine in addition to uracil (some sequence of UUC or UUG), the amino acid coded is leucine, and so forth (Crick, 1963). The implications of such a molecular method of coding genetic or racial "memory" regarding the problem of the central nervous coding of individual "experience" will be discussed later (Chapter 13).

Contrary to the original assumption, which implied that amino acids are assembled directly on RNA templates located in the ribosomes of the cytoplasm, recent investigations suggest that there may be several steps in the process, involving transfer RNA and messenger RNA. It is thought that there are separate low-molecular-weight transfer RNAs for specific amino acids, which "identify" amino acids and carry them to high-molecular-weight messenger RNAs, which serve as templates for protein synthesis. These messenger RNAs depend in an ill-understood manner on temporary association with ribosomes in the cell, which presumably harbor the enzymes necessary for the guidance of protein synthesis.

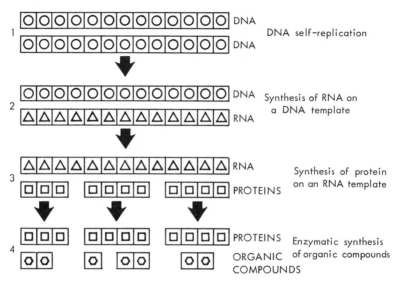

Schematic representation of the decoding of hereditary information carried by DNA in guiding the enzymatic reactions of the organism.

The chain of events that control the biochemical processes of the organism are therefore as follows:

1. The stable genetic blueprint is located in DNA molecules in the chromosomes. These can either duplicate themselves (as in cell division) or reproduce complementary RNA.

2. The RNA molecules leave the nucleus (in the form of transfer and messenger RNA) and become attached to microsomes in the cytoplasm.

3. Microsomal RNA molecules produce complementary protein molecules on their active surface.

4. In turn, the active proteins so produced, such as enzymes, control the various biochemical processes characteristic of the cell.

Thus there is a direct chain in information transfer from the genetic material to proteins, the substances directly engaged in the production

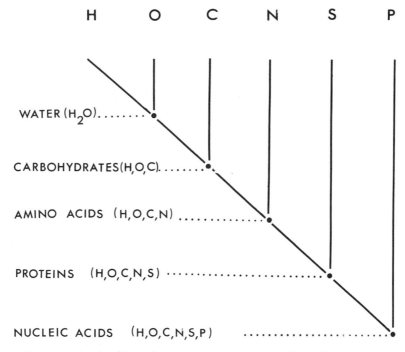

H     O     C     N     S     P

WATER (H$_2$O)..........●

CARBOHYDRATES(H,O,C)..........●

AMINO ACIDS (H,O,C,N) ..............●

PROTEINS (H,O,C,N,S) ...........................●

NUCLEIC ACIDS (H,O,C,N,S,P) .......................●

Atomic and molecular hierarchy in the chemical composition of organic tissue.

control of the chemical transformations of the organism. It is interesting to note that a common mechanism seems to underlie the mode of operation of all components in this chain of biochemical processes. That is, all these macromolecules (DNA, RNA, proteins) are presumed to serve as molding templates or blueprints, on the surfaces of which the simpler molecules of the protoplasmic medium are assembled, reproduced, and transformed into specific compounds of the organism. The Watson-Crick model of the self-replication of double-stranded DNA is essentially such a template theory, and similar template theories have been proposed for the biosynthesis of proteins on single-stranded RNA templates and also for the enzymatic reproduction of simpler biochemical compounds.

**Subcellular Constituents** Within the organism we find sub-atomic constituents built into atoms; atoms combined into molecules; simpler molecules chained together into larger and more complex organic compounds; these then organized into macromolecular, colloidal structures; and we are still not at the end of the complex hierarchy of organic architecture, because these physico-chemical units do not function in isolation but are combined into more complex biotic units. When the biochemist extracts such substances as carbohydrates, lipids, nucleic acids, or proteins from the living cell he often does so by tearing apart structural and functional units, which exist in the living tissue in quite a different form. It is generally assumed that the activities of living systems depend on various combinations and interactions of supramolecular units; unfortunately, little is as yet known about the nature of such organization.

There is evidence that the minimum requirements of a living system is the presence of a genetic information carrier (DNA), a protein-synthesizing template (RNA), a medium of appropriate raw materials (amino acids), an energy source, and, finally, a complex of enzymes which control the essential chemical transformations. Often viruses are described as the simplest living units. Although the more complex viruses may be living organisms, the simplest types (for example, the tobacco mosaic virus) are not truly living systems. Tobacco mosaic virus represents a single RNA nucleoprotein molecule; it contains no water, source of energy or enzymes, and accordingly cannot perform any of the activities that characterize living systems, such as metabolism and reproduction, except when it is brought in contact with a suitable living host. Dislocating the native nucleoproteins, the virus takes over control of the host's biochemical activities and turns the available raw materials into viruses of its own kind.

We do not know of any true organism that is composed of a single nucleoprotein particle with all its essential accessory elements. The simplest of true organisms known, such as bacteria and acellular protists, as well as cells of differentiated multicellular organisms, are composed of several subcellular elements which appear to be essential for organic existence. Most of these structures can be made visible in the living state by means of vital dyes or phase contrast microscopy, or in dead, fixed cells by means of various staining techniques. The identification of other subcellular structures requires the high resolving power of the electron microscope or the application of appropriate biophysical and biochemical techniques.

In all cells two major parts may be distinguished, the cytoplasm and the nucleus. The *cytoplasm* is a translucent structure, surrounded externally by a very thin membrane and containing various organelles, such as the endoplasmic reticulum, microsomes, mitochondria, lysosomes, plastids, and some others.

Little is known at present about the structure and properties of the *cell membrane*. It is a very thin (about 75 Ångstrom in width) double-layered sheath that, when damaged, is regenerated from cytoplasmic material. The membrane is believed to be composed of regularly oriented lipid and protein molecules, and as a porous, semipermeable sieve it regulates the passive as well as active exchange of materials between the

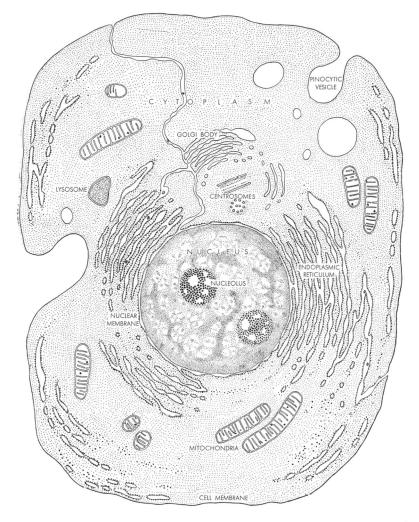

A generalized cell with typical cell constituents. (Courtesy of Dr. Don W. Fawcett)

cytoplasm and its environment. Although certain substances that are continuously utilized or produced, such as oxygen and carbon dioxide, may move in or out through the cell membrane by simple diffusion ("downhill" transport or passive exchange), other substances appear to be "pumped" through the membrane against osmotic concentration gradients and opposing electric potentials ("uphill" transport or active exchange). Thus, for instance, sodium (Na) is actively extruded from the cytoplasm with the result that the internal concentration of this substance is considerably lower than in the surrounding extracellular medium; whereas potassium (K) is actively ferried into the interior of the cytoplasm and its diffusion is prevented. As we shall see later (Chapter 7), the exchange of sodium and potassium ions across the cell membrane of nerve fibers underlies the conduction of nerve impulses. More generally, the maintenance of a characteristic cellular composition is controlled, in an unknown manner, by the cell membrane, which represents a functional barrier between the cell and its environment.

Inside the cell membrane is located the optically homogeneous colloidal cytoplasm, which has both liquid and viscous properties. The fluidity of the cytoplasm is attributable to its high water concentration, whereas its viscosity and elasticity are products of the various macromolecules, which form a complex fibrous framework. A component of this cytoplasmic framework is the *endoplasmic reticulum*, which, as recent electron microscopic investigations have revealed, is composed of a double-layered membrane similar to the membrane of the cytoplasm. Many investigators believe that the endoplasmic reticulum is formed by invagination of the cell membrane and remains continuous with it. It may represent a complex system of canals through which extracellular substances are transported into the interior of the cell. Attached to the endoplasmic reticulum are the *microsomes*, which were originally identified by the centrifugation technique as the RNA-rich components of the cytoplasm. The microsomes can now be seen in electron microscopic pictures as "electron-dense" granules. As we have mentioned before, the microsomes are the sites of protein synthesis in the cell. We shall see later that nerve cells are particularly rich in endoplasmic reticulum, where their large aggregations are recognizable with light microscopy as "Nissl granules."

*Mitochondria* can be seen through a light microscope and a variable number of them, up to several hundred, may be present in a single cell. Under the optical microscope mitochondria have a simple rodlike appearance, but electron microscopy has revealed that they have a compartmentalized structure with external and transverse double membranes resembling the cell membrane. Biochemical studies have shown that mitochondria contain various respiratory enzymes that are essential in energy metabolism, that is, the enzymes of the citric acid cycle, the cytochrome oxidase complex, and others. Mitochondria represent the power plant of the cell in which energy-rich nutrients are transformed in a complex cycle into substances, specifically adenosine triphosphate (ATP), which the cell can readily use for the energization of various biochemical processes. Less well known is another cytoplasmic organelle, the *lysosome*. It is believed that lysosomes contain another group of enzymes, the function of which is to break down larger molecules, such as lipids and proteins, into smaller components that are then used as raw materials by other cellular structures. The lysosome may function as a protective shell to separate these destructive cytoplasmic agents from the rest of the cell. Finally, a group of organelles, called *plastids*, are found in plant cells but not in animal cells. Among other elements, plastids contain the chlorophyll of green plants, which is essential for photosynthetic reactions. The role of these various cytoplasmic inclusions will be discussed in somewhat greater detail in subsequent chapters.

Inside the cytoplasm, and separated from it by a membrane, is the *nucleus*. The nuclear membrane is assumed to regulate the exchange of substances between nucleus and cytoplasm. It may also be important in protecting the chromosomes of the nucleus from the hazards of the intensive everyday activities of the cytoplasm. The chromosomes contain a large concentration of DNA, as previously described. The *nucleolus*, which is located inside the nucleus, is rich in RNA, and it has been postulated that the nucleolus may serve as a mediating mechanism between nucleus and cytoplasm whereby genetic information stored in the nucleus is transmitted to the cytoplasm by way of transfer and messenger RNA.

This description of the basic subcellular constitution of organisms applies to protists as well as to single cells of multicellular organisms. Protists represent the simpler and phylogenetically more ancient mode of biotic organization in which all the multiform functions of the organism are performed by a single "cell." But unicellular organization appears to set a limit to the absolute size and complexity that an organism can attain. Organisms have overcome this handicap by evolving the more complex multicellular organization. Not only phylogenetically but also ontogenetically multicellular organisms are derived from a single cell by a process that is in many respects similar to the division and multiplication of unicellular organisms. However, the cells of multicellular organisms do not separate from the parent cells and do not acquire all the abilities and propensities necessary for independent existence. Instead, the various cells that remain together form a complex hierarchic system by specializing along various lines and performing selected part-functions of the organism.

We shall not deal at this point with the problem of how such a cellular differentiation comes about, nor shall we be concerned with the specific nature of the various cells. The properties and functions of various cells, tissues and organs in the system of multicellular organisms will be considered in the next section.

### SELECTED READINGS

Baldwin, E. *Dynamic aspects of biochemistry.* (3d ed.) London: Cambridge, 1957.

Brachet, J. *Biochemical cytology.* New York: Academic Press, Inc., 1957.

De Robertis, E. D. P., W. W. Nowinski, and F. A. Saez. *General cytology.* (3d ed.) Philadelphia: Saunders, 1960.

Giese, A. C. *Cell physiology.* (2d ed.) Philadelphia: Saunders, 1962.

Heilbrunn, L. V. *Outline of general physiology.* (3d ed.) Philadelphia: Saunders, 1952.

McElroy, W. D. *Cell physiology and biochemistry.* (2d ed.) Englewood Cliffs, N.J.: Prentice-Hall, 1964.

Paul, J. *Cell biology.* Stanford, Calif.: Stanford University Press, 1964.

# 3

# Fundamental Vegetative Processes

**Vegetative Processes and** In an attempt to classify the various
**Animative Activities** activities of organisms we shall first
distinguish between two basically
dissimilar sets of phenomena, the vegetative processes and the animative activities. The vegetative processes are the more fundamental, and are shared by all organisms, plant or animal. The animative activities (including behavioral capacities) are superimposed functions that are not common to all organisms but are prerogatives of animals equipped with a neuromuscular system. The fundamental *vegetative processes* are the following three: metabolism, reproduction, and humoral integration. *Metabolism* is the basis of the self-maintenance of living things; *reproduction* is responsible for the hereditary maintenance of the species; and *humoral integration* permits the coordination of the varied activities of differentiated organisms.

Because organisms are "open systems" that need to have commerce with their environment in carrying out their activities, each of the above functions is combined in plants with vegetative modes of interaction with the environment. Metabolism requires acquisition of external sources of energy and raw materials and the extrusion of waste products; the relatively "passive," or nonbehavioral, way whereby metabolism is attained by sessile plants we shall designate as *vegetative nutrition* and *alimentation*. Reproduction requires in most species the meeting of male and female gametes, fertilization, and the distribution of seeds, spores, and the like in space; this task again is brought about in the plant world for the most part passively, and the process will be designated as *vegetative sexual propagation*. Finally, the integration of the organism requires the ability to respond to environmental changes; the way this integration is accomplished by sessile plants will be called *vegetative modes of adjustment*. Metabolism and vegetative nutrition, reproduction and vegetative propagation, and humoral integration and vegetative adjustment are the three classes of functions that are shared by all living organisms. They may, accordingly, be considered primary, or fundamental, organic processes.

Though plants can successfully maintain themselves by means of these three vegetative functions, animals make extensive use also of *animative activities*. Owing to their inability to use inorganic substances as raw materials, and sunshine as an energy source, the way sessile green plants do, the interaction of animals with their environment is by necessity a more complex task than that of plants. Animals have to search for and locate suitable sources of organic nutrients, they have to manipulate and ingest the detected nutrients, and, quite often, they must also break down mechanically the solid organic substances and prepare them in such a way that they can be utilized by the needy cells and tissues of the body. The more active animal way of life depends on specific animative capacities that are the functions of three types of animal structures: receptors, muscle, and nerves.

The *animative action system* may be considered a secondary super-structure situated on and sustained by the vegetative core of the organism. The animative action system may be activated by internal needs as well as by external stimuli; its main task is the satisfaction of vegetative needs through interaction with the environment. As an illustration of the functioning of the animative action system we may consider the situation where the food stores of an animal are depleted and a metabolic "need" arises. As this need can be satisfied only by acquiring external sources of food, the animal becomes active and begins to search for food. When suitable nutrients are located, the animal approaches them, attempts to acquire them, and, when successful, ingests, masticates, and swallows them. At this point the behavioral sequence concerned with food acquisition comes to an end, and a set of visceral animative activities begin. The food is transported and prepared in the alimentary canal (digestion as an enzymatic process is a vegetative function) and is transferred to the vascular system in which, with the aid of the pumping action of the heart, the digested food is carried to the needy cells. With this the domestic animative activities concerned with alimentation come to an end and the basic vegetative processes begin. The needed substances are incorporated by the various cells and metabolized to satisfy the existing needs.

In summary, it may be said that, insofar as there is an unavoidable necessity for disciplinary subdivisions in the vast science of biology, a useful separation can be made between vegetative processes and animative activities. As conceived, vegetative biology is concerned with all the organic activities of plants and with the corresponding vegetative activities of animals. Animative biology, on the other hand, deals with the neuro-muscular activities of animals, incorporating the subject matter of psychology and a considerable portion of animal physiology. The proposed separation of vegetative processes and animative activities is of course merely a utilitarian step, for the two sets of functions are interconnected aspects of integrated animal functioning.

**METABOLISM AND VEGETATIVE NUTRITION AND ALIMENTATION** *Metabolism* is the fundamental organic function that makes possible living existence. It consists of two complementary processes, anabolism and catabolism. *Anabolism* is the biochemical transformation of various inorganic and organic substances into specific, usually more complex, compounds; it is an uphill process that requires an external source of energy. *Catabolism* is the opposite process of degradation of organic compounds into simpler molecules; it is a downhill process accompanied by the release of free energy. The result of coordinated anabolism and catabolism, where the energy liberated by one is utilized for the synthetic functions of the other, is the complementary process of metabolism. It is through the metabolic process that, notwithstanding its continual expenditure of work and energy, the steady state of the organism is maintained.

The metabolic processes of the organism are guided by *enzymes*. Enzymes are biocatalysts that control the direction and rate of chemical transformations. Enzymes are either pure proteins or conjugated proteins combined with coenzymes. (Some of the coenzymes are related to, or are identical with, relatively simple organic compounds known as vitamins.) Enzymes affect the transformation of a single substance or group of substances, and are usually named after the substance on which they act by the addition of the suffix "ase." Thus carbohydrases break down sugar, cellulose, and other carbohydrates; proteases act on proteins; cholinesterase destroys acetylcholine, and so forth. Sometimes the suffix "ase" is added to the term describing the function of the enzyme; thus oxidases control the transfer of oxygen to various substances, and dehydrogenases affect the transfer of hydrogen. Several enzymes have recently been prepared in pure crystalline form, and their amino-acid composition and properties have been thoroughly investigated.

The exact nature of enzymatic action in general and enzymatic specificity in particular are not well understood. It is generally assumed that enzymatic specificity is determined by the adsorption surface of the protein moiety by means of a template process (as it has been said, the substrate has to fit the enzyme surface as a key its lock). That chemical transformations go on in the cell in controlled steps instead of bursts of explosion, and that these transformations do not require or lead to appreciable temperature changes, are largely to be attributed to the control functions of cellular enzymes.

Enzymes can only guide chemical transformations, they do not energize them. The energy for these processes is obtained from chemical sources through the breakdown of energy-rich organic compounds, such as carbohydrates or, more directly, of adenosine triphosphate. It should be noted, however, that the ultimate energy source of organisms is not of chemical but of photic origin. It is the energy of solar radiation that is utilized by chlorophyll-containing *autotrophic* (self-nourishing) green plants for the synthesis of energy-rich organic compounds by means of photosynthesis. In this process photic energy is transformed into storable chemical-bond energy, which can then be utilized by both plants and "parasitic," or *heterotrophic*, animals for the synthesis of other organic compounds and the energization of various organic processes.

The energy of the sun is stored by carbohydrates through a reductive process (defined as the addition of electrons or hydrogens to a compound) in which water molecules are split, the oxygen is freed, and hydrogen is attached to carbon dioxide. During this phase (namely, in daytime) plants inhale carbon dioxide and exhale oxygen. Reduction, in general, requires energy input; in the photosynthesis of carbohydrates the source is solar energy. The energy stored in this manner by carbohydrates can be released by oxidative processes. Oxidation is defined as the removal of electrons or hydrogens from a compound, a process accompanied by the release of chemical or thermal energy (burning). The end result of the oxidation of carbohydrates is the reverse of photosynthesis; oxygen is consumed and carbon dioxide is released, which is the characteristic of the respiration of animals in general and of the respiration of plants in the dark. The theoretical maximal yield of this oxidative process, for glucose, is about 690,000 calories per mol.

In the cell, the decomposition of glucose involves numerous steps and a variety of pathways, each step being guided by a different enzyme. Two major phases in the cellular decomposition of glucose have been identified. Anaerobic glycolysis is the first phase, in which, through several intermediate steps, 6-carbon glucose is split into 3-carbon pyruvic acid. The second phase is an aerobic one, that is, it requires oxygen; in it 3-carbon pyruvic acid is broken down into 1-carbon carbon dioxide. This occurs in a complex sequence of steps, which is known as the Krebs citric acid cycle. The net energy yield of the anaerobic phase is quite meager. About 24,000 calories per mol of glucose are usefully invested through the transformation of 2 mols of adenosine diphosphate (ADP) into energy-rich adenosine triphosphate (ATP). ATP, which stores about

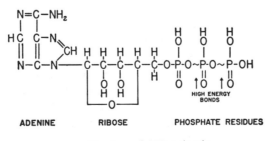

ADENINE          RIBOSE          PHOSPHATE RESIDUES

Structure of ATP molecule

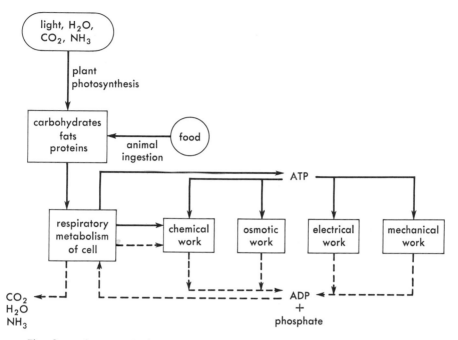

The flow of energy in living systems. Solid lines refer to "high energy" flow, dashed lines to low energy flow. (From Loewy and Siekevitz, *Cell structure and function*, Holt, Rinehart and Winston, 1963)

12,000 calories per mol in its high-energy phosphate bond, is the universal exchange unit of cells, and its energy is easily utilized in a variety of metabolic processes. The energy yield of the second, aerobic, phase is considerable; it leads to the production of about 36 mols of ATP. Thus the total decomposition of glucose leads to a better than 50-percent utilization of the energy stored in it.

**Vegetative Nutrition and Alimentation**    The prerequisite of internal cellular metabolism is *nutrition*, which refers to the acquisition of essential raw materials and energy sources from the environment. The process of extracellular preparation and transportation of nutrients, and excretion of waste products, is referred to as *alimentation*. The term "vegetative nutrition and alimentation" refers to modes of food acquisition, preparation, and transportation, and to the mode of waste elimination, shown by multicellular sessile organisms, such as plants, and by sessile components of motile organisms, such as internal organs in the bodies of animals. Vegetative nutrition and alimentation depend on such physical processes as diffusion and selective membrane permeability, such chemical processes as enzymatic digestion, and such ill-understood biotic processes as "pumping" against diffusion gradients, streaming, and the like.

In contrast, "animative nutrition and alimentation" consists of biochemical activities carried out with the aid of neuromuscular organs and systems. Animative nutrition is exemplified by such interactive processes as the search for, and acquisition of, nutrients; and animative alimentation includes such neuromuscular processes as ingestion and mastication, the gastrointestinal and circulatory transportation of nutrients, and others. In this book we are primarily interested in the animative or behavioral aspects of nutrition. To further our understanding of the latter processes we shall, however, briefly discuss the nature of vegetative nutrition and alimentation.

**Nutrition and Alimentation in Autotrophs**      In the everyday material exchanges of autotrophic plants, of great importance is the absorption of water, carbon dioxide, and some minerals, all of which are necessary for photosynthesis and also for the elimination of oxygen, the main waste product of green plants. These material exchanges do not require specific mechanisms but may be carried out with the favorable intervention of physical processes. For example, in simple algae all these inorganic substances may easily pass in or out through the semipermeable cell membrane by diffusion. Because carbon dioxide and the various essential minerals dissolved in water are constantly being used up by the synthesizing organism, their concentration inside the cell tends to fall below that found in any favorable medium, and so, owing to diffusion, these substances move into the interior of the cell without active soliciting processes. Similarly, oxygen is produced during photosynthesis in large quantities inside the cell; as the inside concentration grows, the substance tends to move outward by diffusion.

Material exchange is a more serious task in multicellular organisms, especially in large plants. In these organisms certain cells and tissues are specialized to perform various nutritive functions: root cells absorb water and its minerals, green leaves absorb carbon dioxide, and other tissues form vascular channels in which various substances are moved up and down the plant with and against the force of gravity. The antigravitational transportation of water and minerals from the roots upward in the woody xylem of plants is believed to be based on such physical processes as capillarity, root pressure, and the cohesion of water ("transpiration pump"). The translocation of organic substances produced in the green leaves through the sieve tubes of the phloem is also attributed to physical factors, such as diffusion from regions of higher concentration (the sites of synthesis) to regions of lower concentration, the turgor pressure built up in the leaf parenchyma, and some other processes. The acquisition and transportation of nutritive materials in autotrophic plants may, accordingly, be attributed largely to appropriate structural adaptations and the exploitation of favorable physical processes. In addition to these "passive" factors, some active selective processes may also be at work. Thus plants acquire certain substances, such as iodine or selenium, in much higher concentrations than exist in the soil from which they are drawn.

**Vegetative Alimentation in Animals**   Nutrition and alimentation are more complex processes in heterotrophic than in autotrophic organisms. Heterotrophs cannot themselves synthesize carbohydrates and various other nutrients (such as "essential" amino acids), which they have to obtain ready-made from some other organic source. Instead, heterotrophs ingest organic compounds produced by autotrophs (or by other heterotrophs) and then transform the alien organic substances into species-specific and organ-specific compounds of their own. There are several plantlike organisms, such as various bacteria, and true plants, such as yeasts and molds, that do not possess chlorophyll and that therefore continually require exogenous sources of carbohydrates. Lacking an animative action system, such heterotrophic organisms cannot of course engage in active pursuit of food objects. Many heterotrophic plants thrive in a parasitic manner on rich organic media. If they feed on organic nutrients already in solution, as do some bacteria and molds in a dissolved carbohydrate medium, then the exchange of materials may be satisfied by diffusion. If, on the other hand, the organic substrate is composed of particulate matter, as is true of various fungi that utilize starch, enzymes (such as amylase) are secreted that make possible external digestion of the large molecules. The broken-down starch can then enter through the cell walls of the fungus by diffusion.

In another large class of heterotrophs, namely animals, nutrition is a complex behavioral process carried out exclusively by animative means. Also, various aspects of alimentation depend in animals on animative structures and functions. The three main groups of substances that animals acquire behaviorally from their environment are, classified according to their physical states, gases (oxygen), liquids (water and substances dissolved or carried by water), and solids (leaves, seeds, fruits, meat, and so on). The active ingestion of these substances is dependent on three animative processes, breathing (inspiration), drinking, and eating. The excretion of gaseous (carbon dioxide), liquid, and solid waste products is also carried out by animative means, and these processes are, respectively, breathing (expiration), micturition, and defecation. Further, the transportation of nutrients throughout the body also necessitates animative mechanisms, such as the muscular contraction of the gastrointestinal tract and the pumping of blood by the heart. Nevertheless, important aspects of the alimentary process are carried out in animals by vegetative means, that is, by nonanimative tissues and processes.

In this context we shall describe briefly the structure and functions of various visceral organ systems, that is, the respiratory, circulatory, lymphatic, gastrointestinal, and urinary systems. Familiarity with the functioning of these structures is necessary for the proper appreciation of their motivational role in behavior and also for an understanding of the mode of neural control of their activities.

**The Respiratory System**    The respiratory system is concerned primarily with acquisition of oxygen and elimination of carbon dioxide. Accessory structures of the respiratory system are the various air passages (mouth, nostrils, pharynx, larynx, and trachea), and its main organs are the gills (in lower aquatic vertebrates) and the lungs (in air-breathing vertebrates). The *lungs* are situated in the chest cavity or thorax, which is divided from the abdominal cavity by the diaphragm. The lungs consist of air passages, the bronchi and bronchioles, and of air spaces, or alveolar sacs, in which the bronchioles terminate. The alveolar sacs are formed of a single layer of cells in intimate contact with blood capillaries.

The respiratory process may be divided into three phases: (1) the external phase, which consists of the movement of air between the environment and the lungs; (2) the intermediate phase, which consists of the exchange of respiratory gases between the lungs and the blood, and of their transportation by the blood; and (3) the internal phase, which is represented by the exchange of oxygen and carbon dioxide between the blood, on the one hand, and between the intracellular and tissue fluids, on the other.

The first phase, sometimes called external respiration, is based on alternating inspiratory and expiratory movements. These are biomechanical *animative* processes produced extrabronchially by the chest muscles and the diaphragm: the volume of the thorax, and with it the air capacity of the lungs, is increased during inspiration and reduced during expiration. Movements of the air are also modified by the skeletal muscles of the air passages and, to some extent, by the smooth muscles of the bronchi and bronchioles.

The second and third phases may be classified as *vegetative* processes insofar as they represent the universal living phenomenon of osmotic exchange of diffusible substances between cells and their media. The walls that separate the alveoli and capillary interior are very thin and permeable; through them the exchange of oxygen and carbon dioxide between the respiratory and circulatory systems takes place. The oxygen concentration or pressure of the alveoli is higher than that of the pulmonary venous blood (which represents blood returned, with its oxygen unloaded, to the tissues); as a consequence, oxygen moves from the alveoli to the blood. The reverse holds for carbon dioxide, which is present in higher concentration in venous blood as a waste product of carbohydrate metabolism;

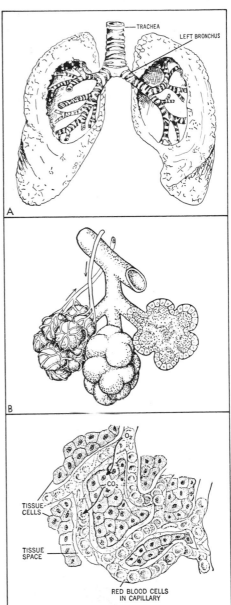

A, the lungs with the trachea and bronchi. Portion of lung tissue removed to show branchings of bronchial tree. (From Best and Taylor, *The living body*, 4th ed., Holt, Rinehart and Winston, 1958)

B, alveoli with associated capillaries; arrows indicate direction of capillary blood flow. (From Whaley et al., *Principles of biology*, Harper & Brothers, 1954)

C, red blood cells in capillaries of alveoli, with arrows indicating direction of flow of $O_2$ and $CO_2$. (From Best and Taylor, *The living body*, 4th ed., Holt, Rinehart and Winston, 1958)

accordingly, carbon dioxide moves in the reverse direction, from the blood to the lungs.

The exchange of respiratory gases between the lungs and the blood thus follows physical principles and does not necessitate special pumping or transfer mechanisms. The oxygen-carrying capacity of the blood, however, is greatly enhanced by the presence of cells furnished with pigments that reversibly combine with oxygen. These cells are the erythrocytes, or *red blood cells*, which contain the pigmented substance, hemoglobin (or hemocyanin in invertebrates). The loose chemical combination of hemoglobin and oxygen is such that they tend to dissociate in regions where the oxygen pressure is low, as in the vicinity of needy cells. It is thus that oxygen carried by the blood from the lungs is unloaded at sites where it is needed, and through the capillaries the oxygen diffuses into the tissue and cell fluids.

**The Circulatory System**     The circulatory system consists of the heart, a pumping mechanism; and a set of ducts: the arteries, veins, and capillaries. The *heart* of vertebrates, which consists of two-to-four alternatingly contracting muscular chambers, is furnished with valves that direct the fluid flow. The blood is carried by the arteries away from the heart and is returned to the heart through the veins; by means of fine capillaries, direct contact with the tissues and cells of the body is maintained. In four-chambered

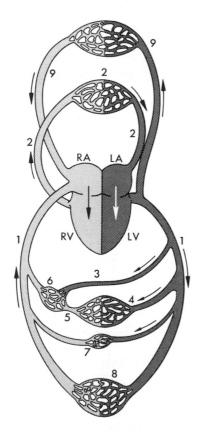

Diagram of the mammalian circulatory system, with arteries, veins, and capillaries. 1, systemic circulation; 2, pulmonary circulation; 3, artery to liver; 4, artery to gastrointestinal tract; 5, portal vein; 6, liver circulation; 7, kidney circulation; 8, capillaries of limbs; 9, arteries, capillaries, and veins of head and neck. (After Best and Taylor, *The living body*, 4th ed., Holt, Rinehart and Winston, 1958)

hearts, like those of birds and mammals, there are two major flow circuits, the *pulmonary* and *systemic circuits*. Through the pulmonary circuit venous blood from the body is carried to the lungs for reoxygenation and unloading of carbon dioxide; the fresh blood returned from the lungs is then recirculated through the systemic route. The heart and its channels represent an animative device that makes possible the rapid mechanical transportation of a highly adapted body fluid, the blood.

The *blood* is a complex fluid that, when artificially centrifuged, can be separated into liquid and viscous components. The liquid portion, called plasma, consists of about 90 percent water and contains such dissolved or dispersed chemicals as salts, glucose, amino acids, proteins, and various hormones. The viscous component is made up of cells. Three blood cell types are distinguished: red blood cells, or erythrocytes; white blood cells, or leucocytes; and platelets, or thrombocytes. The erythrocytes are specialized cells containing, as we have mentioned earlier, hemoglobin. Hemoglobin combines reversibly with oxygen and makes possible the transportation of large volumes of oxygen by the blood, up to 60 times as much as can be carried by water. The red blood cells are formed mainly in bone marrow; limited reserves of them are stored in the spleen. The white blood cells are less numerous in the blood than are the red blood cells. They are capable of ameboid locomotion and are phagocytic, ingesting diseased cells, cell debris, bacteria, and the like. Accordingly, the leucocytes are of great importance in protecting the body from toxic and infectious agents. The platelets, which may be partly the products of disintegrating erythrocytes, have a role in the coagulation of blood when blood vessels are ruptured. The concentration of ions, nutrients, and other metabolic constituents of the blood is, under normal circumstances, relatively stable, with the result that the cells and tissues of the body, irrespective of their changing needs and conditions, are bathed in a fluid medium with constant properties. The maintenance of this constancy is dependent on a complex chain of homeostatic mechanisms, which will be considered later.

**The Lymphatic System**  The lymphatic system consists of fine capillaries, larger vessels, lymph nodes, and two large trunks. The lymphatic capillaries, which have highly permeable walls, penetrate into the body tissues and drain the tissue fluids. The composition of lymph is essentially the same as that of tissue fluids, and it also contains leucocytes in large number, but no erythrocytes. The circulated lymph passes through the lymph nodes, which, together with the leucocytes, act as filters for the removal of microorganisms. Through the large lymphatic trunks the filtered lymphatic fluid is then returned to the circulatory system by way of the subclavian vein. The lymphatic system is, accordingly, essentially a device for the cleansing of recirculated tissue fluids.

**The Gastrointestinal System**   The gastrointestinal system consists of the mouth, pharynx, esophagus. stomach, and intestines. Food ingested by mouth is transferred to the pharynx and esophagus (gullet) and then passed to the stomach. By peristaltic movement the content of the stomach is moved through the length of the small and large intestines, and the remaining waste products are eliminated through the anus. The entire gastrointestinal digestive tract is essentially a single duct with modified components from which

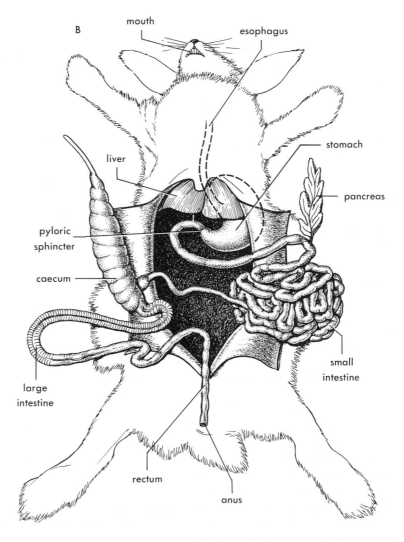

Digestive tract of a mammal, the rabbit. (From Griffin, *Animal structure and function,* Holt, Rinehart and Winston, 1962)

environmental nutrients are transferred to the interior of the body by capillary blood vessels terminating in the walls of the duct. Digestion of solid nutrients taking place in the gastrointestinal tract consists of two aspects: (1) a mechanical or animative one, consisting of mastication, swallowing, and peristaltic movements of the stomach and intestines; and (2) a chemical or vegetative one, with which we shall be concerned here.

In the mucous membranes of the alimentary tract, or outside the tract but with openings into it, are several *exocrine glands* that secrete into the alimentary tract the chemicals essential for the digestion of nutrients. These glands include the salivary and gastric glands, the pancreas and liver, and the intestinal glands. There are three pairs of *salivary glands:* the submaxillary, sublingual, and parotic glands. These glands are composed of secreting cells, finer collecting ducts, and main ducts; the main ducts empty the secreted saliva into the mouth. Saliva acts as a moistening agent, aiding the transportation of the masticated food, and also as a cleansing agent, removing food debris from the mouth. But more importantly, saliva contains an enzyme, ptyalin (salivary amylase), which splits large starch molecules into smaller disaccharides. The salivary amylase is mixed with the food, and the digestion of starch in it continues as the food is passed to the stomach.

The mucous membrane of the stomach contains *gastric glands,* which secrete gastric juice into the stomach. The gastric glands are small tubular structures, several million of which may be present in the stomachs of larger mammalian species. Gastric juice is composed of mucus, hydrochloric acid, and several enzymes. Most of these chemicals are produced by different cell types and may be secreted independently from one another. The chief constituent of mucus is mucin, a glycoprotein. It is believed that mucus protects the epithelial surface of the stomach from the destructive effects of hydrochloric acid. Hydrochloric acid is secreted by the parietal cells of the gastric glands. Hydrochloric acid is instrumental in hydrolyzing starch and proteins, and in maintaining the acidity (high hydrogen-ion concentration) of the gastric juice, which is essential for the optimal enzymatic effect of pepsin. The most important constituent of gastric juice is pepsin, the proteolytic enzyme, which breaks down proteins into smaller fragments called peptides; pepsin, however, cannot disintegrate proteins into amino acids. Rennin is present particularly in younger animals; it clots milk and has a slight proteolytic action. Gastric lipase splits fats, but its role in the digestion of fatty constituents of the stomach content is not very important.

The stomach contents, as they are being broken down by the digestive juices, are turned into a homogeneous viscous fluid, called chyme. In this state the food passes from the stomach into the small intestines, in which the final digestion of food occurs, whereby it is converted into low-molecular-weight products that can pass through the capillaries into the blood stream. The small intestine is by convention divided into three parts, the duodenum, jejunum, and ileum. Connected with the duodenum is an important digestive gland, the pancreas. The *pancreas* contains a variety of secretory cells that empty their products into smaller ducts or alveoli, whence the pancreatic juice passes through a large collecting duct into the duodenum. The pancreatic juice contains a large number of proteolytic enzymes, such as trypsin, chymotrypsin, carboxypeptidases, and aminopeptidases, which are responsible for the successive breakdown of proteins and peptides into absorbable amino acids. The pancreatic juice also contains nucleases, which digest nucleic acids and nucleotides; lipases, which split fats into fatty acids and glycerin; and amylase, maltase, sucrase, and lactase, which decompose starch and disaccharides into absorbable monosaccharides.

In addition to the pancreas, secretory and excretory products in the form of bile are emptied into the duodenum by the liver by way of the gall bladder. The *liver* is the largest gland of the mammalian body. It receives blood from the intestinal tract through the portal vein and delivers blood, with nutrients absorbed from the intestines and partially transformed by the liver, through the hepatic vein. The liver is composed of smaller units called hepatic lobules, which are formed of rows of cells (the liver cords) radiating from a central vein. Among the many vegetative functions of the liver are the storage of sugar in the form of glycogen, the storage of fat, and the detoxication of toxic substances received from the intestines. Bile is secreted by the parenchymal cells of the liver into fine ducts called bile canaliculi, and the collected fluid moves through the large hepatic duct into the gall bladder.

The composition of bile varies greatly with the nutritional condition of the animal. Its most important components are such secretory products as bile salts and such excretory substances as cholesterol and bile pigments; few enzymes of functional importance are present in bile. The bile salts are important in aiding the digestion of fatty substances. As emulsifying agents they increase the surface area of fats and thus promote the digestive action of pancreatic lipases. Another role of bile salts is to keep cholesterol, an excretory product of bile, in solution. Bile pigments are also excretory substances; they derive from the hemoglobin of disintegrating red blood cells. Bile from the liver is transferred to the gall bladder, which is essentially a small muscular pouch. Water is reabsorbed from the gall bladder, and the concentrated bile is emptied periodically into the duodenum.

The absorption of food substances (water, alcohol, and some drugs excepted) is restricted to the small intestines. In the *small intestines* virtually all the digestible components of the ingested nutrients are broken down into absorbable low-molecular-weight substances by the pancreatic enzymes, the bile salts, and the intestinal enzymes. The latter (which in-

clude amylase, maltase, lipase, nuclease, and many others) are produced
by the small intestinal glands situated at the base of the intestinal villi.
The surface of the small intestine is greatly enlarged by macroscopic folds
and by innumerable microscopic fingerlike processes, the villi. The *villi* are
richly supplied by fine blood capillaries; the absorption of monosaccharides,
amino acids, fatty acids, and other digested nutrients occurs here by diffusion. These nutrients are carried from the capillaries by the portal vein
to the liver, where some of the nutrients are stored (for example, glucose
in the form of glycogen) and the rest released for circulation throughout
the body.

The *large intestine* extends from the ileum to the anus. It is commonly
subdivided into several components, the cecum, colon, rectum, and anal
canal. A considerable proportion of the water present in the chyme is reabsorbed from the cecum and colon, but other substances (such as nutrients) are not absorbed. The solid material left in the colon, the feces,
represents waste products. Feces contains all the indigestible ingredients of
food, such as cellulose, and also the waste materials of the circulatory and
lymphatic systems. A large concentration of bacteria is also present in the
feces; these play a role, as intestinal flora, in the breakdown of nitrogenous
substances and the fermentation of carbohydrates.

**The Urinary System**   The last constituent of the alimentary mechanism, the urinary system,
consists of kidneys, bladder, and urethra. The *kidneys* are paired organs
composed of many (several hundred thousand) microscopic structures, the
nephrons. Nephrons are excretory units of the kidney that filter from the
blood certain substances eventually excreted as urine. The nephrons are
composed of the renal glomeruli and renal tubules. The cells of the
glomeruli act as passive semipermeable filters for the removal of various
low-molecular substances that are present in high concentration in the
blood. The glomeruli are rich in capillaries; blood is delivered to them
by way of the renal artery. Each glomerulus has an efferent vessel, through
which blood is brought to the glomerulus, and an efferent vessel, which
terminates in the renal tubules. The latter represent a tortuous path
from which water is reabsorbed by the blood and through which excreted
substances pass through the pelvis of the kidney to a duct called the
ureter, by way of which the urine is passed into the urinary bladder.
The urine is a liquid excretory product that contains various inorganic
and organic waste materials. Of the latter, urea, ammonia, and creatinine
are breakdown products of proteins and amino acids, and uric acid is a
waste product of purines. Normal urine does not contain glucose. By its
excretory functions, the kidney plays an important role in the maintenance
of standard composition of blood and tissue fluid. The kidney is also
involved in the regulation of acid-base balance through its production

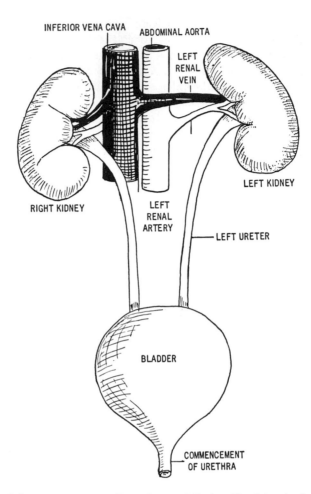

INFERIOR VENA CAVA    ABDOMINAL AORTA

LEFT RENAL VEIN

LEFT KIDNEY

RIGHT KIDNEY    LEFT RENAL ARTERY

LEFT URETER

BLADDER

COMMENCEMENT OF URETHRA

Diagram of the urinary system. (From Best and Taylor, *The living body*, 4th ed., Holt, Rinehart and Winston, 1958)

and elimination of various salts. The urine that is passed, by way of the ureter, from the kidney to the bladder is stored in the latter and emptied periodically by muscular contraction of the bladder through the urethra.

**REPRODUCTON AND VEGETATIVE PROPAGATION**
**Reproduction and Heredity**

Although the maintenance of individual existence requires only continued metabolism, survival of the species depends on self-duplication or reproduction. Before senescence slows down and death puts an end to the existence of the individual, offspring are produced that can carry on a similar existence with rejuvenated strength. There are, of course, individuals or groups of individuals within a species that are not endowed with the ability of self-reproduction and that are nevertheless "alive." But survival of the species requires that at least some individuals reproduce themselves and thus contribute to the perpetuation of the species.

The cleavage (separation) of acellular organisms, such as bacteria, represents the simplest form of reproduction known. Through this process one individual gives rise to two, each of which can independently carry on its own existence. Reproduction is more complicated in multicellular organisms, in which cell division is necessary not only for reproduction but also for embryonic differentiation and growth. In primitive multicellular organisms potentiality for existence as an individual may be latently present in many or all cells of the body; circumstantial factors determine whether a cell becomes differentiated into some specialized structure within the organism or becomes the germ material of a new individual. In most higher multicellular forms, however, these two processes, developmental segmentation and reproductive division, are separated; only specific cells (germ cells or gametes) are usually engaged in, or capable of, reproducing the organism through a morphogenetic process. Further, early in the evolutionary history of life, reproductive cell division became dependent on fertilization.

*Fertilization* is the conjugation of two cells prior to division, a phenomenon occasionally seen even in some acellular organisms. In differentiated organisms two kinds of gametes are produced, and fertilization is a bisexual process. One of the gametes is loaded with nutrients and, associated with a relatively great weight, it is comparatively passive; this is the female gamete or *ovum*. The other gamete contains little if any nutrients and represents essentially a packet of chromosomes in the nucleus; this is the male gamete or *sperm*. The sperm is not only light but motile, being furnished with a flagellum, so that it can actively move about in pursuit of ova. Sperms and ova are produced in some species by a single organism (hermaphrodites), but more commonly separate individuals, males and females, produce sperms or ova exclusively. Whether male and female gametes are produced by a single organism or separately by males and females, organic adaptations exist that permit fertilization of an ovum only by a sperm originating from a different individual. This is the phenomenon of *cross fertilization*, which greatly contributes to hereditary variation. This latter factor may be the adaptive basis of the evolution of bisexual reproduction.

In cells of sexually reproducing organisms there are two sets of chromosomes present in the nucleus, one derived from each parent (diploid cells). Cells specializing in propagation lose one set of chromosomes through *meiotic division* (a necessary process, because otherwise there would be a continual duplication and geometric growth in the chromosome number of conjugating gametes). Meiotic division takes place in cells situated in the spore capsules of plants and in the ovaries and testes of animals, and through this reductive process the normal diploid cells are turned into haploid ones. When sexual conjugation of the gametes takes place, the diploid condition is re-established and the fertilized germ cell is ready for normal mitotic or somatic division.

Cytological studies have shown that *mitotic division* proceeds in several steps. When the cell is not preparing for division or is "resting" (this period is called the interphase), the chromosomes of the nucleus are dispersed as extended threads. In the first, preparatory stage, called the prophase, the chromosomes become condensed, and, in animal cells, a pair of polar spindle apparatus is formed. In the next stages, the metaphase and ana-

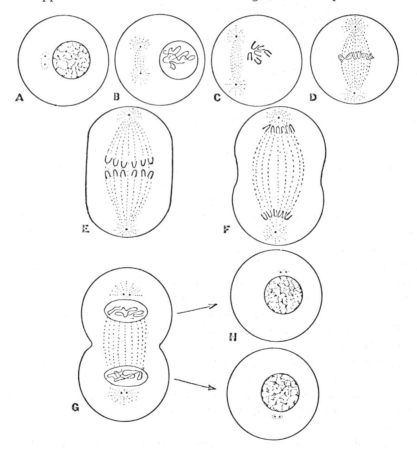

Mitotic division of an animal cell. A, B, C, prophase; D, metaphase; E, F, anaphase; G, H, telophase. (From Best and Taylor, *The living body*, 4th ed., Holt, Rinehart and Winston, 1958)

phase, the duplicated chromosomes are aligned in the middle portion of the spindle apparatus, are pulled apart, and then moved to the opposite poles of the enlarged cell. In the last stage, called telophase, a cleavage furrow appears, new nuclear membranes are formed, and finally the two cells separate. From the biochemical point of view, this complex cytological process represents the segregation of the double set of DNA molecules located in the diploid set of chromosomes, followed by the transference of the reduplicated DNA macromolecules to two separate cells in which, after division in the interphase, the diploid set of chromosomes is reduplicated. This is the process that makes possible the replication of DNA-coded genetic information and its transmittance to daughter cells.

We shall deal here very briefly with the laws of *heredity*. The basic laws of heredity were established by Mendel on the basis of his breeding studies in plants, which were subsequently related to cytological events (modes of chromosomal segregation and recombination) and, more recently, to underlying biochemical processes (guidance of enzyme production by the nucleic acids of the chromosomes). The operation of hereditarily determined regulatory factors in reproduction was well known for a long time and was extensively utilized by farmers and breeders. The commonly held belief was that if both parents shared a trait (for instance, certain body size, shape, or color) the offspring would inherit the trait in pure form, but if the parents had divergent traits, the offspring would inherit a blend or mixture of the two traits. In his careful studies, Mendel found that when a snapdragon with red flowers was mated with another red one, all the offspring were red, and when the reds were mated with white ones, the offspring were pink, apparently a mixture of the two. However, when these pink offspring were mated with each other, half of the new generation was pink, about one-quarter red, and one-quarter white. From this and related experiments Mendel concluded that the genetic determinants of variable traits (which geneticists now call alleles, or allelic genes) never blend but remain segregated. This is Mendel's first law, the "law of segregation" or "law of purity of gametes."

In terms of the chromosome theory, the inheritance of flower color in the snapdragon is interpreted as follows. In homologous regions of chromosome pairs of the reproductive cells of the red snapdragon there are two genes, AA, which together induce the development of the red color of the flowers. When the chromosomes segregate in meiotic division, one of these A genes is retained, and when the gamete is fertilized by another haploid gamete with an A gene, the AA combination is re-established. As expressed by geneticists, the *genotype* of AA leads to the development of the *phenotype* of red color. When, on the other hand, a red snapdragon, AA, is mated with a white one, aa, all the zygotes produced will have a mixed pair of chromosomes, Aa, which lead to the development of pink flowers, a blend of red and white. In the subsequent meiotic segregation of the Aa alleles of the pink flowers, half of the haploid cells will have an A gene, the other half an a gene. Consequently, in the zygotes of these gametes the following combination will occur: AA, Aa, aA, and aa, giving rise to one quarter with red flowers (AA), one half with pink flowers (Aa, aA), and one quarter with white flowers (aa).

The very same process of chromosomal segregation and recombination may also lead to different results. Mendel found that when he bred red-flowered garden peas with white ones, the offspring were all red. But when he interbred these impure red-flowered peas, three quarters of the new seeds produced red-flowered peas and one quarter, white-flowered peas. The assumption had to be made, therefore, that in the garden pea the gene determining red color, A, is *dominant* over the gene producing white color, a, the latter being a *recessive* allele. Thus the combinations of AA and Aa produce red flowers, the former being pure or *homozygous*, the latter a hybrid or *heterozygous*, and only the combination aa can produce white-flowered peas.

Studying the simultaneous inheritance of two or more traits (for instance, the inheritance of seed shape and seed color in the garden pea), Mendel found that the traits were independently inherited. These findings gave rise to the second law of heredity, the "law of independent assortment." This law is easy to reconcile with the modern gene theory which assumes that each gene is represented in the chromosomes by an individual particle. Mendel's second law, however, has only restricted validity, because it applies primarily to genes located in different chromosomes. Genes located in the same chromosome are *linked* and therefore tend to be transmitted in a block. But such a linked transmission is not imperative; as Morgan's elegant studies in the fruitfly showed, there may be *crossing over* between adjacent chromosomes, fragments of the chromosomes being exchanged in the process.

In closing this brief account of the Mendelian laws of inheritance, we must point out that we have dealt here only with the simplest instances of heredity, where certain simple traits are determined by a single set of allelic genes. It is justified to assume, however, that most organic traits, or characters, including the inheritance of behavioral properties, are determined by a multitude of genes whose effects interact with one another in a complex manner during development. (Some examples of the inheritance of behavior traits are considered in Chapter 17.)

Finally, we may refer here briefly to the great advances recently made in the study of the functional relation of hereditary factors, on the one hand, and ensuing metabolic processes, on the other. These advances are to a large extent attributable to the investigations of Beadle, Tatum, and their collaborators (Beadle, 1951). Cultures of the bread mold *Neurospora* were exposed to ultraviolet or x-ray irradiation to produce genetic mutations in them; then alterations in their metabolism in terms of changed nutritional requirements were investigated. Mutant strains that lost the ability to synthesize certain amino acids, vitamins, nucleic acids, and so forth were isolated. These losses in metabolic capacity were transmitted hereditarily. On the basis of these studies, Beadle hypothesized a one-gene–one-enzyme relation, each specific enzyme of the body having a specific gene as its determinant. This hypothesis of Beadle was carried a step further by the more recent studies of Watson, Crick, Ochoa, Nirenberg, and others, referred to above, which are beginning to throw light on how the genes or DNA molecules transfer their coded information to RNA, and how RNA molecules, in turn, determine the specificity of proteins, enzymes included.

**Sex Organs and Sexual Propagation in Plants** The sexual mode of reproduction necessitates the fertilization of ova from one individual by sperms from another. Because they lack a neuromuscular system, the majority of plants rely on external agents, such as air currents or insects, to transport pollen (which produce the male gametes) to the ovules (which contain the egg) and display various structural adaptations to solicit or promote the "cooperation" of these outside agents. Some plants produce syrupy substances or nectar, which is the favorite food source of many insects. To advertise the presence of nectar, the sex organs of plants, the flowers, are equipped with brightly colored petals, liberate various odorous substances, or may have a "conspicuous" appearance. Certain insects are totally dependent on nectar; when they visit the flowers they rub against the anthers of one flower and carry pollen to the stigma of another, thus assisting in sexual fertilization. In some plants there are complicated accessory structures that control, in a passive or nonbehavioral manner, the various steps of this process. In this way sexual interaction is achieved in the absence of a biomechanical capacity for the direct behavioral control of sexual propagation. A similar process is also employed for the dissemination of seeds, which again are carried by the winds, or by animals, usually birds, which are attracted by the external fruity coverings of the seeds. The birds eat the fruits and disseminate the seeds when they are excreted intact in the feces.

This "passive," nonbehavioral mode of interaction with the environment in furtherance of sexual reproduction we shall designate as *vegetative sexual propagation*. This vegetative mode of sexual propagation will be distinguished from another, "active," behavioral method employed by animals, called *animative sexual propagation*. Animals solicit reproduction by such means as the seeking and following of sex partners, various patterns of courtship and mating behavior, and, in some higher species, complex parental activities. (The term "vegetative sexual propagation" used in this study differs from the term "vegetative reproduction" as used in botany.)

**Primary and Secondary** Germ cells are endowed with bisex-
**Sex Organs in Animals** ual potentiality of developing into
male or female individuals. Sex de-
termination depends on the coupling of chromosomes when the ovum is
fertilized by a sperm (the XX combination leading to differentiation into
female sex, XY into male). In addition, sex determination may also depend on as yet ill-understood factors operating during the differentiation
process. Males and females are distinguished by different primary sex organs, different accessory sex organs, and different secondary sex characters.

THE MALE REPRODUCTIVE SYSTEM. The *primary sex organs* of
males are the testes, the paired glands in which the spermatozoa, or sperms,
are produced. The *testes* are located either in the abdominal cavity or, as
in most mammals, in an external pouch, the scrotum. Each testis is di-
visible into lobules within which there are numerous tortuous canals, the
seminiferous tubules. The *sperms* are derived from the epithelium of the
seminiferous tubules. The primordial spermatogonia undergo mitotic division and give rise to primary spermatocytes. The latter undergo meiotic

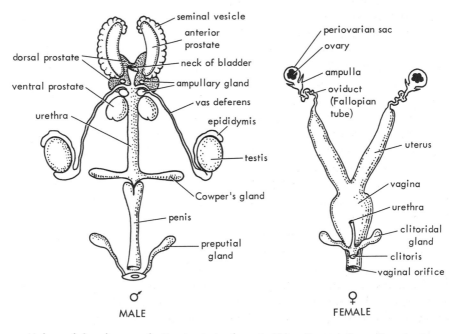

Male and female reproductive tracts in the rat. (After Turner, *General endocrinology*, 3d ed., W. B. Saunders, 1960)

division, as mentioned earlier, and give rise to haploid secondary spermato-cytes. From these latter cells develop the spermatozoa. Spermatozoa are produced in large number in the testes, cyclically in seasonally breeding animals, and year round in other species.

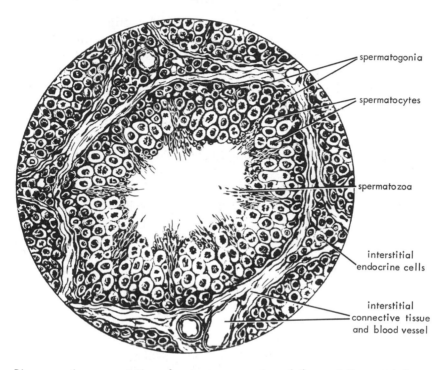

Diagrammatic representation of a transverse section of the seminiferous tubule of a mammal. (After Gillison, *A histology of the body tissues,* 2d ed., E. & S. Livingstone, 1961)

The spermatozoa are conveyed from the testes by *accessory sex organs;* these include the epididymis, vas deferens, seminal vesicles, ejaculatory ducts, Cowper's glands, prostate glands, the urethra, and the penis. Joined with the testis is a convoluted canal, the epididymis, in which the sperma-tozoa are stored. Connected with the epididymis is a long, slender tube, the vas deferens, which receives secretions, the seminal fluid, from the seminal vesicle, Cowper's gland, and prostates. The *seminal fluid* represents the carrying medium in which the sperms are moved through the ejaculatory duct. The ejaculatory duct joins the urethra, which serves as a common passageway with the urinary system for the *ejaculation* of semen (the mix-ture of sperms and seminal fluid). Ejaculation and penile erection are neuromuscular processes, to be discussed later. The *secondary sex charac-ters* differentiating males and females differ widely among different species.

They may include different body size or shape, the development of differential markings or ornaments, be it through different pigmentation, different patterns of feather or hair growth, and the like. The development of secondary sex characters, largely dependent on hormones secreted by the gonads, is discussed in Chapter 17.

THE FEMALE REPRODUCTIVE SYSTEM. The primary sex organs in females are the ovaries. The *ovaries* are paired structures situated, in mammals, in the pelvic cavity. The ovary of mammals (to which this discussion is restricted) may be subdivided into the cortex and medulla. The cortex is covered by the germinal epithelium and contains follicles and corpora lutea. The medulla consists mostly of connective tissue and a rich collection of blood vessels. The germinal epithelium is the source of cells that in the course of the *ovarian cycle* differentiate into follicles and corpora lutea. The cells of the germinal epithelium differentiate first into primary follicles.

The *primary follicle* is a microscopic structure consisting of a primary ovum, the oogonium, surrounded by granulosa cells. As its yolk content increases, the oogonium differentiates into a primary oocyte, and the granulosa cells form a fluid-filled cavity, the vesicular follicle. The vesicular follicle then increases in size, owing to the rapid proliferation of the granulosa cells. Eventually the bulging follicle, called the *Graafian follicle*, ruptures, and the secondary oocyte, which is a product of meiotic division,

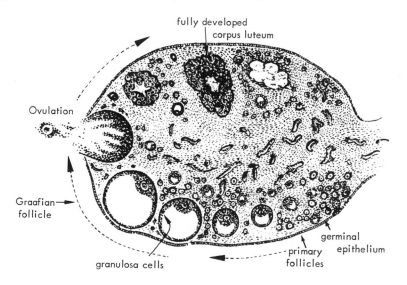

Diagrammatic representation of the ovary, showing the stages in the maturation of the follicles, ovulation, and the formation of the corpus luteum. (After Bell, Davidson, and Scarborough, *Textbook of physiology and biochemistry*, 5th ed., E. & S. Livingstone, 1961)

is released; this is the process of *ovulation*. The granulosa cells of the ruptured follicle accumulate a yellow pigment, and a new structure is formed, the *corpus luteum*. (The follicles, as we shall see later, are a source of estrogenic hormones, and the corpora lutea a source of both estrogens and progestogens.) If the ovum is fertilized by a sperm, the corpus luteum undergoes changes that characterize the corpus luteum of pregnancy; if the ovum is not fertilized, the corpus luteum of menstruation eventually degenerates. At this point it should be noted that the ovarian cycle, and its structural and functional characteristics, vary widely among different species.

The female accessory organs (see page 58) include the oviduct, the uterus, the vagina, and external genitalia. The *oviduct*, a muscular tube with ciliated epithelium, connects the ovary and the uterus and serves as a passageway for the shedding of ova into the uterus. The *uterus* is a paired organ in some species and fused in others, and it is connected through a narrowed caudal neck, the cervix, with the vagina. The uterus is composed of several layers, vascular, muscular, and mucous. The fertilized ovum becomes embedded in the internal mucous layer where a nourishing medium, the *placenta*, is formed in mammals. The fertilized ovum undergoes its morphogenetic development for variable periods of gestation in the uterus, which thus serves as a protective and nourishing compartment for the embryo. The uterus undergoes marked changes during pregnancy, which make possible the accommodation and eventual delivery (parturition) of the growing embryo. Preparation for delivery is associated, in mammals, with the development of, or changes in, the mammary glands and the secretion of milk. The cycling of these complex processes, which begin with fertilization and continue after parturition, depends largely on humoral regulation, to be discussed in Chapter 17.

**Reproduction and Morphogenetic Development** In acellular organisms, development is often an inconspicuous process, because the offspring is quite similar to its parent at the time of division. Development becomes a more complex and more prolonged process in multicellular organisms, in which the fertilized ovum bears no resemblance either to the parents or to the mature individual into which it is gradually transformed. This developmental transformation is variously referred to as embryonic growth, ontogenetic development, or morphogenesis. It is a fundamental aspect of the reproductive process whereby the latent potentialities present in coded form in the germ cell are unfolded and the growing system is endowed with individuality.

When the ovum of an animal is fertilized, a repeated process of cellular division is initiated, and the single cell is transformed into a structure composed of an increasing number of embryonic cells. These cells are

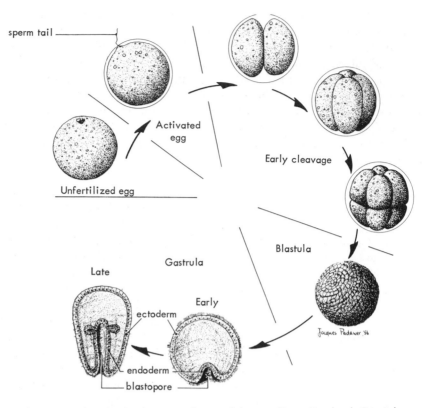

sperm tail

Activated egg

Unfertilized egg

Early cleavage

Blastula

Gastrula

Late

Early

ectoderm

endoderm

blastopore

*Jacques Padawer '56*

Fertilization and early development of a starfish egg. (From Marsland, *Principles of modern biology,* 4th ed., Holt, Rinehart and Winston, 1964)

called, at the earlier stages of development of animal organisms, blastomeres, and the hollow spherical structure that they give rise to is called the *blastula*. The next developmental stage is called gastrulation. This is introduced by a process of invagination in which a group of cells moves downward and, reaching the bottom of the blastula from the inside, forms a two-layered wall. At this stage, the inside layer is called the *endoderm*, which lines the hollow called archenteron or primitive gut; the layer remaining outside is called the *ectoderm*. Later a tissue develops between the ectoderm and the endoderm, called the *mesoderm*, and with it all three layers of the tripoblastic embryo are developed. These layers then give rise, by successive stages of *structural* and *functional differentiation*, to various tissues and organs. In general, the mesoderm gives rise to the vascular, muscular, and reproductive organs of the body, and to such accessory parts as connective and supporting tissues. The cells of the endoderm form the organs of alimentary digestion, and the cells of the ectoderm develop the sense organs and the nervous system.

Cellular differentiation leads to the development of various structurally and functionally distinguishable cell types. A related process in morphogenetic development is the selective association of these different cell types into varied tissues and organs. The exact nature of the formative and integrative aspect of development is as little understood as that of differentiation. Development is essentially an internally controlled process; therefore the interaction among the various cells must be of paramount importance. The differentiated cells may aggregate or segregate, form densely packed tissues or disperse over the body, proliferate at a high rate or divide sluggishly. For instance, it was found by Wilson (1907) a long time ago that the cells of a sponge that were dissociated from one another by being squeezed through a silk sieve restored themselves and reunited to form a normal sponge. Wilson's observation suggested that the individual cells can in some way "recognize" one another. Later, Holtfreter (1943) demonstrated in the embryonic tissue of amphibians that certain cell types adhere to one another because of some unknown affinity, but others do not. Some cells are also characterized by motility; they can thus migrate from the site of production to other parts of the body (Weiss, 1950). Also, some cells that at an early stage of development are compatible with one another may, at a later stage, develop an incompatibility, which leads to their segregation.

That some cells exercise control over others is well established. Spemann (1936) found that cells of the dorsal lip of the blastopore (a region through which the invaginating blastomeres pass during gastrulation) act as developmental "organizers" in the amphibian embryo, inducing the formation of the nerve tube. If the dorsal lip of the blastopore of the early newt gastrula is removed and transplanted underneath the ectoderm cells of another, the first embryo fails to develop a nerve tube, whereas the other develops a second one. The biochemical analysis of this inducer process showed that a number of chemicals may start this differentiation, such as steroids (Needham, 1942), nucleoproteins (Brachet, 1950), and others.

The investigations of Spemann also threw light on the nature of the later phases of differentiation. Studying the development of the eye in amphibians, he found that the optic cup of the forebrain acts as an inducer. The optic cup itself becomes the retina, but simultaneously it induces the overlying epidermis to form a lens. If the optic cup is transplanted into various embryonic regions, its inductive powers are retained, and alien tissue is induced to form a lens. The optic cup, accordingly, is an induction center similar to the dorsal blastopore lip, but a very specialized one that controls the development of one single organ.

If this mechanism of differentiation has universal validity, we may think of the morphogenetic process as one of sequential unfolding in which competent but undifferentiated embryonic cells progressively assume more and more specialized forms and functions under the guidance of localized inductive structures. However, the latent potentialities realized in this process are triggered by the inductive regions but not directed by them. This conclusion is drawn from another set of experiments carried out by Spemann and his collaborators, in which the technique of heteroplastic transplantation was employed (in this procedure embryonic tissue is transplanted from an individual of one species to another of a different, though related, species). When presumptive epidermis from *Hyla* is transplanted into the mouth region of *Triton taeniatus*, the unspecialized tissue of the donor is turned into specific local tissues and organs by the regional inducing power of the host. The structures formed by the alien tissue, however, do not resemble the homologous organs of the host but retain the characteristics of the donor. That is, notwithstanding the fact that the specialization is induced by the host's local organizing powers, the development is controlled by the genetic inheritance of the affected cells.

We shall later (Chapter 13) discuss further the problem of morphogenetic organization with reference to the question of the nature of the regional differentiation of the central nervous system, and the formation of specific neural circuits between receptors and effectors and between different brain structures.

In summary, it may be said that the reproductive multiplication of germ cells and the morphogenetic process represent two important aspects in the organic task of maintaining the species. These two, it should be added, are essentially *intra*organic aspects of the process of species preservation, which, in addition, necessitate other processes involving interaction with the environment. The *inter*organic aspects of development, such as the relation between parents and their offspring, will be discussed in some detail in Chapter 17.

**HUMORAL INTEGRATION AND VEGETATIVE ADJUSTMENTS**    The innumerous activities of the organism are carried out by a multitude of specialized cells, tissues, and organs, whose harmonious functioning requires complex processes of communication and integration. Further, because the existence and welfare of the organism are dependent on its environment, the ability to adjust to varied and changing conditions of the environment is a prerequisite of organic existence.

The best-known organic mechanism serving these functions is the central nervous system, and we are often inclined to think of it as the only organic apparatus of communication and adjustment. The central nervous system is absent, however, in many types of organisms that manifest coordinated organic functioning: there is no nervous system in plants, and it is absent or rudimentary in protozoans and primitive metazoans. As we shall try to demonstrate later, integration of organic activities by means of the central nervous system is a phylogenetically recent development. A more fundamental and ancient system, which is present in plants as well as animals, is the vegetative mechanism of humoral or hormonal communication, integration, and adjustment.

**Hormones** Hormones are chemical compounds that, produced and liberated by various cells, including specialized glandular cells, are carried in the vascular fluid streams throughout the body. "Hormone" means an excitor; however, there are hormones that function as inhibitors, and many of the hormones that facilitate the activities of one group of tissue may retard those of another. The term, therefore, is now quite generally used in a wider sense to incorporate all humorally dispersed chemical substances whose functions are communication between various organs of the body, and the regulation or coordination of organic processes. Hormones are chemically a very heterogeneous group; there is no relation between the hormones of plants and those of animals, and the various groups of animal hormones are chemically quite different from one another (such as steroids, amino acid derivatives, and proteins). Unlike enzymes and nucleoproteins, most hormones are not species-specific. Auxin from one plant, or thyroxine from one animal, may affect the developmental processes of other plants or animals.

All hormones have a few common characteristics. Both plant and animal hormones are effective in very low concentrations. One part of auxin diluted in 100 million parts of water may produce detectable root growth (Audus, 1960); a hormone of the pituitary gland, called pitressin, in a solution of 1 part in 5 billion parts of water, contracts the uterus of a pregnant rabbit (Amberson and Smith, 1948). The exact concentration of a hormone is an important factor of its mode of action. Auxin, for instance, accelerates root growth only in small concentration; in high concentration it retards root growth. Another common characteristic of hormones is their comparatively small molecular weight, a factor that may be important in permitting the easy transportation or diffusion of hormones and their penetration through the walls and membranes of cells. Hormones have no autonomous means of reaching their target organs: in plants they are moved in the fluid streams; in animals they are carried throughout the body in the circulatory system. Most glands do not store hormones in large quantities; after their production and liberation the hormones may be inactivated or destroyed and thus prevented from lingering in the body indefinitely.

The regulation of hormone production in many instances involves feedback mechanisms. An example is the production of parathormone, the hormone of the parathyroid gland, which controls calcium metabolism but is itself controlled by the calcium concentration of the blood. When the calcium concentration of the body falls, the gland is induced to produce more parathormone; when the calcium level of the blood is thus raised, the rate of parathormone production falls. In other instances external stimuli control the rate of hormone production. Lengthened duration of light during the day, for instance, activates in various species of animals the production of gonadotrophic hormones by the pituitary gland; in this manner the seasonal cycling of sexual maturation is controlled.

**Vegetative Integration and**       Organisms have to adjust them-
**Adjustment in Plants**       selves to outside circumstances, uti-
lize the opportunties presented by favorable environmental conditions, and avoid or counteract unfavorable influences. If we investigate the behavior of sessile plants, however, we find that they manifest relatively little active behavior comparable to the quick and constant overt activity of animals. By what physiological methods can plants achieve their adjustment to outside events? Much of what animals achieve by swift animative or neuromuscular action is attained by plants by slower structural and functional adaptations. To facilitate maximal utilization of sunshine, for instance, many green plants have evolved large flattened leaves with extended surfaces in which the chloroplast granules are densely concentrated. To permit absorption of water and minerals dissolved in it, fine capillary rootlets penetrate into the soil, and a vascular system is developed through which large quantities of water can circulate, drawn from the soil by means of propitious physical forces, as described earlier. For protection from harmful outside agents, plant cells are enclosed in hard cellulose coverings, and the whole plant is given structural support by woody fibers of the stem. These and other similar structural adaptations facilitate adjustment to the environment without true behavioral interaction.

In addition to these essentially nonbehavioral interrelations by means of structural adaptations, a limited number of active adjustments also occurs in plants. No matter in what position a seed falls or is placed in the soil, the root grows downward and the shoot upward; later, the lateral roots, branches, and leaves arrange themselves horizontally. This morphogenetic pattern of adjustment, furthermore, is not rigidly set; slight modifications, if necessary, are readily performed. If light consistently penetrates from one side, as with plants growing under the window in a room, the leaves will tend to orient themselves in that direction; or if water is located in a selected part of the soil, the roots tend to grow toward it.

Most of these active types of plant adjustments are regulated by hormones. One of the earliest investigators of the problem of plant adjustments was Darwin (1881), who demonstrated that the bending of canary grass toward the illuminated side is dependent on the sensitiveness of the tip of the leaf sheath, although the bending itself takes place at some distance below it. Darwin found that if the tip of the leaf sheath was removed, or a lightproof material was placed over it, the phototropic bending below the tip did not take place. It was later shown that the communicating "influence," which moved from the tip to the growing regions, was of a chemical nature, because it passed through protoplasmic discontinuities, such as nonliving gelatinous gaps, if such were placed between the tip and the stump. Subsequently some of these humoral agents were isolated and identified and are now known collectively as auxins (Leopold, 1955).

*Auxins* control many important integrative and adjustive functions in plants. The general rate of growth, the unilateral elongation of cells, bud and root formation, flowering, and many other processes are dependent on the control action of auxins. Auxins are produced in various parts of the plant, in particular in regions sensitive to various external stimuli. Carried throughout the body by fluids in the vascular channels of the plant, auxins affect the growth patterns of various responsive tissues. As is well known, plants can respond to a variety of physical stimuli, such as photic, gravitational, chemical, and mechanical. These responses are called tropistic movements or *tropisms*; depending on the nature of the stimulus eliciting them, they are distinguished as phototropism, geotropism, chemotropism, thigmotropism, and so forth.

Tropisms are specified as *positive* when the ensuing response brings the plant, or part of it, toward the stimulus, and as *negative* if the move-

Positive phototropism of the stem of a bean seedling. Successive photographic exposures at 40-minute intervals.

Negative geotropism of the stem of a bean seedling. Successive exposures at 45-minute intervals. (From Marsland, *Principles of modern biology*, 4th ed., Holt, Rinehart and Winston, 1964)

ment produced is away from the stimulus. Most of the responses controlled by auxins are essentially *growth processes*. The bending of the root
or shoot of plants is caused by unilateral growth or elongation of cells;
other plant movements are based on the proliferation of cells in some
regions of the body and on their cessation in other regions. Being growth
processes, these plant adjustments are characterized by relative sluggishness
and irreversibility.

Some plants may also manifest quick and reversible kinds of adjustments. The most common of these is the employment of turgor mechanisms. *Turgor movements* are produced by two forces: the elasticity of cell
walls and the reversible absorption of water by certain specialized cells
and tissues. These specialized cells and tissues are located at the base of
movable parts of the plant (as leaflets, petiole, or modified leaves), and
through loss or uptake of water, opening or closing movements are brought
about. The most familiar of these are the relatively quick closing movements of the modified leaf of the insectivorous Venus' flytrap and the

The folding of the leaflets of *Mimosa pudica*. A, the plant before it was touched;
B, five seconds after it was touched. (By E. H. Runyon, from Marsland, *Principles
of modern biology*, 4th ed., Holt, Rinehart and Winston, 1964)

folding of the leaflets of *Mimosa pudica*. The sleep movements of various plants, and also some of the tropisms, such as the phototropic movements of the sunflower, are produced by turgor mechanisms.

The preceding brief account indicates that adjustive mechanisms have an important function in regulating the interaction between plants and their environment. From the physiological point of view, however, there is little resemblance between the adjustment mechanisms employed by plants and those employed by animals. Animals are furnished with specialized cells, tissues, and organs (receptors, muscle, and nerve) whose function is quick and effective adjustments to external changes; these animative mechanisms of behavioral interaction are not present in developed form in plants. In some primitive plantlike organisms, such as the slime mold (*Myxomycetes*), primordial animative mechanisms, as manifested in ciliary and ameboid movements, are present. The same mechanisms are also shown by the reproductive cells of a few primitive plants (antherozoids and zoospores), which are furnished with flagella. Nevertheless, though rudiments of animative abilities may be present in plants, they never occur in developed form; no plant is equipped with a neuromuscular system.

**Vegetative or Hormonal Integration in Animals**  Animals carry out their overt adjustments to changing environmental conditions almost exclusively by means of animative mechanisms, under the guidance of the central nervous system. The integration of various vegetative processes, however, is dependent on humoral means, that is, on hormones secreted into and carried by the circulatory system. In the animal body, hormones are secreted either by endocrine or exocrine glands. *Endocrine*, or *ductless glands*, have no openings into the body cavities but release their hormones into the blood. Of the endocrine glands, the thyroid, adrenals, and pituitary are the best known in vertebrates. Hormones are also secreted into the blood by some of the *exocrine glands*, that is, glands which secrete nonhormonal products into the body cavities. Among the exocrine glands that also produce hormones, best known are the pancreas, the testes, the ovaries, and the intestines.

The chemical composition of animal hormones varies. The secretion of the thyroid gland, thyroxin, is an amino acid; the hormone of the parathyroids, parathormone, and probably all the hormones of the adenohypophysis are proteins; the hormones of the adrenal cortex, as well as those of the testes and ovaries, are steroids. Also, the targets on which these hormones act vary. Some, as thyroxin, insulin, and possibly epinephrine, influence the functioning of many, if not all, the cells of the body; others, such as the hormones of the ovaries, affect the functioning

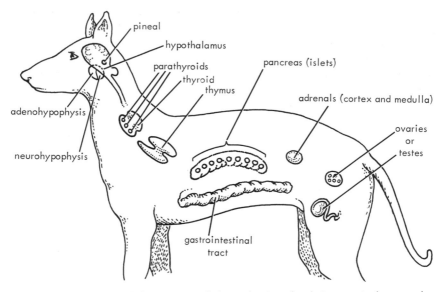

Schematic drawing of the position of the endocrine glands in a typical mammal.

of only selected organs, whereas the hormones of the adenohypophysis interact specifically with endocrine glands and their secretions. The hormones that are presently recognized may be a fraction of those that exist in the animal body; future research will undoubtedly detect many more that have important functions in the regulation of the vegetative activities of the animal organism.

In accordance with the previous distinction of three fundamental vegetative processes, we may somewhat arbitrarily distinguish here three classes of animal (more specifically vertebrate) hormones. First, there are hormones that regulate, in the restricted sense of the term, the metabolic processes of the body. Second, there are hormones concerned with the control of reproductive processes. Finally, there are hormones concerned with the coordination of the activities of all other hormones and that also mediate, in the interest of organismic integration, between the nervous system and the vegetative tissues.

HORMONES COORDINATING METABOLIC PROCESSES. Very important in the control of carbohydrate metabolism is *insulin*, a protein secreted by the beta cells of the island tissues of the *pancreas* (islets of Langerhans). Another metabolic hormone with related functions is *glucagon*, which is produced by the alpha cells of the islets of Langerhans. Insulin insufficiency leads to *diabetes mellitus*, a disease characterized by increased accumulation of glucose in the blood (*hyperglycemia*) and its wasteful elimination through urinary excretion. Injection of excess insulin into the blood stream leads to a marked decrease of the blood sugar level

interlobular septum                    pancreatic acinus

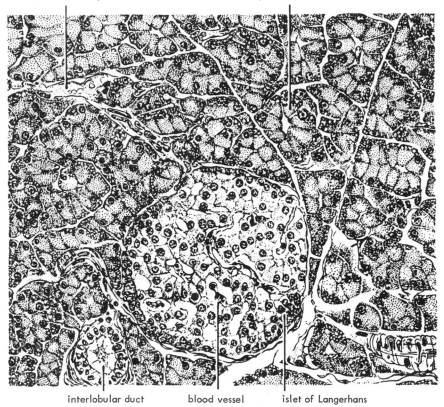

interlobular duct        blood vessel        islet of Langerhans

Drawing of a section of a part of the pancreas in the rat. The islets of Langerhans are the endocrine components of the pancreas; the surrounding acinar tissue forms the exocrine component. (From Turner, *General endocrinology*, 3d ed., W. B. Saunders, 1960)

(*hypoglycemia*). In diabetic animals the production of glycogen by muscles is greatly retarded and the utilization of glycogen stored in the liver is increased; the result is eventual depletion of liver glycogen. The diabetic animal therefore has to utilize other sources of sugar, such as fats and proteins, with consequent increase in food consumption and the wasting of body tissues.

The production and secretion of insulin in the normal animal is a link in the homeostatic equilibrium-maintaining process that assures the constancy of the sugar concentration of the blood. High blood-glucose concentration leads to stimulation of insulin secretion, which then results in an increased utilization and consequent decrease of the glucose level. Low sugar concentration depresses insulin secretion, permitting restoration of the normal level; the latter process is hastened by secretion of epinephrine by the adrenal medulla, because epinephrine induces release of sugar by the liver. The exact mode of action of insulin on sugar metabolism is not known. One of its effects may be the facilitation of the transportation of glucose across the cell membranes into the interior of the metabolizing cells.

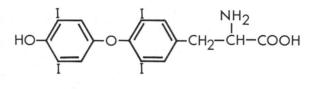

Thyroxin

Another hormone involved in the regulation of metabolic processes is *thyroxin*. Thyroxin is an amino acid produced in the *thyroid* gland; it contains iodine and is generally stored, bound to protein, as iodothy-

secretory epithelium          blood vessel          interfollicular connective tissue

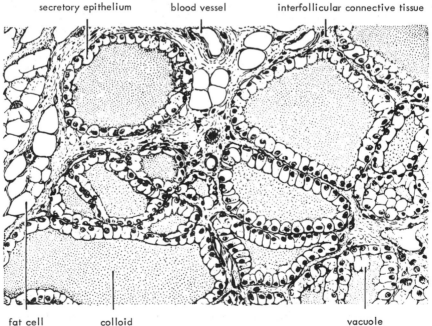

fat cell            colloid                                    vacuole

Drawing of a portion of the thyroid gland of the rat. In this section a few follicles may be seen (there are about 100,000 of them in the thyroid of the rat). The colloid is the secretory product of the follicular epithelium. (From Turner, *General endocrinology*, 3d ed., W. B. Saunders, 1960)

roglobulin. Thyroxin deficiency leads to a fall of the basal metabolic rate; whereas thyroid hyperactivity produces a rise in basal metabolism. The exact mode of action of thyroxin is not known, but it is generally assumed that it hastens oxidative reactions or energy transfer in cells. But thyroxin must also have other effects, because the administration of drugs that accelerate oxidative reactions, such as dinitrophenol, does not eliminate all the thyroid deficiency symptoms. Among other functions, thyroxin affects growth in vertebrates. For example, addition of thyroxin to the medium in which tadpoles are kept produces precocious metamorphosis, whereas removal of the thyroids in tadpoles prevents metamorphosis. The amphibian axolotl, which does not normally metamorphose, is induced to do so by the administration of thyroxin. (Dinitrophenol, the metabolic stimulant, does not have these effects.) In some reptiles and birds administration of thyroxin initiates molting. In young mammals thyroid deficiency leads to a retardation of development, known as cretinism, manifested by such symptoms as inhibited skeletal growth, failure of sexual maturation, and inadequate development of the neuromuscular system. Thyroid activity, as described later, is dependent on the thyroid-stimulating hormone (TSH) of the pituitary.

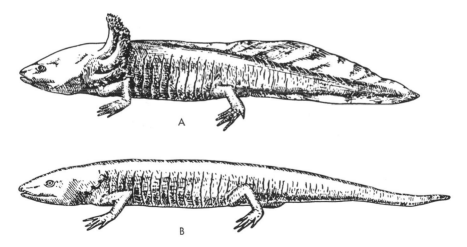

The effect of iodine implantation on the metamorphosis of the American axolotl. A, untreated gilled stage; B, metamorphosis 30 days after implantation of iodine crystals under the skin. Note atrophy of the gills and disappearance of the tail fin. (From Turner, *General endocrinology,* 3d ed., W. B. Saunders, 1960)

Great significance is also attributed in the control of metabolism to the *parathyroid hormone* (PTH) secreted by the parathyroid glands. This hormone (possibly hormones) has not yet been isolated in pure form, but there is suggestive evidence that it is either a polypeptide or a protein. Excessively low or high concentrations of parathyroid hormone lead to degeneration of the skeletal system and also to atrophy of the muscular and nervous systems. These disturbances are caused by abnormal calcium and phosphate metabolism. Total removal of these glands (parathyroidectomy) is fatal in most mammals, although the symptoms can be alleviated by dietary supply of calcium and phosphates. Normal parathyroid activity is homeostatically controlled: decrease in calcium concentration of the blood triggers parathyroid hyperactivity, with resulting elevation of the calcium level; rise in calcium level, in turn, is followed by inhibition of parathyroid activity.

Of great importance in the control of metabolism are also the steroid hormones secreted by the *cortical* component of the *adrenal glands*. The common extraction of the adrenal cortex, called cortin, was found to contain almost 50 different steroids, some of which are active components, others presumably precursors or breakdown products. The active hormones secreted by the adrenal cortex include *corticoids*, which will be discussed here, as well as various sex hormones (androgens, progestogens, estrogens). The corticoids, which have important effects on metabolism, have been distinguished as glucocorticoids and mineralocorticoids.

*Glucocorticoids*, which include, among others, cortisone, cortisol, and corticosterone, play a role in the conversion of fats and sugar into glucose. The *mineralocorticoids*, best known of which are aldosterone and deoxycorticosterone, are essential for the regulation of electrolyte and water metabolism. Bilateral removal of the adrenals produces various metabolic deficits (such as kidney failure, hypoglycemia, muscular weakness); unless relieved by the administration of steroids or dietary salt, the animal dies within a short period. Normal secretion of corticoids (with the exception of aldosterone) is homeostatically controlled by corticotrophin (ACTH) of the pituitary. Rise in corticoid secretion leads to a fall in ACTH secretion, and vice versa. Adrenalectomy is followed by an increased output of pituitary ACTH. Increased corticoid output is also seen following strenu-

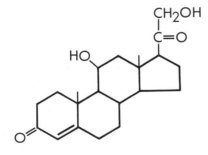

Corticosterone
(A glucocorticoid)

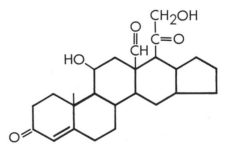

Aldosterone
(A mineralocorticoid)

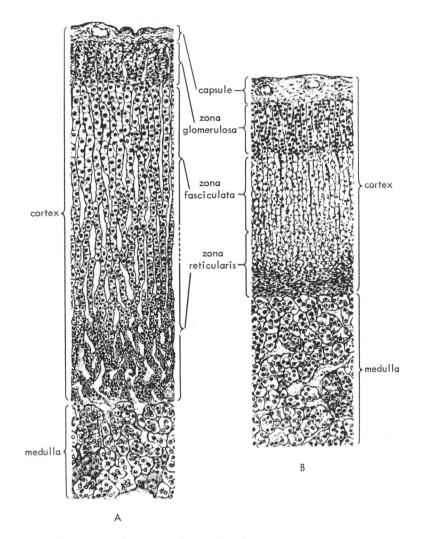

Comparable sections, drawn to scale, of the adrenal gland of (A) a normal and (B) a hypophysectomized rat. The adrenal medulla is not affected by hypophysectomy. In the cortex the width of the zona fasciculata and zona reticularis is greatly reduced in the hypophysectomized rat. The width of the zona glomerulosa, where aldosterone is produced, is not affected by hypophysectomy. (From Turner, *General endocrinology*, 3d ed., W. B. Saunders, 1960)

ous exercise, stress, or trauma. In agreement with this reaction, it was found recently (Mosier, 1957) that the adrenal cortex of wild Norway rats is larger in size, is better vascularized, and its steroid hormone concentration is higher than is found in the domesticated variety. Differential treatment of rats early in life may also lead to changes in adrenal development and corticoid secretion (Levine and Lewis, 1959).

Because we are dealing with hormones involved in the regulation of metabolic processes, we may refer here to certain substances carried by the blood that regulate the functioning of various parts of the gastrointestinal digestive system. The mucosa of the stomach produces a protein, called *gastrin*, which is released in response to mechanical and chemical stimulation produced by food in the stomach. This hormone, in turn, induces the secretion of hydrochloric acid, which is essential for the digestive process. Similar effects, it may be noted, can be obtained in the stomach in the presence of histamine; however, the two substances are different: histaminase, the enzyme that destroys histamine, does not affect the action of gastrin.

The release of another gastric hormone, *enterogastron*, is believed to be stimulated by the presence of fatty substances. The effects of enterogastron are the opposite of those of gastrin: enterogastron inhibits secretion of hydrochloric acid. *Secretin* is another hormone of the gastrointestinal tract. It is a polypeptide produced by cells in the lining of the duodenum. Secretion of this substance is triggered by food passing through the duodenum, and secretin, in turn, stimulates the flow of pancreatic juice and bile formation in the liver. Another hormone secreted by cells of the duodenum is *cholecystokinin*. This substance is chemically related to secretin; it controls the evacuation of the gall bladder.

HORMONES COORDINATING REPRODUCTIVE PROCESSES. The coordination of various aspects of the reproductive process is dependent on hormones. The principal sources of reproductive hormones are the gonads, the testes in males and the ovaries in females. But reproductive hormones, that is, hormones that affect sexual and related processes, are also secreted by other glandular structures, particularly the cortex of the adrenals and the hypophysis.

The male sex hormones, that is, hormones that have a masculinizing effect, are referred to collectively as *androgens*. The principal androgen is

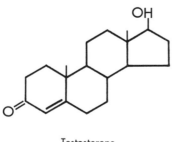

Testosterone

testosterone, which is produced in the testis by the interstitial cells of Leydig. Another androgen produced by the testis is androsterone. Androgens are also produced in smaller quantities by the ovaries and placenta (in the female) and by the adrenal cortex. Androgens play a role in the development and maintenance of virtually all masculine characters of males. First, androgens stimulate sperm production in the testes. This effect is seen in hypophysectomized animals (animals in which the pituitary gland was removed), in which cessation of spermatogenesis can be remedied by in-

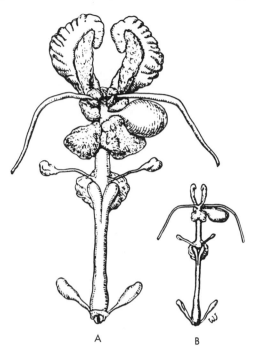

A, the genital tract of a castrated rat that received daily injections of testosterone for 20 days before autopsy. B, the genital tract of a castrated littermate that did not receive replacement therapy. (From Turner, *General endocrinology*, 3d ed., W. B. Saunders, 1960)

A                    B

jection of testosterone. The presence of androgens is also essential for the induction of the development of accessory sex organs. Castration in immature animals prevents the puberal maturation of accessory sex organs and secondary sex characters; these characters do develop if the castrated animal is regularly treated with testosterone. Also, in adults of many species, castration can lead to degeneration of accessory sex organs, and some of the secondary sex characters, which eventually resemble pre-puberal conditions. In contrast, administration of androgens can induce precocious sexual development in young animals and may lead, in some species, to the development of masculine characteristics in females. Likewise, in seasonally breeding species, preseasonal sexual maturation may be induced by injection of testosterone. Secretion of androgens in the normal animal is regulated by the gonadotrophic hormones of the pituitary. Removal of the pituitary leads to degeneration of the testes, cessation of spermatogenesis, and the atrophy of accessory sex organs and secondary sex characters. These regressive effects can be counteracted not only by administration of pituitary gonadotrophic hormones but also by regular treatment with androgens; the suggestion is that the immediate effect of gonadotrophins is on secretion of androgens.

The principal source of female sex hormones is the ovary. The ovary secretes *estrogens*, which stimulate the development of feminine characters in the female, and *progestogens*, which are involved in trriggering gestational changes. In addition, the ovaries also secrete some androgens and a nonsteroid hormone called relaxin. Estrogens, which include estradiol, estrone, and estriol, are secreted by the ovarian follicles and also by the corpus luteum. Progestogens, the most important member of which is progesterone, are secreted by the corpus luteum and, in pregnant females, by the placenta. (The varied effects of sex hormones are discussed in greater detail in Chapter 17.)

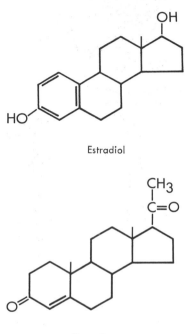

Estradiol

Progesterone

The production and liberation of estrogens and progesterone are important for the cycling of the female reproductive process. The first phase of this cycle is called the *anestrus* or *diestrus*, which coincides with the immaturity of ova, the period when the female is physiologically not ready to be impregnated. During this phase the estrogen level of the blood is low and the accessory sex organs are in a regressive state. With the increasing growth of the follicles and ova the second or *proestrus* phase is introduced. On maturation of the Graafian follicles and in preparation for ovulation, estrogens are secreted into the blood in large quantites, with which the third or *estrus* phase is introduced. The presence of estrogens changes the accessory sex organs: the vagina, oviduct, and uterus become enlarged, and these organs, specifically the uterus, show an increase in contractility. More generally, the estrus female displays receptivity toward males and may thus become impregnated. If impregnation does not occur, the female returns after ovulation to the anestrus (or diestrus) phase, during which the accessory sex organs manifest regressive changes. After a shorter or longer period, which varies greatly in different species, and which is seasonally controlled in many, the described phases are recycled again.

If the female becomes impregnated during estrus, the uterus undergoes proliferative and other changes that prepare it for the reception of the fertilized ovum, the implantation of the blastocysts and their placentation. This reaction may be partially triggered by estrogens but more par-

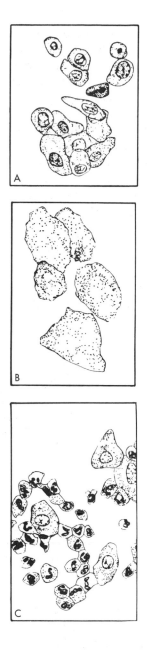

Types of cells present in vaginal smears in various phases of the estrus cycle in the rat. During proestrus (A) the detaching cells are mostly nucleated components of the surface epithelium. During estrus (B) cornified, nonnucleated cells abound. In diestrus (C) leucocytes are present in large number, together with new, nucleated epithelial cells. (After Long and Evans, in Gorham and Bern, *Textbook of comparative endocrinology*, John Wiley & Sons, 1962)

ticularly by progesterone secreted by the corpora lutea, which remain active during pregnancy. When the corpus lutea are excised in rabbits, the embryo fails to develop and is expelled from the uterus; but if progesterone is administered, pregnancy may proceed normally. The manner in which the various sex hormones interact during ovulation and pregnancy is not well understood, and the problem is further complicated by the important regulative role of several pituitary hormones, the follicle-stimulating hormone (FSH), the luteinizing hormone (LH), and the lactogenic hormone, prolactin. If immature females are hypophysectomized, the ovaries and accessory sex organs fail to develop, unless the animals are given remedial treatment with estrogens and progesterone.

HORMONES INVOLVED IN INTEGRATIVE PROCESSES. The *hypophysis*, or *pituitary gland*, located at the base of the brain, is composed of two embryologically, morphologically, and functionally distinguishable structures, the adenohypophysis and neurohypophysis. The adenohypophysis is derived from the mouth pouch of the embryo; the neurohypophysis is

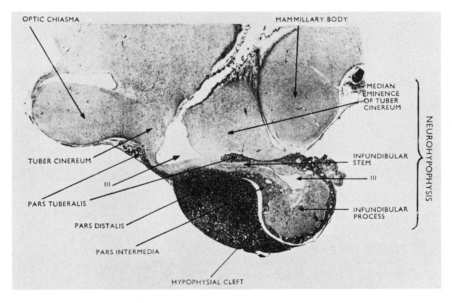

Midline section through the pituitary gland of the dog (with overlying hypothalamus). III, infundibular recess of the third ventricle. (After Richardson, from Bell, Davidson, and Scarborough, *Textbook of physiology and biochemistry*, 5th ed., E. & S. Livingstone, 1961)

derived from the diencephalon of the brain and remains, in the adult, intimately associated with it. We shall be concerned here, first, with the *adenohypophysis*, whose protein secretions interact in a complex manner with virtually all the metabolic and reproductive hormones of the vertebrate body and are involved in the coordination of practically all vegetative processes. Among the various symptoms of removal of the adenohypophysis in young animals are the following: the animal ceases to grow, a fact largely attributable to cessation of skeletal development; the cortex of the adrenal gland and the thyroid gland atrophy; the testes and ovaries remain infantile and the accessory sex organs fail to mature; serious disturbances in carbohydrate, lipid, and protein metabolism ensue; and, finally, because of these and several other deficiencies, the life expectancy of the animal, unless it is given special care, is greatly shortened.

The adenohypophysis is subdivided into three parts: the pars tuberalis, pars intermedia, and pars distalis. At least six hormones of the adenohypophysis were isolated in mammals; most or all of these hormones are secreted by the pars distalis: the somatotrophic or growth hormone (STH); the corticotrophic hormone (ACTH); the thyrotrophic hormone (TSH); the lactogenic hormone, or prolactin (LTH); the follicle-stimulating hormone (FSH); and the luteinizing hormone (LH).

The *growth hormone* (STH), like all other hormones of the pituitary, is a protein. Injection of STH into a normal animal produces increased skeletal growth, which may lead to acromegaly (gigantism). The dwarfism and early ossification of certain skeletal structures seen after hypophysectomy may be attributed to the lack of STH, because injection of purified growth hormone alleviates the symptom. Administration of STH leads also to a facilitation of carbohydrate, fat, and protein metabolism and thus to a general facilitation of somatic development. Unlike the growth hormone, which is not known to affect directly target hormones, the other hormones of the adenohypophysis are characterized by their direct interaction with endocrine glands and are therefore referred to as trophic hormones. The *corticotrophic hormone* (ACTH) is a protein with small molecular weight whose main target is the cortex of the adrenal gland. Injection of ACTH leads to growth of the tissue of the adrenal cortex and increased secretion of the cortical steroid hormones. The interrelation between ACTH and corticoids is a homeostatic one: decreased blood level of corticoids leads to increased pituitary output of ACTH, and, as the level of corticoid secretion rises, the secretion of ACTH decreases. The secretion of ACTH is of great importance under conditions of *stress*, which, by way of activation of corticoid secretion, makes possible the metabolic adjustments necessitated by exertion or exhaustion.

Ser-Tyr-Ser-Met-Glu-His-Phe-Arg-Try-Gly-Lys-Pro-Val⎤
⎡Gly-Asp-Pro-Tyr-Val-Lys-Val-Pro-Arg-Arg-Lys-Lys-Gly⎦
⎣Ala-Glu-Asp-Gn-Leu-Ala-Glu-Ala-Phe-Pro-Leu-Glu-Phe

Sequence of 39 amino acids in ACTH (corticotrophic hormone) molecule from pig.

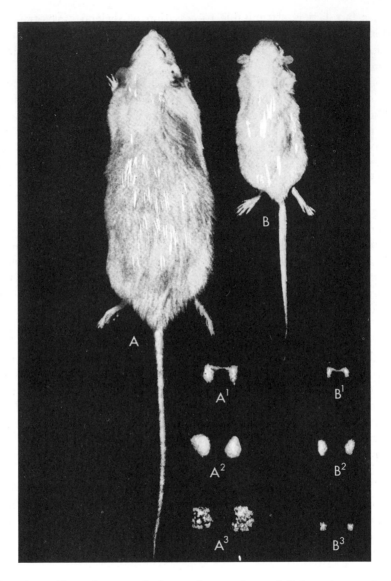

The effects of hypophysectomy in the rat. A, normal control; B, hypophysectomized littermate. $A^1$, $A^2$, $A^3$ and $B^1$, $B^2$, $B^3$ are the thyroids, adrenals, and ovaries from the two animals at the age of 144 days. (After Turner, *General endocrinology*, 3d ed., W. B. Saunders, 1960)

The *thyrotrophic hormone* (TSH) stimulates the growth of the thyroid gland, increases accumulation of iodine by the thyroid, and hastens the secretion of thyroxine. The interaction of TSH and thyroxine is a reciprocal one, TSH secretion being inhibited by rising thyroxine levels of the blood and facilitated by falling levels. The *lactogenic hormone* or prolactin (LH) triggers milk secretion by the mammary glands in mammals (in the pigeon it stimulates secretion of the crop glands), and it is also involved in maintaining the corpora lutea in active secretory state. In the latter capacity it acts synergistically not only with estrogen of the ovary but also with the *luteinizing hormone* (LH) of the adenohypophysis. LH facilitates maturation of the corpora lutea, it induces secretion of estrogens and progestogens, and it may produce ovulation in some species. In the male LH stimulates the production of androgens by the cells of Leydig in the testis. Thus, in general, LH activates the secretory activity of both male and female gonads. Acting synergistically with LH is the *follicle-stimulating hormone* (FSH). In hypophysectomized females, FSH stimulates the growth of the ovarian follicles. Its action may be specific to the female, because administration of FSH does not seem to have gonadal effects in the male.

It may be clear from the foregoing account that the hormones of the adenohypophysis exert a paramount regulatory influence on the secretory activities of the various endocrine glands of the body. This influence is, in at least some instances, a homeostatic one, in which the interrelation between the target hormones of the body and the trophic hormones of the adenohypophysis represents a negative feedback system. But in all probability the role of the adenohypophysis goes far beyond the maintenance of stable concentration of body hormones. There is evidence that through its hormones the adenohypophysis can modify the level of output of the other endocrine glands. In this capacity the adenohypophysis may have a role in the cyclical maturation and regression of various tissues, such as those of the sexual and reproductive organs, and in inducing the metabolic adjustments necessitated by changing environmental conditions, such as those produced by seasonal changes, bodily exertion, and the like. By sharing vascular supply with the neurohypophysis, and a common fluid space with the brain (the entire pituitary is surrounded by the dura mater of the brain), the adenohypophysis, even in the absence of direct nervous connections, is well exposed to brain influences for such functions.

The connections between the brain and neurohypophysis are even more intimate than those between the brain and adenohypophysis. The *neurohypophysis*, as we have mentioned earlier, is of neural derivation, being an outgrowth of the diencephalon. The neurohypophysis consists of the median eminence, the infundibulum (pituitary stalk), and the lobus nervosus (neural lobe). The neural lobe is composed of a rich supply of blood capillaries and of unmyelinated nerve processes that issue from secretory nerve cells located in the hypothalamus of the brain. The

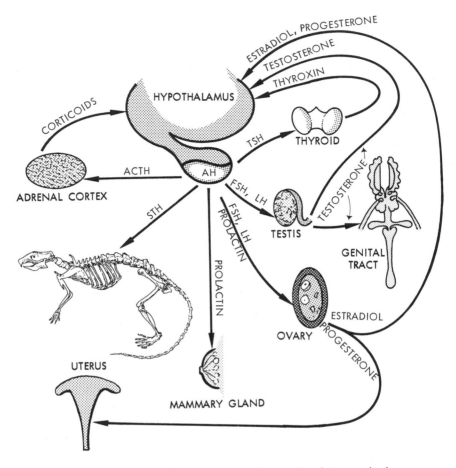

Diagrammatic summary of the most important interactions between the hormones
of the adenohypophysis and their target organs. The feedback effects on the
pituitary by the hormones of these target glands are mediated by way of the
hypothalamus, which controls pituitary activity.

neurohypophysis thus differs from all the foregoing structures in that it
is, according to our system of classification, essentially of animative derivation, though its mode of action resembles other humoral organs. Indeed, the neurohypophysis plays a dual role, transmitting neural influences
to a glandular structure controlling vegetative functions.

It is well established (Bargmann, 1957) that the hormones of the
neurohypophysis are secreted by nerve cells of certain hypothalamic structures (supraoptic and paraventricular nuclei), which are then transported
in the nerve processes to the neurohypophysis and released there into the
blood. That is, the neurohypophysis does not secrete but merely stores

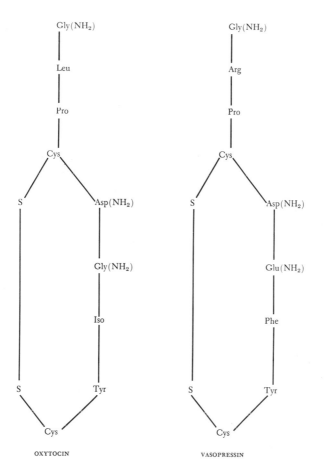

Gly(NH$_2$)

Leu

Pro

Cys

S                    Asp(NH$_2$)

Gly(NH$_2$)

Iso

S                    Tyr

Cys

OXYTOCIN

Gly(NH$_2$)

Arg

Pro

Cys

S                    Asp(NH$_2$)

Glu(NH$_2$)

Phe

S                    Tyr

Cys

VASOPRESSIN

and releases its neurohumors. These hormones are *oxytocin* and *vaso-pressin*. The two substances are closely related (both are octapeptides) and have the following systemic effects: elevation of blood pressure (*pressor effect*); decrease in urine excretion (*antidiuretic effect*); stimulation of milk ejection (*galactogogic effect*); stimulation of contractility of uterus; and alteration of the electrolyte composition of body fluids. Oxytocin is much more effective than vasopressin in causing uterine contraction, whereas vasopressin is more effective as a pressor and antidiuretic agent. In general, removal of the neurohypophysis does not have the serious consequences that removal of adenohypophysis has; in fact, the neurohypophysectomized animal can regulate its water balance and uterine functions, presumably by means of its other humoral mechanisms.

In addition to the neurohypophysis, there is another endocrine gland, the *adrenal medulla*, which has intimate connections with, and is largely controlled by, the nervous system. The cortex and medulla of the adrenal glands are of different embryonic derivation, the former being mesodermal in origin, the latter ectodermal. (The cells of the adrenal medulla may be considered modified postganglionic cells of the sympathetic nervous system.) The adrenal cortex, as we have discussed previously, secretes steroids. In contrast, the adrenal medulla secretes catechol amines, *epinephrine* and *norepinephrine*. Medullary extracts may also contain dopamine, which is a precursor of norepinephrine; in turn, norepinephrine may be converted into epinephrine. Many of the medullary cells contain granules that react with bichromate fixatives, and these cells were named chromaffin cells. The chromaffin reaction is believed to be caused by large concentrations of catechol amines in these cells.

The adrenal medulla is not essential for everyday life processes, but its amine secretions are of great importance during stress or trauma. Both hormones increase blood pressure: epinephrine does so mainly by accelerating heart rate, norepinephrine by constricting blood vessels. Epinephrine is also instrumental in elevating the level of blood sugar; thus, in combination with its effect of accelerating cardiac output, it adjusts the organism's energy output when bodily exertions are made

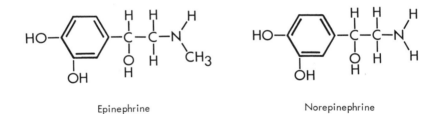

Epinephrine                                           Norepinephrine

or needed. Norepinephrine, in addition to being an adrenal medullary secretion, is an important humoral transmitter agent of the nervous system. In summary, epinephrine and norepinephrine may be considered hormones involved in emergency reactions, as originally proposed by Cannon (1929).

### SELECTED READINGS

Bell, G. H., J. N. Davidson, and H. Scarborough. *Textbook of physiology and biochemistry.* (5th ed.) Baltimore: Williams & Wilkins, 1961.

Best, C. H., and N. B. Taylor. *The physiological basis of medical practice.* (7th ed.) Baltimore: Williams & Wilkins, 1961.

Bloom, W., and D. W. Fawcett. *Textbook of histology.* (8th ed.) Philadelphia: Saunders, 1962.

Sinnott, E. W., L. C. Dunn, and T. Dobzhansky. *Principles of genetics.* (5th ed.) New York: McGraw-Hill, 1958.

Spemann, H. *Embryonic development and induction.* New Haven, Conn.: Yale University Press, 1938.

Stern, H., and Nanney, D. L. *The biology of cells.* New York: Wiley, 1965.

Turner, C. D. *General endocrinology.* (3d ed.) Philadelphia: Saunders, 1960.

Willier, B. H., and J. M. Oppenheimer (Eds.). *Foundations of experimental embryology.* Englewood Cliffs, N.J.: Prentice-Hall, 1964.

————, P. A. Weiss, and V. Hamburger. *Analysis of development.* Philadelphia: Saunders, 1955.

# 4

# Primitive Animative Activities

There are two ways whereby organisms may satisfy their metabolic needs: (1) by synthesizing organic compounds from inorganic substances, as autotrophs do, or (2) by acquiring already synthesized organic substances and then transforming these into species-specific body-building compounds, which is the mode of nutrition of heterotrophs. As we described earlier, chlorophyll-containing green plants utilize inorganic materials, such as water, carbon dioxide, and some minerals, and with the energy obtained from the rays of the sun transform these materials into carbohydrates, lipoids, and proteins. In contrast, animals, which are incapable of utilizing solar energy to synthesize energy-rich organic compounds from energy-poor inorganic precursors, are perforce "parasitic" on other living things and obtain from them their essential organic nutrients.

This difference in the mode of nutrition was probably one of the major determining factors that led to the evolutionary divergence of plants and animals. Being heterotrophic, the typical animal has to search for and locate sources of food supply, it has to follow the tracks of its prey and overpower its victims, and it has to remain forever agile in order to satisfy its various basic needs. The animal way of life necessitates sensitivity and motility, it requires constant readiness for action, and its success depends on the individual's ability to manipulate its environment. The way of life of animals is more hazardous than that of plants, but it is a mode of existence that permits them to acquire a greater degree of mastery over their surroundings than sessile, nonbehaving plants can display.

Are these capacities shown by animals basically different from the vegetative processes, or are they merely specializations derived from properties of the vegetative system? In spite of the fact that, as organic functions, the vegetative and animative processes have much in common, recent experimental findings suggest that the mechanisms of animative activities, even on the molecular level, are distinguishable in certain respects from the vegetative processes. Whereas vegetative processes are largely dependent on *humoral* events guided by *corpuscular proteins* (that is, enzymes), in animative activities of paramount importance are certain *biomechanical* events carried out by *fibrous proteins*. These fibrous proteins are not known to occur in differentiated plants, but they are present in large concentration in various animal tissues, including cilia, flagella, muscle, and nerve, and also in connective tissue, hair, and a few other parts of the body. (The antherozoids and zoospores of some primitive plants, but not the anthers of differentiated plants, may contain such fibrous proteins. Furthermore, the fibrous spindle apparatus of dividing animal cells is not present in dividing plant cells.)

These fibrous proteins may be merely static, structural elements (as keratin of feather and wool, or collagen of tendon); if they are, their contribution does not differ from the fibrous carbohydrate (cellulose) of plants. Other fibrous proteins, in particular the *actomyosin* complex of muscle, are of vital importance as special functional constituents of animal tissue that make possible the transformation of chemical energy into mechanical work, endowing animals with the capacity for quick and reversible overt action. The involvement of such fibrous proteins in muscular contraction has been demonstrated with muscle models. An example is the extracted actomyosin thread studied by Szent-Györgyi (1951). Actomyosin, which represents two fibrous proteins, actin and myosin, can be easily extracted from freshly minced muscle and formed into threads of macroscopic size. When adenosine triphosphate (ATP) is added to this preparation, contraction of the thread is induced. This effect is similar to that produced by ATP on intact muscle, though the work performed by contracting muscle fibers is considerably greater than that of this muscle model.

The glycerol extracted fibrous components of muscle represent another example of a muscle model (Weber, 1955) that, although nonliving, exhibits the mechanical behavior of living muscle. In this preparation the membrane is destroyed and all the soluble proteins are extracted, together with other chemical constituents of muscle, including ATP. Such a fiber cannot be made to contract by electric stimulation; it exhibits the rigor of dead muscle. On addition of ATP, however, these fibers behave as though they were alive, and will contract and then relax. This function is attributed to the insoluble components of the muscle; the work performed by these threads is practically equivalent to the work capacity of living muscle.

Because overt animative activity is a product of the contractility of muscle, the role of the contractile fibrous protein molecules is of central importance in the animative system. Whether or not fibrous protein molecules play such an important role in the two other cellular constituents of the animative system, that is, in specialized receptors and nerves, remains to be determined.

Before dealing in detail with the properties of the three distinctive cell types and organs of the animative system of differentiated organisms

(receptors, nerve, and muscle) an attempt will be made in the following pages to trace some of the main steps in the *phylogenetic evolution*
of the animative action system. In protozoans and primitive metazoans,
specialized receptor, nerve, and muscle cells are either absent or only
rudimentarily developed. But, as will be observed, the primitive contractile tissue, be it the plasmagel of an ameba, the flagellum or cilia
of protists, or the myocytes found in sponges, is by itself capable of all
the fundamental animative activities that, on higher levels, become the
separate tasks of specialized animative cells.

**Ameboid Action**    Animative capacities are manifested
in the most rudimentary form in a
group of unicellular animals of which amebas are the most familiar repre-
sentatives. The typical ameba is of microscopic size and is lacking in
permanent shape. Its cytoplasm is considered to be composed of two
parts, an outer viscous portion, *plasmagel*, and an inner freely moving
liquid part, the *plasmasol*. Reversible colloidal changes from the gel to
the sol state are believed to be responsible for the formation of *pseudopods*, cytoplasmic protrusions of transient nature that make possible locomotion in ameba and also a primitive mode of interaction with external
objects. Ameboid activity, as the characteristic behavior of amebas is
called, may also be observed in cells of a great variety of animal types,
including mammals, where the phagocytes of the blood and lymph employ ameboid motility in locomotion and feeding.

When an ameba moves on a solid surface, the plasmasol of its interior
flows forward in the direction of its locomotion. It is assumed that this
action is caused by a lack of gelation in the transient front end of the
animal and the squeezing action exercised by the gelated hind end. The
fluid plasmasol of the interior rushes forward under the pressure and
forms a pseudopod in the more elastic transient anterior region. The
fluid moving forward is then slowed down by the elastic cell membrane,
is deflected sideways, and as it flows backward gelates again. That is, the
overt motility of the ameba is attributed to protoplasmic flow produced
by reversible colloidal changes in the cell interior.

Amebas are capable not only of moving about but also of exhibiting
organized behavior; that is, they have discriminative as well as adjustive
capacities. Amebas manifest rudimentary sensory capacities when they
move toward or away from sources of stimuli, though differentiated sensory
mechanisms are not present. When the forward-moving pseudopod of an
ameba comes in contact with an object, or if it is excited by photic or
chemical stimuli, two characteristic changes may occur. The point stimulated may become motionless while the surrounding cytoplasm flows

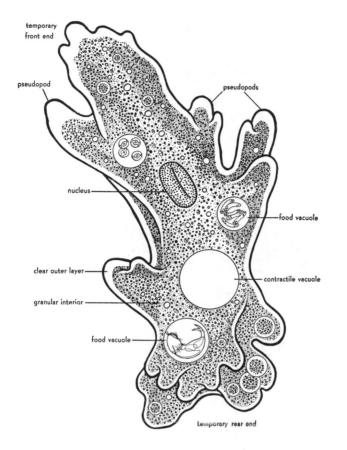

The form and major components of an ameba. (From Buchsbaum, *Animals without backbones*, rev. ed. Copyright 1938 and 1948 by The University of Chicago Press)

Colloidal changes in the cytoplasm during locomotion in the ameba. (From Buchsbaum, *Animals without backbones*, rev. ed. Copyright 1938 and 1948 by The University of Chicago Press)

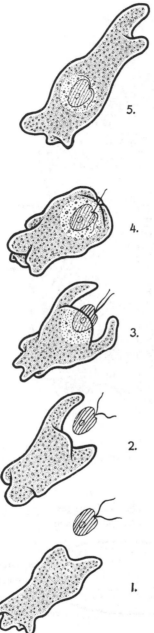

5.

4.

3.

2.

Ingestion of a flagellate by an ameba.
(After Schaeffer, *Ameboid movement,*
copyright 1920 by Princeton University Press, from Buchsbaum, *Animals
without backbones,* rev. ed., The University of Chicago Press, 1948)

1.

forward; this is the ameba's positive response. This reaction is of great
importance in the feeding of the animal, because it is in this way that
it flows around small objects, such as a diatom or microbe, to ingest

them. When the stimulus is of great intensity, as when the front of the animal is pierced with a glass rod or illuminated with an intense light beam, then not only the stimulated region but its whole surrounding is induced to gelate. As a consequence, the sol cytoplasm is squeezed in the opposite direction, and thus the animal reverses its direction of locomotion and moves away from the stimulus source. This is the negative response of the ameba; its function is evidently the protection of the animal from intense and harmful stimuli.

If this interpretation is correct, it may be concluded that stimulation leads in all instances to gelation of the surface region of the ameba. When weak stimulus is applied, the gelation is restricted to the locus of stimulation, and the forward flow of the cytoplasm in the surrounding region is not stopped. However, when the stimulus is intense, extended gelation is produced around an area beyond the impact of the stimulus, with the result that cytoplasmic flow in this direction is completely halted. This conclusion is supported by the fact that if an ameba is subjected to stimulation over its entire surface, or if the applied local stimulus is prolonged, the total surface of the ameba becomes gelated and the animal rounds up into a ball.

According to the preceding account, the motility of amebas is based on colloidal changes of the cytoplasm. To produce work resulting in movement, however, the gelated parts of the cytoplasm must also exert pressure on the liquefied parts. The colloidal theory has therefore recently been amended to include another hypothetical mechanism, a mechanism similar to that presumed to operate in the contractile molecules of muscle (Goldacre and Lorch, 1950). The assumption is that

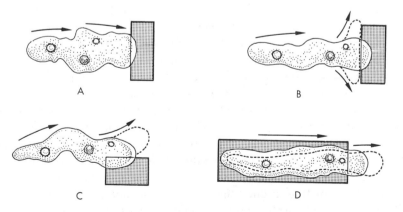

Negative response of ameba to local intense illumination (indicated by rectangular area). Arrows indicate flow direction of plasmasol. (Modified drawing, after Mast, from Gary N. Calkins and Francis M. Summers, *Protozoa in biological research*, Columbia University Press, 1941)

some protein constituents of the cytoplasm of amebas may exist in a corpuscular or fibrous form. If a large proportion of these proteins is fibrous, the cytoplasm assumes a viscous gel form, whereas predominance of globular proteins makes the protoplasm more fluid. Work is performed by the proteins in a fibrous state, when they are assumed to be endowed with contractility in a manner resembling contractile muscle proteins.

The primitive action mechanism of the ameba may be considered an organic system superimposed on the vegetative "core" of the organism. The vegetative functioning of the ameba is dependent on the maintained activity of its nucleus, as shown by the facts that enucleated amebas show abnormal metabolism and fail to reproduce themselves. Animative activity in the ameba is not so intimately connected with nuclear activity, because the enucleated ameba, as long as it survives, behaves very much like the normal animal. The two systems, of course, are not independent. The rate of overt activity in the normal ameba, for instance, is closely related to metabolic needs. After ingestion of large quantities of digestible particles, amebas become quiescent for a considerable period of time, but if the substance acquired is not digestible, overt activity continues (Schaeffer, 1920).

**Ciliary Action**    Molecular contraction can lead to significant work production only if (1) the contracting elements are oriented parallel to the axis of contraction and (2) the fibrous molecules are tied to one another to form larger units. Such an arrangement is not present in the cytoplasm of amebas. The pseudopods of certain protists, as the axopods of *Heliozoa*, mark an advance in this direction, because in them there are signs of a regular arrangement of the contracting molecules (as evidenced by birefringence under a polarizing microscope). These axopods show some resemblance to the specialized threadlike locomotor organelles, the cilia and flagella. The exact phylogenetic connection between the ameboid and ciliary mechanisms is not known, but such a relation may exist. In *Myxomycetes*, for instance, there is a stage of development when flagella are used in locomotion, and another when locomotion is based on ameboid motility. Similarly, *Chrysamoeba* may at times lose its flagellum and exhibit ameboid motility. It is conceivable that in these two phases of the organisms' existence the same basic material components are made use of, but that the presumed contractile molecules are organized into a stable structure in one stage, and remain unorganized in the other.

The *cilia* are relatively simple appendages specialized to serve motor functions. For convenience they are usually divided into two classes, (1) *flagella*, long filaments present singly or in small number on the surface of cells, and (2) *cilia proper*, shorter fibers usually present in

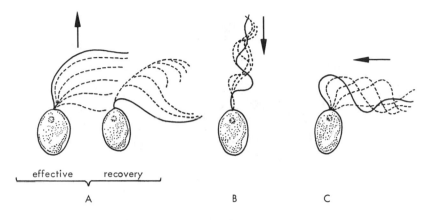

effective    recovery

A            B            C

Modes of locomotion in the flagellate, *Monas*. Arrows indicate the direction of locomotion as a consequence of the differing types of undulatory activity of the flagellum. (After Krijgsman, from Prosser and Brown, *Comparative animal physiology*, 2d ed., W. B. Saunders Company, 1961)

larger numbers. Flagella work in an undulatory fashion, in which waves pass along the filament from base to tip; cilia work more like oars, as a pendulum or in a hooklike fashion (Gray, 1928). Ciliary movement is generally used in an aqueous milieu or on a surface covered with a liquid film. If the ciliated body is small, the body is transported by means of ciliary activity; if the body is too large relative to the work capacity of the cilia, ciliary motion causes the liquid medium to move past the body. In the latter instance locomotion is not achieved, but such ciliary activity may be useful in feeding and other essential functions. Ciliary activity is widespread in a great variety of lower animal species, and it is also found in some specialized cells of highly evolved animal types, as in the epithelial lining of body cavities, and elsewhere.

Rhythmic beating of cilia situated in a single row. (After Gelei, from Buchsbaum, *Animals without backbones*, rev. ed. Copyright 1938 and 1948 by The University of Chicago Press)

It was recognized recently with electron microscopy that cilia and flagella from the most diverse sources are built according to the same pattern, consisting of two central filaments that are surrounded by nine equidistant double-barreled peripheral filaments arising from the same

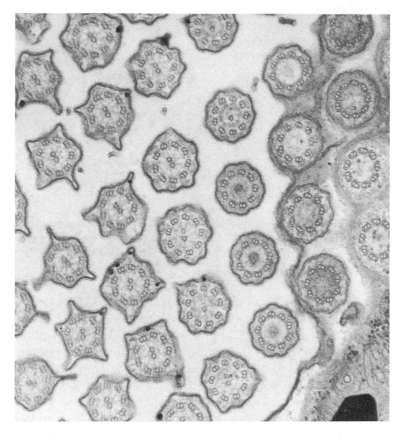

Electron micrograph showing cilia in cross section in the oral groove of *Paramecium*. (Courtesy of Dr. Keith Porter)

number of basal bodies. Some atypical cilia were demonstrated, but the nine-plus-two pattern is widespread. X-ray diffraction patterns of bacterial flagella resemble closely those of keratin and myosin, and biochemical analysis of flagellar preparations showed that the flagellum is made up of a protein named "flagellin." On the basis of these findings, and allied evidence, Astbury et al. (1955) suggested that cilia and flagella may be considered monomolecular muscle fibers.

To illustrate the nature of overt activity achieved by means of ciliary movement, we shall consider here briefly the behavior patterns of two familiar protists, the relatively simple flagellate, *Euglena*, and the more complex ciliate, *Paramecium*.

*Euglena* is a protist that is frequently classified with plants, for it is equipped with chloroplast granules, can synthesize carbohydrates by means of photosynthesis, and contains starch. However, it lacks the typi-

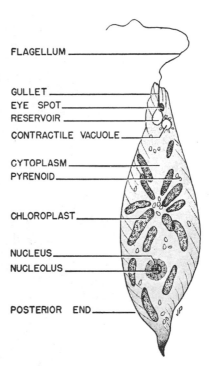

FLAGELLUM

GULLET
EYE SPOT
RESERVOIR
CONTRACTILE VACUOLE

CYTOPLASM
PYRENOID

CHLOROPLAST

NUCLEUS
NUCLEOLUS

POSTERIOR END

The flagellate, *Euglena*. (From Marsland, *Principles of modern biology*, 4th
ed., Holt, Rinehart and Winston, 1964)

cal cellulose wall of plants and manifests a typical animal trait, motility.
The locomotion of *Euglena* is dependent on its flagellum, the beating
of which pulls the organism forward. The flagellum arises from the flagellar
swelling near the anterior part of the body where the gullet is located. A
conspicuous structure on the body of *Euglena* is an "eyespot," a pigmented
region that casts a shadow on the flagellar swelling and controls the organism's orientation to light. *Euglena* responds positively to sources of mild
illumination, but when it moves into an intensely illuminated region it
displays a quick negative response; with changed flagellar beating it escapes
into dimmer surroundings. The scope of behavior in *Euglena* is extremely
limited. Because it is essentially autotrophic it requires no overt activity to
satisfy its nutritive needs; the locomotor ability of *Euglena* is presumably
used merely for the selection of optimal habitats.

The ciliary action mechanism is used more efficiently by *Paramecium*.
The surface of *Paramecium* is covered by hundreds of cilia that beat in
a rhythmic fashion and move the animal, at a relatively great speed, in
various directions. The cilia are used like oars; striking backward, they
move the animal forward. The direction of paddling can be reversed;
then the animal swims backward, or, if the change is partial, sideways.

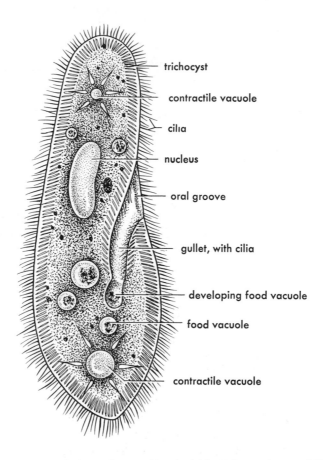

trichocyst

contractile vacuole

cilia

nucleus

oral groove

gullet, with cilia

developing food vacuole

food vacuole

contractile vacuole

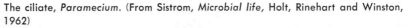

The ciliate, *Paramecium.* (From Sistrom, *Microbial life,* Holt, Rinehart and Winston, 1962)

The sideways movement occurs when the animal moves from a more favorable to a less favorable environment, or when it bumps into a solid object. This negative escape response continues until the animal chances to reach an acceptable surrounding, a mode of response termed by Jennings (1906) "trial-and-error behavior." Jennings, in his extensive study of the behavior of *Paramecium*, also demonstrated that the extent of backward locomotion depends on the intensity of noxious stimulation. When strong stimuli are applied to *Paramecium*, its backing becomes more conspicuous; consequently, it is carried farther away from the source of stimulation than when stimulation is mild.

Much of the time of *Paramecium* is spent on locomotion, apparently in search of food. There is little discrimination in food selection; all kinds of small particles, including indigestible ones, are ingested. Ingestion is achieved by means of the oral cilia, the beating of which produces water current that moves particles into the gullet. When a noxious substance reaches the gullet, the beating of the oral cilia is reversed and the substance is ejected. No specialized receptors are present in *Paramecium*, and no motor organs other than the cilia, but the animal is capable of selecting an optimal environment, satisfying its nutritive needs, and escaping from danger by means of this relatively simple action mechanism.

**Myoid Action** According to the presented hypothesis, both ameboid and ciliary activity are products of contractile protein molecules, which make possible the transformation of chemical energy into mechanical work. Contraction as the basis of movement, however, is merely an assumption in these transformations. Although direct tissue contraction is often thought to be the exclusive property of specialized contractile cells found in differentiated multicellular animals, that is, muscle, there is evidence of gross overt contraction in certain protists and in primitive metazoans. *Euglena*, for instance, in addition to flagellar locomotion, also employs a form of squirming action, produced by contracting fibrils or myonemes in the cytoplasm, which is referred to as "euglenoid movement."

Likewise, in certain ciliates, as in *Stentor* and *Vorticella*, evident contraction may be the basis of the animal's behavior. *Stentor* is a trumpet-shaped ciliate, which swims about in search of favorable habitat. Its feeding habit is a sessile one; it attaches itself to the leaf of a water plant or similar object, stretches its stalk to full length, and obtains food by producing water current with its oral cilia. If *Stentor* is offered a noxious substance it not only reverses the beat of the oral cilia but the stalk bends sideways, or, if stimulation is intense, the stalk contracts. This mode of action is made possible by the longitudinally arranged contractile fibers (or myonemes) in the stalk, which, because of their obvious musclelike action, may be called a myoid mechanism. A similar mechanism is present in the stalk of the sessile *Vorticella*, which coils up when the animal's body, the bell, is stimulated.

We may also consider under the heading of myoid action system some of the behavioral mechanisms employed by the most primitive of multicellular animals, *sponges*. A simple sponge has a cylindrical saclike structure, and on its upper part there is a large opening, called the osculum. Around the osculum is a circular sheet of cells, the myocytes, which contract when stimulated, thus closing the opening of the osculum. The exterior of the body is covered with flattened epithelial cells, interspersed with pore cells (porocytes), which have pores leading to the interior of the body. The inside wall is covered with collar cells equipped with flagella. Sponges are sessile animals, which feed themselves by

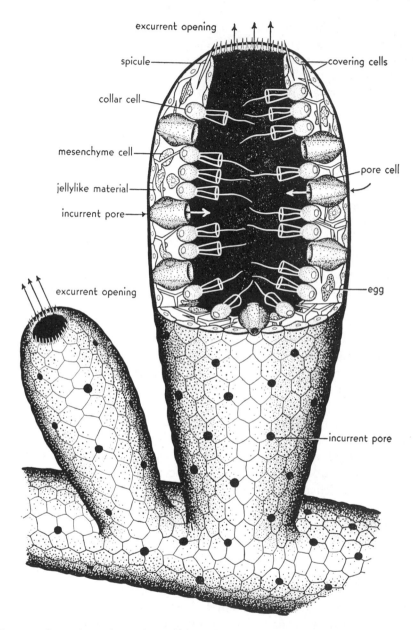

excurrent opening

spicule

covering cells

collar cell

mesenchyme cell

pore cell

jellylike material

incurrent pore

excurrent opening

egg

incurrent pore

Two members of a colony of sponges. In the larger member the upper part is cut away to show the internal organization. (From Buchsbaum, *Animals without backbones*, rev. ed. Copyright 1938 and 1948 by The University of Chicago Press) creating water currents that move inward through the pores and then out through the osculum. The currents are produced by the collar cells, which beat with their flagella and then capture the food particles obtained. Between the layer of epithelial cells and collar cells is a jellylike layer of cells showing ameboid motility. The ameboid cells ingest and digest the acquired nutrients; they also transport the digested food to other parts of the body. The function of the contractile cells, the myocytes and porocytes, is to close the openings of the body when the water currents bring noxious substances or when the temperature of the water is too high.

The behavior of sponges, accordingly, is dependent on all three primitive action mechanisms, ameboid motility, ciliary beating, and myoid contraction. Coordination among these action mechanisms does not exist in sponges. There are no specialized receptor cells in the sponge, and there are no specialized communicating nerve cells. Each myocyte acts independently of the others, and each myocyte, as Parker (1919) pointed out, combines sensitivity with its contractile property. When, on stimulation, a number of myocytes combines in closing the osculum, the reaction can be attributed indirectly to stimulation of the relaxed cells by contracting cells. The process is very slow; it takes about 3 minutes for the osculum to close.

**Differentiation of Animative Action Mechanisms**    Differentiated animative action has three aspects: (1) information gathering, (2) coordination or programming of action, and (3) the execution of action. In protozoans and lower metazoans all these aspects of animative activity are performed by a single structure, the undifferentiated cell. In higher forms, on the other hand, structural differentiation permits the performance of these functions by separate cells or organs. Considered from the evolutionary point of view, muscle cells were probably the first of the differentiated animative cell types. In some active parts of the body of coelenterates, such as *Actinozoa*, muscle cells contract in direct response to external stimuli without the intervention of other cell types. These muscle cells resemble the myocytes of the osculum in sponges, which, as previously described, respond to stimulation by contraction, then pass excitation along to the other myocytes and in this way eventually close the osculum. The evolutionary priority of muscle cells as differentiated components of the animative system may suggest the vital importance of effective biomechanical action in this system.

The second step in the evolutionary differentiation of animative action may be represented by the two-cell type mechanism present in the tentacles of various polyps, consisting of an epithelial receptor cell and epithelial muscle cells. The differentiation of nerve cells, interposed between receptor and muscle cells, represents the third step in the evolution of this system. In its most primitive form such a triple mechanism may also be observed in coelenterates, as in the bell of medusae, in which nerve cells form a diffuse network through which excitation may pass from one part of the body to other parts.

**Evolution of Diffuse Nervous Systems**    Nerve cells appeared first during evolution, as far as we can judge from surviving species, in coelenterates. Coelenterates are known in two forms, as polyps and as medusae (which may represent two phases in the individual's life cycle). *Polyps* lead predominantly a sedentary life; the

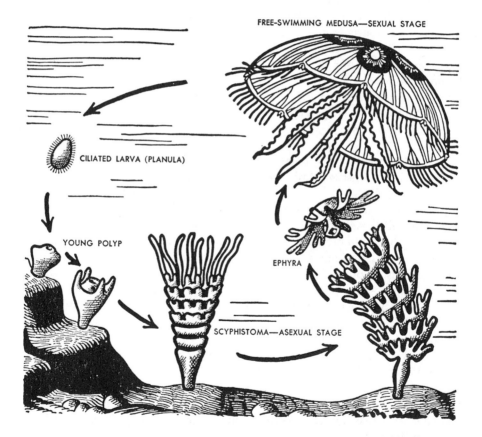

FREE-SWIMMING MEDUSA—SEXUAL STAGE

CILIATED LARVA (PLANULA)

YOUNG POLYP

EPHYRA

SCYPHISTOMA—ASEXUAL STAGE

The life cycle of a coelenterate, *Aurelia*. The animal passes through a free-swimming, ciliated larval stage, then a sedentary polyp stage, and a free-swimming medusa stage. (From Buchsbaum, *Animals without backbones*, rev. ed. Copyright 1938 and 1948 by The University of Chicago Press)

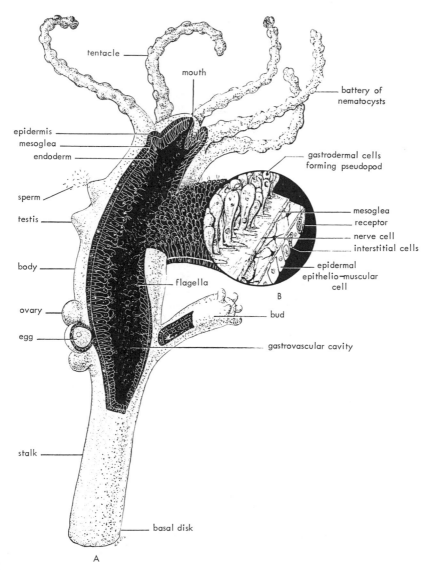

The structure and some cell types of *Hydra*. The cellular composition of a tentacle shown diagrammatically on the right at higher magnification. (From Johnson et al., *General biology*, rev. ed., Holt, Rinehart and Winston, 1961)

aboral end of the body is attached to a substratum, and the tentacles move about in search of food. *Medusae* move freely by means of rhythmic pulsations of their bells. In spite of this variability in appearance and function, the basic structure of polyps and medusae is very similar. The

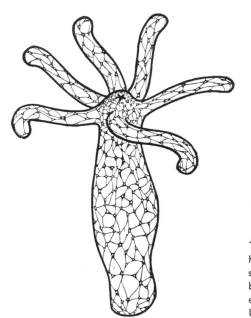

The subepidermal nerve net of hydra. Highest concentration of nerve cells is seen in the mouth region. (From Buchsbaum, *Animals without backbones*, rev. ed. Copyright 1938 and 1948 by The University of Chicago Press)

body is composed of two layers of cells, the ectoderm, a protective epithelium equipped with nerve cells and muscle cells (epitheliomuscular cells), and the endoderm, which lines the digestive cavity. The ectoderm is separated from the endoderm by a thin layer of jellylike material, the mesoglea, the forerunner of the mesoderm.

In the tentacles of polyps rudimentary nerve cells (protoneurons) are present, which perform the dual function of receptors and nerves. These protoneurons are the forerunners of the differentiated nerve cells intercalated between receptors and effectors. Such differentiated nerve cells are also present in coelenterates; they form a subepidermal *diffuse network* beneath the cells of the ectoderm. These comparatively simple neurons are of the bipolar or multipolar type, and the elongated nerve processes communicate with one another. The rate of impulse conduction in coelenterate nerves is very low: in sea anemones it varies between 0.146 and 0.211 meter per second (Parker, 1918). Conduction is self-propagating, as in more highly differentiated nerves (Chapter 7), and under certain conditions the initiated impulse may spread through the whole body without decrement in intensity. This action, however, is not typical. The propagated impulse tends to weaken and die after it has traveled a certain distance, not because conduction is decremental, but because there is a need for facilitation at synaptic junctions (Pantin, 1950).

Conduction in nerve nets is essentially diffuse; the initiated impulse tends to travel through the nerve cells in all directions. In the more active type of medusae, as in the umbrella-shaped jellyfishes, a nerve ring may be present around the margin of the bell, in which both nerve cells and nerve processes are concentrated. The nerve ring does not differ in essentials from other parts of the nerve net, except that excitation can be transmitted through it more directly from the tentacles to the bell. In the actinian, *Metridium*, a modification of the diffuse network may be observed, insofar as bipolar cells are present whose fibers run largely in a single direction; this system has been called through-conducting (Pantin, 1950).

Subepidermal diffuse networks are also present in echinoderms and balanoglossids. In the *starfish*, for instance, the peripheral plexi control the activities of the tube feet, the spines, and other organs.

The position of the nervous system of echinoderms may be considered intermediate between the completely diffuse, peripheral system of coelenterates and the centralized systems of higher invertebrates and vertebrates. In echinoderms conducting strands of nerves are present in the oral ring and radial nerves, which run directly from one part of the body to others. But, then, true switching centers, or ganglions, which relay impulses along different paths, are absent. In general, it may be stated that the peripheral diffuse network has been retained only in animals that lead a sessile or sluggish existence; in more active animal types it was replaced by centralized systems. In line with this statement is the fact that subepidermal networks are retained in higher forms, as in vertebrates, in or near body structures that carry on with their routine functions in a relatively sluggish manner, as in the gastrointestinal system.

**Evolution of Centralized Nervous Systems** The basic characteristic of a centralized nervous system is the segregation of communication lines, the *fiber tracts*, from centrally located switching stations, the *nerve centers*, or *ganglia*, where interaction among, and coordination of, various body parts may take place. A primitive group of animals in which such a centralized nervous system is present is represented by flatworms, as in the well-known *Planaria*. Flatworms represent primitive animal forms whose body structure is characteristic of most of the higher type of animals (insects and vertebrates): they are bilaterally symmetrical, have a specialized anterior end or head, and have a differentiated ventral and dorsal surface.

Receptor cells are scattered over the entire body of *Planaria*, but their greatest concentration is at the frontal end. Among the sense organs located in this region are the paired auricular receptors, which mediate chemical and tactile sensitivity, and the paired eyes, which respond to

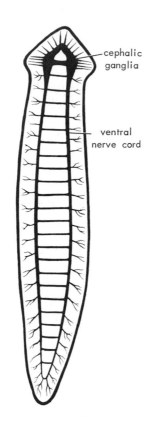

cephalic ganglia

ventral nerve cord

Cephalic ganglia and nerve trunks in a planarian. (Modified from Buchsbaum, *Animals without backbones*, rev. ed. Copyright 1938 and 1948 by The University of Chicago Press)

photic stimulation. Flatworms achieve locomotion by means of ciliary and muscular movement. The smaller flatworms, and the undeveloped larger types, move mainly by cilia, which are located on the ventral side of the body and move the animal forward by beating backward. Bigger flatworms may use ciliary locomotion when gliding slowly, but when they are irritated they hasten away quickly by muscular waves passing from the frontal end backward (Hyman, 1951).

The relatively complex behavior of planarians is controlled by a centralized nervous system located in the head portion of the body. In the lower order of flatworms, as *Acoela* and *Polycladida*, cephalization is only rudimentary. In the body of these lower orders are several nerve trunks, in which nerve cells are scattered, a fact suggesting the flatworm's derivation from the primitive nerve nets. In the higher order of flatworms, as planarians, the number of longitudinal trunks is reduced to two, and the diffuse nerve cells are few; neurons in the cephalic ganglia, however, are increased in number.

Evidently, there is centralized neural control of behavior in planarians. The role of cephalic ganglia in the regulation of planarian behavior has been studied for some time. Earlier studies established that the directed locomotion of planarians toward or away from sources of photic or chemical stimuli is seriously interfered with by removal of the cephalic ganglia. For instance, such an animal may be unable to locate food, though it will readily ingest food with which it comes accidentally in direct contact. More recent studies have exploited the unusual regenerative capacity of planarians to study the role of the cephalic ganglia and nerve trunks in the control of behavior in general and in memory storage in particular. Some of these studies are discussed in Chapter 13.

**SELECTED READINGS**

Buchsbaum, R. *Animals without backbones.* (2d ed.) Chicago: University of Chicago Press, 1948.

Bullock, T. H., and G. A. Horridge. *Structure and function in the nervous systems of invertebrates.* 2 vols. San Francisco: Freeman, 1965.

Hall, R. P. *Protozoa.* New York: Holt, Rinehart and Winston, 1964.

Hyman, L. H. *The invertebrates.* New York: McGraw-Hill, 1951. Vol. 2.

Jennings, H. S. *Behavior of the lower organisms.* Bloomington: Indiana University Press, 1962 (reprint of 1906 edition).

Maier, N. R. F., and T. C. Schneirla. *Principles of animal psychology.* New York: McGraw-Hill, 1935.

Parker, G. H. *The elementary nervous system.* Philadelphia: Lippincott, 1919.

Prosser, C. L., and F. A. Brown. *Comparative animal physiology.* (2d ed.) Philadelphia: Saunders, 1961.

PART **II**

# ELEMENTARY
# MECHANISMS
# OF ANIMATIVE ACTION

If animative activity is analyzed into its functional constituents, three basic processes may be distinguished. One process, not necessarily the first in sequence, is concerned with the gathering and securing of *information* about conditions of the body and its environment. This process is dependent on physical and chemical influences on the organism, which can serve as environmental stimuli. The utilization of stimuli by the organism as sources of information requires *transducer* functions, and the various organic transducers are collectively known as receptors. Another process is the *control* or coordination of animative activities, and it consists of two major aspects, the transmission and processing of information. The transmission of information from one part of the body (or the nervous system) to another is dependent on the *conductile* property of nerve fibers; the neural processing of information is based on complex *synaptic* functions with the aid of which impulses are sorted out, amplified, inhibited, biased, or otherwise modulated, then integrated and channeled along various transmission routes. The third process, not necessarily the last in sequence, is the *effector* or motor process, consisting of various adjustments produced by the body. This accomplishment is to a large extent dependent on the muscular system, which is capable of producing mechanical work.

# 5

# Transducer Mechanisms and
# Receptor Organization

Exposed protoplasm is profoundly affected by a variety of physical and chemical forces; this property is sometimes referred to as "irritability." The irritability of living tissue is the basis of the sensitivity of organisms to stimuli. However, to obtain protection against the harmful effects of various extraneous forces, cells and tissues are usually furnished with protective coatings, which greatly diminish their sensitivity. The tough cellulose wall of plants is one of the main causes of plant insensitivity; in animals, similarly, the exterior of the body is usually coated with horny epidermis or with various other kinds of inanimate coverings (such as cuticle or shell) so that the sensitivity of animal tissue is also greatly reduced.

To be able to register changes in their environment and obtain information about external events, animals developed various receptors that, as small peepholes, may be scattered over the entire surface of the body or, as large observation windows, are concentrated at strategic points of the body. Although there are receptors that respond indiscriminately to a great variety of stimuli, others are specialized to register selectively specific kinds of stimuli. This receptor specialization offers at least two advantages to the organism. First, it permits classification or sorting out at the receptor level (and thus the peripheral coding) of some of the specific properties of the stimulus. Second, it makes possible increased sensitivity or acuity through the development of specialized transducer mechanisms for specific types of stimuli.

**Structure and Variety of Receptors**  In its simplest form a receptor may be composed of fine branches of an afferent nerve that are directly affected by stimulating agents. More complex receptors contain various organic transducers that respond to specific physical or chemical forces and generate bioelectric impulses that, in turn, serve as intraorganic signals of external stimulation. Most differentiated receptors have a complex structure in which three common components may be distinguished: (a) accessory, nonsensory structures that promote the information-gathering process; (b) transducer structures that are directly affected by stimuli; and (c) conducting afferent nerves, forming part of, or being in contact with, the transducers, which transmit to the central nervous system in a coded form the signals generated by the receptors.

The *accessory structures* attached to sense organs are of varied origins and composition, and their only common characteristic is their function, namely, the promotion of receptive processes. For instance, in the case of the eye there are accessory structures such as the cornea and lens, which help focusing light to form a clear optic image on the transducer proper, the retina; and there are also several types of muscles, such as the oculomotor, the ciliary, and the sphincter muscles of the iris, which help in scanning the environment, in shaping the curvature of the lens, and in controlling the amount of light admitted. Such accessory structures are also present in other differentiated sense organs. Apart from facilitating responsiveness to the class of stimuli to which the receptor is adapted (called "adequate" stimuli), some of the accessory structures also tend to diminish the effectiveness of, or interference by, improper stimuli.

The *transducer, or sensory, elements* of receptors are generally, though not exclusively, derived from dendrites of nerve cells. In the olfactory epithelium of the nose, for instance, one pole of a nerve cell (the proximal cilia) serves as the receptor or transducer element; its other pole, the axon, transmits the generated impulse to the central nervous system. In other sense organs, as in the eye, nonneural transducer cells are present, the rods and cones. The transducer elements of receptors are generally sensitive to a single class of stimuli, be it mechanical, chemical, thermal, or photic. Some of the elements may be specifically sensitive to a narrow, selected range within a given type of energy form, that is, to a particular range of mechanical vibration, to a specific class of chemicals, and so forth. With the help of these organic transducers the external stimulus is translated into an energy form, a bioelectric potential, which can be transmitted through the afferent nerves to the central nervous system as a coded signal. The electric event initiated by stimuli in the transducer component of receptors is called the *receptor generator potential*. This receptor potential, as was recently demonstrated in several types of receptors (Gray, 1959), is a *graded* bioelectric current whose amplitude is a function of the intensity of the applied stimulus (Chapter 7). For this reason, the transducer process at this level is considered an *analog* coding mechanism (magnitude of stimulus is coded analogously as potential amplitude).

The transducer elements, as stated before, are either directly equipped with conducting nerve fibers or are in immediate contact with afferent neurons. The function of the *afferent nerve fiber* is to transmit the local potentials generated by the sensory elements to the central nervous system. As we shall see later, the analog signals of the transducer mechanisms are changed into frequency-coded *digital* signals and propagated through the conductile elements of nerves (the axons), with unchanging amplitude and velocity, to specific receiving stations in the central nervous system.

**Classification of Receptors**     Receptors may be classified usefully in at least three ways: (1) in terms of their specific morphological identity; (2) in terms of the properties of the external stimuli to which they respond; and (3) in terms of the functions they subserve within the organism.

The first of these classifications is based on gross observation and anatomical considerations. The eyes, ears, and nose are obviously dissimilar receptors, which require separate consideration. This commonly employed classification, which is the best first approach, meets with some difficulty when the attempt is made to relate sense modality to receptor structure in the less specialized receptors of the viscera, muscles, and skin. Also, the dependence of a particular sensory function on a specific morphological structure is not universal. For instance, the mediation of auditory function by the ear is restricted to vertebrates; in other classes of animals quite different structures mediate this function.

The second system of classification is based on the physical property of the external agent to which receptors respond, and it distinguishes mechanoreceptors, chemoreceptors, thermoreceptors, and photoreceptors (in some species, as in fish, there may also be electroreceptors; Machin, 1962). Such a grouping lumps together several morphologically dissimilar receptors. Thus such distinct receptors as the ear and vestibular apparatus, the various somesthetic and kinesthetic receptors of skin and muscle, and a variety of visceral receptors are all classified as mechanoreceptors. The disadvantage of the exclusive use of such a system of classification is that it does not distinguish among a variety of receptors that not only are morphologically quite different from one another but subserve distinct functions within the organism.

The third system of classification is the functional one in which the different receptors are grouped according to their organic functions. There are several such classifications; one of them, derived from an earlier classification by Sherrington and used here, includes the following: (1) domestic receptors and (2) relational receptors. The *domestic receptors* include all sense organs concerned with gathering of information about changes taking place within the body, whereas the *relational receptors* are concerned with the task of obtaining information about external events.

The *domestic receptors* include (1) the visceral receptors (visceroceptors), (2) the injury, or pain, receptors (nociceptors) and (3) a few postulated intracerebral receptors. The *visceral receptors* consist of a variety of relatively simple mechanical, chemical, and thermal receptors located in the interior of the body; they report such events as the state of distention of various hollow viscera (stomach, heart, lungs, bladder, and the like) and the chemical and thermal changes in the solute and particulate substances passing through these visceral channels. The visceral reports are used for monitoring domestic changes—both developing deficiencies ("needs") and tensions—that upset the internal equilibrium of the body. The *injury, or pain, receptors* respond to noxious chemical and thermal effects that are damaging to body tissues. These are receptors with protective functions that respond to the traumatic effects produced by stimuli rather than to the external stimuli themselves. In the third class of domestic receptors are the *intracerebral receptors*. This group of hypothetical monitoring devices, thought to be located within the central nervous system, record the temperature and chemical composition of the vascular, ventricular, and interstitial fluids of this unique compartment of the body.

The second group of receptors, the *relational receptors*, includes a great variety of sense organs concerned with external events or with functions that are directly involved in the organism's interrelation with the environment. The three classes of relational receptors are (1) the posture receptors, (2) the proximal receptors (exteroceptors), and (3) the distal receptors (teleceptors). Of these, the *posture receptors* are all mechano-receptors, which transmit feedback information about the position of the effector organs of the body (say, the limbs) in relation to one another, as well as changes of the body as a whole with relation to the coordinates of external space. The latter function is mediated by the *vestibular apparatus*, a complex receptor system that records the position of the head with respect to gravity and responds also to acceleration. Changes in the position of parts of the body to one another, whether related to the maintenance of stance or locomotion, are received by the various *kinesthetic receptors* (proprioceptors) located in the skin, muscles, and joints.

The *proximal receptors* (exteroceptors), located in the skin, include mechanical, thermal, and chemical receptors that respond to direct contacts of the body with various external agents. Of these, the *tactile* (touch) and *temperature* (heat and cold) receptors are distributed over the entire body surface; the *gustatory* (taste) receptors, in contrast, are restricted to the mouth region. The *distal receptors* (teleceptors) transmit information about the presence of objects or the occurrence of events some distance away from the organism, by responding to mechanical, chemical, or photic "signals" emitted by the events or objects. In vertebrates the teleceptors are complex, paired organs located in the anterior part of the body, the head. The nose (or olfactory apparatus) is a chemical teleceptor, which responds to volatile molecules (mostly organic) emitted by various substances and carried by air and water. The ear or auditory apparatus is a mechanical teleceptor, which responds to high frequency mechanical vibrations, produced by various agents and transmitted through

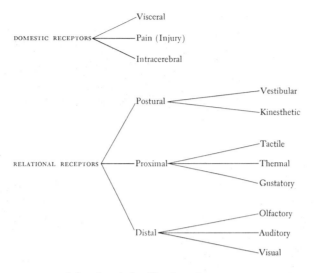

A functional classification of receptors.

the media of air, water, or solids. The eye is an optic teleceptor, which responds to light reflected or emitted by different distant objects.

**DOMESTIC RECEPTORS** Visceral Receptors. The visceral organs of the animal body, which compose the gastrointestinal, cardiovascular, and urogenital organ systems, are in the immediate service of vegetative needs. By means of animative mechanisms (mostly smooth muscles) these organs perform vegetative functions—such as digestion, excretion, circulation, and reproduction. As mechanisms primarily in vegetative service, the visceral organs are to a large extent activated by vegetative or humoral means, hormones and related substances, which accelerate or inhibit the rate of activity of these "autonomic" mechanisms with reference to the homeostatic needs of the body. As neuromuscular mechanisms, however, the visceral organs are also intimately connected with the rest of the animative system of the body, and their "autonomy" is only partial insofar as they are under the control also of the central nervous system. To exercise control over the visceral organs, the nervous system has both afferents and efferents innervating these structures. The visceral afferents are in contact with visceral receptors, or, in the absence of specialized receptors, their freely branching endings serve as receptors. Our knowledge of the structure and functions of the visceral receptors is most inadequate. The little information available suggests that these visceral receptors are either mechanoreceptors or chemoreceptors, with the possibility of some thermoreceptors.

The viscera are essentially hollow tubes surrounded by smooth, cardiac, and sometimes skeletal muscle, through which solid, liquid, or gaseous

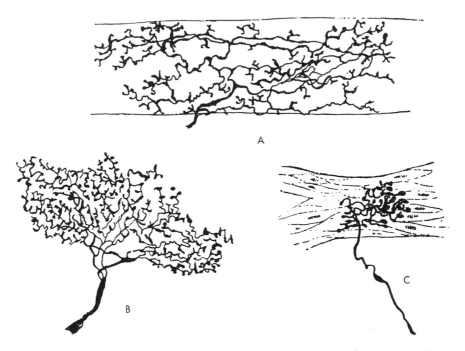

Free afferent nerve endings in various visceral structures. A, on a large pancreatic blood vessel (after Castro); B, in endocardium of dog (after Smirnow); C, in bronchial musculature of child (after Larsell and Dow). (From Truex and Carpenter, *Strong and Elwyn's human neuroanatomy*, 5th ed. The Williams & Wilkins Co., 1964)

substances pass. The visceral mechanoreceptors signal changes in the sustained (or static) tone, the phasic contraction, and the distention of these tubes. Such receptors are present in the vicinity of the lungs, in the heart, stomach, bladder, uterus, and some other visceral organs, including blood vessels. The visceral chemoreceptors, located inside these hollow tubes, respond to the chemical composition of substances circulating inside the tubes, such as the composition of air in the lungs, the properties of blood in the heart and blood vessels, and so forth. Few visceral receptors have been adequately investigated either by morphological or physiological techniques. Most of our information about them comes from indirect studies on visceral afferents, in particular, those coursing in the vagus nerve.

A rich network of free dendritic nerve endings is present in the cardiovascular system in the atrium, in the aorta, in several veins, and in the walls of the arteries supplying the aortic body. Frequency of impulse discharge in some afferents from these structures is linearly related to the blood pressure, whereas the discharge frequency of other afferents is

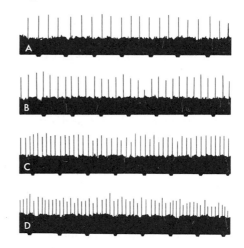

Steady (nonadapting) discharge from a single fiber of the carotid sinus nerve in response to increasing perfusion pressure of heart. A, 40 mm Hg; B, 80 mm HG; C, 140 mm Hg; D, 200 mm Hg. Time marker on base of traces is 0.2 second. (From Bronk and Stella, The response to steady pressures of single end organs in the isolated carotid sinus. *Amer. J. Physiol.,* 1935, **110,** 708–714)

linearly related to blood volume (Paintal, 1953). These afferents apparently function as mechanoreceptors.

In contrast, other receptors of the cardiovascular system, which are present in the arch of the aorta and in the carotid body, respond to the chemical composition of the blood and discharge maximally during oxygen deficiency, or asphyxia. In single fibers of these chemoreceptors, discharge frequency is increased with an increase of carbon-dioxide concentration, with a decrease of the pH, and with lowered oxygen concentration (Uvnäs, 1960).

Similarly, distention of the lungs produces discharge in single fibers in the vagus nerve, where the frequency of discharge and the number of fibers discharging are related to the rapidity and magnitude of distention or increase in lung volume. The mechanoreceptors signaling these events may be located in the peribronchial region (Widdicombe, 1954). Under normal conditions, the afferents are silent or may discharge with low frequency during expiration and at high frequency during inspiration (Oberholzer and Tofani, 1960).

Mechanical or chemical irritation of the respiratory passages (larynx, trachea, bronchi, or that of the lung itself when stimulated through a catheter) produces coughing. This respiratory protective reflex is mediated by separate mechano- and chemoreceptor afferents. Likewise, mechanical receptors of the bladder signal its distention (discharging at an increased rate with an increase of bladder volume) and thus make possible the afferent control of periodic micturition. Mechanical and chemical receptors present in the gastrointestinal system are responsible for vomiting, a protective reflex, which can be elicited by direct stimulation of various parts of the alimentary canal.

In addition to the visceral receptors so far considered, which control internal visceral functions of routine nature, other visceral receptors signal internal changes that call for complex environmental transactions. Thus Cannon established in his classical studies that stomach contractions occur after the stomach becomes empty and that the contractions serve as signals of food-need (hunger) and have a role in the initiation of feeding behavior. Likewise, dehydration of the mucous surfaces of the mouth and throat produces sensory signals of water-need (thirst), which then initiate water-procuring behavior and drinking. Relatively little is known of the properties of these visceral receptors, though they are, together with various central nervous control mechanisms, of importance in the regulation of eating, drinking, and other existential activities. (The metering function of the gastrointestinal system with reference to the regulation of food and water intake is further considered in Chapter 16).

INJURY OR PAIN RECEPTORS.  The injury receptors or nociceptors have a high stimulus threshold; that is, they are activated by stimuli of high intensity. In man, stimulation of these receptors produces the subjective sensation of pain, and in all vertebrates painlike manifestations may be observed with excessive stimulation of sensory surfaces or the damaging of various body tissues. It is generally assumed that the pain receptors are dendritic branches, or free nerve endings, of small-diameter nerve fibers, which are present in tissues all over the body, as in visceral organs, muscles, fascia, tendons and joints, and in the skin, particularly the epidermis. The basis of this assumption is the evidence of the presence of pain sensitivity in organs that contain such free nerve endings but are devoid of specialized receptors (for example, cornea and dental pulp).

It was widely held in the past that "pain" may be produced by excessive stimulation of any receptor or afferent pathway—that it is not caused by stimulation of separate nociceptors. But several observations contradict such an assumption. As was first shown by von Frey, pain-sensitive spots may be present in parts of the skin where no other sensation can be aroused—a fact that suggests the separate existence of nociceptors. Similarly, several investigators (for example, Cattell and Hoagland, 1931) have shown that excessive stimulation of an isolated receptor, say, tactile receptor, does not necessarily produce pain. Furthermore, by various artificial means, such as asphyxia, the sensation of touch or warmth may be abolished with the survival of pain (Sweet, 1959). This dissociability of pain sensation from the other skin sensations has also been observed at different levels of the central nervous system where the afferents of nociception appear to travel separately from the other cutaneous afferents.

These fine nerve endings have a high stimulus threshold and are excited only by stimuli that produce actual damage in the various tissues of the body. If the skin, for instance, is pricked sufficiently to produce pain, most of the skin points will redden subsequently, a finding that suggests local irritation (Lewis, 1942). Likewise, the heat threshold for pain is in the range of about 45°C, a temperature level that produces cutaneous flare and histologically demonstrable irreversible damage to tissue (Benjamin,

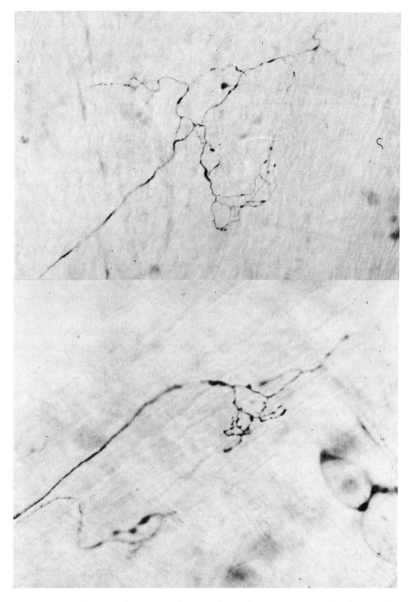

Free nerve endings, and nerve endings with small expansions, in the fascia of the hand. (From Miller et al. Pattern of cutaneous innervation. In Montagna (Ed.), *Advances in the biology of skin.* Pergamon Press, 1960, vol. 1, *Cutaneous innervation,* p. 42. Photo courtesy of Dr. Malcolm Miller)

1953). These free nerve endings are, moreover, nonspecific receptors; that is, they can be stimulated by mechanical, thermal, and electric as well as chemical stimuli. (That a certain degree of specialization may be present in some injury receptors is indicated by the fact that in some tissues only specific types of stimuli produce pain; muscle, for instance, may be pierced or cut without pain, though it is very sensitive to chemical stimulants.) It has been suggested (Lewis, 1942, for example) that the adequate stimulus of pain is some chemical produced or released by the injured tissue; perhaps histamine or some other substance (Sweet, 1959). Such a mechanism would explain the nonspecificity of injury receptors and their high stimulus threshold.

INTRACEREBRAL RECEPTORS.   In general, brain tissue is devoid of the type of receptors that abound in skin, muscle, and viscera; and mechanical or thermal stimulation of the exposed brain (with a few regions excepted) does not produce sensations in man. There is, however, suggestive evidence of the existence of some chemoreceptors and thermoreceptors in specialized brain regions. For instance, in the respiratory centers of the medulla neural receptors are thought to exist that respond directly to the carbon-dioxide concentration of the blood (Oberholzer and Tofani, 1960, p. 1118). Receptors that respond to the osmotic pressure of the blood were postulated to exist in the supraoptic and paraventricular nuclei of the hypothalamus (Verney, 1947). Highly sensitive thermoreceptors also appear to be present in the hypothalamus, because slight local increase in temperature produces immediate sweating (Benzinger, 1959). There is even some evidence of the existence of photoreceptors in the brains of birds. Their presence was indicated in a study (Benoit and Assenmacher, 1959) in which maturation of the gonads of drakes was induced, after sectioning of the optic nerves, by direct photic stimulation of the hypothalamus and rhinencephalon with a quartz rod. To what extent the postulated intracerebral receptors are involved in the regulation of the various homeostatic states or behavioral functions of the body in general, and of the metabolic processes of the unique environment of the brain in particular, remains to be elucidated.

**RELATIONAL RECEPTORS**

**Posture Receptors**

The task of the posture receptors is threefold. First, they provide information about mechanical forces that, acting on the organism, affect the maintenance of standard stance or posture. Second, they gather information about the tonus (state of contraction) of muscles. Third, they register the position of muscles and joints with relation to each other and their skeletal attachments.

Although all posture receptors are mechanoreceptors, two distinct types may be distinguished. The first group is made up of relatively simple receptor elements scattered over the entire body in muscles, tendons, and the skin. These receptors, called proprioceptors or kinesthetic receptors, register changes in the tonus and position of muscles and their appendages. The second type, located in the head, is known as the vestibular or labyrinthine apparatus. This is a more complex system of mechanoreceptors with accessory organs that register the position of the head with relation to gravity and respond also to linear and angular acceleration in space.

KINESTHETIC RECEPTORS. Three classes of receptors concerned with proprioception have been recognized. The first, the muscle spindles, are located within strands of skeletal muscle; the second, the Golgi tendon

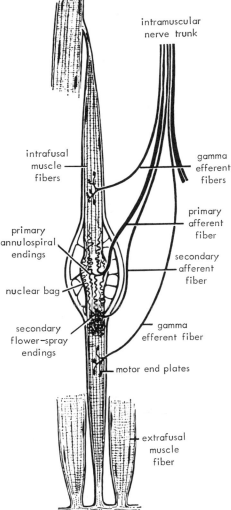

A muscle spindle with parts of the muscle fibers (called in this context extrafusal muscle fibers) in which they are embedded. (After Barker, from Truex and Carpenter, *Strong and Elwyn's human neuroanatomy,* 5th ed. The Williams & Wilkins Co., 1964)

organs or corpuscles, are located in tendons near skeletal joints; the third, the Pacinian corpuscles, are situated in the fascia of muscles, in periosteum, and in skin surrounding muscles.

The *muscle spindles* are specialized receptors found in skeletal muscle. They are spindle-shaped connective-tissue capsules, supplied with two types of afferent terminals, the flower-spray and annulospiral endings. Enclosed in the capsules are several muscular filaments, the *intrafusal*

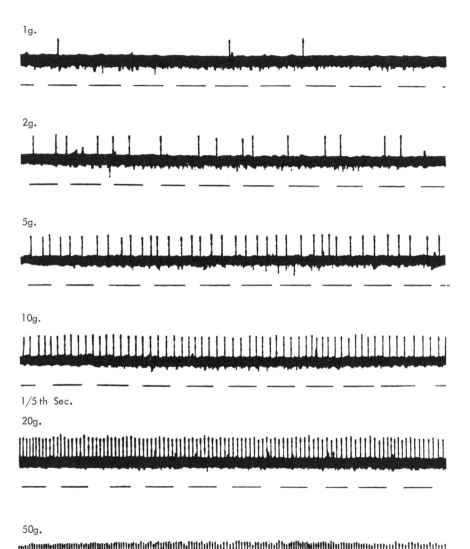

Oscilloscopic recording of discharges in the sciatic nerve from a single stretch receptor in response to application of increasingly heavier loads. The loads were applied 1 second before the onset of the oscilloscopic trace. Time marker below trace, 0.2 second. (After B. L. Andrew, from Bell, Davidson, and Scarborough, *Textbook of physiology and biochemistry*, 5th ed. E. & S. Livingstone, 1961)

muscle fibers, which are innervated by a small-diameter motor fiber, the centrifugal gamma efferent. The centrifugal efferent is believed to control the tonus, or state of contraction, of the intrafusal muscle fibers within the muscle spindle. The muscle spindle, which is embedded in muscle, is oriented parallel to the skeletal (extrafusal) muscle fibers. As a consequence, the contraction of skeletal muscle slackens the pressure on the muscle spindle, decreasing its impulse discharge; stretching the muscle, on on the other hand, exerts pressure on the spindle, leading to an increase in its signal discharge (Granit, 1955). That is, the muscle spindle is designed specifically to respond to passive stretching of the muscle; as such, it is believed to initiate the stretch reflex. The stretch reflex, the contraction of muscle when pulled, is of primary importance as an antigravity response and as a mechanism compensating for passive displacement of body parts. In tetrapod animals (Chapter 10) this reflex makes standing possible (an antigravitational activity). The sensitivity of muscle spindle to stretch can be increased by contraction of the intrafusal muscle fibers by way of

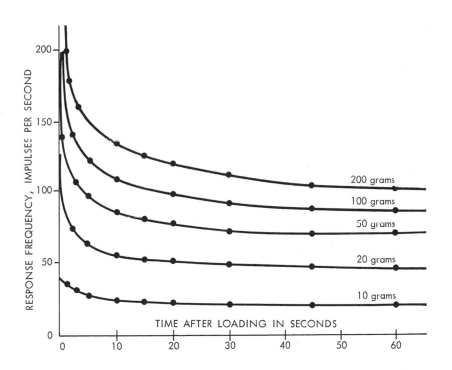

Response of a muscle spindle to stretching with different weights. Response frequency (ordinate) declines rapidly after 1–2 seconds (abcissa), following which little adaptation (decline in frequency) is seen. (Matthews, Nerve endings in mammalian muscle. *J. Physiol.* (London), 1933, **78**, 1–53)

the gamma efferents (which leads to increase in the width of the spindle) or lessened by their relaxation; this is the probable function of the efferent control of the intrafusal muscle fibers (Granit, 1955).

Unlike the muscle spindle, which responds primarily to passive stretch, the *Golgi tendon organ* is assumed to respond to muscular tension, irrespective of how produced, whether by passive stretch or active contraction. The Golgi tendon organs, located in tendons near their muscular orgins, are composed of encapsulated tendon fascicles, inside which unmyelinated branches of relatively large myelinated afferents terminate. The sensitivity of tendon corpuscles to tension may be based on the relative inelasticity of the fibrous substance of which they are composed.

The *Pacinian corpuscles* are present, particularly in the neighborhood of joints, in the fascia of muscle, in tendon sheaths, periosteum, deeper layers of skin, and mesentery. The Pacinian corpuscle consists of a central core embracing a nerve ending, surrounded by coaxial spheroid laminae, which are separated from one another by spaces filled with fluid. If compressed, a displacement of the laminae takes place (Hubbard, 1958), which may be the stimulus for the excitation of the interior nerve ending. As investigations of Gray and his associates have shown (Gray, 1959), stimulation of the Pacinian corpuscle produces an electric receptor or generator potential in the unmyelinated central portion of the nerve, the magnitude of which is proportional to the intensity and rapidity of the applied mechanical stimulus. If the generator potential reaches a maximum value, it produces an action or spike potential in the myelinated portion of the nerve that is propagated at constant intensity and velocity in an all-or-none manner (Chapter 7).

A common property of all postural receptors, as will be described later, is a sustained discharge during prolonged stimulation ("slow adaptation"), a characteristic which is absent in many other types of receptors that discharge only at the onset or the termination of stimulation. In closing this brief account of the structure and functions of proprioceptors, it should be added that tactile receptors (to be discussed later) also may play a role in postural feedback signaling, particularly in the execution of manipulatory activities with fingers and mouth where the movements are constantly adjusted to the texture, size, and form of the objects manipulated.

VESTIBULAR RECEPTORS. Receptors that record the position of the animal's body in general, and head in particular, with respect to gravity are present in most freely moving animals. In lower organisms these receptors are called statocysts. A *statocyst*, in its simplest form, is a spherical sac containing a small but comparatively heavy granule (made of secreted particulate substances or grains of sand), the *otolith*. A portion of the statocyst is covered with sensory hairs that, as mechanoreceptors, are stimulated by changes in the position of the otoliths. The latter occur whenever

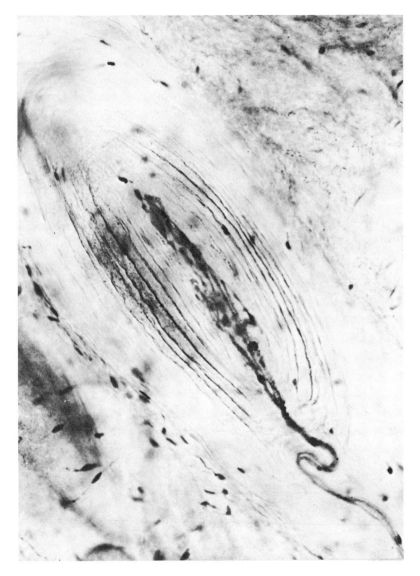

Pacinian corpuscle with an encased terminal nerve fiber. (From Miller, et al. Pattern of cutaneous innervation. In Montagna (Ed.), *Advances in the biology of skin.* Pergamon Press, 1960, vol. 1, *Cutaneous innervation,* p. 28. Photo courtesy of Dr. Malcolm Miller)

the position of the body changes with relation to gravity, or when the body is moved, accelerated or decelerated. The mode of operation of these statocysts was well illustrated in the classical demonstration of Kreidl

(1893). During molting, crabs lose their statocysts and insert grains of
sand picked from the ground into the newly forming statocysts. Iron and
nickel dust were placed at the bottom of the aquarium, and the animals were induced to use these as otoliths. After the insertions were
made, the animals could be forced to turn on their backs by placing a
magnet over their heads. That is, the animals behaved as though the
direction of gravity had changed by 180°. Under normal conditions the
statoliths are moved in a similar way by gravity when the head is tilted
or when the body is accelerated. The sensory signals sent through the
nerves to the central nervous system are then used to produce the compensatory movements for the maintenance of postural equilibrium.

The mechanoreceptor system concerned with spatial orientation and
equilibration in vertebrates is the *vestibular apparatus*. The vestibular apparatus (together with the auditory apparatus) is located in the *inner ear*.
It consists, in higher vertebrates, of three semicircular canals and two sacs,

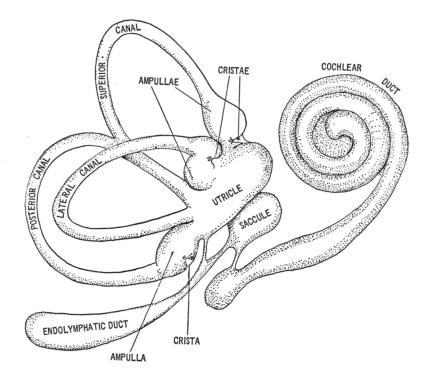

Diagram of the vestibular labyrinth. Each of the three canals has a dilated end,
called ampulla. In each ampulla the hair cells are located in the crista, and the
cilia of the hair cells project into the gelatinous cupula. (From Best and Taylor, *The
living body*, 4th ed. Holt, Rinehart and Winston, 1958)

the utricle and saccule, all of which are filled with endolymph. The three semicircular canals are at right angles to one another, oriented in the three dimensions of space (they are called, respectively, the posterior, superior, and lateral canals). The epithelium of the ampullae of the semicircular canals contains the sensory cells, the cilia of which project into a gelatinous substance, the cupula. The receptor tissue of the utricle and saccule is the macula, which is covered by a gelatinous substance containing the otoliths. The vestibular apparatus is innervated by myelinated afferents that pass toward the central nervous system in the vestibular branch of the eighth cranial nerve.

The orientation of the three semicircular canals suggests that they are designed to analyze rotatory movements of the head in space. It is assumed that the movements of the head set up endolymphatic currents, which are transmitted to the hair cells embedded in the damped cupula (Gernandt, 1959). The endolymphatic currents and the deflection of the cupula have actually been visualized in fish by the injection of dye (Steinhausen, 1933) or oil droplets (Dohlmann, 1935) into the canals. For the utricle and saccule, which are homologous with the statoliths of other organisms, the specific stimulus appears to be the force of gravity (though the movements of the otoliths over the macula in all probability can also serve to analyze linear acceleration). Electrical recordings from afferents of the vestibular apparatus suggest the presence of a sustained, low-frequency discharge at rest and an increased rate of discharge as a result of acceleration.

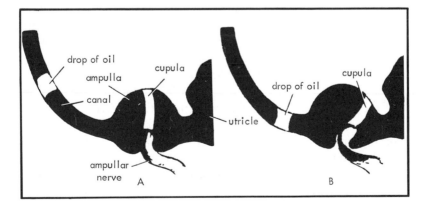

The position of the cupula in the ampulla before (A) and during (B) angular acceleration. Note changed position of oil droplet in the endolymph during acceleration. (After Dohlmann, Some practical and theoretical points in labyrinthology. *Proc. Roy. Soc. Med.,* 1935, **28**, 1371–1380)

**Proximal Receptors**  The proximal or contact receptors include a group of *cutaneous* sense organs that are sensitive to mechanical, thermal, or chemical stimuli generated by objects that come in direct contact with the surface of the body. Unlike the cutaneous injury (pain) receptors, which have a high-stimulus threshold and respond to tissue damage produced by various stimulants, the contact receptors have a lower threshold and respond directly or indirectly to the external stimuli themselves. That is, these contact receptors are, as Sherrington classified them, exteroceptors, which signal changing conditions in the immediate surrounding of the body. Of these proximal receptors, the widely distributed low-threshold tactile receptors (mediating the sense of "touch") are mechanoreceptors; the receptors mediating "warmth" and "cold" are thermoreceptors; and the gustatory ("taste") receptors of the mouth are chemoreceptors.

Until the end of the last century the cutaneous receptors were generally assumed to mediate one sense modality (referred to subjectively as "feeling") with different submodalities or qualities (warmth, cold, touch, and pressure). As a result of the work of Blix and Goldscheider, and particularly of von Frey, who showed that by using *punctate stimulus sources* different cutaneous qualities could be evoked separately from one another from different skin spots, the various cutaneous sensations came to be considered as different sense modalities.

Whether the cutaneous senses are considered different modalities or different qualities of the same modality is of little significance. In support of the former argument, however, efforts were made toward the end of the last century to associate the various cutaneous modalities with different classes of skin sensory endings identified by histologists (Meissner, Merkel, Retzius, Dogiel, and others). But these attempts were largely unsuccessful. For one thing, no reliable associations could be established between psychologically demonstrable *punctate sensory maps* of the skin and the histological distribution of different sensory endings. For another, modern histological studies (Weddell et al., 1955; Winkelmann, 1960; Miller et al., 1960) have cast doubt on the existence of the diversity of distinct cutaneous receptors described by earlier histologists. It is now believed that most of the cutaneous receptors represent modifications of a few basic types, with gradual transition from one to the other. There may be three such basic types: (1) free nerve endings without specialized tips; (2) fiber endings with expanded tips; and (3) fiber endings with encapsulated sheaths.

TACTILE RECEPTORS.  The tactile receptors are mechanoreceptors of low threshold, which are sensitive to gentle pressure or touch. In areas of the skin covered by hair, and wrapped around the base of hairs, are nerve fibers without specialized endings or fibers with expanded tips. The hairs to

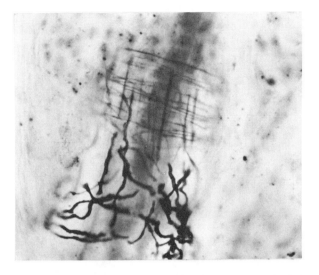

Nerve network around a hair follicle in the skin of a cat. (From Winkelmann. Similarities in cutaneous nerve end organs. In Montagna (Ed.), *Advances in the biology of skin*. Pergamon Press, 1959, vol. 1, *Cutaneous innervation*, p. 51. Photo courtesy of Dr. R. K. Winkelmann)

which the nerve endings are attached may be considered accessory organs that act as amplifying levers. In fact, hairs present in some skin areas function exclusively as specialized tactile accessory organs, as is true of vibrissae found on the snout of various mammals. In hairless parts of the body, such as the palm of the hands or fingertips of primates, for instance, similar free nerve endings are present, as well as specialized nerve endings equipped with various types of endings; these were in the past distinguished as Meissner, Vater-Pacini, and Golgi-Massoni corpuscles, and Merkel discs. Although these end organs may indeed be identified histologically in the skin, they represent, as mentioned earlier, transitional forms within a limited class of sensory nerve endings; there is no evidence that they subserve different functions.

Tactile sensitivity differs in different parts of the body; it is highest around body orifices, such as the mouth, and in the fingers in primates. Parts of the body that show acute tactile sensitivity are characterized by low absolute sensory threshold, low difference threshold, accurate somatotopic localization, and fine resolving power. *Absolute sensory threshold* is defined as the minimal stimulus magnitude that will elicit a sensory response (in man, this usually implies subjective sensation). In man, when a small tip is used for stimulation, the absolute tactile threshold is about 0.5 grams per millimeter in the lips and fingers, but is much higher in other parts of the body (Dallenbach, 1935).

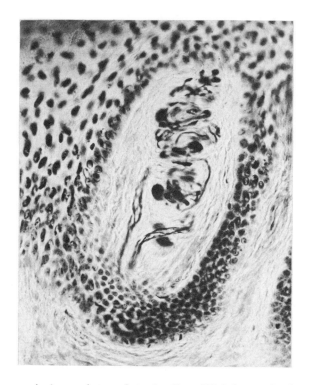

Meissner corpuscle from a human fingertip. (From Winkelmann. Similarities in cu-
taneous nerve end organs. In Montagna (Ed.), *Advances in the biology of skin.*
Pergamon Press, 1960, vol. 1, *Cutaneous innervation,* p. 54. Photo courtesy of Dr.
R. K. Winkelmann)

The *difference threshold* is defined as the amount of increment or decrement in stimulus magnitude required to perceive a change in stimulus
intensity. According to Weber's law, the difference threshold ("just notice-
able difference") is a constant ratio of the magnitude of stimulus
($\triangle I/I=K$). This ratio or Weber fraction holds only within limited ranges
of stimulus magnitude, and it is different for different sense modalities
(smaller for more sensitive receptors than for less sensitive ones).

*Somatotopic localization* refers to the ability of localizing the site of
bodily stimulation. Tactile localization was investigated originally by
Weber, who determined the magnitude of the "error of localization" over
different parts of the body.

Related to the *accuracy* of tactile somatotopic localization is tactile
*resolving power.* This power is measured most conveniently as the *two-
point discrimination* threshold with a caliper with blunt tips. Accuracy in
somatotopic localization and acuity in resolving two adjacent tactile points
are highest in parts of the body also distinguished by a low absolute

threshold (that is, mouth and fingers). Tactile receptor sensitivity and acuity are believed to be correlated with the degree of receptor density in different areas of the skin (Ruch, 1960).

Accordingly, tactile receptors are well suited to the analysis of the size, weight, texture, and shape of objects and also to providing feedback information regarding the accuracy of executed motor activities in general and manipulatory activities in particular.

THERMAL RECEPTORS. In 1882 Blix discovered, and soon afterward others confirmed, the existence of separate *punctate warmth* and *cold spots* in the skin. These sensory spots can be stimulated by both adequate (temperature) and nonadequate (such as electrical) stimuli. The cold spots are generally more numerous than the warm spots, though there is wide variation from one region of the body to the next (Dallenbach, 1927). Both of these receptors, of course, respond to "warmth," but the cold receptors are stimulated by a lower range of radiant or contact temperature than are the warmth receptors. On the basis of some experimental evidence, von Frey asserted that the Krause end bulbs of the skin are the specific cold receptors, and the Ruffini cylinders the warmth receptors. This claim has since been disproved by several investigators in experiments in which the sensory spots on the skin of human subjects were first mapped for the distribution of warmth and cold spots and then the skin removed and prepared histologically. In these experiments a point-to-point relation between specific sensory spots and specific underlying cutaneous receptors could not be demonstrated. In fact, thermal sensations can be evoked in areas in which encapsulated endings or specialized receptors are absent and only free nerve endings are present (Sinclair et al., 1952; Hagen et al., 1953; Lele, 1954).

Although specific end organs cannot be ascribed to the subjectively determined warm and cold spots, or to thermoreceptors in general, the subjective dissociability of cold and warm sensory spots is considered by many psychologists sufficient justification for postulating independent warmth and cold receptors. The thermoreceptors, it has been argued, might be histologically undifferentiable free nerve endings that are nevertheless functionally differentiated at the receptor level. According to others (for example, Weddell et al., 1955), the differentiation of warmth and cold (as well as other cutaneous sensory qualities) may depend on neural coding processes based on different patterns of afferent discharge by the same receptors. Whatever may be the situation at the receptor level, the existence of separate afferents mediating warmth and cold is supported by the work of Zotterman and his collaborators (Zotterman, 1959), who recorded electric discharges from single afferents of the skin. These thermal afferents are myelinated fibers of relatively small diameter that terminate mostly in the spinal cord. The afferents responding to cooling, discharge persistently to a wide range of thermal stimuli, with a maximum discharge

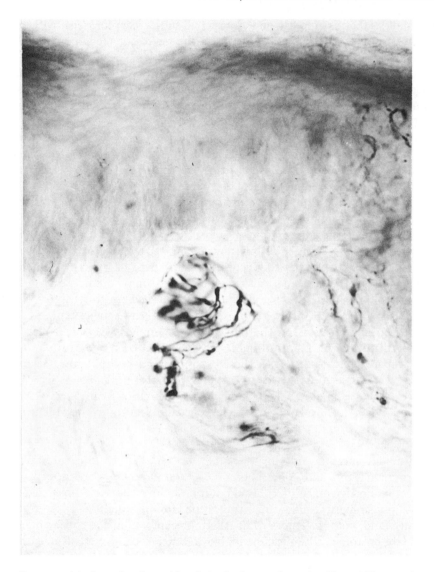

Krause end bulb under the epidermis in the human fingertip. (From Miller et al. Pattern of cutaneous innervation. In Montagna (Ed.), *Advances in the biology of skin*. Pergamon Press, 1960, vol. 1, *Cutaneous innervation*, p. 28. Photo courtesy of Dr. Malcolm Miller)

rate when the temperature is in the range of 30–32°C, whereas afferents sensitive to warmth discharge maximally at about 37–40°C.

It has been recognized for some time that the thermal receptors of the skin do not operate as conventional thermometers, recording merely the temperature of the external medium, but that they are also registering

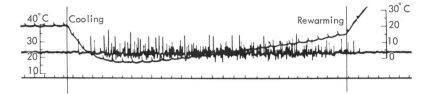

Action potential discharges from an afferent of a cold receptor from the lingual nerve of the cat. Responses are initiated by cooling the tongue (indicated on the left side on the trace showing the temperature changes). Spike discharge ceases when the tongue is rewarmed. Time in 20 milliseconds. (After Hensel et al. From Zotterman, Thermal sensations. *Handb. Physiol.*, Sec. 1, **1**, 431–458)

relative changes in skin temperature. Present in the skin is a temperature gradient that is a function of the internal body temperature and the temperature of the environment. Objects that do not alter this gradient affect neither the cold nor the warmth receptors. This condition occurs when contact is established with objects that have the same temperature as the exterior of the skin or with objects that are poor thermal conductors. Temperature changes that affect this gradient by lowering the external skin temperature (that is, produce heat loss) evoke the sensation of cold; changes that raise the external skin temperature produce the sensation of warmth. The sensory threshold of thermal receptors is variable. The most sensitive thermal receptors may be those located in the facial pit of snakes, which can detect a temperature difference of about 0.002°C (Bullock and Diecke, 1956). The thermal threshold of the skin receptors of mammals is much higher, of the order of 0.15°C (Kenshalo et al., 1960).

The function of thermal receptors is at least twofold. First, they supply information about temperature changes in the environment in order to permit the homeostatic regulation of body temperature (this function need not be restricted to warm-blooded animals). Second, the thermoreceptors supply information about the temperature of objects with which the body comes in contact, as an important aspect of the object's physical properties.

GUSTATORY RECEPTORS. Although the majority of contact receptors are mechanoreceptors, a group of chemoreceptors, the taste buds, also belong to this group. In lower aquatic vertebrates, the gustatory receptors are present over the entire body surface (Parker, 1922) in a manner resembling the cutaneous receptors. In higher vertebrates, however, the gustatory receptors are restricted to the mouth region. In higher terrestrial vertebrates, the primary function of gustatory receptors is the regulation of the ingestion of nutrients (eating and drinking), because it is mainly by gustatory discrimination that ingested substances are accepted or rejected.

In mammals, the *taste buds* are found embedded in ridges (fungiform or circumvalate papillae) in the mucous membranes of the tongue, and

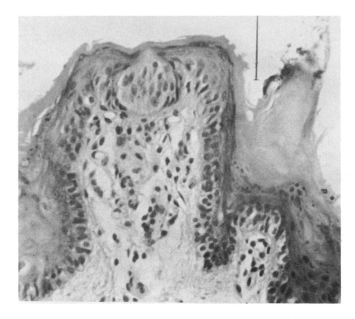

A fungiform papilla in the rat tongue with a taste bud close to the surface. (Figure 1, from Kimura and Beidler. Microelectrode study of the taste receptors of rat and hamster. *J. cell. comp. Physiol.*, 1961, **58**, 132. Photo courtesy of Dr. Beidler)

in the palate, pharynx, and larynx. Each taste bud consists of approximately 10 to 15 *taste cells*; each taste cell has elongated, villilike processes, which project into the aqueous medium covering the mucous membranes. It is assumed that these villi are the sites of the gustatory transducer processes. The taste buds are innervated by fibers of the chorda tympany and glossopharyngeal nerves; on the average, each taste bud may receive two nerve fibers. Recent studies indicate that the taste cells are in a continual turnover; some degenerate and are replaced by new cells that are produced by mitotic division (Beidler, 1961.)

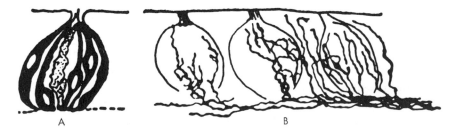

A, taste cell with supporting cells. B, similar taste cells with the nerve fibers stained. (After Retzius, from Pfaffmann, The sense of taste. *Handb. Physiol.*, 1959, Sec. 1, **1**, 508)

Dissolved or soluble substances are the adequate stimuli of taste. On the basis of human experience four taste qualities are generally distinguished: salt, sour, bitter, and sweet. *Salty* taste is most commonly associated with sodium chloride, or common salt, though many other salts may produce similar sensory qualities. *Sour* is associated with acids, though not all acids taste sour. The acidity of many fluids, and their sourness, is often dependent on the degree of hydrogen-ion dissociation. Alkaloids, in general, are *bitter*; they include various noxious substances, such as caffeine, nicotine, strychnine, and others (Moncrieff, 1951). *Sweet* taste is usually associated with such organic substances as carbohydrates and amino acids, which are the main nutrients of herbivorous and omnivorous animals. Some substances, however, that do not fall under this category (such as saccharine) also may be sweet. High concentrations of otherwise sweet-tasting substances may acquire a bitter taste. In many vertebrates sweet-tasting substances are generally ingested, and bitter substances (such as quinine) rejected. Apparently the sensory qualities mediated by the gustatory receptors are related to certain basic properties of fluids and soluble substances, such as their nutritive value (sweetness), their electrolytic properties or pH (acidity), their osmotic properties (saltiness), and their toxicity (bitterness). The more complex taste sensations of subjective experience are based on olfaction; they therefore disappear when olfaction is eliminated (for example, during a common cold).

There is some evidence that the different taste qualities may be mediated by different taste buds or taste cells. It has been known for a long time that different parts of the tongue are selectively sensitive to sweet, sour, and bitter, though sensitivity to salt is said to be widespread. Similarly, certain drugs may selectively affect certain taste sensations: gymnemic acid, for instance, dulls sensitivity to sweet and bitter but leaves sensitivity to salt and sour unaffected (Shore, 1892). However, electrophysiological studies involving the insertion of microelectrodes into single cells of taste buds suggest that the individual cells may respond to more than one class of chemicals (Kimura and Beidler, 1961). Likewise, early microelectrode studies by Pfaffmann (1959) suggested that single gustatory nerve fibers may respond to several classes of chemicals, though they too show highest sensitivity to stimuli associated with one or two of the four taste qualities. More recent studies by Zotterman and his associates (Zotterman, 1961, 1963) indicate the presence in various mammals of single fibers that respond exclusively to sweet (sucrose and the like), bitter (quinine), salt (NaCl), or acid (acetic acid, for example). In some mammals, such as the cat, no "sweet" fibers appear to be present (as carnivorous animals, cats ingest carbohydrates sparingly); in others (frog, rabbit) the existence of a fifth type of taste fiber, fibers sensitive to pure water, is claimed (Zotterman, 1961).

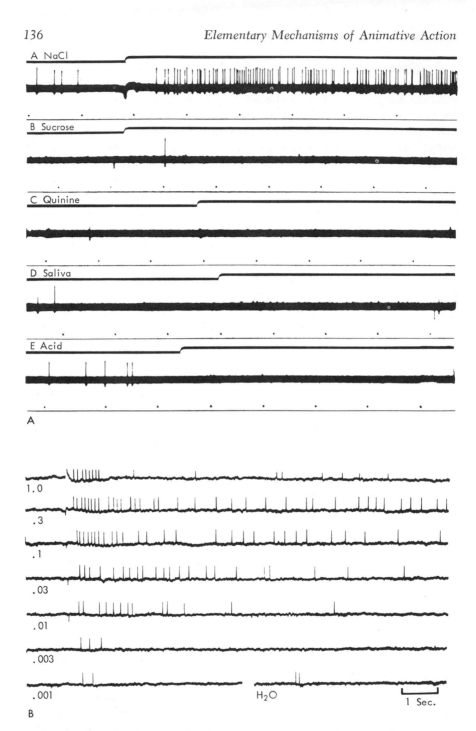

A, recording of action potentials from a single gustatory fiber. This element responds to a salt solution but not to the other substances tested. Time in seconds.

(*continued on the page opposite*)

**DISTAL RECEPTORS**     Olfactory     Receptors. *Bipolar cells* embedded in the olfactory mucosa are the transducer elements of the olfactory system. They are specialized nerve cells from which several cilia issue at the apical end, and a fine axon at the basal end. The number of olfactory receptors is extremely high; in the rabbit mucosa they are estimated to be in the neigh-

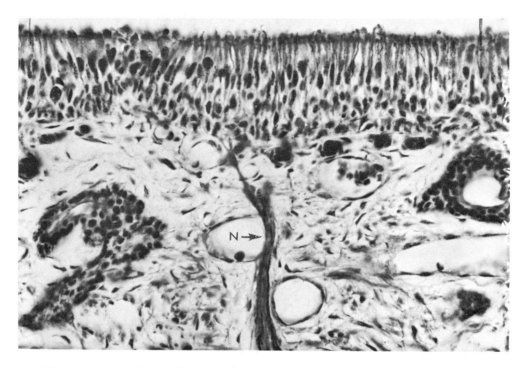

Olfactory mucosa of the rabbit, stained with Bodian's silver method. N, collection of olfactory nerve fibers. (From De Lorenzo. In Zotterman, Ed., *Olfaction and taste.* Pergamon Press, 1963. Photo courtesy of Dr. A. J. De Lorenzo)

borhood of 100 million (Allison, 1953). The olfactory receptor cells are surrounded by rod-shaped *sustentacular cells*, which also have cilia but no axons. Olfactory glands opening into the epithelium secrete a mucous substance that covers the cilia; it is generally assumed that this is the site of the olfactory transducer process.

(From Konishi and Zotterman. In Zotterman, Ed. *Olfaction and taste.* Pergamon Press, 1963, p. 220)

B, changes in discharge frequency of a single fiber to changing concentration of salt solution. (From Pfaffman, Gustatory nerve impulses in rat, cat, and rabbit. *J. Neurophysiol.,* 1955, **18,** 429–440)

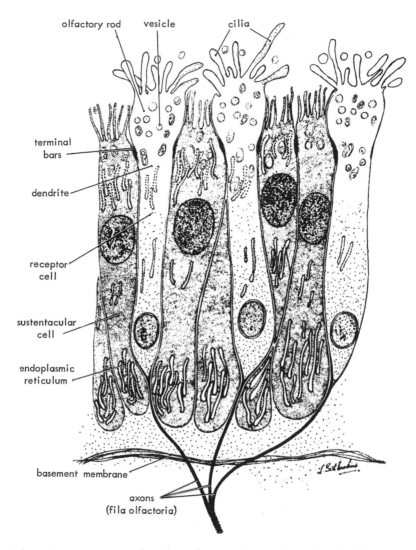

olfactory rod    vesicle         cilia

terminal
bars

dendrite

receptor
cell

sustentacular
cell

endoplasmic
reticulum

basement membrane

axons
(fila olfactoria)

Schematic representation, based on electron microscopic studies, of olfactory receptor and sustentacular cells. (From de Lorenzo. In Zotterman (Ed.), *Olfaction and
taste*. Pergamon Press, 1963, p. 8)

The axons of the bipolar cells pass directly to the central nervous system
in the olfactory nerve. These axons are of very small diameter (0.1–0.4
micra), and conduct impulses of long duration (3–5 milliseconds) at
an extremely low velocity (0.2 meters per second). They terminate in
the *olfactory bulb*, a complex laminated structure analogous to the retina
of the eye. In the olfactory bulb the widely branched processes of the
axons of the bipolar cells synapse with the dendrites of the secondary

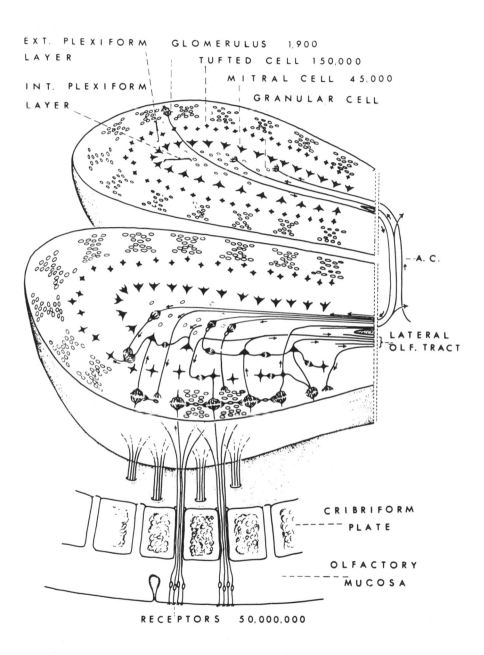

EXT. PLEXIFORM LAYER

INT. PLEXIFORM LAYER

GLOMERULUS 1,900

TUFTED CELL 150,000

MITRAL CELL 45,000

GRANULAR CELL

A.C.

LATERAL OLF. TRACT

CRIBRIFORM PLATE

OLFACTORY MUCOSA

RECEPTORS 50,000,000

Schematic drawing of the olfactory bulbs. Olfactory fibers terminate in the glomer-uli where synaptic relation is established directly or by way of the granule cells with the mitral cells. (From Moulton and Tucker. Electrophysiology of the olfactory system. *Ann. N.Y. Acad. Sci.,* 1964, **116,** 380–428) neurons, the *mitral cells*, in specialized regions, called *glomeruli*. The axons of the mitral cells form the bulk of the *lateral olfactory tract*, which proceeds to the brain. In addition to the mitral cells, several other types of neurons are found in the olfactory bulb. Among these are the *tufted cells*, whose axons cross to the opposite olfactory bulb by way of the anterior commissure. The olfactory bulb also contains several types of short-axoned neurons, together with *granular cells* with rich dendritic networks but no axons.

Volatile substances dispersed in air or dissolved in water are the adequate stimuli of olfaction. Nasal inhaling and sniffing are the accessory functions, which serve in forcing air past the olfactory epithelium. The volatile substances that the olfactory receptors respond to are mostly of organic origin, emitted by flowers, fruits, decaying flesh, scent-producing glands of animals, and the like. On the basis of subjective considerations such odor qualities as floral, camphoraceous, musky, pungent, and putrid have been distinguished. Minute quantities of some chemicals can be detected by smell; for some of them the threshold is in the range of a few molecules (De Vries and Stuiver, 1961).

All odorous substances have some common properties. By the nature of the stimulus, all odorous substances are volatile; however, there are volatile substances that have no odor, and relatively involatile substances may be highly odorous. The substance has to be water- or lipoid-soluble, presumably to permit penetration through the mucous secretions to the cilia. Most odorous substances show characteristically strong absorption in the infrared region of the light spectrum (Barnes et al., 1943; Beck, 1950), a fact that gave rise to the suggestion that molecular oscillation plays an important role in the olfactory transducer process. But this theory has been severely criticized (Moncrieff, 1951; Pfaffmann, 1951; Adey, 1959). More recently, a *steric theory* of olfaction has been proposed (Moncrieff, 1951) and investigated (Amoore, 1964). According to this theory, the stereochemical properties of molecules (their size and shape) rather than their composition determine what odors they evoke. More specifically, the theory assumes that receptor sites with different configurations are present in the olfactory mucosa and that the odor of dissolved chemicals is determined on the basis of their fit into these receptor sites. In a preliminary investigation (Amoore, 1964), 21 camphoraceous substances of diverse chemical composition were all found to have ellipsoidal molecules about 7.7 Ångstrom long, 6.0 Ångstrom wide, and 5.3 Ångstrom high.

The electrical changes accompanying olfactory stimulation have been investigated (1) by placing electrodes over the olfactory mucosa, (2) by recording activity from the olfactory nerve, and (3) by lowering electrodes into the olfactory bulb. Ottoson (1956) studied the electrical response of the mucosa to puffs of odor directed to the same area. He found an electrical potential change at the site of stimulation with an initial, brief

| | TOP SILHOUETTE | FRONT SILHOUETTE | RIGHT SILHOUETTE |
|---|---|---|---|

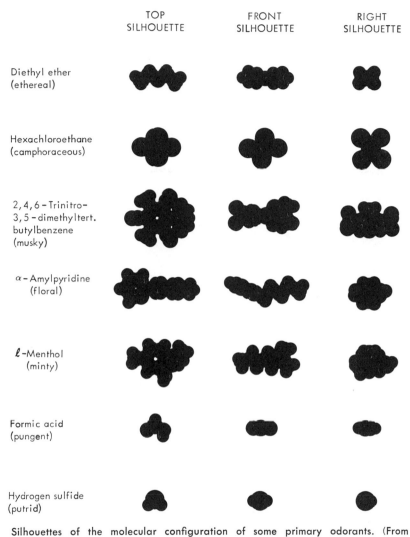

Diethyl ether (ethereal)

Hexachloroethane (camphoraceous)

2,4,6-Trinitro-3,5-dimethyltert. butylbenzene (musky)

α-Amylpyridine (floral)

ℓ-Menthol (minty)

Formic acid (pungent)

Hydrogen sulfide (putrid)

**Silhouettes of the molecular configuration of some primary odorants. (From Amoore. Current status of the steric theory of odor. Ann. N.Y. Acad. Sci., 1964, 116, 457–476)**

positive component, and a large negative one. This mucosal response was named by Ottoson the *electro-olfactogram*, or EOG. With microelectrodes lowered into the mucosa, the EOG was of greatest amplitude near the surface, a fact suggesting that summated activity at the cilia is the source of this electric potential. The shape of the potential differs when different odorants are applied to the mucosa, whereas its amplitude is a function of the concentration of the applied chemical (Gesteland, 1964). Ottoson

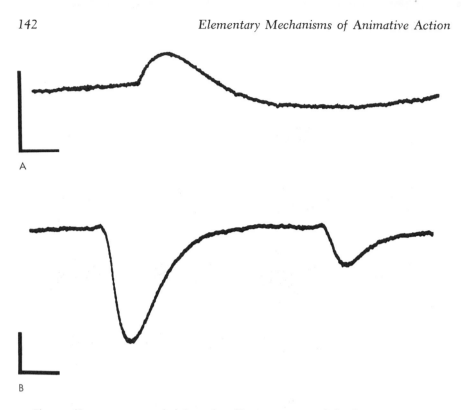

Electro-olfactograms recorded from the olfactory mucosa of the frog in response (A) to a puff of ethanol vapor and (B) to puffs of petroleum ether. Note that in the latter record the second puff, delivered 6 seconds after the first, gives a decreased response. Calibration markings in the left corner: horizontal line, 1 second; vertical line, 1 millivolt. (From Gesteland. Initial events of the electro-olfactogram. *Ann. N.Y. Acad. Sci.,* 1964, **116,** 440–447)

(1963) proposed that the EOG is analogous to the generator potentials recorded in other sense organs.

Because of their thinness, electric discharges of single olfactory fibers are not easy to obtain. Recently, successful recording of unit activity from isolated olfactory fibers of the frog was reported (Gesteland et al., 1963). This study suggests limited odor specificity of single olfactory fibers. A technically easier method is the recording of electrical discharges from isolated strands of the olfactory nerve that contain a limited number of fibers (Beidler, 1961; Tucker, 1963). These latter studies indicate that the magnitude of integrated responses in such nerve strands is a function of the chemicals used and their concentrations. Olfactory-nerve activity is characterized by relatively rapid adaptation; the nerve discharge declines rapidly after prolonged exposure to a chemical stimulant. The olfactory nerve discharge can also be modulated from the central nervous system via the sympathetic fibers of the ethmoidal nerve; the increase in sympathetic activity is accompanied by an increase in the olfactory response to the same stimulus. Apart from these preliminary results, no systematic study is available on the electrical correlates of olfactory sensory activity, though there is quite a number of reports on the electrical activity of the olfactory bulb.

We have referred earlier to the complex architecture of the *olfactory bulb*; hence electrical recordings from the olfactory bulb in conjunction with stimulation of the olfactory receptors is even more difficult to interpret than recordings from the mucosa or olfactory nerve (Moulton and Tucker, 1964). During stimulation of the nose with odorants, large rhythmic potentials that are superimposed on the spontaneous EEG activity of the olfactory bulb may be recorded from the bulb. These potentials were named by Adrian (1950) "induced waves." Recording the single-cell (or unit) activity of the bulb, Adrian (1953) found that some units responded to a restricted class of chemicals and not to others, provided that the concentration of the chemicals was kept low. At higher concentrations the response specificity of the units was lost. In another study (Walsh, 1956), certain odorous substances were found to increase the spike discharge of isolated cells; other chemicals suppressed the discharge activity of the cells. These exploratory investigations indicate a degree of odor specificity at the level of the olfactory bulb. At this point we may mention that the olfactory bulb receives, in addition to its afferent input, centrifugal efferent fibers. This fact was originally recognized by Cajal (1911), who distinguished two centrifugal systems. The existence of centrifugal projection to the olfactory bulb was confirmed recently (Cragg, 1962; Powell and Cowan, 1963); these fibers presumably originate in rhinencephalic structures (Chapter 8).

In almost all vertebrates olfaction is of great importance in recognizing and localizing nutrients, predators, and mates, because all these vaporize scents that can serve as signals of the existence and whereabouts of these vitally important objects. In addition, in some vertebrates, in particular those that live in murky water or are active at night, olfactory information may be of paramount importance in permitting the animal's orientation to its environment. Olfaction is of lesser importance in arboreal and avian than in aquatic and terrestrial species; the former are referred to as *microsmatic*, the latter as *macrosmatic*, animals. Olfaction is altogether absent in a few species, such as the porpoise, which are called *anosmatic* animals (as a lung-breathing mammal the porpoise cannot use its nose under water for olfaction).

AUDITORY RECEPTORS. The ears are mechanoreceptors specialized to register vibrations produced by distant objects and transmitted as pressure waves through water and air. The waves thus propagated can serve as broadcasting signals of the presence and location of sound-emitting objects.

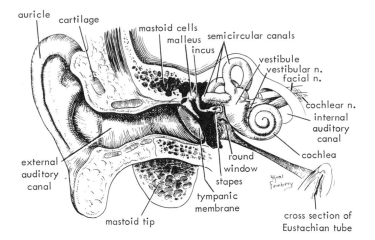

auricle
cartilage
mastoid cells
malleus
incus
semicircular canals
vestibule
vestibular n.
facial n.
cochlear n.
internal
auditory
canal
external
auditory
canal
round
window
stapes
tympanic
membrane
cochlea
mastoid tip
cross section of
Eustachian tube

Semidiagrammatic drawing of the ear with the semicircular canals and the cochlea. (Modified from Davis and Silverman, *Hearing and deafness*, rev. ed. Holt,
Rinehart and Winston, 1960)

The ear is conventionally subdivided into three parts: the external, the
middle, and the inner ear. The external and middle ear are accessory organs
of audition; the inner ear contains the transducer mechanisms of hearing.

The *external ear* includes the auricle and the meatus (auditory canal),
which function jointly in concentrating and channeling sound waves. The
*tympanic membrane* (ear drum) across the canal serves as a partition between the external and middle ear.

The *middle ear* is filled with air and contains three small bones or
*oscicles*: the malleus, incus, and stapes. The *malleus* is in contact with the
tympanic membrane; together with the incus, it vibrates with the air waves
transmitted by the tympanic membrane. The *incus* transmits these vibrations to the *stapes*, which is in contact with the membrane of the *oval
window*. The three oscicles of the middle ear are so arranged that they act
as a mechanical lever system, amplifying the energy of sound signals received at the tympanic membrane when it is transmitted to the oval
window.

The *inner ear* is a complex of cavities filled with fluid. Part of these
form the vestibular apparatus, discussed above; the rest form the auditory,
or cochlear, apparatus. The *cochlear apparatus* is essentially a tube, in
higher vertebrates with several spiral coils, that has two openings with
covering membranes, the *oval* and *round windows*. Throughout its length,
the cochlear tube is divided into three compartments by *Reissner's membrane* and the *basilar membrane*. The two outer compartments, filled with
perilymph, are the scala vestibuli and scala tympani; the middle compartment, filled with endolymph, is the scala media. (The endolymph shows a

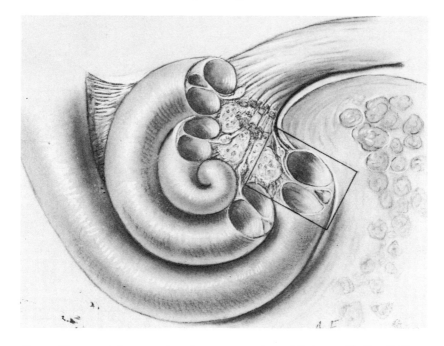

The cochlea, partially opened to show cross sections of its turns with the distribution of the nerves. (From Davis and Silverman, *Hearing and deafness,* rev. ed. Holt, Rinehart and Winston, 1960)

high concentration of potassium and a low concentration of sodium—a source of the resting endocochlear potential, which is 80 millivolts positive with respect to the perilymph and surrounding tissues.) On the basilar membrane in the scala media is the *organ of Corti,* containing the sensory hair cells, which are in contact with the *tectorial membrane.*

The afferents of the auditory system are bipolar neurons whose cell bodies are located in the *cochlear* and *spiral ganglia.* The dendrites of these neurons innervate the hair cells; their axons pass by way of the eighth cranial nerve to the cochlear nucleus in the medulla. In addition to these afferents, a number of feedback efferent fibers originating in the medulla (olivocochlear bundle) are also believed to reach the cochlea (Rasmussen, 1946, 1955).

*Pressure waves* propagated by such elastic media as air, water, or solids are the adequate stimuli of audition. The lowest *frequency* of pressure waves that mammals respond to is in the range of 10–50 cycles per second, the upper limit varies in different species from about 10,000 to 100,000 cycles per second. Sound *intensity* is conventionally measured in decibels. A *decibel* is $\frac{1}{10}$ of a bel, where 1 bel is defined as the common logarithm of the ratio between a reference intensity (usually 0.0002 dynes per square

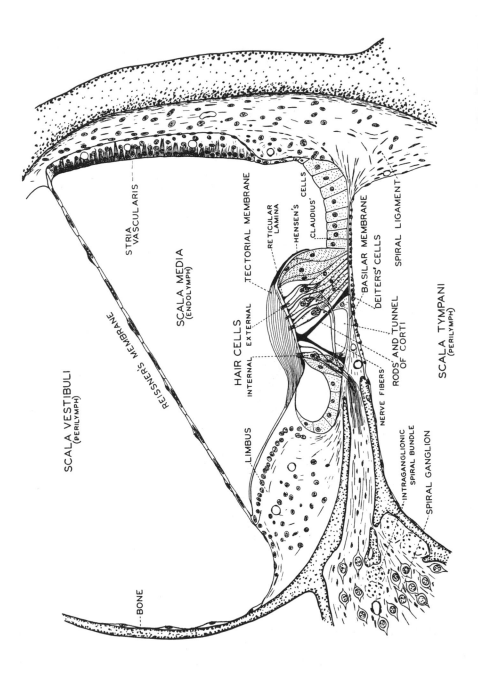

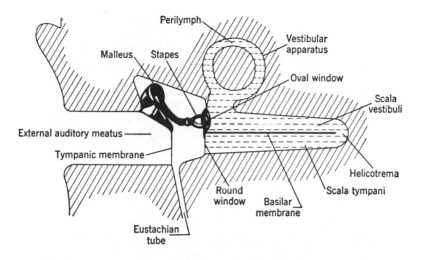

Highly schematic diagram of the ear, showing the cochlear and vestibular channels filled with perilymph. (From Békésy and Rosenblith. In Stevens, Ed., *Handbook of experimental psychology.* John Wiley & Sons, 1951, p. 1076)

centimeter) and the sound that is being measured. The intensity range varies from a lower limit near thermal background noise (Brownian motion) to an upper limit set by injurious effects on the sense organ (about 130 decibels). The differential threshold for frequency (pitch) and amplitude (loudness) varies in different species, but a high level of differential sensitivity is the rule in most of them (Davis, 1959).

When the ear is stimulated by sound waves, the fluid in the cochlea, enclosed between the oval and round windows, is forced to move, and this movement is assumed to stimulate the cochlear receptors. If electrodes are placed over the round window, they will record alternating electric potentials that follow faithfully, within a limited range, the frequency and amplitude of the sound stimulus. This electric potential, which when connected with an amplifier and loudspeaker, can reproduce the original sound pattern, was called by Wever and Bray the *cochlear microphonic*. It is believed that the shearing force of the moving tectorial membrane over the hair cells produces this effect. The cochlear microphonic response has no measurable latency, and it may be analogous to the receptor generator potentials observed in some other sense organs, which are characterized by graded potentials that follow the amplitude and frequency of the

(See *facing page.*)

Cross-sectional drawing of the cochlear canal in the second turn of the guinea pig's cochlea (the position indicated by the rectangle in the figure on page 145). (From Davis and Silverman, *Hearing and deafness,* rev. ed. Holt, Rinehart and Winston, 1960)

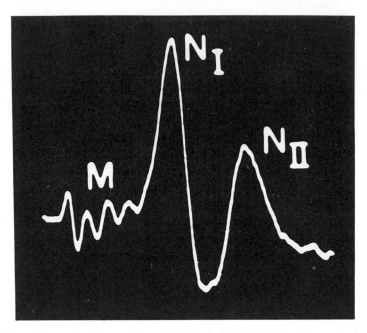

Oscilloscopic record of the cochlear microphonic (M) and of the subsequent electric responses of the auditory nerve (NI, NII). (From Galambos. Suppression of auditory nerve acturty by stimulation of efferent fibers to cochlea. *J. Neurophysiol.*, 1956, **19**, 424–437)

applied stimulus. Electrodes placed over the auditory nerve or inserted into single auditory afferents display a different discharge pattern (Tasaki, 1954). In response to a single click, one or a few spike discharges with a latency of 1–2 milliseconds may be recorded. If the click is intense, the spike discharges increase and may outlast the duration of the applied stimulus. These discharge patterns are of all-or-none character, followed by a refractory period with no discharge.

The problem of *auditory frequency analysis* (pitch discrimination) was first considered by Helmholtz. According to his resonance theory, in a more limited sense referred to as a *place theory*, different portions of the basilar membrane of the spiral cochlea resonate at different frequencies. Thus the hair cells in the different regions of the cochlea are deformed and excited selectively. Some support for such a place theory has come from studies in which portions of the cochlea were destroyed; the findings suggest that the basal turns of the organ of Corti respond to high-frequency tones, and the apical turns to low frequency tones. In a similar vein, electrical recordings from single auditory fibers have shown that fibers from the apical turns of the cochlea are activated preferentially by low-frequency

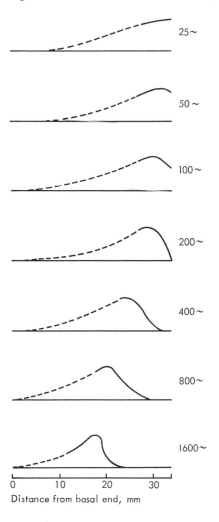

Traveling waves in the cochlea, on stimulation of the ear with sounds of different frequency. Solid lines in curves represent actual measurements; broken lines, extrapolated. (From *Experiments in hearing* by G. Von Békésy. Copyright © 1960. McGraw-Hill Book Company. Used by permission)

tones; although, according to this evidence, fibers from the basal turn respond to any frequency (Tasaki, 1954). Despite the fact that the place theory in general is supported by modern investigations, the studies of Békésy (1960) indicate that Helmholtz's original assumption that the basilar membrane resonates with sound is incorrect. Békésy's investigations, which involved direct microscopic observation of the mechanical behavior of the cochlear membranes under pressure, suggest instead that *traveling waves* are produced in the basilar membrane and that they reach maximal displacement at different sites with different frequencies (for other theories, see Wever, 1949).

The place theory is also supported by electrophysiological recordings made in different way stations of the auditory portion of the central nervous system. These structures show a *tonotopic organization;* that is, neurons in different regions respond preferentially to sounds of different frequency. In addition to frequency (or pitch) analysis, the ears can also analyze accurately the intensity (or loudness) of sounds. *Sound intensity* is correlated with amplitude of the pressure waves, and its coding may be dependent on the discharge frequency of single fibers or the activation of fibers with different thresholds. Finally, *auditory localization* is dependent on the functioning of two ears, permitting the *binaural analysis* of differences in the arrival time of and phase differences in the sound waves.

Audition can be utilized in a variety of behavioral processes. Approaching objects generate sound waves; thus predators and prey may be identified from a distance. Auditory signals are widely used in social communication. Sounds emitted by members of a group can be appreciated by other members and in this way permit the coordination of their communal activities. Finally, some animals, particularly those living in visually impoverished environments, such as caves, emit high-frequency sounds that, when reflected by objects, permit their localization; this function is called *echo location.* Echo location is well known in bats (Griffin, 1958), but it is also used by porpoises (Kellogg, 1958) and many other animals. In this context we may mention that in fish and amphibians an organ related to the ear, the *lateral line* organ, is used for registering water currents produced or reflected by objects.

OPTICAL RECEPTORS. The reliance on olfactory and auditory information is limited to some extent, because numerous objects and events (particularly inorganic types) are not associated with the vaporization of odorous chemicals or the generation of sound waves. A more common source of "telecommunication" signals is light, which, as electromagnetic radiation, is transmitted through various transparent or translucent media (air or water) and reflected by all kinds of opaque objects, whether organic or inorganic. The great speed with which light is transmitted, and the physical regularities of its propagation, refraction, and reflection, make it the most dependable of all broadcasting signals that the organism can utilize. Moreover, because various life processes are dependent on light, the presence of light is associated with sources of food, and the sunlit milieu represents a propitious environment for organic activities.

*Optic radiation* is physically defined as electromagnetic vibration with wavelengths in the range of about 200 to 10,000 millimicra. The vertebrate eye, unlike some other optical instruments, is sensitive only to a limited range of optical waves, between 400 and 750 millimicra; this latter is the range of *visible light.* Some organisms may respond to shorter or longer wavelengths, the ultraviolet and infrared range, respectively. Light is utilized by virtually all animals as a means of obtaining information about events in their environment.

The simplest eyes are seen in some flagellate protists, such as Euglena. The *stigma* of Euglena consists of a swelling at the base of the flagellum, a light-sensitive spot, which is shaded by a mass of orange-pigmented granules. The light-sensitive spot, as recent electron microscopic studies have shown (Wolken, 1958), is composed of about 50 fine rods. The shading by the pigment permits the coarse determination of the direction of the light source. More complex photoreceptors are the *ocelli*, seen in Coelenterates. The ocelli are composed of photosensitive cells embedded in pigmented substances. In their simplest form, the ocelli constitute flat patches on the surface of the body. More complex ocelli are cup-shaped structures sunk into a pit; some of them may also be covered with a protective coating or equipped with a light-focusing lens. The flat ocelli may be useful in discriminating light intensity but are probably ineffective in locating directly the light source. The cup-shaped ocelli with pinhole openings are better suited for analyzing the direction of light source; in contrast, the ocelli with optic lenses may permit rudimentary discrimination of size or shape. *Complex eyes*, which may be found in higher molluscs, in insects, and vertebrates, are equipped with various mechanisms that make possible the projection of a faithful image of the optical world onto the photosensitive transducer surface of the eye, the retina.

The *vertebrate eye* is composed of accessory optical mechanisms and a photosensitive transducer system. The accessory mechanisms make possible the scanning of the surrounding, the regulation of the amount of light admitted, and the focusing of a relatively accurate optic image on the photosensitive surface. The latter is a transducer system that translates light signals into the impulse code of the central nervous system. The vertebrate eye functions essentially as a modern automatic camera, and though it is in many respects less accurate than a good optical instrument, some of its functions (achieved with the help of the central nervous system) cannot as yet be matched by the most complex of man-made optical instruments.

Scanning of the visual surrounding is accomplished partly by body and head movements, and partly by rotation of the eyes in the eye socket by the extraocular muscles. Light enters the eye through the *cornea*, which is a modified portion of the sclerotic coating of the eye. The spherical surface of the cornea is to a large extent responsible for the refraction of the light entering the eye, and it contributes to the focusing of the optical image on the retina. The surface of the cornea is protected and kept moist by the watery secretion of the *lacrimal gland*. Light passing through the cornea enters the anterior chamber of the eye, which is filled with a fluid, the *aqueous humor*, and reaches the lens through the opening of the *iris*, the pupil. The *sphincter* and *dilator* muscles of the iris vary the bore of the *pupil* and control the amount of light that may reach the lens in a manner similar to the operation of the diaphragm of a camera.

The *lens* is a transparent biconvex structure with elastic properties. The lens and cornea jointly form the *dioptric system* of the eye, converging the incident light rays in such a way that their focal point coincides with the

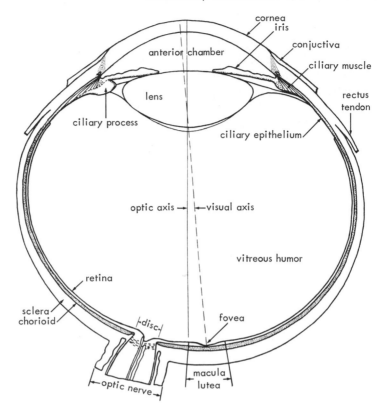

Diagrammatic section of the human eye. (Modified from Salzman. In Walls, *The vertebrate eye and its adaptive radiation*. Cranbrook Institute of Science, 1942)

photosensitive surface of the retina. The curvature of the normal "relaxed" lens brings to focus on the retina the parallel light rays coming from distant objects (objects at infinity); in this state the eye is said to be *emmetropic*. For focusing on near objects, the dioptric power of the lens has to be increased; this process is called accommodation. In *accommodation* the curvature of the elastic lens is increased by a complex process including the contraction of the ciliary muscles, with a consequent increase in the dioptric power of the eye. Light leaving the lens passes through the *vitreous humor* of the interior chamber of the eye. The wall of the interior chamber is formed by a sclerotic coat, the inner surface of which is covered by the pigmented *choroid layer*, which, as an absorbing surface, reduces light scatter. Covering the choroid layer in the far end of the interior chamber is the retina.

The *retina* is a complex multilayered structure that for convenience may be subdivided into three major layers: the exterior portion of the retina is

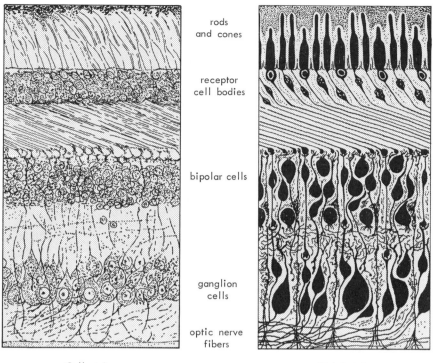

rods
and cones

receptor
cell bodies

bipolar cells

ganglion
cells

optic nerve
fibers

Cell stain                    Golgi stain

The layers of the human retina from a peripheral region near the fovea (region III of Polyak). The left figure is a schematic drawing of the retina in Nissl-stained material; the right figure is a schematic drawing from the same region from Golgi-stained material. (Slightly modified, from Polyak, *The vertebrate visual system*. The University of Chicago Press, 1957)

formed by a layer of *ganglion cells* and their fibers; below this is situated an intermediate layer composed of *bipolar, horizontal,* and *amacrine* cells; at the bottom of the retina and partly in contact with the pigmented choroid is the layer of rods and cones, which are the transducer elements of the eye. That is, light falling on the retina first reaches the optic nerve fibers and their ganglion cells and, lastly, the receptors themselves. This is an anomalous situation in vertebrates that is absent in the similarly complex eyes of cephalopod molluscs (like sepia or octopus) and in the mosaic eyes of insects.

The *rods* and *cones* are the transducer elements of the eye, which translate the energy of photic signals into electrochemical energy that, in turn, initiates the transmission of bioelectric signals through the optic nerves to the central nervous system. The rods and cones have certain common properties, but they also differ from one another in many respects. It has

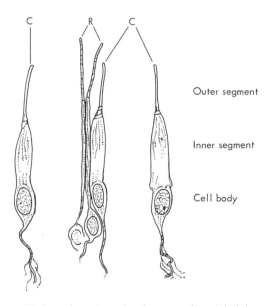

Rods (R) and cones (C) from the retina of a rhesus monkey. (Slightly modified, from Polyak, *The vertebrate visual system.* The University of Chicago Press, 1957)

been suspected for a long time that rods are associated with vision in the dark or under conditions of dim illumination, called *scotopic vision*, whereas the cones are associated with vision in the day or bright illumination, called *photopic vision*, and with color discrimination, or *chromatic vision*. The retinae of some nocturnal species may contain almost exclusively rods; the retinae of other species with expressed diurnal living habits, however, may have an almost-pure cone composition (Walls, 1942). In the retinae of many vertebrates, such as carnivores and primates, both rods and cones are present. In these species the rods are relatively more numerous in the periphery of the retina, but the cones predominate in the center, called the *area centralis* or *fovea*. In a narrow region of the retina, where the optic nerve exits, both rods and cones are absent; this region is the optic disc, which, because of its insensitivity to light, is called the *blind spot*.

In addition to their nucleated cell bodies, rods and cones are composed of two parts, an outer and an inner segment. Recent electron microscopic studies have revealed (Sjöstrand, 1953; De Robertis, 1960) that the *outer segment*, which may be in contact with the pigmented choroid, is composed of a pile of narrow, double-membraned discs. These discs contain the photochemical pigments that serve as transducers. The outer segment is in contact with the *inner segment* by way of modified cilia that resemble in structure the primitive cilia previously described (Chapter 4). The inner segment is rich in mitochondria; it is therefore believed to play a role in

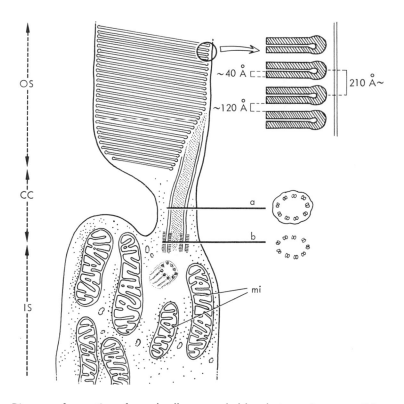

Diagram of a portion of a rod cell as revealed by electron microscopy. OS, outer segment; CC, connecting ciliated segment; IS, inner segment. The pile of double-membraned discs of the outer segment shown enlarged in the upper right corner. a and b, the connecting cilium and its basal body in cross section; mi, mitochondria in the inner segment. (Slightly modified, after de Robertis, Nowinski, and Salz. *Cell biology,* 4th ed. W. B. Saunders Company, 1965.

the energization of the photochemical processes that go on during illumination of the retina. Biochemical studies have shown (Wald, 1959) that pigmented chemicals may be extracted from the rods and cones that undergo a series of reversible transformations when exposed to light. The photosensitive chemical extracted from the rods is called *rhodopsin;* it is a conjugated protein composed of *retinene* (a carotenoid) and a protein or lipoprotein called *opsin.* (Less commonly, as in freshwater fish, the analogous substance extracted from rods is porphyropsin.) The substance extracted from cones is called *iodopsin* (a less commonly occurring cone pigment is cyanopsin). Rhodopsin extracted from rods in the dark is purple, but it bleaches to yellow and white when exposed to light. Chemically, this bleaching indicates the dissociation of rhodopsin into colorless

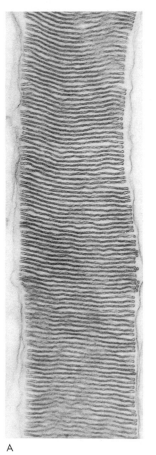

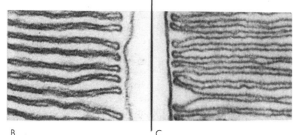

Electron micrographs of cones and a rod from the retina of a monkey. A, the double-membraned discs from the outer segment of a cone in the fovea; B, the double-membraned discs of a cone at higher magnification; C, the double-membraned discs of a rod from the same preparation. Note that the intradisc space is greater in the rod than in the cone, whereas the interdisc space is smaller. (From J. F. Dowling. Foveal receptors of the monkey retina: fine structure. *Science,* 1965, **147,** 57–59. Copyright 1965 by the American Association for the Advancement of Science. Photo courtesy of Dr. John Dowling)

A                    B                         C

opsin, and the yellow retinene or the colorless vitamin A. In the intact eye, and to some extent also in suitable extracts, this process is a reversible one, and rhodopsin is regenerated in the dark from retinene, vitamin A, and opsin.

The ability of rhodopsin to transform photic energy into chemical energy must be related to its efficiency, as a pigment, in absorbing or trapping light. On the basis of this assumption, several investigators have made photometric measurements of the *absorption spectrum* of extracted, unbleached rhodopsin with light of different wavelengths. Wald and his collaborators (1935) extracted from the retina of chickens rhodopsin and iodopsin, and found that their spectral absorption curves agreed well with the sensitivity spectra of dark-adapted and light-adapted pigeons, respectively. The absorption spectrum of rhodopsin from a variety of species was found to correspond closely to the sensitivity curve of the dark-adapted

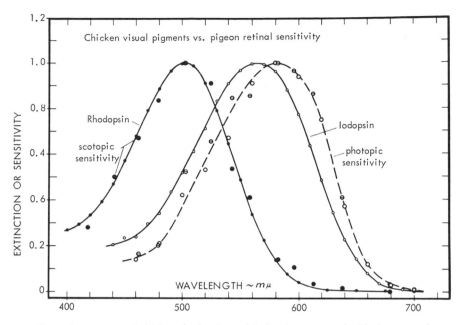

Absorption spectra of chicken rhodopsin and iodopsin, compared with the spectral sensitivities of dark-adapted and light-adapted pigeons. (After Wald. The photoreceptor process in vision. *Handb. Physiol.*, 1959, Sec. 1. **1**, 671–692)

eye (scotopic vision), with an absorption maximum and sensitivity maximum at about 500 millimicra. Similarly, the absorption curve of iodopsin extracted from the chicken retina could be related to the photopic sensitivity curve of pigeons, though there was a shift of about 20 millimicra toward the red end of the spectrum. From these and related findings it was concluded that the properties of rod and cone vision derive, at least partly, from the properties of their photosensitive pigments.

The difference in the absolute *sensitivity threshold* of the light-adapted and dark-adapted eye is considerable. After a period of about 30 minutes in the dark, the sensitivity of the eye is increased several thousand times. This increase in visual sensitivity is attributed to a switch from the use of cones under conditions of light-adaptation to rods under dark-adaptation. (This is often referred to as the *duplicity theory* of vision.) In bright light rhodopsin is maximally bleached and is not regenerated; under such conditions the rods cannot function, and vision is mediated largely by cones. In dim light the high-threshold iodopsin of the cones is not appreciably affected, and vision is mediated by the regenerating low-threshold rhodopsin. Hecht and his collaborators (1942) found that as few as 3–8 light quanta may be sufficient to produce visual sensation in the light-adapted eye of man.

Whereas the high degree of visual sensitivity is attributable to the rods, the great acuity or resolving power of the eye is the function of the cones. *Visual acuity* refers to the ability of seeing separately neighboring points of light or dark, a function which makes possible the perception of optical detail. Obviously, the resolving power of the eye is limited by the size of its receptors, the "retinal mosaic," and it also depends on the mode of interaction between the receptor elements and the associated nerves that transmit the optic signals. Measured in terms of visual angle, *visual resolution* in the fovea of man was found to be about 20 to 30 seconds of arc; separate points within this angle tend to fuse. In the peripheral parts of the retina the "minimum separable" is much larger.

This finding has been related to the fact that in the fovea single cones may establish synaptic relation with separate bipolar neurons, particularly the *midget bipolar cells* found in this region (Polyak, 1957). These bipolar cells, in turn, tend to have a one-to-one relation with ganglion cells or *midget ganglion cells*. In this manner, the exact locus of stimulation, or its "local sign," may be resolved by the foveal retinal "mosaic." In contrast, in the periphery of the retina a large number of rods converge on single bipolar cells, thus the utilization of single receptor elements for the resolution of visual detail is prevented. It should be added that the great advantage of having several rod cells synapse with single bipolar cells is that the energy of the excitation of many rods may summate to produce a discharge of a bipolar cell at low levels of illumination. This may be one of the explanations of why peripheral rods have a considerably lower sensitivity threshold than foveal cones have. (In man there are about 125 million rods, and 4–7 million cones, against only 1 million ganglion cells and nerve fibers.)

One of the most intensively studied, but as yet poorly understood, aspects of the visual receptor process is *chromatic vision*. Under photopic conditions, stimulation of the retina (that is, of the cones) with light of different wavelengths produces qualitatively distinct *hue* sensations, extending in the visible spectrum from red to violet. (These hues, together with their characteristic brightness and saturation, are referred to as *colors*). Now it has been known for a long time that all the specific color sensations may also be produced by the appropriate mixtures of the three *primary colors*, red, green, and blue (violet).

This phenomenon of color mixing gave rise to the familiar *trichromatic theory* of color vision, associated with the names of Young and Helmholtz. The theory postulated the existence of three types of cones, each of which responds maximally to wavelengths of one of the primary colors. Integration of the differential levels of excitation of these three types of hypothetical cones would then be the basis of color discrimination. The trichromatic theory has recently obtained confirmation in experiments in which the absorption spectra of single cones were determined in primate retinae

(Marks et al., 1964). Three groups of cones were identified, with absorption maxima at about 445, 535, and 570 millimicra, corresponding to the violet, green, and yellow regions of the spectrum. Comparable results were also obtained by Brown and Wald (1964), who identified three types of cones with absorption maxima at about 450, 525, and 555 millimicra. The latter investigators were also able to measure the absorption of single rods, which were found to have their maxima at about 505 millimicra (see page 160).

Electrophysiological studies of the events taking place in the retina as a result of photic stimulation fall into two classes. During illumination (1) electrodes placed over or inserted into the eye record a complex polyphasic response called the *electroretinogram* (ERG). Between the back and the front of the eye is a resting retinal potential, the basal ends of the receptor cells being positive with respect to the apical ends. The ERG response during illumination is due partly to a change in this potential, and it partly reflects the generated nerve potentials. Various attempts have been made to analyze the source and significance of these complex waves, and to extract information from them that may shed light on the retinal receptor process (Granit, 1959; Brindley, 1960). More direct information about the electrical events accompanying stimulation can be gained (2) from *micro-electrode recordings* from single retinal fibers or cells, and with gross and microelectrode recordings from the optic nerve.

The pioneering work of recording from *single retinal fibers* in the horseshoe crab and the frog was the accomplishment of Hartline (1938); his studies were extended by several other investigators, such as Granit (1947, 1955), Kuffler (1953), Lettvin et al., (1959), Hubel and Wiesel (1959). Hartline found in the frog some fibers that responded when light was turned on, and discharged steadily during illumination; these were called *on-fibers*. Other fibers gave a burst of spikes when light was turned on, then became inactive, to give a new burst when light was turned off; these were called *on-off fibers*. Finally, still other fibers gave discharges only when visual stimulation was discontinued; these were called *off-fibers*. The nature of these discharging units was further clarified by Kuffler and others, who used small reflected light spots in order to explore the response properties of single retinal cells or fibers. With this technique it was shown that single units tend to respond to illumination of a circumscribed area in the visual environment, the *receptive field*, and that two major types of units may be distinguished, *on-center units* and *off-center units*. The on-center units are characterized by an increase of spike discharges when the center of the receptive field is illuminated (on-response) and inhibition of discharges when the periphery of the receptive field is illuminated (off-response). The opposite holds for off-center units. These findings suggest a complex organization in the retina where receptors and nerves interact with each other both synergistically and antagonistically. The intricate histological organization of the retina, indeed, could permit such

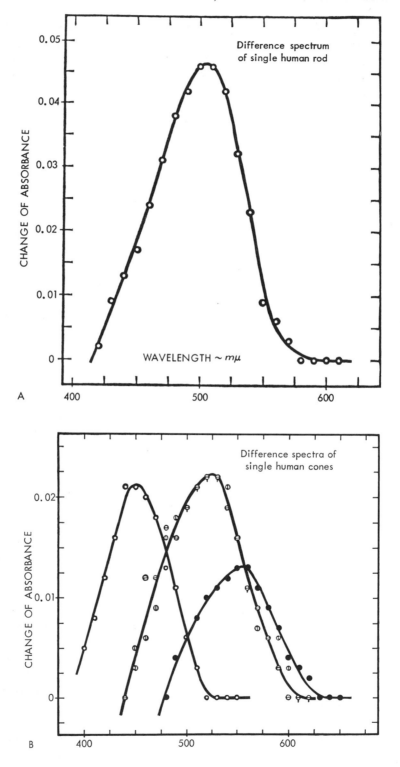

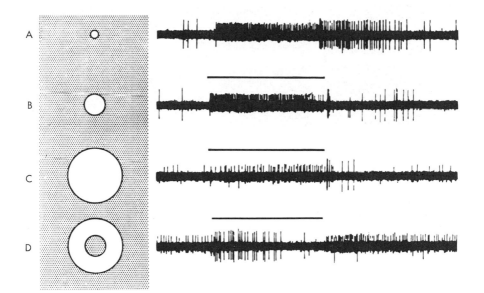

An "on-center" unit with antagonistic peripheral surround from the lateral geniculate nucleus of the cat. (Similar units are commonly found also in the retina.) Illumination of part of the center of the receptive field of this cell (the duration of
illumination is shown by the line above the oscilloscopic traces) produces increased
discharge frequency (A). Maximal discharge is obtained when the entire center is
illuminated (B). When both the "on"-center and "off"-periphery are illuminated,
discharge frequency is greatly reduced (C). The spontaneous activity of the unit is
inhibited if the center is masked and only the periphery is illuminated, with an increase in discharge on cessation of illumination (D). (From Hubel and Wiesel. Integrative action in the cat's lateral geniculate body. *J. Physiol.* (London), 1961, **155,**
385–398)

an interaction. In fact, in the retina of lower vertebrates, such as the frog
(Lettvin et al., 1959), evidence was obtained of a more complex organization, single units being able to respond differentially to such properties of
the visual environment as sharp edges or moving small objects ("bug de-
tectors").

(See facing page.)

Difference spectra of single rods and cones from the parafoveal region of the human retina. (Difference spectra are obtained by subtracting the absorption values
obtained with bleached receptor elements from those obtained in the dark.) A,
difference spectrum of a single rod with an absorption maximum at about 505
millimicra. B, difference spectra from three types of cones with maxima at about
450 millimicra ("blue" receptor), 525 millimicra ("green" receptor), and 555 millimicra ("red" receptor). (From P. K. Brown and G. Wald. Visual pigments in single
rods and cones of the human retina. *Science,* 1964, **144,** 45–52). Copyright
1964 by the American Association for the Advancement of Science.

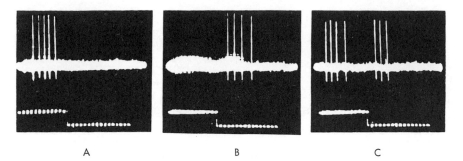

A                    B                    C

Responses of a single ganglion cell in the cat's retina. A single light spot 0.2 milli-meters in diameter (duration of illumination indicated by upward position of the lower trace) produced an "on" response in A. When the light was moved 0.5 milli-meters away, the ganglion cell responded with an "off" response to the same stimulus, as shown in B. In the region between A and B an "on-off" response was obtained, as shown in C. (From Kuffler. Discharge patterns and functional organiza-tion of mammalian retina. *J. Neurophysiol.*, 1953, **16**, 37–68)

We may, finally, refer here briefly to the work of Granit (1943, 1955), who recorded with microelectrodes the response of single fibers of the retina in a variety of vertebrate species to light of differing wavelengths. Granit found that under conditions of dark-adaptation maximal discharges could be obtained from all fibers with a 500 millimicra light source; this finding corresponds to the scotopic maximum of rods obtained with other techniques. Under light adaptation, however, there could be distinguished in several species two classes of fibers, which Granit has called "dominators" and "modulators." Fibers responding maximally at 560 millimicra were called the dominators; this wavelength is the photopic maximum as de-termined by ERG recording, and it also represents the average response of the modulators. The modulators represent a group of fibers that respond dif-ferentially to selected, narrow regions of the spectrum which roughly represent red, green, blue, and possibly a few other colors. Granit postu-lated that the *dominators* mediate intensity or brightness discrimination, and the modulators analyze color at the level of the retina. Because these recordings were obtained from fibers that issue from ganglion cells and that therefore are removed by at least one set of neurons (the bipolar cells) from the rods and cones, these results need not reflect directly on the be-havior of the rods and cones themselves.

**Some General Properties of Receptors**    All the receptors described share a common function; namely, they gather information about prevailing or changing conditions in the organism's internal or external environment. This function is accomplished in different (and as yet little understood) ways by means of transducer mechanisms whereby mechanical, thermal, chemical, and photic forms of energy, the *peripheral stimuli*, are converted into intraorganic *neural signals* that can be utilized by the central nervous system for its information-gathering functions.

RECEPTOR GENERATOR POTENTIAL. There is accumulating evidence (Gray, 1959; Davis, 1961) that the first step in the initiation of a nerve signal is the production of a local, electrical *generator potential* at the receptor-neural juncture (this reaction can occur between two cells or two components of a single cell). The generator potential, under propitious circumstances, may be converted into a *spike*, or *action, potential*, transmitted by way of the axon of the nerve, and made available for central nervous processing. That the direct action of a peripheral stimulus is the generation of a local potential was first demonstrated clearly in the Pacinian corpuscle. In this receptor a graded generator potential may be recorded from the unmyelinated fiber endings encased in the corpuscle, and the action potential is initiated outside the capsule in the axon at the first node of Ranvier of the myelin sheath. Such generator potentials are also produced in all probability in most or all other sensory structures, as in the olfactory epithelium, the cochlea, the retina, and others. The basic difference between a generator potential and an action potential is that the former is a *graded, local* electrical event whose *variable magnitude* (amplitude) depends on the strength of the applied stimulus, whereas the latter displays an essentially *invariant amplitude* that is conducted *nondecrementally* (self-propagation) along the entire nerve axon.

TEMPORAL AND SPATIAL SUMMATION AND INHIBITION. Whether or not an action potential can be initiated in a nerve axon will depend on the magnitude of the generator potential produced by the transducer action of the stimulus. Weak or *subthreshold* stimuli cannot initiate an action potential and will therefore fail to produce a nerve signal that is transmitted in an obligatory fashion along the axon. It has been shown by various techniques, however, that subthreshold stimuli delivered in quick succession to a receptor may produce spike potentials. This additive phenomenon is referred to as *temporal summation*. Summation effects may also be produced by stimulation of adjacent receptors that converge on or synapse with a single nerve element, as is true of the rods of the retina; this is the phenomenon of *spatial summation*. Summation decreases the threshold (that is, increases the sensitivity) of receptors, because the energy yield of weak stimuli is built up in a cumulative fashion. Summation is also of importance for the coding of stimulus intensity: owing to the time required for summating subthreshold generator potentials, the discharge frequency of axons will be lower when the applied stimulus is weak than when it is intense.

The increase in sensitivity obtained through temporal and spatial summation occurs at the expense of acuity or resolving power. The resolution (prevention of fusion) of temporally or spatially contiguous stimuli is

achieved through the opposite processes of *temporal* or *spatial inhibition.*
Temporal inhibition has been observed with generator potentials; for instance, the receptor potential of the Pacinian corpuscle is depressed for a
few milliseconds after the delivery of a stimulus (Gray and Sato, 1953).
Temporal inhibition is more easily demonstrated by recording action potentials, and this inhibition is at least partly caused by the refractory
cycle of nerves (Chapter 7). The phenomenon of spatial inhibition, also
known as *lateral inhibition*, is well established. The reciprocal organization
of visual receptive fields by means of antagonistic surrounds illustrates the
way lateral inhibition can lead to "sharpening" the boundary and de-
limiting the spatial locus of the stimulus. The combined use of two classes
of receptor elements, those that employ summation and those that are
utilizing antagonistic organization, can provide both low-sensory threshold
and high level of acuity in a single receptor system.

THE CODING OF SENSORY INFORMATION.   The circumstance that receptors are affected preferentially by their *adequate stimuli* (the eyes by
optic stimuli, the ears by acoustic stimuli, and so forth) should make possible the direct, peripheral coding of the primary physical property of the
stimulus. This hypothesis is merely a rephrasing of Johannes Müller's
"doctrine of specific nerve energies," which also implied that *modality-
specificity* (stimulation of the eyes always giving rise to vision, of the ears
to audition, and so on) is attributable to the structural or functional specificity of the nerves transmitting peripherally evoked signals or to the specificity of their anatomical connections within the brain. Although we
know now that the signals ("nerve energies") transmitted by different afferent systems are basically alike (that is, the spike discharges transmitted
through optic fibers may be indistinguishable from the spikes of the auditory fibers), nevertheless it is still justifiable to postulate that specific receptors in combination with their unique central nervous connections can
code sensory modality. It is for this reason that stimulation of a receptor
by nonadequate stimuli produces receptor-specific sensation; for instance,
stimulation of the retina mechanically, chemically, or electrically produces
visual sensations in man.

The coding of *sensory qualities* within a single modality (say, different
colors in vision or different tones in audition) may be dependent on more
complex processes. According to one theory, the discrimination of different
sensory qualities is made possible by the presence of different receptor
elements or afferent fibers within a single receptor system, which respond
selectively to different stimulus qualities; examples of such a postulated
coding mechanism are the place theory of pitch discrimination and the
trichromatic theory of color vision. According to another theory, sensory
qualities are coded by a single set of sensory elements through their differential patterns of discharge; an example of this is the pattern theory of
somesthetic discrimination that we have previously considered. Neither

theory has been established beyond doubt for any single sensory system, and there is no compelling reason to postulate that sensory quality is coded in the same manner in different receptor systems.

Some information is available at present about the peripheral coding of various stimulus dimensions or *sensory attributes*, such as their intensity (loudness, brightness, and so on), geometric pattern, and spatial location. *Stimulus intensity* can be coded in at least three ways, and there is evidence of the operation of all of them in one or another of the sensory systems. One way of coding intensity is by the *frequency of discharges* of single receptor elements, because with increasing stimulus intensity the frequency of afferent discharge increases in many sensory systems. Another way of coding intensity is by the number of jointly discharging elements; the *recruiting* of more and more discharging afferent fibers as stimulus intensity is raised has also been demonstrated in a variety of sensory systems. Finally, related to the latter, is the coding of intensity by means of elements or fibers with different *sensory thresholds*, receptor elements with higher sensitivity threshold being activated as the intensity of the stimulus increases. The exact role of any of these possible methods of coding in the various sensory systems remains to be established; it is not unlikely that more than one method is often used for the sake of redundancy of information.

The coding of the *spatial location* of a stimulus source, and its *shape* or *configuration*, are dependent on topographically arranged receptor mosaics in some sensory systems. The accurate optic projection of the visual field on the retinal mosaic, the topographic arrangement of the somesthetic and kinesthetic receptors over the body surface, and the maintenance of accurate *retinotopic* and *somatotopic* projection by the afferents of these receptors in the central nervous system make possible the coding of the spatial source, or "local sign," of the stimulus. (Auditory localization is achieved in a different manner by a binaural mechanism.) In the coding of stimulus configuration, which is obviously a more complex task than the coding of the locus of a point source, the topographic properties of these receptors are presumably utilized. Some of the central nervous mechanisms involved in the coding and decoding of stimulus patterns will be considered later. We should mention here, however, that some aspects of the coding of stimulus configuration may occur at the receptor level, at least in the visual system of lower vertebrates. This is suggested by the work of Lettvin and his collaborators (1959), which showed that single retinal fibers in the frog can respond selectively to simple configurational properties of the visual world. The retina, of course, is distinguished from other receptors by being essentially a central nervous structure in which complex interaction among the receptor and neural elements may take place, as exemplified by lateral inhibition and related phenomena.

STIMULUS AND RECEPTOR ACTIVITY. It is often assumed that receptors are passive organs activated by the energy of the delivered stimuli.

This is erroneous. It is well established that receptors can discharge "spontaneously" in the absence of stimulation. Adrian and Matthews (1928) were the first to show spontaneous spike discharge in the optic nerve of eels; since their pioneering work the spontaneous activity of the unstimulated retina was reported by several investigators as a characteristic property of the optic system in a variety of species. The spontaneous discharge of the auditory, vestibular, somesthetic, kinesthetic, and other sense organs is also well established (Granit, 1955). Accordingly, it would be wrong to state that the action of stimuli is the initiation of receptor action (although their effect may be acceleration of ongoing activity); rather, one should say that stimuli modulate the endogenous level of activity of receptors. Indeed, we may recall that the effect of stimulation need not be the acceleration of spike discharge but may as well be the converse, namely, the inhibition of ongoing activity. What mechanism maintains this "spontaneous" activity, however, is not known.

Different receptors respond to their adequate stimuli in different ways. The afferents of some receptors, particularly those that supply information about the homeostatic condition of body components (the visceral receptors) or the tonic state of body parts (the kinesthetic receptors), display a relatively high rate of *sustained* firing. In such receptors the application of a stimulus either accelerates or inhibits the rate of ongoing activity. We may speculate that by such a mechanism the organism can obtain information about both *negative* and *positive deviations* from the steady state, or *standard level*, set by its homeostatic mechanisms. In other receptors, especially those that provide information about changing external events, the low rate of endogenous discharge may be accelerated both at the onset of a stimulus and at its cessation. In such receptors prolonged stimulation produces *adaptation*, a decrease in the rate of discharge with time, which after a period may reach the "spontaneous," or endogenous, level. Then, as stimulation is discontinued, there may be a new burst of discharge, signaling the removal of the stimulus (off-response). Presumably, such receptors cannot provide information about steady conditions, only about changing events.

The mechanisms of sensory adaptation are not known. Explanations in terms of receptor fatigue or receptor and nervous refractoriness are not altogether sufficient, because adaptation occurs in many instances with very low rates of repetitive stimulation. Furthermore, adaptation does not usually occur, or there may be a recovery from it, if the repeated stimulus conveys important information. For instance, adaptation to repeated clicks (both in terms of electrical activity of certain brain structures and in terms of overt signs of "attention") is abolished by associating the clicks with painful stimulation (Galambos et al., 1956; see Chapter 13). Adaptation, instead, appear, to be an active inhibitory process that emanates from the central nervous system. The central nervous modulation of receptor activity, which may as well be facilitatory in nature, is referred to as *centrifugal control*. Simple examples of the centrifugal control of receptors are modulatory effects exerted on the accessory organs of the receptors, as in the pupillary reflex of the eye, the tympanic reflex of the ear, and the modulatory effects of the gamma efferent system on the intrafusal muscle fibers of the muscle spindles. Of more complex nature, and less well understood, are direct modulatory effects on the receptors or transducers themselves. The problem of centrifugal control of sensory activity is discussed further in Chapter 14.

### SELECTED READINGS

Békésy, G. von. *Experiments in hearing.* New York: McGraw-Hill, 1960.

Brindley, G. S. *Physiology of the retina and the visual pathway.* Baltimore: Williams & Wilkins, 1960.

Davson, H. *The eye.* New York: Academic Press, 1962. 4 vols.

Geldard, F. A. *The human senses.* New York: Wiley, 1953.

Granit, R. *Receptors and sensory perception.* New Haven, Conn.: Yale University Press, 1955.

Montagna, W. (Ed.). *Cutaneous innervation.* Oxford: Pergamon Press, 1960.

Polyak, S. *The vertebrate visual system,* H. Klüver (Ed.). Chicago: University of Chicago Press, 1957.

Ruch, T. C., and J. F. Fulton. *Medical physiology and biophysics.* (18th ed.) Philadelphia: Saunders, 1960.

Walls, G. L. *The vertebrate eye and its adaptive radiation.* New York: Hafner, 1963.

Wever, E. G., and M. Lawrence. *Physiological acoustics.* Princeton, N.J.: Princeton University Press, 1954.

Zotterman, Y. (Ed.). *Olfaction and taste.* New York: Pergamon, 1963.

# 6

# Contractile Mechanisms and Effector Organization

The varied animative activities, all of which are directed toward overt performance, would be futile without the cooperation of organs that can transform biochemical energy into mechanical work. In animals, mechanical work is commonly produced by contractile substances that are capable of reversible shortening and lengthening. As we have described earlier, in the simplest protists, as in ameba, such contractile substances are present in the undifferentiated cytoplasm. In other unicellular organisms, as in ciliates and flagellates, differentiated contractile organelles (cilia and flagella) and myonemes perform the same function. In primitive metazoans, as in sponges, partially differentiated contractile cells may be present in addition to ameboid and ciliary mechanisms. In more complex metazoans, from coelenterates to vertebrates, large numbers of differentiated contractile muscle cells are present, which, organized into complex organs, can execute mechanical work of great complexity. In vertebrates, two main types of muscles are distinguished, smooth and striated muscles, with some intermediate types (cardiac muscle). Smooth muscles are primarily responsible for domestic, visceral activities; in contrast, striated muscles, with the help of skeletal attachments, execute relational activities, that is, are concerned with overt behavior.

**Smooth Muscle and Visceral Motor Activity** Smooth muscle is composed of spindle-shaped cells about 3–8 micra wide and 15–500 micra long. There is a single nucleus in the middle portion of the cell, and faintly visible longitudinal striations, produced by the *myofibrils*, may be seen with suitable staining. The cells lie more or less parallel to one another and are held together in sheets and bands by connective tissue. Smooth muscle is present in the alimentary canal from the middle of the esophagus to the anus; in the gall bladder, hepatic ducts and bladder; in the trachea and the bronchi of the lungs; in the blood vessels and the larger lymphatic tubes; in the testes, epididymis, prostates, uterus, oviducts, and vagina;

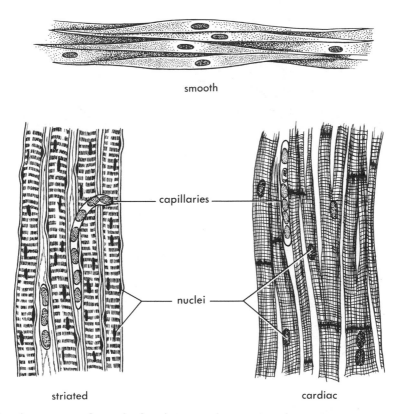

smooth

capillaries

nuclei

striated                              cardiac

The three types of muscle found in vertebrates. Smooth muscle consists of separate cells, whereas in skeletal muscle the cells are fused. Cardiac muscle represents an intermediate form with partial fusion. (From Griffin. *Animal structure and function*. Holt, Rinehart and Winston, 1962)

and, finally, in various scattered positions, as piloerectors around hair in the skin, as constrictors of the iris in the eye, and so forth. Some of these smooth muscles form *circular rings* around tubular organs; others are *longitudinally oriented*. In some parts of the body both types are present, and by their reciprocal contraction and relaxation they can change the bore and length of the hollow organ to which they are attached and thus propel liquid or viscous substances in selected directions.

In general, the contraction of smooth muscles is slow but sustained. The contraction is initiated, in at least parts of the muscle, by efferents of the autonomic nervous system that synapse directly with some of the muscle fibers. The initiated contraction can then be transmitted to adjacent muscle cells that are not directly innervated. Denervation of smooth muscle, however, does not lead to cessation of the "autonomic"

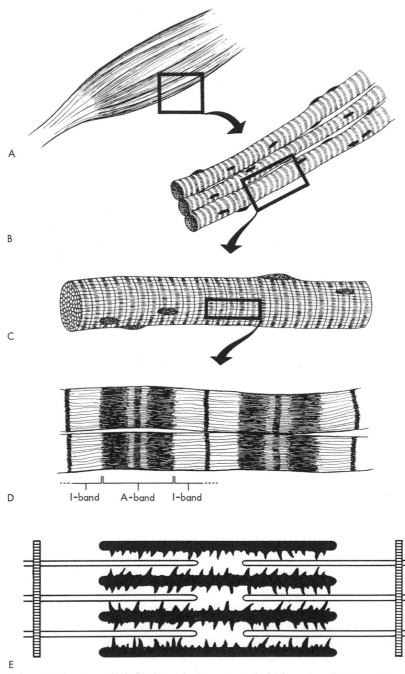

A

B

C

D          I-band    A-band    I-band

E

Schematic drawings of skeletal muscle at successively higher magnifications: (A) an
entire muscle; (B) several muscle fibers; (C) a single muscle fiber as it appears at
high magnification with a light microscope; (D) two myofibrils, as they appear at

activities of visceral organs; humoral agents circulating in the body may also cause contraction and relaxation of smooth muscle. An example of such humoral action is the contractile effect of oxytocin of the neurohypophysis on the pregnant uterus. Relatively little is known about the mechanism of contraction in smooth muscle. Most of our knowledge of the biophysical and biochemical processes involved in muscular contraction has been gained from studies on striated muscle.

**Striated Muscle and** Unlike smooth muscle, which con-
**Skeletal Motor Activity** tracts slowly, striated muscle is characterized by quick contraction and
relaxation. Striated muscle is composed of muscle fibers that may be 10–100 micra thick and several centimeters long. These muscle fibers have several nuclei and are formed by the fusion of many embryonic cells, or myoblasts. "Striated" muscle is striped both longitudinally and transversely. The longitudinal striation is produced by numerous longitudinally arranged myofibrils, which are 1–2 micra thick and very long, and are embedded in the cytoplasm, called the sarcoplasm. These fibrils display a pattern of transverse striation similar to that seen in the muscle fiber as a whole. The cross striation is produced by alternating dense, dark segments (A-band) and less dense, light segments (I-band) along the myofibrils. The light I-band is bisected by the Z-band; portions of the muscle fibers extending from one Z-band to the next are called sarcomeres.

The myofibrils are the last structural elements visible at highest optical magnification. Further magnification with the electron microscope reveals that the myofibrils are made up of longitudinal filaments of macromolecular dimensions. Recent studies revealed the regular arrangement in myofibrils of two types of filaments, a thicker one of about 100 Ångstrom width and 1.5 micra length, and a thinner one of about 50 Ångstrom width and 2.0 micra length (Huxley and Hanson, 1960). The thicker filaments extend from one end of the A-band to the next, but the thinner filaments run between the Z-bands and are partially interdigitated with the thick filaments.

As earlier work has indicated, the fibrous component of muscle contains a protein called actomyosin, which is formed through the combination of two other fibrous proteins, actin and myosin. Recent biochemical and electron microscopic investigations have revealed that the thick filaments referred to are made up largely of myosin; the thin filaments are composed of actin. Cross links connect the two types of protein filaments, and muscle contraction is assumed to be based on the interaction between

high magnification with an electron microscope; and (E) the thick and thin molecular components of muscle, as seen under the highest magnification with an electron microscope. The thinner bands are believed to be composed of actin, the thicker ones of myosin. (From Griffin, *Animal structure and function*, Holt, Rinehart and Winston, 1962)

actin and myosin, which is manifested as forced sliding of the interdigitat-
ing elements along the long axis of the filaments (Huxley and Hanson,
1960).

In addition to these fibrous proteins, muscle fibers also contain various
other subcellular organelles. Mitochondria are abundant in muscle, and
it is assumed that with their oxidative enzymes, mitochondria are involved
in processes that supply energy for the work performed during contraction.
The main energy source of muscular work is the carbohydrate, glycogen,
which is oxidized to yield energy, but there is some evidence that immediate energy transfer is dependent on the high-energy phosphate bond
of adenosine triphosphate (ATP), which, in interaction with actomyosin,
is converted into adenosine diphosphate (ADP) with the liberation of
considerable energy. As was first shown by Szent-Györgyi (1951), nonliving
actomyosin threads extracted from muscle contract on addition of ATP.

Skeletal muscle fibers are organized into large bundles and attached at
both ends by tendons to accessory structures, usually the bones of the
*skeletal system*. Muscles attached to bones may act as *adjustable braces*,
holding the various bones of the body together and developing tension to
counteract mechanical displacement effects. The mechanical work performed by *holding muscles* is an increase in static tonus, or *isometric
contraction* (the development of increased tension without shortening or
change in the length of the muscles). Holding muscles, which have a
characteristic appearance ("red muscle"), contract and relax relatively
slowly and can remain in a state of contraction for a long time. The color
of these holding muscles is caused by "red fibers" with a large concentration of *myoglobin* in the sarcoplasm, presumably concerned with supply
of adequate quantities of oxygen during prolonged contractions. "White
muscle," on the other hand, is composed mostly of "white fibers," which
contain little myoglobin. These fibers compose the *moving muscles*, and
they can contract and relax quickly. These muscles are said to display
*isotonic contraction* (change in length but not in tension). It should be
pointed out, however, that the distinction between "red" and "white"
muscles, between holding and moving muscles, and between isometric
and isotonic contraction, are relative distinctions; some muscle types
belong to neither group, others can function both in holding and
moving, and, finally, in most instances of muscular contraction isotonic
and isometric effects are mixed to various extents, one or the other pre-
dominating.

The skeletal muscles producing overt movement may be said to have
proximal and distal ends. The *proximal end*, or *origin*, of the muscle is
attached to a structure that can be made rigid by the holding muscles;
this structure may be a bone attached to the vertebral column or a bone
of a limb. When the muscle is shortened as a consequence of contraction,
its *distal end*, or *insertion*, turns another bone around its joint. The mobile

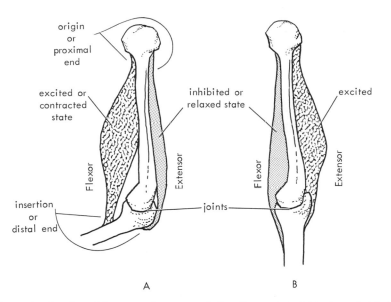

origin
or
proximal
end

excited or
contracted
state

inhibited or
relaxed state

excited

Flexor

Extensor

Flexor

Extensor

insertion
or
distal end

joints

A                                    B

The mode of action of flexors and extensors in bending and straightening a jointed
limb. During bending (A) the contracting flexor acts as the agonist, and its antagonist, the extensor, is relaxed. When the limb is straightened (B), the flexor,
now the antagonist, relaxes, and the extensor in contracted.

skeletal attachments, like the limbs and digits, are usually supplied with several groups of muscles, which can either stabilize a skeletal structure or move it in different directions. The muscle that initiates a given movement is the "prime mover," or *agonist*, of that movement. During contraction of the agonist, another muscle, its *antagonist*, which tends to move the skeletal attachment in the opposite direction, relaxes. When the skeletal part is to be returned to its original position, the original agonist relaxes, and the antagonist contracts. This is the principle of *reciprocal organization*, which is characteristic of the coordination of the vertebral skeleto-muscular system (Chapter 10). In addition to the agonists and antagonists, several *synergistically* contracting, or supporting, muscles may be activated during the execution of a movement. It is because of this complex organization that muscular movement in the normal organism is highly variable, smooth, and precise.

Contraction of skeletal muscle is under the exclusive control of efferent or motor fibers of the central nervous system; denervation of skeletal muscle produces immediate *paralysis*. (However, it was reported recently [Bajusz, 1964] that, unlike "white" muscle fibers, "red" muscle fibers may resist atrophy for some time after severance of their sensory and motor attachments; the indication is that red muscle fibers are less functionally dependent on neural control.) These efferent fibers are usually of large

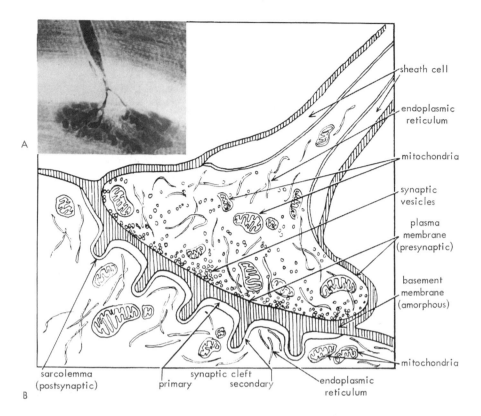

Motor end-plate. A, photomicrograph of a motor fiber with end-plate terminating
on one of the muscle fibers; B, schematic drawing of a single synaptic element of
an end-plate as revealed by electron microscopy. (From Elliott, *Textbook of neuroanatomy*, J. B. Lippincott Company, 1963)

diameter, originating in motor cells in the spinal cord or medulla. Before
reaching the muscle fibers, the efferents branch into finer processes and
then establish contact with muscle fibers.

The region where efferent nerves and muscle fibers come in contact is
called the *end plate*. This is a specialized region, and descriptions are available of its detailed organization (Couteaux, 1960; Robertson, 1956; Zacks,
1964). Electrical recordings with a variety of techniques (Fatt, 1959) have
established that efferent impulses reaching the end plate set up a graded
electric potential, called the *end-plate potential*. This potential, if of
sufficient magnitude, depolarizes the muscle membrane and, following
some latency, this electrical event leads to contraction of the muscle.
Muscle contraction is associated with a recordable action potential. (The
dependence of contraction on membrane depolarization is not well understood.) When a single pulse is transmitted, the muscle contracts with a

*twitch*, because, on cessation of the action potential, the muscle immediately relaxes. To maintain steady contraction, called *tetanic contraction*, the delivery of repetitive pulses is required. (The frequency of stimulation necessary for continuous contraction is inversely related to the duration of a single twitch in a given muscle type.) Under normal functioning, movement in the body is produced by such tetanic contractions.

Transmission through the neuromuscular junction is dependent on neurochemical transmitter substances. The presence of a special transmitter mechanism at the neuromuscular junction was deduced by Claude Bernard in the middle of the last century. Studying the paralyzing effect of the Indian arrow poison, *curare*, Bernard found that neither impulse transmission through the efferent nerve nor the contractility of the muscle was abolished by this poison. Instead, curare appeared to *block transmission* of the nerve signal at the junction of nerve and muscle. That transmission at the neuromuscular junction is of chemical nature was first shown by Dale; the transmitter substance was later identified as *acetylcholine* (Dale, 1937), one of the several neurohumors secreted by the cells of the nervous system.

### SELECTED READINGS

Fatt, P. Skeletal neuromuscular transmission. *Handb. Physiol.*, Sec. 1, **1,** 199–213.
Huxley, H. E. Muscle cells. In J. Brachet and A. E. Mirsky (Eds.), *The cell.* New York: Academic Press, 1960. Vol. 4.
Romer, A. S. *The vertebrate body.* (2d ed.) Philadelphia: Saunders, 1955.
Zacks, S. I. *The motor end plate.* Philadelphia: Saunders, 1964.

# 7

# Neural Conducting and
# Relaying Mechanisms

By means of its receptors the organism gathers information about its own state and about events in its environment, and with the aid of muscles various mechanical operations are performed in the service of its needs. But receptors and effectors cannot function by themselves. Transmission, decoding, and storing of receptor information, and the programing, initiation, and feedback regulation of muscular activities are dependent on the central nervous system, which is the conducting, relaying, and coordinating mechanism of the animative action system. The central nervous system may be considered the governing organ of animative activities; with the help of two peripheral extensions, the receptor and effector systems, it regulates the visceral and behavioral functions of the organism.

The nervous system is composed of nerve cells, or *neurons*, and supporting *glia cells*, and it is richly supplied with blood vessels. Some of the properties of the nervous system, such as impulse conduction, can be best understood by studying the nature of single neurons. Other aspects of neural functioning, which derive from the complex interaction of numerous types of neurons, require investigation of the operation of organized aggregates of neurons. In the following sections we shall first review the morphological and functional properties of nerve and glia cells; subsequently we shall consider briefly some of the known aspects of multineuronal interaction.

**MORPHOLOGY OF NEURONS AND GLIA CELLS** **Neurons** The idea that the nervous system is composed of discrete cells with their fibrous processes (cells that are in contact with one another but not fused) is known as the *neuron theory*. The neuron theory was proposed toward the end of the last century by Waldeyer, on the basis of the work of several neuroanatomists and histologists (His, Forel, van Gehuchten, Cajal, and others). Protagonists of the opposing "reticular theory" (Gerlach, Golgi, and others) believed that nerve cells with their

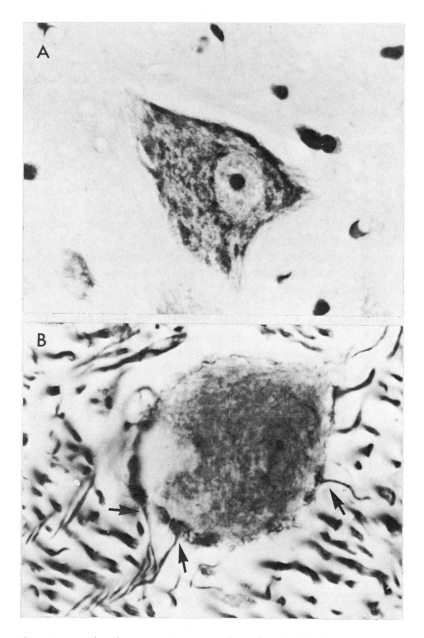

Photomicrographs of neurons. A, neuron from the reticular formation of a rat stained with gallocyanin chromalum to show structure of cell body; B, neuron from the cochlear nucleus of a rat with Bodian fiber stain. Arrows show fibers terminating on the neuron with synaptic end boutons. (Unpublished photomicrographs, Das and Altman)

fibrous processes form a continuous syncytial network. Modern research, employing improved staining procedures and new microscopic techniques (phase contrast and electron microscopy), has given additional support to the neuron theory.

All neurons are composed of a cell body, or soma, and two structurally and functionally distinguishable processes, the dendrites and axons. Let us first consider briefly the properties of the *cell body*, which is the vegetative or trophic (nourishing) center of the neuron. The soma of nerve cells resembles in many ways other cells, but it also has many differential characteristics. As in all cells, the center of the cell body is occupied by a nucleus. The nuclei of differentiated nerve cells are virtually always in a resting state (absence of mitosis); from this observation (and additional evidence) it was concluded that after embryonic development neurogenesis (the formation of new neurons) ceases in the brain. This conclusion in all probability holds for the largest class of neurons, namely, neurons with long axons (macroneurons), but does not apply, as we shall see later, to a less numerous class of neurons, those with short axons (microneurons).

The cytoplasm surrounding the nucleus of the neuron is distinguished by the unusually dense distribution of granular chromatin material, known as the *Nissl granules*, or Nissl substance. Recent studies have established that the Nissl granules are identical with the endoplasmic reticulum of other cells and contain RNA-rich microsomes in large quantities. Nerve cells contain considerable amounts of proteins (50–70 percent of the dry

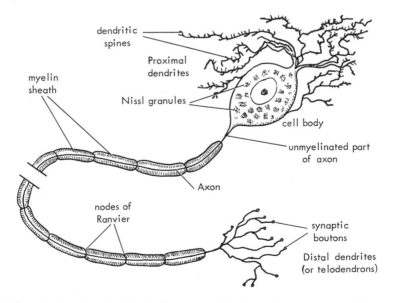

Schematic drawing of a "typical" neuron. (This type of neuron is most closely related to a motor neuron.)

weight of the cell), and the presence of large concentrations of RNA suggests high protein turnover. High protein metabolism was, in fact, established independently by biochemical and radiochemical (including autoradiographic) means. Although the exact significance of the unusually high protein turnover of nerve cells is not understood (it is matched only by some enzyme-secreting glandular cells), there is some evidence that the functioning of nerve cells is dependent on protein metabolism and that increased neuronal activity (induced by behavioral activation) is accompanied by heightened RNA (Hydén, 1962) and protein metabolism (Altman, 1963). In addition to high protein metabolism, and presumably associated with it, nerve cells also show high turnover of glucose and great oxygen consumption, and also a high rate of utilization of some specific amino acids, such as glutamic acid (Elliott, 1962).

On the basis of differential structural and functional characteristics two types of nerve processes are traditionally distinguished, dendrites and axons. Both dendrites and axons are specialized fibrous structures that are involved in impulse generation and transmission. The *dendrites*, which are always unmyelinated, can conduct only graded potentials; in contrast, the axons, which may or may not be myelinated, can also transmit all-or-none spike potentials. Following this definition, we may distinguish two subtypes

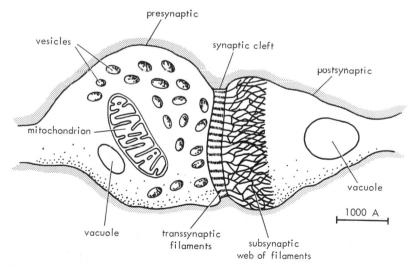

B

Diagram of a synapse in the cortex. Synaptic vesicles are present in the presynaptic bouton, together with mitochondria. Transsynaptic filaments serve as a bridge between the pre- and postsynaptic membranes. A subsynaptic web of filaments may be seen underneath the postsynaptic membrane. (From De Robertis. *Histophysiology of synapses and neurosecretion*. Pergamon Press, 1964)

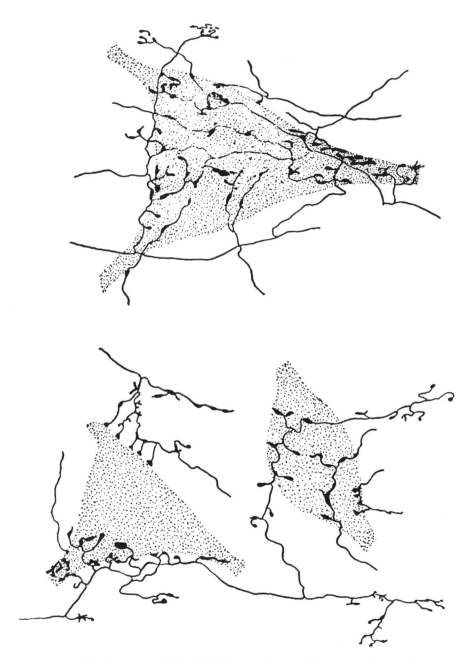

Preterminal arborizations of distal dendrites with terminal boutons ending on large cell bodies in the spinal cord. (From Lorente de Nó. Transmission of impulses through cranial motor nuclei. *J. Neurophysiol.*, 1939, **2**, 403)

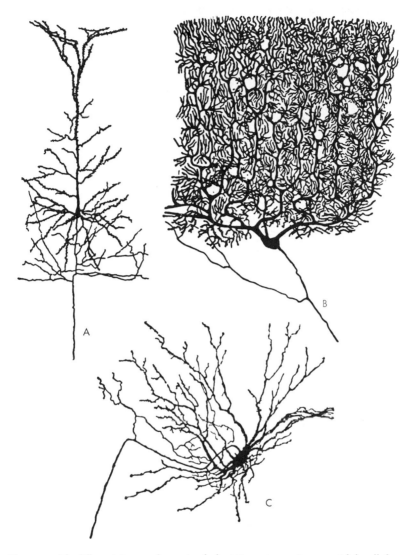

Neurons with different types of proximal dentrite systems: A, pyramidal cell from cerebral cortex; B, Purkinje cell from cerebellum; C, ventral horn motor cell from spinal cord. Reprinted by permission of the author and The Rockefeller Institute Press from Rall. *Biophys. J.*, 1962, **2** (Supplement), 156, 1.

of dendrites and axons: proximal and distal dendrites, and proximal and distal axons.

The *proximal dendrites* are in synaptic contact with the terminal components of other nerves (or, peripherally, with those of receptors). These proximal dendrites, which contain fine tubules of unknown function, are often furnished with *spines*, which may represent added surfaces for synaptic contact. Most recent electron microscopic pictures (De Robertis, 1964) also indicate the presence of a web of fine filaments near the subsynaptic membrane of the proximal dendrite. When excited, the proximal dendrites conduct *postsynaptic* generator potentials in the direction of the soma of the neuron, or centripetally. The proximal dendrites represent the *generator region* of the neuron, and it is of great significance that they cannot themselves stimulate transsynaptically the terminal branches of the nerves with which they are in contact. That is, they act as valves, or diodes, transmitting excitation in one direction only (called *orthodromic* conduction).

The *distal dendrites*, or telodendrons, represent the preterminal collaterals and the presynaptic terminal branches of axons. They are often furnished with specialized end-feet, or boutons, in which mitochondria and small vesicles are located. These *vesicles*, which are about 200–500 Ångstrom in size and are believed to contain neurohumoral substances, are the other component of the synaptic junction at which impulse transmission from one neuron to another takes place. The presynaptic and postsynaptic membranes are separated from each other by clefts or intracellular spaces of about 200 Ångstrom. The distal dendrites may synapse with the proximal dendrites of other neurons or directly with

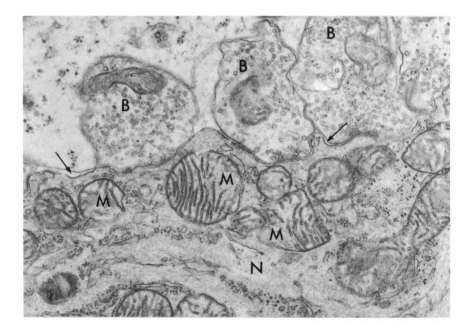

Electron micrograph of a motor neuron in the spinal cord with terminal boutons of other neurons. N, neuron cytoplasm; M, mitochodria; B, boutons with vesicles. Arrows pointing to synaptic cleft. (Photo courtesy of Dr. Keith Porter)

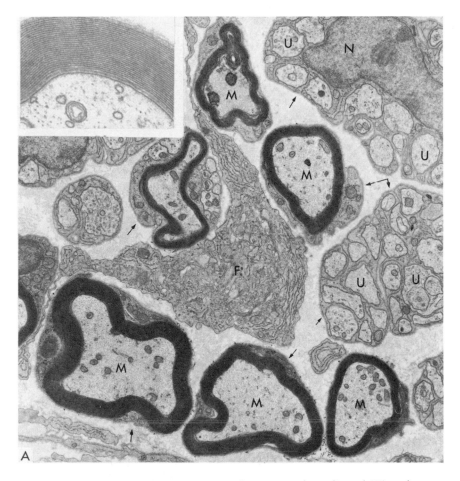

Electron micrograph of the cross section of a nerve with myelinated (M) and un-myelinated (U) axons. In both cases the axons may be seen partially surrounded by the cytoplasm of Schwann cells (arrows). N, nucleus of a Schwann cell; F, prob-ably a fibroblast. (Photo courtesy of Dr. Keith Porter). Insert in top left corner: the spiral lamellae of the myelin sheath. (From Bloom and Fawcett. *Textbook of histol-ogy*, 8th ed. W. B. Saunders Company, 1962)

their cell bodies. (The distal dendrites of motor neurons terminate on muscle with a specialized structure, the end-plate.)

The axons may be myelinated or unmyelinated. The myelin sheath is a fatty insulating substance formed by a type of supporting cell, the *Schwann cell*, in the peripheral nervous system, and presumably by *oligodendroglia cells* in the central nervous system. In peripheral nerves the cytoplasm of the Schwann cell winds around the axon, depositing double-membraned concentric layers around it. In large axons the myelin sheath is interrupted at periodic intervals, where the *nodes of Ranvier*

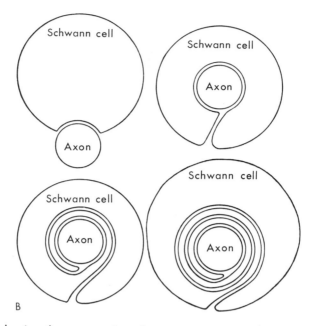

Diagrams showing the process of myelination. The Schwann cell envelopes the axon by forming a spiral wrapping around it. (After B. Geren-Uzman. From Bloom and Fawcett. *Textbook of Histology*, 8th ed. W. B. Saunders Co., 1962)

are formed; at these points the axon is exposed. The axon is made up of a fine lipoprotein membrane, which plays a major role in impulse transmission and contains a semifluid axoplasm. In the axoplasm are present fibrous proteins that in the living state appear to be oriented parallel to the long axis of the axon. The width of axons varies from less than 1 micron to about 20 micra, whereas their length varies from less than a millimeter (in the central nervous system) up to a meter in some species, as in the "nerve fibers" of the peripheral nervous system.

If we define axons as nerve processes that may be myelinated, and conduct all-or-none spike potentials, we have to distinguish two types of axons, proximal axons and distal axons. *Proximal axons*, which occur in unipolar and bipolar neurons only, conduct spike potentials centripetally. *Distal axons*, which exist probably in all differentiated neurons, conduct spike potentials centrifugally. In terms of the conventional classification, the proximal axons of unipolar and bipolar neurons are considered dendrites, because they conduct nerve impulses centripetally. Such a classification, however, disregards the facts that these proximal nerve processes are commonly myelinated, and conduct spike potentials in a manner indistinguishable from the distal axons (Bodian, 1962).

We may distinguish two major classes of vertebrate neurons: macroneurons and microneurons. *Macroneurons* are characterized by having long axons, which make possible the transmission of impulses over long distances. Typical macroneurons are the afferent, commissural, relay, and efferent neurons. The *afferent neurons* (sometimes called primary afferents) are characteristically unipolar or bipolar cells, whose cell bodies are located in the spinal and cranial ganglia. The proximal dendrites of these afferent neurons are in direct contact with receptors or themselves serve as free-ending receptors. As described earlier, the unipolar and bipolar receptor neurons are furnished with both proximal and distal axons that conduct spike potentials from the periphery to the central nervous system. The internuclear *relay neurons* transmit impulses over shorter or longer distances between different brain regions (they are often described as afferents when they interconnect central nervous sensory structures, and as efferents when the connections they make are between motor structures). The *commissural neurons* (which may sometimes be merely collaterals of other neurons) interconnect, across the midline, homologous portions of bilaterally symmetrical neural structures. The *efferent* or *motor neurons* are represented by the large ventral horn cells in the spinal cord, and related neurons in the cranial nerve nuclei, whose axons leave the central nervous system to establish contact with peripheral

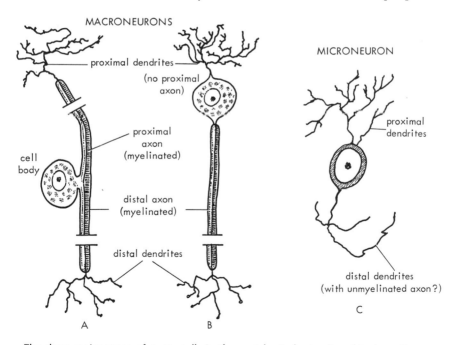

The three major types of nerve cells in the vertebrate brain. A, a bipolar cell or primary afferent neuron from the spinal ganglion. This type of neuron is unique in having both proximal and distal axons. B, a common type of neuron with a long distal axon. These two types of neurons are macroneurons. C, small neuron with a short axon or without an axon. These microneurons always have proximal and distal dendrites.

skeletal muscle or the autonomic nervous system. The pyramidal cells of the cerebral cortex, which share many structural and functional characteristics with the ventral horn neurons, may also be classified with the efferent neurons.

*Microneurons,* (granule cells or stellate neurons), are nerve cells with short axons that terminate within the structure in which their cell bodies are located. Microneurons are sparsely furnished with cytoplasm, presumably because the trophic requirements of neurons with short axons are lower than the requirements of neurons with long axons. These short-axoned cells represent *interneurons,* which establish connections among neurons located in different components or layers of a given structure. In some parts of the central nervous system the cell bodies of microneurons form distinct layers. Examples are the granule cells of the olfactory bulb, which form a distinct granular layer and also contribute to the glomerular and mitral cell layers; the granule cells of the dentate gyrus of the hippocampus, which form its conspicuous granular layer; the granular layer of the cerebellum formed by innumerable granule cells in this region; and a few others. In other regions these microneurons are interspersed with macroneurons; an example is the cerebral cortex, in which short-axoned stellate cells or Golgi type II neurons mingle with larger types of long-axoned neurons.

Of some interest is the recent finding from our laboratory (Altman and Das, 1965b) that in the rat the majority of microneurons in the structures referred to are formed after birth. This finding was established with the technique of autoradiography. Rats of different ages were injected with radioactively labeled thymidine (thymidine is a specific precursor of chromosomal DNA) in order to tag the cells that are preparing to multiply at the time of injection (DNA is metabolically stable, and only multiplying cells require thymidine). The cells utilizing the radioactive thymidine can then be easily visualized with autoradiography, and we can also follow their movements and transformations over time. With this procedure we were able to establish that undifferentiated cells multiply at a high rate in the brains of young rats and that these proliferating cells become subsequently transformed into either microneurons or glia cells. The possible functional significance of these interneurons, and of their postnatal origin, will be discussed further in connection with some of the neural theories of memory and learning (Chapter 13).

**Glia Cells**   Glia cells are intermingled with neurons in all parts of the nervous system, and they greatly outnumber nerve cells in most regions, particularly in higher mammals. Several types of glia cells are distinguished. We have already referred to the Schwann cells found in the peripheral nervous system. In the central nervous system, oligodendrocytes, astrocytes, and microglia cells are distinguished (oligodendrocytes and astrocytes are col-

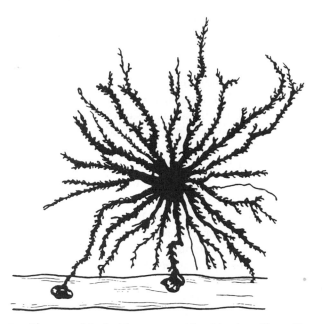

An astrocyte with some of its feet in contact with a blood capillary. (From Nakai. *Morphology of neuroglia.* Igaku Shoin, 1963)

lectively known as neuroglia cells). As we mentioned earlier, *oligodendrocytes* may be responsible for the myelination of axons in the central nervous system. With their protoplasmic and fibrous processes, *astrocytes* surround neurons and blood capillaries, and they may regulate the exchange of materials between nerve cells and blood vessels.

A curious phenomenon is the pulsatile activity of some glial elements (Pomerat, 1951). Perhaps these glia cells may represent the local transport mechanisms of the central nervous system that selectively admit or extract various substances from the blood stream and pump it to the nerve cells. Neuroglia may multiply in the nervous system under normal conditions (Altman, 1963); when the brain is traumatized, glia cells tend to proliferate extensively (gliosis). Presumably the glia cells participate in neuronal degenerative and regenerative processes and respond also to increased functional demands. A special type of glia cells, the *microglia*, have phagocytic properties and assist in the removal of waste products and debris.

**PROPAGATION OF NERVE SIGNALS**   It has been known for a long time that if the nerve of an isolated nerve-muscle preparation is stimulated (be it electrically, mechanically, or otherwise), the associated muscles will contract; that is, the excitation is transmitted from the nerve to the muscle. In the first half of the last century, Du Bois-Reymond showed that under such circumstances electric current flows through the nerve fibers; he therefore concluded that impulse transmission in nerve is electrical. For some time afterward it was assumed that electrical transmission through nerve is similar to conduction through an inanimate electrical conductor. However, evidence slowly accumulated to suggest that conduction along nerve followed principles different from those of electric conduction through passive core conductors.

Soon after Du Bois-Reymond's demonstration, Helmholtz measured the speed of nerve conduction, which, compared with transmission through a metal wire, was found to be a relatively slow event. It was later demonstrated (Adrian, 1914) that, provided the applied stimulus to the nerve was of sufficient magnitude, an impulse of constant intensity was generated, which could not be further enhanced by increasing the strength of the stimulus. That is, the magnitude or amplitude of the conducted nerve impulse (spike, or action, potential) is independent of the intensity of the initiating stimulus; this phenomenon is referred to as the *all-or-none principle* of neural conduction. Similarly, once an impulse was generated, the stimulus initiating the process could be removed, and the impulse would be propagated along the entire length of the axon with constant intensity and velocity; that is, conduction of the nerve spike is a *nondecremental, self-propagating* process.

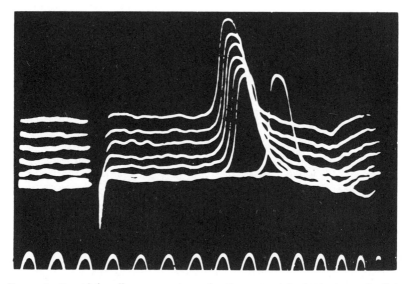

Demonstration of the all-or-none nature of action potentials. As the strength of the applied stimulus is increased (shown from bottom upward) there is a gradual diminution in the latency of the response in this myelinated nerve, but the amplitude of the action potential remains unaltered. (From Tasaki. *Handb. Physiol.*, 1959, Sec. 1, **1**, 80)

After transmission of the action potential, the nerve enters a phase of absolute inexcitability, called the *absolute refractory period*, followed by other phases, the *relative refractory periods*, during which the stimulus threshold is changed. These refractory periods are interpreted to represent metabolic recovery cycles during which the normal excitability of the nerve is re-established. In sum, conduction of nerve signals along the axon is not a passive event, one that is sustained by the applied stimulus; it is rather an internally energized process, which is merely triggered or released by the stimulus. This realization initiated an intensive search for the mechanisms underlying neural conduction.

**Types of Electrical Potentials in Nerves** As it is now realized, propagation through nerves is based on a property common to all living cells, plant or animal. This is the presence of a *resting electric potential* across the cell membrane, the exterior of the cell membrane being normally positive with respect to the cell interior. This resting electric potential is attributable to the differential distribution of ions in the interior of the cell and its external medium. The unequal distribution of ions is made possible by the semipermeable cell membrane, which permits certain ions to move freely across the membrane but prevents the exit or entry of others. At the same time an active transport process of unknown nature takes place, by which certain substances are drawn in and others pumped out of the cell against osmotic and electric gradients.

In animal cells (for example, muscle cells) the resting electric potential is associated with greater potassium-ion ($K^+$) concentration in the cell interior than in its external medium, and greater sodium-ion ($Na^+$) concentration in the cell's surroundings than inside the cell. When the cell surface is disturbed, changes are produced in the electric polarization of the membrane. As a result of such disturbance, the potential difference across the membrane, which is about 60–90 millivolts in different cell types, can be altered in four different ways:

1. The membrane polarity may be further increased (this action is called *hyperpolarization*);
2. The polarity may be reduced (*hypopolarization*);
3. The polarization may be abolished (*depolarization*); or finally,
4. The polarity difference may be *reversed*.

In the latter situation the exterior of the cell becomes negative with respect to the interior, a phenomenon associated with the breakdown of the barrier for, and the sudden influx of, sodium ions.

In most cell types membrane polarization is presumably associated with the regulation of the electrolytic properties of the cell interior and, in all probability, serves no other major functions. In some animal cells, such

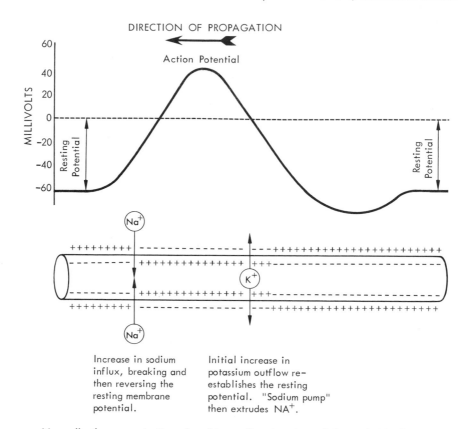

DIRECTION OF PROPAGATION

Action Potential

MILLIVOLTS

Resting Potential

Resting Potential

| Increase in sodium influx, breaking and then reversing the resting membrane potential. | Initial increase in potassium outflow re- establishes the resting potential. "Sodium pump" then extrudes NA⁺. |

Normally the concentration of positive sodium ions is much lower inside the axon than in the external medium. The cell interior is therefore negative with respect to the outside. The action potential is initiated by the breakdown of the cell bar- rier to sodium ions, which rush into the cell interior and make the interior positive with respect to the cell exterior. The consequent outflow of positive potassium ions is the initial step in the regeneration of the resting potential and the negativity of the cell interior.

as receptor and muscle cells but particularly in nerve cells, the membrane potential and the various membrane events associated with it are utilized for an additional function, namely, as means of propagating signals from one part of the body to another. With the help of the greatly elongated membrane surfaces of the nerve fibers, signal propagation over great dis- tances is made possible.

The signal produced and transmitted by a typical neuron may consist of three distinct functional components associated with three distinct structural components of the neuron. *Postsynaptic generator potentials* are produced in the proximal dendrites of the nerve cell or in its soma. The *action potential* is transmitted by the myelinated or unmyelinated axon

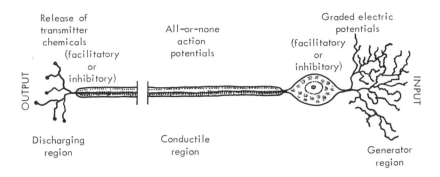

Release of transmitter chemicals (facilitatory or inhibitory)

All-or-none action potentials

Graded electric potentials (facilitatory or inhibitory)

OUTPUT

INPUT

Discharging region

Conductile region

Generator region

Functional properties of the major components of a typical neuron. (Modified after Grundfest. Synaptic and ephaptic transmission. *Hand. Physiol.*, 1959, Sec. 1, 1, 147–197)

and its collaterals. Finally, the action potential produces a *presynaptic discharge potential*, which leads to or is associated with the liberation of chemical transmitter substances from terminal endings of the telodendrons or distal dendrites. The liberated chemical diffuses through the synaptic cleft and produces transsynaptically postsynaptic generator potentials.

**Generator Potentials** The potential initiated at the generator region of the neuron is called the *receptor generator potential* if it is initiated by receptors in the proximal dendritic branches of afferents in the peripheral nervous system, or the postsynaptic generator potential if it is generated in the central nervous system by presynaptic distal dendrites of other neurons. These generator potentials are graded, and decrementally conducted electric impulses, whose intensity and propagation are functions of the magnitude of the applied stimulus (Hodgkin, 1938; Katz, 1947).

Generator potentials may be based on two types of processes, hypopolarization and hyperpolarization (Eccles, 1959, 1964). As we stated before, in *hypopolarization* or partial depolarization the normal resting potential is reduced. This action is considered an excitatory or facilitatory one, because it makes easier further depolarization, and eventual reversal of membrane polarity or spike generation, by other depolarizing processes (*excitatory postsynaptic potential*, EPSP). *Hyperpolarization* implies increase in the normal polarization of the membrane, an event considered inhibitory, because it makes subsequent spike generation by other potentials more difficult (*inhibitory postsynaptic potential*, IPSP).

These generator potentials may be recorded from the dendritic processes and from the soma of the neuron, but, being decremental in nature, they do not spread to the axon except when current flow is increased to a certain critical magnitude. When such an increase takes place, and depolarization of the axon membrane reaches the required intensity, a *spike potential* is initiated in the axon. Such action is seldom obtained from a single generator potential, though there are some specialized monosynaptic regions in the brain where it may take place. More commonly, spatial and temporal summation of generator potentials is required to initiate a spike.

*Spatial summation* refers to the initiation of local potentials synchronously in several points of the generator region, such as when potentials are transmitted by many of the presynaptic boutons that terminate on the neuron. *Temporal summation* refers to the arrival of repetitive potentials that, if they follow one another fairly rapidly (before the effects of the previous potentials decay), may summate in generating a spike.

**Action, or Spike, Potentials**   When the excitatory postsynaptic generator potentials spread to the axon region with sufficient intensity, a spike potential is produced, and this spike is transmitted nondecrementally over the entire length of the conductile element. Although initiation of a spike (the generator process) is an *optional* phenomenon, because it depends on the complex interplay

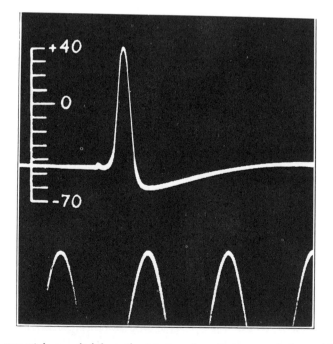

Action potential recorded from the interior of a giant axon of the squid. (From Hodgkin and Huxley. Resting and action potentials in single nerve fibers. *J. Physiol.* [London], 1945, **104,** 176–195)

of facilitatory and inhibitory effects, once the spike has been initiated its transmission is *obligatory*.

Hodgkin, Huxley, Cole, Katz, Keynes, and others have made an intensive study of the events underlying the conduction of spike potentials. These investigators used the giant axons of the squid, which may be almost 1 millimeter in diameter and into which microelectrodes may be inserted for the study of electrical changes during and after the discharge of spike potentials. The studies also utilized the radioactive tracer technique in order to follow the movements of ions during impulse propagation. Other investigators, such as Eccles and his collaborators, have studied the process of impulse propagation by recording with intracellular electrodes the activity of motor neurons in the spinal cord.

The theory that emerged from these studies provides an accurate, although still incomplete, account of the events underlying the propagation of spike potentials. When the resting nerve axon is stimulated, there is produced an *electrotonic current flow* that is conducted passively over a distance and then decays. This current flow produces hypolarization in the form of a local *prepotential*, seen in intracellular recordings from motor neurons; this is a graded response similar to the generator potentials previously described. As the prepotential reaches a critical magnitude, presumably depolarization, the membrane becomes permeable to sodium ions ($Na^+$), and the influx of sodium ions leads to the actual *reversal of membrane polarity*. This reversal of membrane polarity was recorded directly with microelectrodes inserted into the giant axon of the squid (Hodgkin and Huxley, 1945).

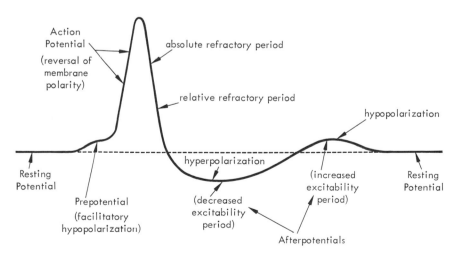

Some of the characteristics of the different phases of an action potential recorded intracellularly from the soma of a neuron.

The sudden influx of sodium ions is responsible for the rising phase of the action potential, a phase that lasts about 1 millisecond in vertebrate neurons. This period is followed immediately by a declining phase during which potassium ions ($K^+$), which are present in larger concentration inside than outside the cell, flow outward and repolarize the surface membrane. Transmission of a spike potential is followed by an afterpotential characterized by hyperpolarization, and, before the membrane potential returns to its resting level, there may be also a phase of hypopolarization. The exact origin of these *afterpotentials* is not known; presumably they are consequences of phases in the metabolic recovery process during which sodium is neutralized or extruded by the hypothetical "sodium pump." These afterpotentials are of some significance, because they affect the excitability cycle of the axon.

When potential reversal takes place in one region of the axon, the negativity of the external surface at the active region causes electrotonic current flow (catelectrotonic potential) to the neighboring areas, leading to breakdown of the membrane potential in this new region, and to the repetition of the whole cycle of events. Accordingly, the propagation of the spike potential is attributed to passive current flow from active to nonactive regions; in contrast, the maintenance of constant spike or volley intensity (nondecremental conduction) is attributed to repeating booster processes produced by the reversible influx and outflow of ions across the axon membrane.

The *speed of impulse conduction* varies in different types of nerves. In general, thicker fibers conduct faster than do thinner fibers; and thickly myelinated fibers conduct faster than do thinly or nonmyelinated fibers. Impulse conduction in nonmyelinated vertebrate fibers of about 1 micron in diameter may be in the range of 1 meter per second, whereas in the largest myelinated mammalian axons, which are about 20 micra in diameter, the speed of conduction may be as high as 120 mps. On the basis of electrical recordings made in peripheral nerves, Gasser (1941) distinguished A, B, and C fibers. *A-fibers* include several types of fast-conducting, myelinated somatic fibers. The *B-fibers* are the somewhat slower-conducting, myelinated autonomic fibers. *C-fibers* are the unmyelinated slowest-conducting components of peripheral nerves. High conduction velocity in myelinated axons is attributed to a special process, called *saltatory conduction*. As described earlier, the myelin sheath is interrupted in vertebrate axons at the nodes of Ranvier. There is some evidence that the active process of spike generation occurs at the nodes, where the axon is exposed to the extracellular fluids, and that the impulse is then swiftly propagated passively (or "jumps") from one node to the next through the internodal space by the faster process of electrotonic current flow. Consequently, the larger the internodal distance, the higher the speed of conduction.

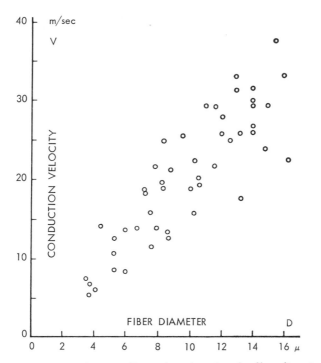

Conduction velocity in single nerve fibers plotted against the fiber diameter in the sciatic nerve of the bullfrog. (From Tasaki. *Handb. Physiol.,* 1959, Sec. 1, **1**, 78)

**Signal Transmission through Synapses** When the rapidly propagated spike potential reaches the preterminal, or presynaptic, region of the neuron, the all-or-none signal is transformed again into a graded, decremental potential whose action is determined by the regional characteristics of the preterminal fibers. These *presynaptic discharge potentials* generated by the spike potential are analogous to the end-plate potentials recorded at neuromuscular junctions. These presynaptic potentials lead to the generation of postsynaptic potentials in the proximal dendrites and soma of the neurons on which they terminate—a generation that may be either *excitatory* or *inhibitory* in nature. There is some experimental evidence (Eccles, 1964) that transmission through synaptic junctions is not electrical, that the synaptic cleft represents a shunt preventing electrical interaction between the presynaptic and post-synaptic membranes. The suggestion was made that synaptic transmission is mediated by neurohumoral transmitter substances in a manner that is analogous to neuromuscular transmission. It was further hypothesized that these neurochemicals are produced in the terminal boutons by the synaptic vesicles, and are released during stimulation. Diffusing through the inter-synaptic spaces, these presynaptic neurohumors are presumed to affect the generator regions of the proximal dendrites or soma of the postsynaptic neuron, producing graded potentials. Depending on the specific chemical released, the postsynaptic effect may be facilitatory (hypopolarization) or inhibitory (hyperpolarization or depolarization).

However, there is at present only indirect evidence in favor of a *chemical theory* of neuro-neuronal synaptic transmission. The chemical theory can easily explain one-way conduction through synapses and neuronal chains in general. When the soma, or axon, of a neuron is stimulated, the initiated spike is conducted in both directions, *orthodromically* (toward the distal dendrites), as well as *antidromically* (toward the proximal dendrites). But whereas the orthodromically conducted impulse may be transmitted by way of the distal dendrites across the synapse to excite the adjacent neuron, the antidromically conducted impulse stops short, and it is not transmitted by way of the proximal dendrites to contiguous neurons. This basic property of transneuronal transmission is difficult to account for by an electrical theory of synaptic transmission but finds easy explanation if one assumes that synaptic action is not an electrically propagated but humorally transmitted process, and that the neurohumors responsible for it are selectively localized at the distal dendrites in the synaptic vesicles.

Other phenomena, such as delayed summation and repetitive firing, are also more easily explained by a chemical theory, because chemical transmitters, if not immediately inactivated by enzymes, may have longer-lasting effects than an electrically propagated impulse has.

Further, there is good evidence, as described earlier, that neuromuscular transmission is mediated by a neural secretory substance, acetylcholine. Acetylcholine has also been demonstrated in sympathetic ganglia, where it is liberated in amounts proportional to the number of impulses delivered to the ganglion (Feldberg and Gaddum, 1934). There is some experimental evidence that acetylcholine is also present in some areas of the central nervous system, together with cholinesterase, the enzyme that inactivates acetylcholine. Acetylcholine, when injected into the nervous system, has a stimulating effect.

In many parts of the central nervous system adrenaline and noradrenaline (Vogt, 1954) and serotonin (Costa and Aprison, 1958) are present in varying concentrations, and these substances too may represent neurohumoral synaptic transmitters. Several investigators have postulated that certain synaptic junctures in the central nervous system are *cholinergic* (the mediator being acetylcholine), whereas others are *adrenergic* (the mediator being adrenaline and related substances); but there is as yet no definitive evidence in favor of this hypothesis.

Whatever be the physical or chemical nature of synaptic transmission, it is characterized by distinct properties. One of these is the optional nature of propagation at this juncture. The all-or-none signal brought to this relay point may or may not "jump" the synaptic gap to continue its course along the next neuron or neurons. If it has any effect, the effect may may be facilitatory or inhibitory. If, as a result of summation (temporal or spatial), a postsynaptic spike is produced, the reaction occurs after considerable delay, *synaptic delay*, which is about 0.2–0.3 millisecond in duration (Eccles, 1964).

The synaptic region represents a complex modulator region at which transmission of a spike potential is conditional, being dependent on the interplay of facilitatory and inhibitory effects exercised by many other neurons and perhaps also by nonneuronal chemical effects mediated by the fluids surrounding the neurons. Although the axons may be considered relatively simple message-relaying cables, the synaptic regions are the *choice points* at which complex "decisions" are made concerning how and along what pathways messages will be relayed. The great complexity of central nervous control functions must be caused by the delicate and highly variable discharging and generator processes occurring at the synaptic regions.

### SELECTED READINGS

Brazier, M. A. B. *The electrical activity of the nervous system.* (2d ed.) New York: Macmillan, 1960.

Eccles, J. C. *The physiology of nerve cells.* Baltimore: The Johns Hopkins Press, 1957.

————. *The physiology of synapses.* New York: Academic Press, 1964.

Erlanger, J., and H. S. Gasser. *Electrical signs of nervous activity.* Philadelphia: University of Pennsylvania Press, 1937.

Field, J. (Ed.). *Handb. Physiol.*, 1959, Sec. 1, Neurophysiology, **1**.

Glees, P. *Neuroglia: morphology and function.* Oxford: Blackwell, 1955.

Ochs, S. *Elements of neurophysiology.* New York: Wiley, 1965.

Ruch, T. C., and J. F. Fulton. *Medical physiology and biophysics.* (18th ed.) Philadelphia: Saunders, 1960.

Truex, R. C., and M. B. Carpenter. *Strong and Elwyn's Human neuroanatomy.* (5th ed.) Baltimore: Williams & Wilkins, 1964.

# 8

# Basic Structure of the
# Vertebrate Nervous System

Neurons seldom operate in isolation but are found banded together into networks of varying complexity. In these networks there is interaction among the various cellular elements that bring information from, and carry instructions to, various parts of the body. To understand neural functioning, a consideration of the properties of the isolated nerve cell must be followed by a study of the structural and functional organization of neuronal networks and the nervous system as a whole. Because the nervous system of vertebrates is a product of a long historical process, proper appreciation of its complex achitecture and organization also requires that we give due consideration to its evolutionary origins. The progressive growth and diversification of the nervous system, in fact, can be traced with some accuracy through phylogeny from primitive metazoan beginnings to the great complexity present in higher vertebrates, particularly in mammals.

**ORIGINS OF THE NERVOUS SYSTEM**
**Peripheral Nerve Nets and Peripheral Ganglia**

In the lowest metazoans, such as sponges, nerve cells are absent. The contractile cells in the osculum of sponges, as previously described (Chapter 4), respond directly to external stimuli, without the mediation of nerves. In coelenterates, such as hydra, primitive nerve cells are present, forming a subepidermal nerve net or plexus. In some parts of the body of coelenterates, such as in the marginal and oral rings of medusae, the nerve nets are organized into a through-conducting system, resembling in some respects the multisynaptic pathways of higher forms (Pantin, 1952). The speed of impulse transmission through these nerve nets is relatively slow, generally less than 1 meter per second, and the generated impulse, if it is not facilitated, usually dies away along its course (Prosser and Brown, 1961). The peripheral nerve plexus of coelenterates may be considered the simplest type of nervous system; it is capable of initiating and controling gross, sluggish movements that characterize the action repertoire of these animals. It is a diffuse system, which in higher forms is not used for guiding relational activities, although the nerve plexus is retained in the interior of the body as a mechanism for the coordination of several slower and less complex "autonomic" visceral processes.

**Ganglionic Centralization and the Beginnings of Cephalization** The beginnings of peripheral ganglionic organization, with suggestions of a more compact peripheral aggregation of neurons near the organs innervated, is seen in echinoderms (though in this phylum the diffuse network remains the major form of neural organization). The nerve cells in the radial nerves of the arms of *starfish* coordinate most of the activities of the arms, the spines, and other appendages. These structures show a large degree of autonomy, which is attributed to local "reflexes" mediated by regional networks (Smith, 1950). Some central control is also present in the starfish, exerted by the nerves of the oral ring, which, by connecting with the radial nerves of the arms, permit the harmonious cooperation of the arms in righting and locomotion. True *peripheral ganglia*, a gathering of cell bodies near the organs innervated, is seen in flatworms, for instance, in *planaria*. To permit coordination of local activities with ongoing activities elsewhere, these peripheral ganglia are connected with one another by nerve trunks, in which true axons, often giant axons, are present.

In annelids, such as the *earthworm*, a subepidermal nerve plexus is still present, but the main control of locomotion is performed by centrally situated ganglia, which are connected with one another by a *ventral nerve cord*. Each ganglion supplies nerve fibers to a few segments of the body, and the organized transmission of peristaltic waves in locomotion is dependent on the nerve cord connecting the various segments. Here again the beginnings of central organization of neurons are evident, where the ganglia of local segments of the body are aligned along a central cord and are, at least partially, controlled by the *cephalic ganglion*. The cephalic ganglion receives fibers from several important sense organs located in the anterior part of the body. Ganglionic organization is particularly well developed in *gastromolluscs*, where four pairs of ganglia are present, the cerebral, pedal, pleural, and visceral ganglia. Each of these mediates local functions with a great degree of autonomy, but there is considerable interaction among the ganglia. The pedal ganglion, for instance, controls locomotion, but locomotion is also affected by the cerebral ganglion. Removal of the cerebral ganglion is followed by an increase in locomotor activity, as though this ganglion exercised an inhibitory effect on the pedal ganglion (Prosser and Brown, 1961). In higher molluscs, the *cephalopods*, a high degree of centralization is apparent, a trend that may also be observed in various other phyla, in particular, in arthropods. In general, the trend of evolution, within and through phyla, is from diffuse nerve nets to scattered peripheral ganglia, then to an aggregation of the latter into a centralized nervous system.

In animals with differentiation of the anterior end or head of the body from the posterior parts, where various receptors concerned with teleception are located, corresponding differentiation takes place in the organization of the nervous system. At the focal region of inflow of afferents from the specialized receptors are cephalic ganglia that connect within the body with other ganglia and exercise control over them in accordance with information obtained from the head receptors. The trend is toward cephalic dominance, expressed structurally as increased growth and differentiation of the cephalic ganglion, a progressive process referred to as *cephalization*. In flatworms, for instance, there is an enlargement of the nerve chords in the frontal part of the body, associated with an afferent bundle that comes from the eyes. Though various activities, including eating, may persist in planaria after removal of the brain, adequately directed behavior requires the intact cephalic ganglion, or brain. Similarly, in annelids, such as the earthworm, there is a frontal enlargement in the nervous system where afferents terminate from the anteriorly located tactile, chemical, and optic receptors. After removal of the brain, the earthworm can move about, feed, copulate, and even burrow, but these activities are slowed down considerably and show lack of proper coordination. Cephalic dominance is obvious in all higher invertebrates, for example, in cephalopod molluscs like squids, and arthropods like bees and ants.

**Protochordate and Primitive** In the protochordate *Amphioxus*
**Vertebrate Nervous Systems** (lancelet), the elongated body is built of many separate *segments*. The segments, not unlike those in annelids, can contract alternatingly on the right and left and thereby produce an undulatory wave that, passing down the length of the body, moves the animal forward. The typical chordate trait of *Amphioxus* is the *notochord*, an elastic cartilageous rod that runs along the entire length of the body. Above the notochord on the *dorsal* side of the body (not on the ventral side, as in annelids) is a tubular *nerve cord*, which gives off nerve bundles laterally, to the right and left, to the segments of the body. *Sensory* and *motor nerves* enter and exit separately through the *dorsal* and *ventral roots* of the chord, respectively, each ventral root nerve innervating three segments of the body: a main central segment and one segment on each side of the central one. The chord is uniform along its entire length, without appreciable enlargement in the frontal part, because *Amphioxus* is not equipped with specialized head receptors.

The anatomy of the body and the nervous system of *Amphioxus* is generally assumed to illustrate the beginnings of the evolution of protochordates, the animal types from which the vetebrates are derived. The notochord of *Amphioxus* is present in all vertebrates during the early stages of embryonic development, and in some primitive aquatic vertebrates, such as cyclostomes (for example, the lamprey), it survives in adults as the core of the vertebral rod. From the cartilageous notochord evolves the bony vertebral column of higher vertebrates, and the tubular, dorsal nerve cord is differentiated into the more complex spinal cord.

Among surviving vertebrates, *cyclostomes* represent the simplest types, and may be usefully studied in an attempt to reconstruct vertebrate origins. Although many of the primitive traits of cyclostomes may be regressive, there is reason to believe that they illustrate sufficiently well the earliest types of vetebrates, most of which are extinct. *Petromyzon* (lamprey) is an elongated aquatic organism in many respects resembling fish. It leads a semiparasitic existence by attaching itself by its circular, jawless mouth to fish or other aquatic animals. When compared with a lancelet, the lamprey shows many progressive traits. It has a definite head with specialized sense organs: two deeply sunk eyes and two nasal sacs. The frontal part of the lamprey's spinal cord is greatly enlarged to form a brain, and this brain is encased in a primitive, rudimentary skull. The lamprey's *spinal cord* is a thick-walled tube in which three layers may be

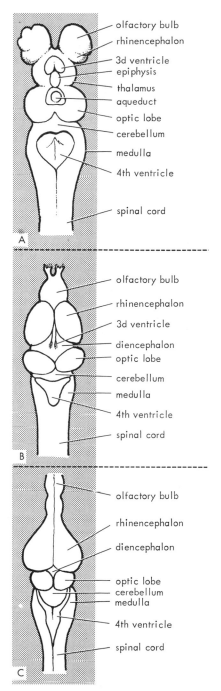

Dorsal view of the brain of (A) lamprey (after Sterzi); (B) frog (after Gaupp); and (C) lizard (after Frederikse)

differentiated: an outer layer of white matter composed of nerve fibers, a middle layer of gray matter composed of nerve cells, and a central ependymal layer lining the central canal. There are dorsal and ventral spinal nerves for each segment of the body; the afferent and efferent fibers in them appear to be nonmyelinated. Ten anterior pairs of nerves have their exit through an opening in the skull; these nerves may therefore be considered cranial nerves.

The cranial portion of the nerve tube in the lamprey differs in appearance from the spinal cord. The most posterior part of the brain represents a transition area from the spinal cord, called medulla, a region where the afferents from the lateral line organ and from the auditory receptors are presumed to terminate. Fibers of the vestibular apparatus also terminate in this region or continue to a dorsal appendage, the cerebellum. The optic tracts terminate in the optic lobes of the midbrain; the olfactory fibers, in the anterior part of the brain, terminate in the olfactory bulb, whence fibers are relayed to the rhinencephalon. In addition to these suprasegmental cranial structures are rudiments of the diencephalon in the lamprey, formed by the epithalamus (habenula) and hypothalamus. These latter structures are in all probability intimately related to two endocrine glands, the epiphysis (pineal gland) and hypophysis (pituitary gland). The central nervous system of the lamprey represents the common core of the vertebrate brain to which, in higher vertebrate forms, new structures were added during evolution.

**GROSS STRUCTURE OF THE**   In describing the anatomical organi-
**MAMMALIAN NERVOUS SYSTEM**   zation of the nervous system of
                                        higher vertebrates, the first useful
distinction that can be made is between the peripheral branches and the central portion of the nervous system. To the peripheral nervous system belong all neural elements that are situated in the body outside the vertebral canal and cranial cavity. These include (1) the primary afferent neurons and their proximal processes, which collect information from the interior and periphery of the body; (2) the distal axons of final motor neurons, which issue from the central nervous system and carry impulses to the effector organs of the body; and (3) the sympathetic and parasympathetic ganglia and plexuses, which innervate the various visceral organs. The central nervous system includes all neural structures that are situated inside the vertebral column and the cranium. The central nervous system is conventionally divided into the following gross morphological structures: the spinal cord, medulla and pons, cerebellum, mesencephalon, diencephalon, rhinencephalon, basal ganglia, and the cerebral cortex.

**Peripheral Nervous System**   THE AFFERENT AND EFFERENT
                                      NERVES. The afferent and efferent
fibers of the limbs and trunk of the body are collected in the spinal nerves; those of the head, in the cranial nerves. The spinal nerves are attached to

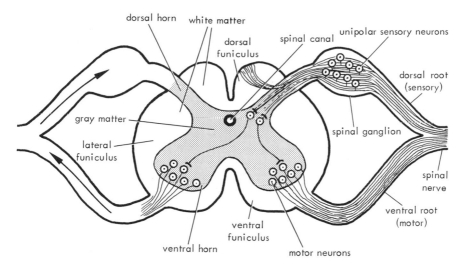

**Cross section of the spinal cord, with dorsal and ventral roots.**

the spinal cord by the ventral and dorsal roots, which are present symmetrically on the right and left sides. The ventral roots contain all the motor nerve fibers that issue from the ventral horn cells of the spinal cord, the *final motor neurons,* and synapse with skeletal muscles of the limbs and trunk. The dorsal roots contain the *primary sensory fibers,* whose unipolar cell bodies are located in the dorsal root ganglia outside the spinal cord. These afferents are in contact with the various receptors of the skin and deeper structures, including the viscera. The spinal nerves are segmentally arranged, the motor fibers of each nerve supplying a separate *myotome,* and the sensory fibers a distinct *dermatome,* of the body. The 31 *spinal nerves* of mammals are conventionally divided into 8 pairs of cervical nerves; 12 pairs of thoracic nerves; 5 pairs of lumbar nerves; 5 pairs of sacral nerves; and 1 pair of coccygeal nerves. The *cranial nerves* are attached to the brain in a somewhat irregular manner. Although some cranial nerves have both sensory and motor components (for example, the vagus, glossopharyngeal, facial, abducens, trigeminal, trochlear, oculomotor), others are composed entirely of motor (accessory) or sensory fibers (vestibular-cochlear, optic, olfactory). One of the cranial nerves, the optic nerve, is, strictly speaking, not a peripheral nerve but a central nervous fiber tract.

SYMPATHETIC AND PARASYMPATHETIC GANGLIA.    In many spinal nerves and cranial nerves, motor fibers that innervate the viscera are present. These fibers do not directly establish contact with the visceral organs but end in peripheral ganglia of the visceral or autonomic nervous system. The peripheral ganglia may belong either to the sympathetic or parasympathetic system (Langley, 1921). The ganglia of the *sympathetic system* form a

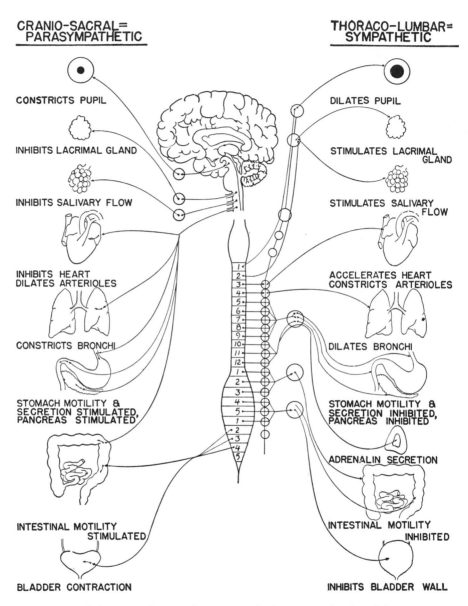

CRANIO-SACRAL=
PARASYMPATHETIC

THORACO-LUMBAR=
SYMPATHETIC

CONSTRICTS PUPIL

DILATES PUPIL

INHIBITS LACRIMAL GLAND

STIMULATES LACRIMAL
GLAND

INHIBITS SALIVARY FLOW

STIMULATES SALIVARY
FLOW

INHIBITS HEART
DILATES ARTERIOLES

ACCELERATES HEART
CONSTRICTS ARTERIOLES

CONSTRICTS BRONCHI

DILATES BRONCHI

STOMACH MOTILITY &
SECRETION STIMULATED,
PANCREAS STIMULATED

STOMACH MOTILITY &
SECRETION INHIBITED,
PANCREAS INHIBITED

ADRENALIN SECRETION

INTESTINAL MOTILITY
STIMULATED

INTESTINAL MOTILITY
INHIBITED

BLADDER CONTRACTION

INHIBITS BLADDER WALL

Diagram of the sympathetic and parasympathetic systems, showing their antagonistic effects on various visceral organs. (From Johnson et al. *General biology*, rev.
ed. Holt, Rinehart and Winston, 1961)

nerve trunk (sympathetic trunk) that extends from the base of the skull
to the terminal region of the vertebral column. There are about 3 pairs
of *sympathetic ganglia* in the neck region, about 10 pairs in the thoracic
region, and several in the region of the abdomen and pelvis. Efferents

constituting the thoracolumbar *preganglionic* outflow synapse in these sympathetic ganglia, where new, *postganglionic* efferents arise. These postganglionic sympathetic efferents are distributed to the various viscera, around which they form extensive plexuses. The ganglia of the *parasympathetic system* are not organized into a trunk but are commonly located near the organs innervated. A *cranial* and a *sacral* outflow of preganglionic efferents terminate in the parasympathetic ganglia. The preganglionic fibers synapse here with postganglionic, unmyelinated parasympathetic efferents, and these contact the various visceral organs.

Both the sympathetic and parasympathetic postganglionic efferents exercise their action on viscera by means of neurohumoral secretions. The majority of postganglionic efferents of the sympathetic system liberate adrenaline (Cannon and Rosenblueth, 1937); they are accordingly referred to as *adrenergic* fibers. The postganglionic parasympathetic efferents liberate acetylcholine (Dale and Feldberg, 1933); these efferents are therefore called *cholinergic* fibers. Most (though not all) visceral organs are supplied by both sympathetic and parasympathetic fibers; and, as is well known, these two efferents may have antagonistic effects. For instance, the activity of the heart is accelerated by sympathetic stimulation and inhibited by parasympathetic stimulation; conversely, gastric motility is inhibited by sympathetic stimulation and accelerated by parasympathetic stimulation. In general, as Cannon has postulated (1939), sympathetic activity prepares the body for exerted overt action, whereas parasympathetic activity furthers recuperative processes and re-establishment of the homeostasis of the internal milieu. Hess (1954) termed the former effect *ergotropic*, the latter *trophotropic*. However, some functions that cannot be classified as emergency activities, such as maintenance of body temperature in warm-blooded animals, also depend on sympathetic and parasympathetic innervation (Chapter 11).

**The Central Nervous System**     Although some of the conventional regional subdivisions of the central nervous system are of limited functional significance, they all serve as useful landmarks for brain parcellation. A more meaningful classification in terms of functional organization will be presented later.

GRAY AND WHITE MATTER. The first useful distinction that can be made in the central nervous system is between gray and white matter. *Gray matter* is composed mostly of nerve and glia cells and their processes, and is poor in or devoid of myelinated fibers. It is found aggregated in the center of the spinal cord, as *nuclei* in the brain stem and forebrain, and as a covering layer of *cortex* over the surface of the cerebellum and the cerebral hemispheres. *White matter*, on the other hand, is composed mostly of myelinated nerve fibers (it is the fatty myelin sheath of nerve axons that lends such structures their whitish appearance in properly fixed, unstained tissue). The white matter forms the exterior of the spinal cord, and it is seen as big tracts and commissures in the brain stem and fore-brain. Gray matter generally represents "brain centers," where synaptic contacts are established by incoming and outgoing fibers, whereas white matter is made up of "pathways" or "lines" connecting the "centers."

The common structural subdivisions of the central nervous system, as-cending from the tail, or *caudal* end, toward the head, or *rostral* regions, are as follows: spinal cord, medulla and pons, cerebellum, mesencephalon, diencephalon, rhinencephalon, basal ganglia, and cerebral cortex.

THE SPINAL CORD. The spinal cord is the oldest and relatively simplest part of the central nervous system. It is a long cylindrical structure situated inside the vertebral canal, running parallel to the long axis of the body and controlling the activities of the trunk and limbs. The spinal cord extends caudally from the lumbar vertebrae to the bony opening of the skull, the *foramen magnum*, where it is continuous with the *medulla oblongata*. Externally the spinal cord is enveloped in various covering mem-branes, the *pia, arachnoid,* and *dura.* In its center region is the *spinal canal,* which is continuous with the greatly enlarged ventricles of the brain and is filled with the *cerebrospinal fluid.* Although functionally the spinal cord is a *segmental* structure, the segmental organization is not apparent in the core of the column, which is continuous and relatively uniform. Ex-ception to this is the presence, in quadruped vertebrates, of the *cervical* and *lumbar enlargements,* the regions where the nerve fibers and cell bodies innervating the front and hind limbs are located. The segmental organiza-tion of the spinal cord, however, is made apparent by the mode of organiza-tion of the spinal nerves. Thirty-one pairs of spinal nerves, each composed of dorsal and ventral roots, connect the spinal cord with the peripheral nervous system, and these divide the spinal cord (and the body) into so many segments.

The structure of the spinal cord can be usefully studied by analyzing both its horizontal and vertical organization. If a cross section through the spinal cord is made at any point, the gray matter may be seen in the center region in the form of the letter H, surrounded by white matter (figure on page 203). The upper arms of the gray matter represent the right and left *dorsal horns,* into which the dorsal-root afferents funnel; its lower, widened limbs represent the right and left *ventral horns,* in which large motor cells are situated. These large cells are the final motor neurons from which the efferent fibers of the ventral root arise. The muscles of the trunk and limbs are innervated exclusively by fibers of these neurons. The middle gray matter, linking the two wings across the midline, is the gray *commissural* region, which associates the two lateral halves of the spinal gray matter. The H-shaped gray matter divides the white matter surrounding it roughly into four regions: the dorsal, ventral, and two lateral (right and left) *funiculi.*

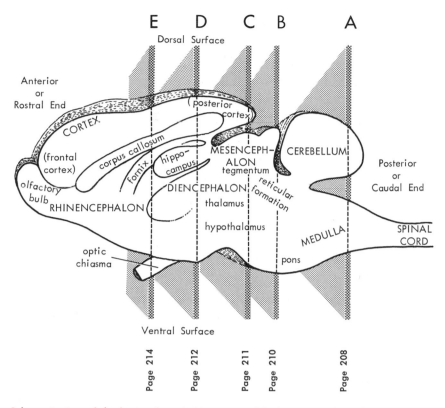

E     D     C  B     A

Dorsal Surface

Anterior
or
Rostral End

CORTEX

(frontal cortex)

olfactory bulb

RHINENCEPHALON

corpus callosum

fornix

hippo-campus

posterior cortex

MESENCEPH-ALON
tegmentum

DIENCEPHALON
thalamus

reticular formation

hypothalamus

CEREBELLUM

Posterior
or
Caudal End

MEDULLA

SPINAL
CORD

optic chiasma

pons

Ventral Surface

Page 214    Page 212    Page 211  Page 210    Page 208

Schematic view of the brain of a primitive mammal (rat) cut in median plane. Vertical broken lines (A–E) indicate some of the coronal levels at which sections illustrated in the following pages were cut.

To understand the internal organization of the spinal cord, we may now consider its vertical architecture. The funiculi are made up actually of columns of fibers. Four major classes of fiber tracts may be distinguished: (1) short fiber tracts that connect adjacent spinal segments with one another, called *fasciculi proprii*; (2) fiber tracts that cross to the other side through the midline, the *commissural fibers*; (3) *long ascending fiber tracts* that carry afferent impulses rostrally to the brain; and (4) *long descending fiber tracts* that bring efferent impulses from the brain to the spinal cord. (The distribution of various fiber tracts in the white columns in terms of origin, function, and destination will be described later.) Not only the fiber tracts but also the various cellular aggregations or nuclear groups in the gray matter can be considered to be essentially columns, most of which extend continuously through all the segments of the spinal cord. Thus the dorsal horn cells form the dorsal (or posterior) gray column; the ventral horn cells, the ventral (or anterior) gray column.

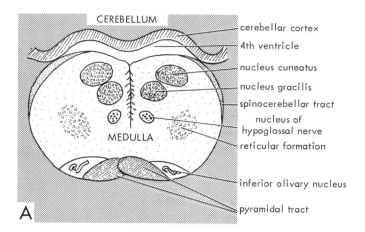

Schematic diagram of the medulla in the rat. This coronal section is cut at level A, as indicated in the figure on page 207.

THE MEDULLA AND PONS.  The *medulla oblongata* is a modified and enlarged extension of the spinal cord. Like the spinal cord, it is essentially a *segmental structure*; the modifications present in it are due partly to the fact that the medulla is related, through the cranial nerves, to a highly specialized region of the body, the head. The head, as the anterior part of the body of subhuman vertebrates, is equipped with specialized receptors that are not present in the trunk and limbs; it also contains a variety of organs (those concerned with food and water intake and breathing) that require modified neural control mechanisms. In addition, the medulla oblongata also represents a crossroad through which large ascending and descending fiber tracts funnel.

A cross section through the posterior part of the medulla shows some of the characteristic landmarks of the spinal cord still present. The major change at this level is the appearance of a nuclear group dorsally, the *nuclei gracilis* and *cuneatus*, where the large fiber tracts ascending in the dorsal funiculus terminate and give rise to a new fiber tract, the medial lemniscus. The *medial lemniscus* then crosses (*decussates*) in this region to the opposite side. Ventrally there appears a distinct eminence, the *pyramid*, which is formed by the massive, descending pyramidal tract, which decussates in this region. In more rostral cross sections of the medulla, the original landmarks of the spinal cord are almost all gone. The central canal, pushed to the dorsal surface of the medulla, widens into the *fourth ventricle*, and entirely new cellular and fibrous structures make their appearance. These include laterally and dorsally the *cochlear* and *vestibular nuclei*, and ventrally the *inferior olivary nucleus* with its unique configuration. In the transition region of the medulla and pons new fibrous structures make their appearance: the *cerebellar peduncles* laterally and dorsolaterally, and the *pontine* fiber tracts and nuclei ventrally. These structures are in intimate contact with the cerebellum, which is situated dorsally over the pons.

THE CEREBELLUM. The cerebellum represents the first *suprasegmental structure* as we pass from the caudal parts of the central nervous system rostrally. It is situated dorsally off the main axis of the nervous system, connected with it by several large fiber tracts. These fiber tracts are the superior, middle, and inferior cerebellar peduncles. The *inferior cerebellar peduncle* contains afferents and efferents that connect the cerebellum with the spinal cord and medulla. The *middle cerebellar peduncle* is composed of fibers that come directly from the pons but relay impulses from the cerebral cortex. The *superior cerebellar peduncle* contains mostly efferent fibers to the brain stem (reticular formation and motor nuclei) and thalamus.

The cerebellum, like the spinal cord and medulla, is an ancient vertebrate structure present in rudimentary form in lampreys. In lower vertebrates, the cerebellum is intimately connected with the lateral line organs nd the vestibular apparatus; its connections in higher forms become more varied, including virtually all afferent systems and perhaps all major portions of the brain including the neocortex. The cerebellum of mammals may be usefully divided into two major parts: the flocculonodular lobe and the anterior lobe of the hemispheres, which form the paleocerebellum; and the middle lobe of the cerebellar hemispheres, which forms the neocerebellum. The *flocculonodular lobe* is presumed to represent the cerebellum of the lowest vertebrates; it is associated mainly with the vestibular system. The *anterior lobe*, situated above the fissura prima, is

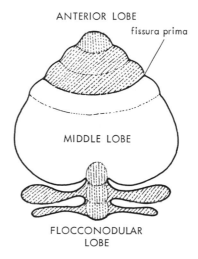

ANTERIOR LOBE

fissura prima

MIDDLE LOBE

FLOCCONODULAR
LOBE

Highly simplified diagram of the major subdivisions of the cerebellum.

present in all vertebrates that have limbs. The bulk of the cerebellum is composed of the middle lobes of the hemispheres.

In the cerebellar hemispheres the white matter is situated interiorly, and the gray matter forms the exterior surface (in which it differs from the spinal cord). The cerebellar gray matter, or cortex, forms a highly convoluted surface, giving rise to numerous folia, sulci, and lobules. The cerebellar cortex is uniform over its entire surface, being composed of three layers: (1) the superficial *molecular layer*, (2) an intermediate layer composed of a row of *Purkinje cells*, and (3) the inner *granular layer*. Several nuclei (dentate, emboliform, fastigial) are also present in the cerebellum. The axons of the Purkinje cells, which represent the efferents of the cerebellar cortex, synapse in these nuclei, and here fibers originate that leave the cerebellum by way of the cerebellar peduncles. The main function of the cerebellum is the regulation of the varied motor activities of the animal by means of complex feedback circuits.

THE MESENCEPHALON. The mesencephalon, or midbrain, is an ancient suprasegmental structure that merges caudally with the pons and

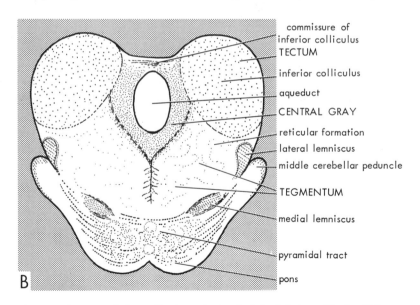

commissure of
inferior colliculus
TECTUM

inferior colliculus

aqueduct

CENTRAL GRAY

reticular formation

lateral lemniscus

middle cerebellar peduncle

TEGMENTUM

medial lemniscus

pyramidal tract

pons

B

Schematic diagram of the midbrain at the level of the inferior colliculus. This coronal section is cut at level B, as indicated in the figure on page 207.

rostrally with the diencephalon. It may be divided into three parts: (1) the tectum, (2) the central, or periaqueductal, gray, and (3) the tegmentum. The *tectum* forms the roof of the midbrain. In lower vertebrates the tectum is present as a single pair of eminences with major input from the eyes; it is therefore also called the optic lobe. In mammals, the tectum is differentiated into two pairs of eminences or colliculi, the *inferior* and

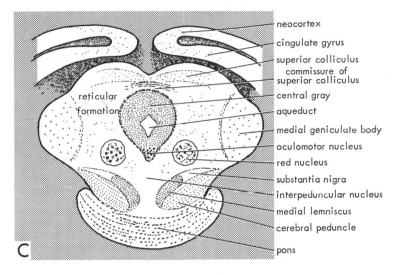

neocortex
cingulate gyrus
superior colliculus
commissure of superior colliculus
central gray
aqueduct
medial geniculate body
oculomotor nucleus
red nucleus
substantia nigra
interpeduncular nucleus
medial lemniscus
cerebral peduncle
pons
reticular formation
C

Schematic diagram of the midbrain at the level of the superior colliculus. This coronal section is cut at level C, as indicated in the figure on page 207.

*superior colliculi.* The colliculi are suprasegmental afferent centers: the input to the inferior colliculus is from the auditory system, and that to the superior colliculus from the visual system. The central gray surrounds the central canal, which is here called the *cerebral aqueduct.* Embedded in the ventral portion of the central gray are several cranial nuclei, including the oculomotor nucleus.

The ventral portion of the mesencephalon is the *tegmentum.* Large portions of the mesencephalic tegmentum are collectively known as the *reticular formation,* which is believed to extend caudally, through the medulla, to the spinal cord, and rostrally into the diencephalon. In addition to the reticular formation, several large motor nuclei are also present in the tegmentum; most prominent of these is the *red nucleus,* formed partly of very large neurons, and the *substantia nigra.* The cerebral peduncle forms the ventral border of the tegmentum; it is made up of pyramidal tract fibers that come from the cortex and course downward to the medulla and spinal cord. In rostral sections of the mesencephalon two structures appear laterally, the medial and lateral geniculate bodies; as thalamic nuclei these are classified with the diencephalon.

THE DIENCEPHALON. The diencephalon is continuous with the midbrain caudally, and large portions of it are in intimate contact with the cerebral cortex through a large fiber tract, the cortical radiation. The diencephalon may be divided into four parts: (1) thalamus, (2) epithalamus, (3) subthalamus, and (4) hypothalamus.

THE THALAMUS. The thalamus is a paired ovoid mass formed around the *third ventricle* (which is continuous with the aqueduct) and

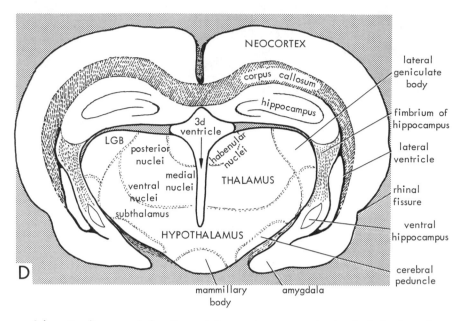

NEOCORTEX

corpus callosum

hippocampus

3d ventricle

LGB

posterior nuclei

habenular nuclei

medial nuclei          THALAMUS

ventral nuclei

subthalamus

HYPOTHALAMUS

D

lateral geniculate body

fimbrium of hippocampus

lateral ventricle

rhinal fissure

ventral hippocampus

cerebral peduncle

mammillary body          amygdala

Schematic diagram of the diencephalon and cortex at the level of the lateral geniculate body. This coronal section is cut at level D, as indicated in the figure on page 207.

composed of a large number of nuclei. A fibrous Y-shaped sheath within the mass of the thalamus, the internal medullary lamina, divides the thalamus into three parts, the medial, anterior, and lateral nuclear groups. In addition to these, a posterior group of nuclei is recognized in the caudal transitional region of the thalamus; thus there are four major nuclear groups. Within each of these nuclear groups several different nuclei are distinguished either by their spatial position or cellular configuration.

Several nuclei situated near the third ventricle form the *medial group of nuclei*. These include the midline, dorsomedial, ventromedial, and centromedian nuclei. The connections of these nuclei are mainly with the brain stem and basal ganglia, although there exist sparse connections with the cerebral cortex (frontal cortex). The *anterior nuclear group*, situated between the bifurcating arms of the internal medullary lamina, represents a relatively small part of the thalamus on its frontal border. The connections of this group are mainly with the hypothalamus (mammillary bodies) and rhinencephalon (cingulate gyrus). The *lateral group of nuclei* lies between the internal medullary lamina and the internal capsule. This large mass of nuclei is usually divided into a ventral and dorsal portion. The *ventral nuclear group* (lateroventral, posteroventral, posteromedial, and posterolateral) receives the ascending somesthetic and kinesthetic projections, and fibers that arise here are projected onto the somesthetic and motor areas of the cortex. The *dorsal group of nuclei* (dorsal lateral and posterior lateral) receives fibers from other thalamic nuclei and sends fibers to the cortex. In addition to these, the reticular nucleus, situated on the border of the internal capsule, is also grouped with the lateral nuclei. Finally, the *posterior group of nuclei*, which is partially continuous with several midbrain structures, includes the lateral and medial geniculate bodies, the pulvinar, and a few other nuclei. The *lateral geniculate body* receives fibers from the optic tract, and it sends projection fibers to the striate cortex. The *medial geniculate body* receives auditory afferents and sends fibers to the auditory cortex in the temporal lobe. The pulvinar receives fibers from the former two (and some other) thalamic structures, and it sends fibers to the cortex. At this point it should be added that the connections of the thalamus and the cortex are usually two-way connections; thalamic nuclei that send fibers to specific regions of the cortex also receive, directly or indirectly, reciprocal fibers from the same or adjacent cortical regions.

Another classification of thalamic nuclei is made in terms of intracerebral connections and phylogenetic considerations. On this basis, three groups of thalamic nuclei may be distinguished: (1) the intrinsic nuclei; (2) the extrinsic projection, or relay, nuclei; and (3) the extrinsic association nuclei. To the *intrinsic nuclear group* belong nuclei that are present in lower vertebrates without a cerebral cortex and that, in vertebrates with a cortex, do not have direct cortical connections. This group includes the intralaminar, midline, anterior, and possibly the reticular nuclei. To the *extrinsic projection nuclei* belong all nuclei that receive direct afferents from the various sensory systems and relay impulses to the various projection areas of the cortex. Among these are the lateral and medial geniculate bodies and the lateroventral, posteroventral, posteromedial, and posterolateral nuclei. Finally, to the *extrinsic association nuclei* belong the pulvinar, the dorsal lateral, the posterior lateral, and a few other thalamic nuclei, which do not receive direct input from the great afferent systems but are in intimate contact with the association areas of the cortex.

The Epithalamus. The epithalamus belongs to the most ancient part of the diencephalon. In mammals it is represented by a single nuclear group, the *habenular nuclei*, which are situated in the dorsal region of the thalamus. The habenular nuclei are connected with the epiphysis, or pineal gland (whose functions are not known), and are associated indirectly with the rhinencephalon and a tegmental nucleus. In all probability these nuclei are concerned with visceral functions.

The Subthalamus. The subthalamus is situated ventrally in the posterior part of the diencephalon. Caudally it is continuous with the midbrain tegmentum and is also functionally associated with it. Its main components are the subthalamic nucleus, zona incerta, and Forel's fields. The diencephalic extensions of the red nucleus and substantia nigra may also be grouped with it. The subthalamus is intimately associated with the basal ganglia, and it represents a motor outflow of the so-called extrapyramidal system.

THE HYPOTHALAMUS.  The hypothalamus is situated below the thalamus and forms the ventrolateral wall and ventral floor of the third ventricle. It is in intimate contact with the hypophysis or pituitary gland. Although a small structure, the hypothalamus is composed of a relatively large number of nuclei with distinct functions. These nuclei have been classified in various ways. It will be sufficient at this point to consider four groups of nuclei: (1) the anterior nuclei (which include the supraoptic and paraventricular nuclei); (2) the middle nuclei; (3) the lateral nuclei; and (4) the posterior nuclei (which include the mammillary bodies). The afferents of the hypothalamus are from the mesencephalic tegmentum, the rhinencephalon, the epithalamus, and basal ganglia, and there are sparse connections with the cortex. These afferent fibers reach the hypothalamus by various routes; most important of these are the *medial forebrain bundle, fornix,* and *stria terminalis.* The major outflow of the hypothalamus is to the neurohypophysis, and to various visceral nuclei of the diencephalon, mesencephalon, pons, and medulla. As will be described later, the hypothalamus is one of the major suprasegmental centers controlling visceral functions.

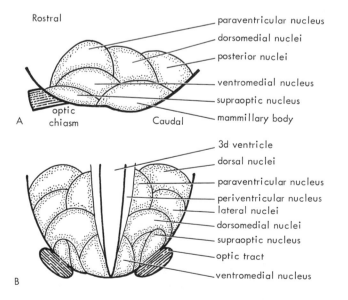

Schematic diagram of the nuclei of the hypothalamus. A, the hypothalamus in sagittal section; B, in an anterior coronal section.

THE BASAL GANGLIA.  The basal ganglia are present beneath the cerebral hemispheres in the form of large masses of gray matter. They are phylogenetically old structures, which form a considerable part of the fore-brain of lower vertebrates (particularly birds). In mammals, the basal ganglia include the *caudate nucleus* and *lentiform nucleus*, which, to-gether, are also known as the *corpus striatum*. The lentiform nucleus is divided into a more laterally placed portion, called *putamen*, and a more medial part, the *globus pallidus*. In addition to these nuclei, several other subcortical nuclei are grouped with the basal ganglia. On the basis of morphological considerations, the claustrum is included with the basal ganglia; on the basis of functional considerations, the subthalamus, sub-stantia nigra, red nucleus, and tegmentum (including the reticular forma-tion) are occasionally classified with the basal ganglia.

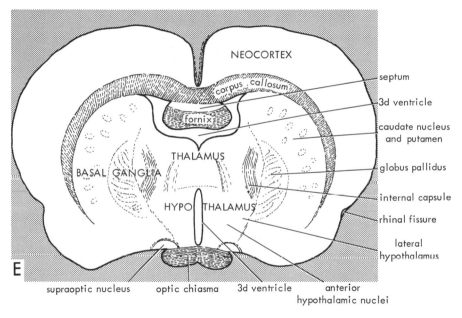

Schematic diagram of the basal ganglia and anterior portion of diencephalon. This coronal section is cut at level E, as indicated in the figure on page 207.

The afferent connections of the basal ganglia are not well known. They receive fibers from the thalamus, and possibly also from the brain stem, and there is intimate connection with the cortex. Their efferents pass mostly to the substantia nigra, red nucleus, subthalamus, and hypo-thalamus, forming a major part of the extrapyramidal efferent system.

THE RHINENCEPHALON.  "Rhinencephalon" is a vaguely defined term referring to ancient parts of the forebrain that are directly or indi-

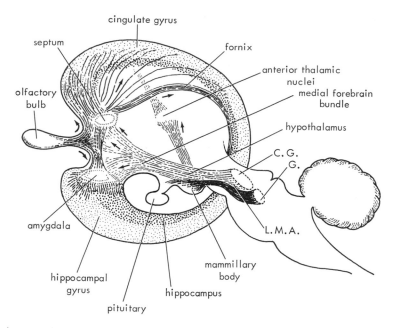

Schematic drawing of the limbic system in primates. (After MacLean. *Handb. Phys-iol.*, 1958, Sec. 1, **3**, 733)

rectly associated with the olfactory system or with structures and functions dependent on olfaction. It includes the olfactory bulb and tract, as well as the pyriform lobe, the amygdaloid body, the septal nuclei, and the hippocampus. Three large fiber tracts, the fornix, the anterior commissure, and the medial forebrain bundle, are connected with the various rhinencephalic structures and also with the hypothalamus. Some anatomists also include with the rhinencephalon various older cortical structures (allocortex), such as the cingulate gyrus, the entorhinal cortex, and the orbitofrontal and temporal pole. These rhinencephalic structures are sometimes grouped together as the *limbic system*.

Although the topography of the rhinencephalon is relatively simple in lower vertebrates, it is quite complex in mammals (particularly in higher mammals). This increasing complexity is attributed to the fact that various parts of the rhinencephalon became separated from one another during phylogeny and were displaced by invading, newer cerebral structures. Looking at the ventral surface or base of the brain of a mammal, we may see the *olfactory bulb* and *tract*, together with the amygdaloid body and the pyriform area. The *amygdaloid body* is composed of several nuclei; some of these have direct olfactory connections, but others do not. The *pyriform area* is formed of the lateral olfactory gyrus and the hippocampal gyrus. The *septum* is situated in the midline region beneath the corpus callosum. The *hippocampus* represents the most ancient part of

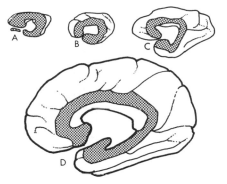

Schematic drawings showing the limbic system (hatched sections) in relation to the neocortex in the rabbit (A), cat (B), monkey (C), and man (D). Note the relative decline of the limbic system in higher mammals. (After MacLean. *J. Neurophysiol.*, 1954, **11**, 29–44)

the cerebral cortex (archicortex); it has no direct olfactory connections. Its two major components are the *dentate gyrus* and *Ammon's horn*. In lower mammals it forms a considerable part of the forebrain, surrounding the midbrain and thalamus dorsally and laterally. In higher mammals parts of it are present as a thin ring (hippocampal rudiment) extending from the region of the olfactory gyrus, over the dorsal surface of the corpus callosum, to the posterior enlarged region, where it is continuous with the *fornix*. This latter is an arched fiber tract, which connects the hippocampus with the hypothalamus (mammillary body).

THE NEOCORTEX. The paired cerebral hemispheres are the most conspicuous components of the brain of mammals, covering large portions of underlying "subcortical" structures. The cerebral hemispheres are formed partly of three-layered allocortical structures and, to a greater extent, of the six-layered neocortex or isocortex. Whereas the *allocortex* is an ancient component present in most lower vertebrates, the neocortex is absent in submammalian vertebrates. The *neocortex*, which is derived phylo- and ontogenetically from the simpler allocortex, is a mammalian acquisition, and there is a progressive growth in the size and complexity of the neocortex as we ascend with the phyletic scale through various orders of mammals. The neocortex is relatively small in marsupials (such as the kangaroo), insectivores (such as the shrew), and even rodents (such as mice and rats); there are obvious signs of increase in size as well as complexity in carnivores (such as cats and dogs) and particularly in primates. This progressive growth may be seen within various orders as well as within single groups or species. In primates, for instance, a considerable relative growth in the size and complexity of the neocortex may be seen when we compare simpler forms (tree shrews, lemurs, tarsiers) with more advanced types (monkeys and apes). Paleontological evidence (Edinger, 1948) suggests similar growth of the cortex within single species, such as the horse; this was indicated by a comparison of the skull casts of simpler, extinct forms (*Eohippus, Mesohippus, Merychippus*) with the brain of modern horse.

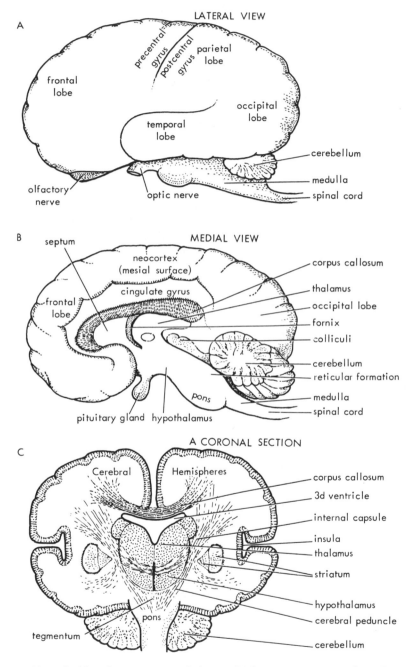

Three highly schematic views of the cerebral cortex in man. A, lateral view; B, medial view; C, a coronal section through the thalamus.

The two symmetrical cerebral hemispheres consist of white and gray matter. The internally situated *white matter* is composed of afferent (corticopetal) and efferent (corticofugal) fibers that connect the cerebrum with other parts of the central nervous system; these fibers form the *internal capsule*, or *cortical radiation*. A massive fiber tract of commissural fibers, the *corpus callosum*, connects the two cerebral hemispheres. The *gray matter* or *cortex*, which is several millimeters thick, is composed of cellular layers, traversed by radially and horizontally oriented fibers. In higher mammalian species the cortex is convoluted, a condition that permits enlargement of the surface of the cortex within the limited space provided by the cranium. Some of the *gyri* (ridges) and *sulci* (fissures) thus formed serve as landmarks for the various subdivisions of the cortex. In primates, most important of these is the *central sulcus*, which divides the anterior from the posterior cortex. Generally speaking, the sensory areas of the cortex are situated in the posterior half; the motor areas, in the anterior half of the cortex.

A more common subdivision of the cortex is into *lobes*. The anterior part of the cortex in front of the central fissure is the *frontal lobe*. The large area below the lateral fissure is the *temporal lobe*. The region surrounded anteriorly by the central fissure and ventrally by the lateral fissure is the *parietal lobe*. The posterior pole of the cortex is known as the *occipital lobe*.

Histological studies with the Golgi staining technique have revealed the presence of four major types of neurons in the neocortex:

1. Cells with descending long axons, particularly pyramidal cells, which pass through the white matter as projection or commissural fibers;

2. Cells with short axons ramified around the cell body (stellate, or Golgi type II, neurons);

3. Cells with ascending axons (Martinotti cells);

4. Cells with horizontal axons (cells of Cajal).

These cortical neurons may be in contact with afferents coming from the thalamus, with association or commissural fibers coming from distant parts of the cortex, or with association fibers coming from neighboring areas and fields.

The neurons and fibers in the cortex are arranged in layers. Classically, six cellular layers are distinguished in all regions of the neocortex, though in many regions some of these layers may be undeveloped and in other regions may be subdivided into numerous sublayers. The conventionally distinguished *six cortical layers* are distinguished as follows.

1. The molecular or *plexiform layer* consists of comparatively few cells arranged parallel to the surface of the cortex, and composed largely of axons and dendrites that come from the underlying layers.

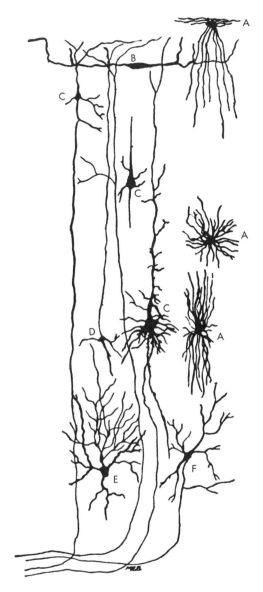

Different types of cells in the cerebral cortex stained with the Golgi technique. A, glia cells; B, horizontal cells of Cajal; C, pyramidal cells; D, cells of Martinotti; E, stellate cell; F, fusiform cells. (From Ranson and Clark. *The anatomy of the nervous system*, 10th ed., Saunders, 1959, p. 349)

2. The *external granular layer* is composed of small cells; their dendrites terminate in the first layer, but their axons pass to the lower layers.

3. The *external pyramidal layer* contains small- or medium-sized pyramidal cells.

4. The *internal granular layer* is composed of small multipolar cells that, particularly in the sensory projection areas, are very densely packed. These cells are in contact with afferents coming from the thalamus. Layers 1 through 4 compose the outer zone of the cortex.

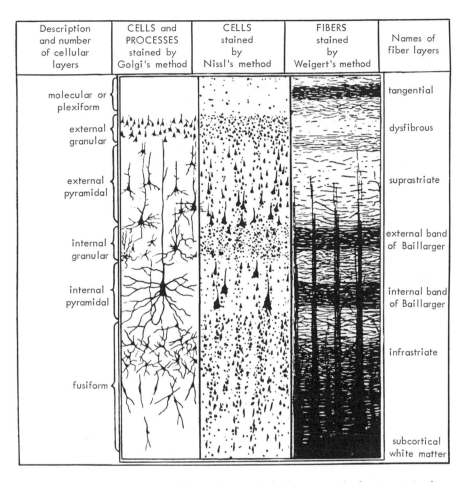

| Description and number of cellular layers | CELLS and PROCESSES stained by Golgi's method | CELLS stained by Nissl's method | FIBERS stained by Weigert's method | Names of fiber layers |
|---|---|---|---|---|
| molecular or plexiform | | | | tangential |
| external granular | | | | dysfibrous |
| external pyramidal | | | | suprastriate |
| internal granular | | | | external band of Baillarger |
| internal pyramidal | | | | internal band of Baillarger |
| | | | | infrastriate |
| fusiform | | | | subcortical white matter |

Diagrammatic presentation of the six layers of the human cerebral cortex stained with different techniques. (After Brodmann. *Vergleichende Lokalisationslehre der Grosshirnrinde*. Barth, 1909)

5. The *internal pyramidal layer* contains many pyramidal cells that, in the motor areas, may be of very large size (Betz cells). It is from this layer that the bulk of the *pyramidal efferents* arise.

6. The *fusiform layer* contains small fusiform cells. Layers 5 and 6 comprise the inner zone of the cortex.

These horizontal layers cannot be distinguished clearly in all regions of the neocortex, and their delimitation is often based on arbitrary criteria. However, the stratified composition of the cortex is an undeniable fact, and areal classifications based on *cytoarchitectonic* differences (for ex-

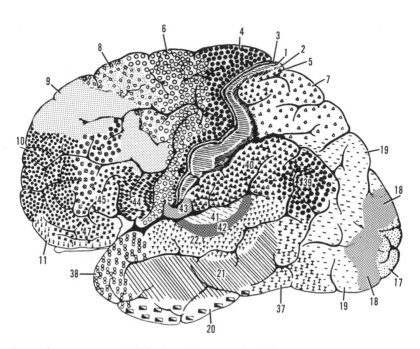

Cytoarchitectonic areas of the lateral aspect of the human brain. (According to Brodmann. *Vergleichende Lokalisationslehre der Grosshirnrinde.* Barth, 1909)

ample, Brodmann, 1909) have, as physiological evidence suggests, functional significance. For instance, Brodmann's cytoarchitectonic area 17 corresponds with the visual projection area, areas 41 and 42 with the auditory projection area, areas 3, 1, and 2 with the somesthetic projection field, and area 4 with the motor cortex. The sensory projection areas are characterized by the excessive development of the granular layers (*granular cortex*); the motor areas, by the better development of the pyramidal layers (*agranular cortex*). The extreme parcellations of some neuroanatomists on the basis of cytoarchitectonics, however, are probably not justified (Lashley and Clark, 1946).

**THE MAIN AFFERENT PATHWAYS AND CENTERS**    In the preceding chapter we have considered the organization of the central nervous system from a morphological point of view, classifying its parts on the basis of gross structural landmarks. As a first step toward a description of the functional organization of the nervous system, we shall present a subdivision in terms of sensory and motor functions subserved by the system's component parts. In subsequent chapters this subdivision will be followed by another made in terms of classes of animative activities that are controlled by the different functional divisions of the central nervous system.

**Segmental Afferent Pathways**    As described previously, the cell bodies of the segmental, primary afferent neurons are located outside the central nervous system in the spinal nerve ganglia. The centripetally conducting proximal processes of these first-order neurons serve as receptors (or are in contact with specialized receptors), whereas their centrifugally conducting distal processes enter the spinal cord or medulla by way of the dorsal sensory roots. These primary afferent neurons serve as exclusive input lines from the receptors to the central nervous system; in their absence transmission of peripheral sensory information is impossible.

The simplest neural unit that can control a visceral or somatic function is one that is composed of at least two neurons, a primary afferent neuron and a final motor neuron. Such a unit can transmit signals, or "stimuli," and initiate a motor action, or "response," forming what is called a *monosynaptic reflex arc.* An example of this is the stretch reflex, the contraction of passively stretched muscle. This reflex is dependent on afferent impulses generated by stretch receptors (muscle spindles), which are relayed in the spinal cord directly to motor neurons to produce the compensatory contraction of the stretched muscle (Lloyd, 1955). Monosynaptic neural units are the simplest relay mechanisms in the vertebrate nervous system; they are adequate only for a few relatively simple functions. The majority of animative activities is controlled by multisynaptic neural units.

The simplest *multisynaptic neural chains* are composed of three neurons, an interneuron, or *internuncial cell,* being interposed between the primary sensory and the final motor neurons. Various segmental spinal reflexes are mediated by such units. These internuncial cells are located in the spinal cord in the dorsal gray column; they may have numerous short processes (Golgi type II neurons), as well as long processes that connect the right and left halves, and the different segments, of the cord. These intercalated cells make possible also the modulation and control of the activities of the reflex arc by other neural circuits whose neurons synapse with the internuncial cell.

Both the two- and three-neuronal reflex chains represent monoafferent systems in which the sensory signals are transmitted by the primary sensory neuron, which synapses directly, or by way of an internuncial, with the motoneuron. Such *monoafferent* pathways mediate most segmental and intersegmental reflexes in the spinal cord and medulla. In contrast, all suprasegmental pathways are characterized by the presence of an additional relay of at least one, but more commonly two, afferent neurons.

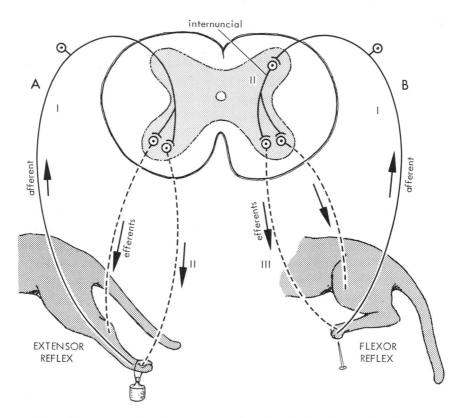

internuncial

A

B

I

II

I

afferent

afferent

efferents

efferents

II

III

EXTENSOR
REFLEX

FLEXOR
REFLEX

Schematic representation of a monosynaptic and a simple polysynaptic reflex arc.
A, path of the monosynaptic (two-neuron) stretch reflex, which leads to an extensor response when the limb is stretched. B, the three-neuron nociceptive flexor
reflex. I, II, III are the neuron elements of the reflex arcs.

**Direct, Oligoafferent**    The afferent pathways of all the
**Suprasegmental Pathways**    major sensory systems are composed
of a set of direct relays of afferents.
(These direct-projection pathways are distinguished from an indirect or
diffuse pathway to be described later.) In all these direct afferent pathways
the unipolar or bipolar primary afferent neurons synapse on the same, or
*ipsilateral*, side with second-order neurons. These *second-order afferents*
are located in the dorsal gray column of the spinal cord or homologous
regions in the medulla in all afferent systems except the olfactory and
optic (in the olfactory system the second-order neuron is in the olfactory
bulb; in the visual system it is in the retina). The axons of all the second-
order neurons decussate, forming a tract, or lemniscus, whose terminal
branches end *contralaterally* in the relay nuclei of the thalamus (the only

exception to this is the olfactory tract, which does not have direct thalamic projection). In the thalamus the second-order neurons synapse with *third-order neurons,* and the axons of the latter proceed by way of the thalamocortical radiation to the projection areas of the cortex on the ipsilateral side. In the main afferent systems some second-order fibers do not reach the thalamus, but terminate in parts of the brain stem (mostly the mesencephalon) that have no direct afferent connections with the cortex.

In the following pages we shall present a brief account of the direct *corticopetal pathways* of the main sensory systems. We shall describe for each system (1) the course of the primary afferent fibers; (2) the relay nucleus or nuclei where the primary afferents synapse with second-order neurons; (3) the course of the secondary afferent fibers; (4) the relay nuclei in which the secondary afferents synapse with third-order neurons; (5) the course of the tertiary afferent fibers; and (6) the projection areas in the cortex where the tertiary afferents terminate. We shall also refer briefly, where known, to the various "association" centers that are intimately connected with the afferent projection pathways, as well as to the feedback or centrifugal connections of some of the afferent systems.

PAIN AND THERMAL PATHWAYS AND CENTERS. Because the afferents of pain and thermal receptors follow similar courses, their afferent pathways will be considered together. The primary neurons of both systems, like those of all other cutaneous receptors, are located in the spinal and cranial sensory ganglia. Their small diameter axons terminate near their point of entry in the *substantia gelatinosa* in the dorsal gray column. Here they synapse with second-order neurons, the axons of which cross immediately to the opposite side and form a bundle of fibers known as the *lateral spinothalamic tract* (some of these fibers synapse with internuncials and mediate local reflexes). More and more fibers are added to this tract as it ascends through the spinal cord and medulla; a particularly large contribution is made by the spinal nucleus of the *trigeminal,* or fifth, cranial nerve. The fibers of the lateral spinothalamic tract terminate partly in the region of the *mesencephalic reticular formation* and partly in the *posterolateral ventral nucleus* of the thalamus. The axons of the third-order neurons located in the posterolateral ventral nucleus of the thalamus pass through the *internal capsule* and terminate in the somesthetic projection area of the cortex in the *postcentral* gyrus.

TACTILE PATHWAYS AND CENTERS. The afferent fibers associated with tactile receptors form two separate ascending pathways. The axons of the primary neurons forming one of the pathways ascend several segments and then synapse with second-order neurons in the dorsal gray-column nuclei. The axons of these second-order neurons decussate in the spinal cord and form the *ventral spinothalamic tract.* This tract is believed to join the lateral spinothalamic tract and to give collaterals off to the

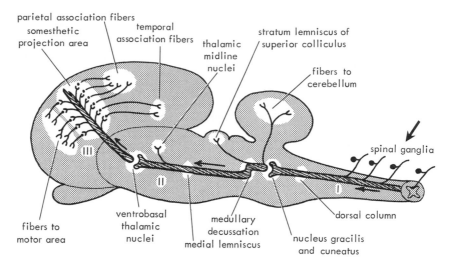

parietal association fibers
somesthetic
projection area
temporal
association fibers
thalamic
midline
nuclei
stratum lemniscus of
superior colliculus
fibers to
cerebellum
spinal ganglia
III
II
I
fibers to
motor area
ventrobasal
thalamic
nuclei
medullary
decussation
medial lemniscus
dorsal column
nucleus gracilis
and cuneatus

**The suprasegmental tactile pathway, with relay afferents (I, II, III) and relay nuclei and projection centers.**

reticular formation and the midline and posterior nuclei of the thalamus; it terminates in the *posterolateral ventral nucleus* of the thalamus. Fibers of this pathway, it has been postulated, mediate coarse touch and pressure, in contradistinction to the fiber system of the other tactile pathway that mediates gentle touch and fine tactile discrimination. The axons of the primary afferents of this second pathway (which is composed of fibers of large diameter) ascend uncrossed in the *dorsal funiculus* and terminate at the level of the medulla in the *nucleus gracilis* and *nucleus cuneatus*. The axons of the second-order neurons originating in these nuclei immediately decussate, form the *medial lemniscus*, and terminate in the *posterolateral ventral nucleus* of the thalamus. The axons of the third-order neurons located in this thalamic nucleus then pass to the precentral *somesthetic cortex*. The electrophysiological investigations of Woolsey (1947) and his collaborators suggest that there are, in fact, two somesthetic projection areas in the cortex of various mammals (labeled SI and SII), the second somesthetic area being situated ventrally to the first one on the lateral surface of the cortex.

The tactile fibers ascending in the dorsal funiculus are arranged in an orderly fashion, fibers of successively higher segments of the body being situated laterally with respect to those coming from lower segments. A more or less accurate topographic, or *somatotopic*, representation of the body surface is maintained throughout the pathway (Rose and Mountcastle, 1959). In the posterolateral ventral nucleus of the thalamus and in the somesthetic cortex (SI), the body representation of tactile spots reflects

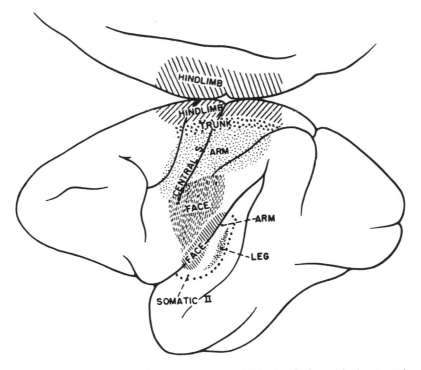

Somatotopic representation in the monkey, established with the evoked potential technique. (Based on work by Woolsey and Fairman. From Terzudo and Adey, Sensorimotor cortical activities. *Handb. Physiol.,* Sec. 1. **2,** 801)

the density of peripheral innervation in the various parts of the body. In lower mammals, such as the rabbit (in which corticalization is not far advanced), the cortical tactile representation is largely restricted to the face and head with minimum representation of the limbs. In carnivores (the cat, for example) there is adequate cortical representation of the limbs; in higher primates the fingers also are well represented (Woolsey, 1958). In addition to ascending projection from the tactile receptors to the cortex, recent anatomical (Brodal et al., 1956; Walberg, 1957; Chambers and Liu, 1957) and physiological (Hernández-Peón, 1961) investigations also suggest the existence of a feedback, or *centrifugal*, pathway, from the cortex to the first-order sensory nuclei. It is believed that by way of these centrifugal fibers the transmission of afferent information is modulated by the higher receiving centers (Granit, 1955).

PROPRIOCEPTIVE PATHWAYS AND CENTERS.  Proprioceptive fibers from muscles, tendons, and joints pass in two separate pathways. One of these pathways is associated with the second tactile projection system. In this

RAT                    DOG                    CAT

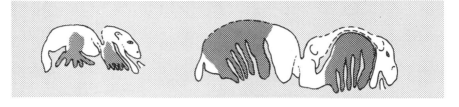

MARMOSET                    MACAQUE

Body representation in the somesthetic cortex in a series of mammals. Dotted areas mark digit representation; note the increasing relative representation of the digits from rodents to the macaque monkey. (After Woolsey. From Paillard. The patterning of skilled movements. *Handb. Physiol.*, Sec. 1, **3**, 1681)

pathway the axons of the first-order neurons ascend in the dorsal funiculus and terminate ipsilaterally in the nuclei gracilis and cuneatus. Fibers of the second-order neurons cross, ascend in the medial lemniscus, and terminate in the posterolateral ventral nucleus of the thalamus. (Some proprioceptive fibers proceed from the cuneate nucleus to the cerebellum.) Fibers of the thalamic, third-order neurons pass by way of the internal capsule to the somesthetic cortex. The topographic cortical representation of this fiber system is similar to that of the tactile fibers. The second proprioceptive pathway connects with the cerebellum. In this pathway the axons of the first-order neurons synapse with cells in the nuclei of the dorsal gray horn. Second-order neurons arising here ascend to the cerebellum in two separate fiber tracts, the *ventral* and *dorsal spinocerebellar tracts*.

THE VESTIBULAR PATHWAYS AND CENTERS. The primary neurons of the vestibular system are located in the *vestibular ganglion* in the inner ear, and their axons form the vestibular portion of the *eighth nerve*. Most of the vestibular fibers entering the medulla proceed to the *vestibular nuclei* (the medial, lateral, superior, and descending vestibular nuclei); some axons, however, go directly to the *cerebellum*. The major connections of the vestibular nuclei are by way of internuncials with the motor nuclei of the ocular muscles, the reticular formation, the cerebellum, and motor nuclei of the spinal cord. The various postural reflexes mediated by the vestibular system are discharged through these pathways. In addition to these routes, ascending vestibular fibers also project to the cortex. The exact course (for example, the thalamic relay nucleus) of this ascending pathway is not known, but the existence of projection to the cortex was established by electrophysiological methods (Gernandt, 1959).

THE GUSTATORY PATHWAYS AND CENTERS. The afferents of the taste buds course in cranial nerves, which also contain a large number of segmental somesthetic and kinesthetic afferents. These nerves include the *chorda tympani* (which joins the facial nerve), the *glossopharyngeal,* and the *vagus.* In the medulla the gustatory afferents form the *solitary tract;* they terminate in the *solitary nucleus.* The second-order gustatory afferents terminate in the contralateral *arcuate nucleus* of the thalamus (adjacent to the somesthetic projection of the face area). The third-order thalamic fibers terminate in the *somesthetic area* of the cortex in the vicinity of the face representation (Pfaffmann, 1959). Thus, in terms of afferent connections, the gustatory system may be considered a specialized part of the somesthetic system.

THE OLFACTORY PATHWAYS AND CENTERS. The olfactory afferents are of suprasegmental derivation; they occupy a unique position among the afferent systems because they do not have a direct thalamocortical projection. The primary neurons of this system are the sensory cells themselves, which are embedded in the nasal epithelium. The very fine, unmyelinated axons of these neurosensory cells enter the brain directly, and end in the *olfactory bulb* in basketlike terminal processes, called *glomeruli.* Here the primary fibers synapse either with the *mitral* or with the *tufted cells* (the second-order neurons of the olfactory system), whose axons make up the *olfactory tract.* The axons of the tufted cells form the *medial olfactory tract,* which cross in the anterior commissure to the contralateral olfactory bulb. The axons of the mitral cells form the *lateral olfactory tract,* which is continuous with the pyriform area in the basal aspect of the brain. These second-order fibers establish connections with the *olfactory tubercle,* the *prepyriform area,* and parts of the *amygdala.* If the olfactory system has connections with other parts of the "rhinencephalon" (such as the septal area, cingulate gyrus, and hippocampus), the connections must be indirect. Such indirect connections, suggested by electrophysiological evidence, may also exist with the anterior thalamic nuclei, the mammillary bodies, and the habenular nuclei (Adey, 1959). The olfactory connections of these latter structures, which control visceral and allied functions, may reflect the importance of olfaction in such processes.

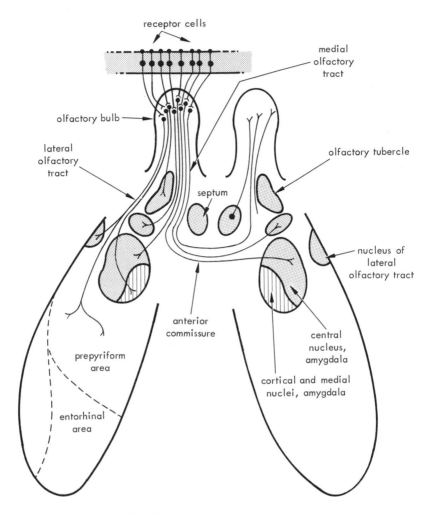

Simplified diagram of the olfactory pathway. (After Allison. The morphology of
the olfactory system in vertebrates. *Biol. Rev.,* 1953, **28**, 195–244)


THE AUDITORY PATHWAYS AND CENTERS.   The primary neurons of
the auditory system are bipolar cells located in the *spiral ganglion* in the
inner ear. The dendrites of these cells innervate the hair cells of the organ
of Corti; their axons form the auditory portion of the *eighth nerve*. The
axons of the primary auditory neurons enter the medulla, and their collaterals terminate in the *dorsal* and *ventral cochlear nuclei*. Some of the
fibers of the second-order neurons that originate in the cochlear nuclei end
in the contralateral *superior olivary nucleus;* but the main bulk of
fibers cross in the *trapezoid body* near the midline and form the *lateral
lemniscus*. Some of the fibers in the lateral lemniscus terminate in the
diffuse nucleus of the lateral lemniscus; the bulk reaches the *inferior*

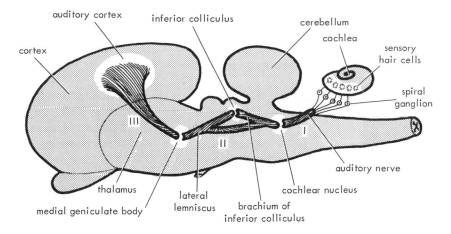

Simplified diagram of the auditory pathway. Many important components of the system are not represented.

*colliculus.* Most of the second-order auditory fibers terminate in this mesencephalic nucleus; a few, however, may continue to the medial geniculate body. The axons of the collicular fibers form the brachium of the inferior colliculus and terminate in the thalamic nucleus of the auditory system, the *medial geniculate body.* Accordingly, only a few fibers reaching the medial geniculate nucleus are truly second-order afferents; the majority represent third- or higher-order fibers, which have synapses in the various subthalamic nuclei referred to. The axons of cell bodies located in the medial geniculate body give rise to thalamocortical fibers, which project to the *auditory cortex* in the temporal lobe. By means of the evoked potential technique, two auditory cortical areas have been identified in the cortex (Woolsey, 1947). In both areas (referred to as AI and AII), as well as in the various nuclei mentioned previously, are indications of a *tonotopic* representation (Galambos and Davis, 1943; Rose et al., 1959); that is, single neurons in these areas may respond selectively to tones of specific frequencies.

A composite view of the various areas in the cortex of the cat that have auditory functions. AI, first auditory area; AII, second auditory area; EP, posterior ectosylvian area; IN, insular region; SII, second somatic area; TE, temporal area. (After several investigators. From Ades. Central auditory mechanisms. *Handb. Physiol.* 1959, Sec. 1, **1,** 597)

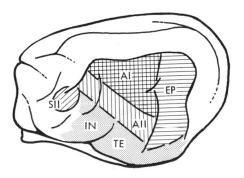

In addition to this complex ascending system, a descending centrifugal pathway is also present in the auditory system. The cortex sends reciprocal fibers to the medial geniculate body; and from the region of superior olivary nucleus a centrifugal bundle, the *olivary-cochlear bundle*, passes to the cochlea.

THE VISUAL PATHWAYS AND CENTERS.   The last afferent system to be considered is the optic tract, which in many vertebrates is the largest and most complex of all the afferent systems. The primary neurons of the visual system are the *bipolar cells* in the retina, which synapse with the rods and cones. The second-order neurons are also located in the retina; they are the *ganglion cells*, which synapse with the bipolar cells. Accordingly, the optic "nerve" fibers, which issue from the ganglion cells, are analogous to the lemniscal fibers of the auditory, somesthetic, and other systems; that is, they are central nervous tracts rather than peripheral nerves. The neural parts of the retina are loci of complex interaction among sensory, neuronal, and various supporting cells. Fibers of the optic nerve decussate inside the skull at the base of the brain; the region of decussation is called the *optic chiasm*. (As a convention, the prechiasmal part of the tract is called *optic nerve*; the postchiasmal portion, *optic tract*.)

In lower vertebrates (which have lateral eyes) the decussation of the optic nerve is complete. The effect of the decussation is that the left visual field is projected to the right half of the brain, and vice versa. This arrangement is in conformity with the decussation of the second-order afferents and thus contralateral projection of all other major afferent systems.

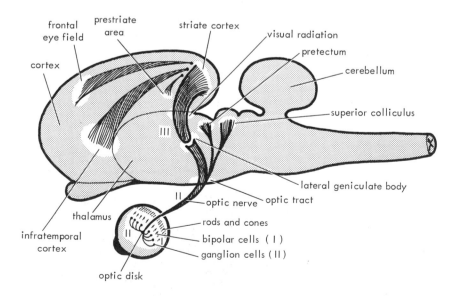

Simplified diagram of the visual pathway.

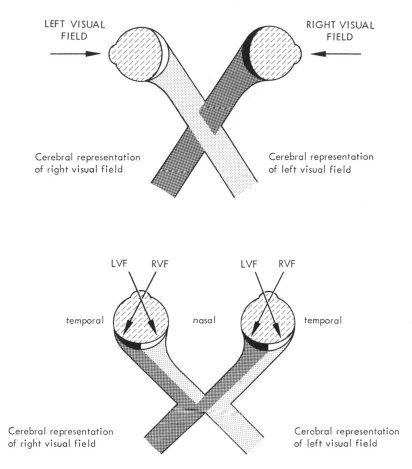

LEFT VISUAL FIELD

RIGHT VISUAL FIELD

Cerebral representation of right visual field

Cerebral representation of left visual field

A

LVF    RVF        LVF    RVF

temporal        nasal        temporal

Cerebral representation of right visual field

Cerebral representation of left visual field

B

Contralateral projection of the visual field in animals with lateral and medial eyes. A, in animals with lateral eyes (lower vertebrates, for instance) decussation of the optic tract is complete. B, in man, with medially placed eyes, the temporal half of the retina has ipsilateral projection, the nasal half contralateral projection. The effect of this hemidecussation of the optic tract is that the principle of contralateral projection of the visual field is preserved. LVF, left visual field; RVF right visual field.

In contrast, the decussation of the optic tract in higher vertebrates that have medially displaced eyes is incomplete, and in higher primates that have medial eyes there is a hemidecussation. In *hemidecussation* the temporal halves of the retina project homolaterally, whereas the nasal halves project contralaterally. The result is that the left visual field is projected to the right half of the brain, and vice versa. That is, the function of partial or hemidecussation is to preserve the system of contralateral stimulus projection in animals in which the eyes are displaced medially from the primitive lateral position.

In lower vertebrates (from fish to birds) the optic-tract fibers terminate in the optic tectum of the mesencephalon, the homologue of the *superior colliculus* of mammals. In lower mammals many optic fibers terminate in the superior colliculus, but as we ascend the phylogenetic scale in mammals, more and more optic-tract fibers are channeled to the thalamic relay nucleus of the visual system, the *lateral geniculate nucleus*. In higher vertebrates the majority of second-order visual fibers terminates in this thalamic nucleus, which is differentiated into a complex laminar structure in which homolateral and contralateral optic fibers are segregated. The third-order neurons arising in the lateral geniculate nucleus send their axons through the visual radiation to the striate cortex in the occipital lobe. The *striate cortex* has a typical granular cytoarchitecture, and there is on its surface a rather accurate topographic or *retinotopic* representation of the visual field. Optic fibers also reach, directly or indirectly, various other structures. Direct optic fibers terminate in the *pretectal region* (which is a diencephalic extension of the superior colliculus); among other functions, this pathway mediates the pupillary reflex. The posterior nucleus of the thalamus, the pulvinar, and the prestriate cortex also receive an indirect optic input.

**Diffuse, Polyafferent Suprasegmental Pathways** In addition to the fast-conducting direct afferent pathways, sometimes referred to as the *lemniscal system*, there is physiological and anatomical evidence for the existence of a high-threshold and slow-conducting *extralemniscal system*, located in the brain stem and in associated portions of the thalamus. This diffuse ascending system apparently receives afferent input from all the sensory systems and relays them to higher brain centers through a complex chain of neurons with short and long axons. The function of the extralemniscal ascending system may not be primarily the transmission of sensory information; nevertheless, recent physiological and behavioral investigations suggest that it has an important role in related processes ("arousal," "vigilance," and "attention").

It was originally assumed (Magoun, 1950) that the afferents of the extralemniscal system are made up of collateral branches of the lemniscal system, which then synapse with cells of the bulbar and midbrain *reticular formation*. Neurons of the reticular formation, in turn, were assumed to transmit impulses through multicellular channels to the *midline* and *reticular nuclei* of the thalamus, which are considered the diencephalic extensions of the reticular formation. The existence of an extralemniscal ascending afferent system has since been duly confirmed. For instance, placement of a lesion in the path of the lateral lemniscus, which severs the direct auditory pathway, does not prevent auditory im-

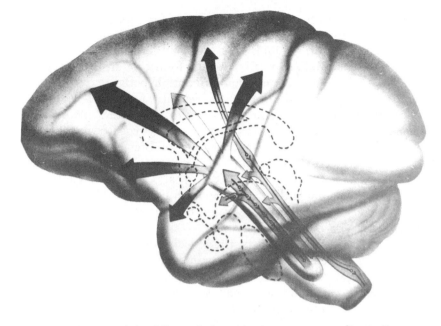

Schematic diagram of the diffuse reticular activating system, according to Magoun and his collaborators. (From Magoun. The ascending reticular activating system and wakefulness. In Delafresnaye, Ed., *Brain mechanisms and consciousness.* Charles C Thomas, 1954)

pulses from reaching the cortex, as long as the core of the brain stem remains intact (Galambos, 1961).

It now appears more likely, however, that in addition to (and possibly instead of) collaterals of the lemniscal system, the extralemniscal system is fed by afferents that pass in separate, phylogenetically older tracts of the central nervous system (Bishop, 1959). Collins and O'Leary (1954) presented physiological evidence that the higher-threshold fibers of the somesthetic system course in the lateral column of the spinal cord and produce evoked potentials in the reticular formation of the midbrain; the lower-threshold fibers of the dorsal columns, in contrast, give rise to evoked potentials in the ventral nuclei of the thalamus. There is also anatomical evidence that many fibers of the spinotectal and spinothalamic tracts terminate in the reticular formation and intralaminar nuclei of the thalamus (Mehler, 1957; Nauta and Kuypers, 1958). Thus the extralemniscal system is made up at least partly of fibers that are destined to reach specifically the reticular formation. This may hold not only for the somesthetic but for various other sensory systems. A recent anatomical study has shown, for instance, that there are no collaterals to the brainstem reticular formation from the optic tract and lateral geniculate body

(Altman, 1962). Instead, there is provision for input to the reticular formation by way of the phylogenetically older collicular fiber system (Altman and Carpenter, 1961).

Afferent impulses relayed to the reticular formation are presumed to be transmitted to the tegmentum, subthalamus, hypothalamus, and a few other motor structures with which the reticular formation has intimate connections. Impulses may also be relayed to the cortex, mainly by way of the reticular nuclei, which have widespread neocortical connections (Rose, 1952). As the original investigations of Bremer (1935), and the more recent studies of Morrison and Dempsey (1942), and Magoun and his collaborators (Magoun, 1950) indicate, the major effect of impulses ascending through these extralemniscal pathways is an alteration of the "spontaneous" electrical activity of the cortex, associated with behavioral awakening and arousal.

In addition to ascending effects, the reticular formation is also a source of descending influences. In addition to affecting motor activity, reticular descending impulses regulate the transmission of sensory information through the direct, lemniscal afferent system. A feedback reticular influence has been demonstrated to affect the discharge of muscle spindles (Granit and Kaada, 1952) by way of the gamma efferents. Transmission of somesthetic and kinesthetic afferent impulses may also be regulated by the reticular formation, through its effects on transmission in the dorsal-root nuclei (Hagbarth and Kerr, 1954), the nuclei gracilis and cuneatus (Scherrer and Hernández-Peón, 1955), and the trigeminal sensory nucleus (Hernández-Peón and Scherrer, 1955). Retinal impulse transmission (Granit, 1955) and cochlear impulse transmission (Brust-Carmona et al., 1960) can also be affected by centrifugal effects emanating from the reticular formation.

The extralemniscal pathways, accordingly, represent an important part of the afferent system of the brain. The possible differential roles of the lemniscal system (which may be likened to major thoroughfares) and of the extralemniscal system (which compares with winding country roads) will be considered later.

**MAIN EFFERENT PATHWAYS** The direct control of muscular
**AND CENTERS** activity is the responsibility of
**Segmental Efferent Pathways** motor neurons located in the ventral horn of the spinal gray matter and in the motor nuclei of several cranial nerves. The axons of these motoneurons, which leave by way of the spinal and cranial nerves, form the *final motor path*, so called because all motor effects in the body are exercised through them. The motoneuron and muscle fibers it innervates form what Sherrington called the *motor unit*, which is the ultimate functional entity of the somatic motor system. Because the motoneurons are

the exclusive exit paths of the efferent system, their destruction leads to paralysis of the skeletal muscles innervated by them.

The motoneurons play, accordingly, the role of executors of central nervous efferent commands, which may come from segmental or suprasegmental sources. We have considered earlier the monosynaptic reflex arc (the mechanism of the stretch reflex), in which the primary afferent neuron synapses directly with the final motor neuron. In these reflex arcs, we may assume, the impulses transmitted by the afferent neurons trigger the discharge of motoneurons. Somewhat more complicated, and more prevalent, is the control of motoneuron activity by multisynaptic reflex arcs, in which internuncial neurons are interposed between the primary afferent neurons and final motoneurons. In this arrangement impulses transmitted by the afferents are relayed to the internuncials, which in turn play on the motoneurons. The internuncial system permits the convergence of facilitatory and inhibitory effects from a variety of sources. As a rule, not only segmental but suprasegmental influences are transmitted to the motoneurons by way of internuncials rather than by direct synaptic contact with the motoneurons.

**Suprasegmental Efferent Pathways**     Usually two major suprasegmental efferent pathway are distinguished, the pyramidal and the extrapyramidal systems. The fibers of the *pyramidal system* originate in the cortex, pass through the internal capsule, decussate in the medulla, and terminate on internuncial cells in the medulla and spinal cord. It may be considered a direct-descending throughway system, the efferent analog of the direct-ascending lemniscal pathways. The *extrapyramidal efferents* originate in the cortex and various subcortical structures, such as the basal ganglia, the subthalamus, and the hypothalamus. They form a diffuse chain of efferents that converge on the substantia nigra and motor cells of tegmental nuclei and the reticular formation. On this basis the extrapyramidal system may be considered the descending or efferent analog of the ascending, diffuse extralemniscal afferent pathway.

THE PYRAMIDAL EFFERENT PATHWAY. The pyramidal efferents come to a large extent from the *precentral motor cortex* (area 4), and to a lesser extent from various other regions of the cortex. Although the large pyramidal or Betz cells found in the fifth layer of the motor area contribute their large axons to the pyramidal system, the greater proportion of pyramidal fibers appears to originate in the smaller pyramidal cells found in all agranular areas, in the anterior (for example, premotor) as well as posterior (for example, postcentral) cortex (Lassek, 1954). As is well known, a topographical or *myotopic* representation of the body surface exists in the motor cortex, with different points controlling the motor activities of different body parts. This topographical arrangement (which was first demonstrated by means of electric stimulation in 1870 by Fritsch

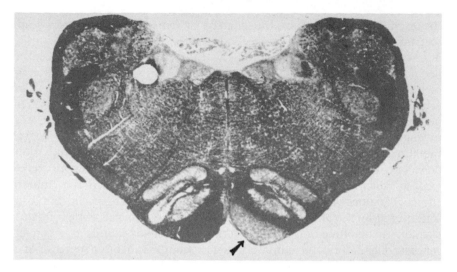

The right pyramid in the medulla (arrow) is degenerated as a consequence of removal of the right cortex of cat, Weil stain. (From Patton and Amassian. The pyramidal tract; its excitation and function. *Handb. Physiol.*, 1960, Sec. 1, **2**, 838)

and Hitzig) does not accurately reproduce the image of the body; some parts of the body are represented in much wider cortical areas than are others. In lower mammals, cortical motor representation is largely restricted to the face and forelimb regions, but, in primates, considerable representation is extended to the digits of the hind and forelimbs (in man there is a shift to increased representation of the fingers and also the mouth regions involved in speech functions). These observations (Woolsey, 1958; Penfield, 1958), as well as evidence obtained from ablation studies (Tower, 1940), indicate that the major function of the corticospinal pyramidal tract is the control of *skilled movements* (oral "manipulation" in lower mammals; digital manipulation in primates and a few other mammals; see Chapter 12).

THE EXTRAPYRAMIDAL EFFERENT PATHWAY. Unlike the corticospinal pyramidal tract, which is a phylogenetically recent acquisition of mammals, the extrapyramidal system is an ancient suprasegmental pathway present in all vertebrates. The extrapyramidal efferents originate in the cortex, the caudate nucleus, and the putamen. The two latter structures (forming the striatum) send efferent fibers to the external pallidum and substantia nigra; the external pallidum, in turn, projects to the hypothalamus, the subthalamic nucleus, the region of the red nucleus, and the tegmental reticular formation in general (Jung and Hassler, 1960). Because the caudate nucleus, the putamen, and pallidum also receive a large afferent projection from the intralaminar nuclei and the reticular nuclear complex (the centromedian nucleus, for instance, degenerates

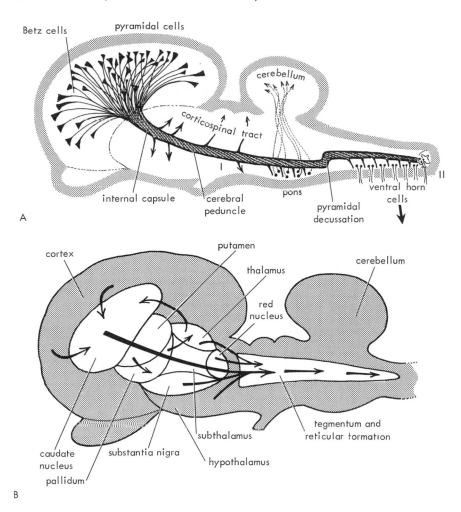

Schematic diagrams of the pyramidal (A) and extrapyramidal (B) motor pathways. The interconnections of the subcortical extrapyramidal system are not well established.

after destruction of the caudate nucleus and putamen), the extrapyramidal system is primarily a part of a subcortical circuit intimately associated with the reticular formation. Though essentially a subcortical mechanism, the extrapyramidal system also receives efferents from the cortex. This interaction presumably permits the cortical regulation of extrapyramidal activities and the elicitation of motor activity from the cortex after severance of the pyramidal tract.

Ablation and stimulation studies carried out on animals do not as yet make possible a clear conceptualization of the functions of the extrapyramidal system. Bilateral destruction of large parts of the caudate nucleus in cats and monkeys (Mettler and Mettler, 1942) produces *hyperactivity* (the animals walk incessantly), whereas bilateral destruction of the pallidum produces *hypoactivity* (the animals become inactive and can maintain for a long time any posture imposed on them). The exact nature of these striatal functions is not understood; nevertheless, experiments and more extensive evidence from clinical studies of human beings suggest that the extrapyramidal system is intimately involved in the control of posture and rhythmic motor activities, particularly locomotion. All the striatal syndromes in man are characterized by *dyskinesias*, such as parkinsonism, athetosis, tics, and so forth.

**SELECTED READINGS**

Cajal, S. Ramón y. *Histologie du système nerveux.* 2 vols. 1909–1911. Reprinted: Instituto Ramón y Cajal, 1952–1955.
Crosby, E. C., T. Humphrey, and E. W. Lauer. *Correlative anatomy of the nervous system.* New York: Macmillan, 1962.
Gardner, E. *Fundamentals of neurology.* (4th ed.) Philadelphia: Saunders, 1963.
Herrick, C. J. *Introduction to neurology.* (5th ed.) Philadelphia: Saunders, 1931.
————. *Neurological foundations of animal behavior.* New York: Holt, Rinehart and Winston, 1924.
Ranson, S. W., and S. L. Clark. *The anatomy of the nervous system.* (10th ed.) Philadelphia: Saunders, 1959.
Rasmussen, A. T. *The principal nervous pathways.* (4th ed.) New York: Macmillan, 1958.

# 9

# Techniques of Studying
# Brain Structure and Function

**NEUROANATOMICAL TECHNIQUES** A simple but rewarding approach
**Gross Neuroanatomy** to the study of the nervous system
is gross anatomy. The brains of
larger species, such as sheep, dog, or man, can be dissected to visualize
the various morphological subdivisions of the brain and to isolate the
bulkier pathways that connect these structures. Until the introduction, in
the last century, of microscopy and staining techniques into the field of
neuroanatomy, information regarding the morphology of the nervous
system was gained exclusively from gross dissection studies. Such studies
permitted the identification of the major structural units of the brain
(which to this day serve as landmarks in brain parcellation), the comparison of the brains of various phyla, and the tracing of the evolution of
the brain through phyla and species. The structural similarities of some
components of the brain, such as the spinal cord, medulla, and brain
stem, in such diverging phyla as fish, amphibians, and mammals, were
recognized early. So was also the phenomenon of progressive encephalization: the absence of a cerebral cortex in the lowest vertebrates and its
progressive enlargement in various mammalian phyla and species.

The comparative, gross-anatomical investigation of the nervous systems
of various animal species is still a fruitful approach, particularly the
comparison of brains of related species with divergent ways of life. An
example of such an investigation is the recent study of Evans (1952),
which indicates gross differences in the brain stems of fish, depending on
whether they are surface feeders (and rely largely on vision) or bottom
feeders (and utilize mainly tactile and olfactory information). On the
other hand, the gross anatomical approach has not only its limitations but
its pitfalls. For instance, the assumption that the morphological units of
the brain are also functional entities has long hampered neurological
investigation. More refined investigations suggest that there may be a more
intimate connection between various morphologically distinct structures
(for example, the relay nuclei of the thalamus and cortex) than between

subcomponents of a single morphological structure (such as the relay and midline nuclei of the thalamus). Also, preoccupation with certain obvious morphological features, such as the fissurization of the cortex, has proved to be fruitless.

**Microscopic Neuroanatomy** The microscopic study of the nervous system began in the last century. For two hundred years after the discovery of the compound microscope virtually no use was made of it in the study of the fine structure of the nervous system. However, after the introduction of adequate fixatives and particularly of various stains (aniline dyes, metallic salts), the microscopic study of the nervous system became a widely and energetically pursued line of investigation. (It deserves to be pointed out that the introduction of fixatives and dyes originated in unrelated industrial fields. Good fixatives were prepared for use in the tanning industry; the synthetic aniline dyes were invented for use in the textile industry. This dependence on technological advancement characterizes the entire history of neurological research. For instance, modern neurophysiological advances have been intimately connected with such discoveries as the string galvanometer, the cathode-ray oscilloscope, modern electronic amplifiers, computers, and so on.)

*Fixatives* are substances that prevent decay in organic tissue after the death of the organism. They are chemical solutions that precipitate, sublimate, denature, or otherwise preserve some of the major molecular constituents (proteins, nucleic acids) of the tissue. Fixatives used in neurological investigations are acids (such as acetic acid), alcohols, formalin (a hydrous solution of formaldehyde), certain metallic salts, and various combinations of these substances. To fix adequately the cellular and subcellular components of nervous tissue, it is essential that the fixative employed penetrate quickly to all parts of the brain after the death of the animal. Ideally this purpose is achieved by *perfusing* the body (through the heart) or brain (through the carotid artery) with the fixative immediately after death, or by actually killing the animal by such perfusion. Submerging the brain in a fixative, without perfusion, is less satisfactory because of the slow penetration of fixatives. Another method of preserving tissue is *freezing*. More recently the *freeze-drying* technique has also been widely used. The latter technique permits preservation of water-soluble cellular constituents, interferes less with the natural state of other substances, and eliminates some of the artifacts produced by fixatives.

The next step in the preparation of brain tissue for staining is the cutting of sections. Cutting requires that the brain be sufficiently hardened. This state is achieved by *embedding* the brain (or blocks cut from it) in paraffin, nitrocellulose (celloidin), carbowax, or some other hard substance; or by using frozen blocks. Cutting is then done on a *microtome*. There are several types of microtomes; all have vises to hold the tissue block, a well-sharpened blade to do the cutting, and a feed mechanism, which advances either the block or the knife in regulated, equal steps to permit cutting of uniformly thin sections. The cut section is usually attached to a glass plate, the embedding material is removed (dissolved chemically), and the section is then ready to be stained.

A great variety of tissue *stains* is being used in neurological research. For our purpose we may group these stains into three classes: entire-neuron stains, cell-body stains, and nerve-fiber stains. An example of the first type of relatively nondifferential stain is the *Golgi stain*, introduced by Golgi in 1873, which employs metallic salts. This method of metallic impregnation permits identification of the cell body, together with its axonal and dendritic processes, in a single preparation. To this day there is no better method to produce a comprehensive picture of neurons. Unfortunately, the Golgi stain is nonspecific (it reacts with glia cells as well as with blood vessels), and it is capricious: it stains an occasional neuron rather than all neurons.

Examples of *cell-body stains* are the various *Nissl stains*, which employ basic dyes that have a specific affinity for the "chromatin" substances of the cell body, particularly the DNA nucleoproteins of the nucleus and the RNA nucleoproteins of the nucleolus and cytoplasm. The first Nissl stain, methylene blue, was introduced by Nissl in 1894; since then the technique has been used widely with a variety of basic dyes. Nissl stains are useful not only in the investigation of the cell composition of normal brain tissue but for the tracing of neural connections. When the axon of a cell is cut, a change occurs in the distribution of the chromatin material. This phenomenon is referred to as *retrograde degeneration* or *chromatolysis*; this permits the tracing of the cellular origins of fibrous tracts. In some pathways, related chromatolytic changes have been observed in neurons deprived of their major afferent connections. This change is referred to as *transneuronal degeneration*. The cells presumably degenerate as a consequence of reduced stimulation. Transneuronal changes may be observed in the lateral geniculate body some time after the cutting of the optic nerve. In structures that have multiple input, transneuronal degeneration is not likely to occur.

There are several types of *fiber stains*. Some of them react with components of the axon, others with the myelin sheath covering the axon. Axon and collateral staining is done most satisfactorily with silver. The *silver-impregnation* method was introduced by Ramón y Cajal, who contributed more than any other person to the microscopic study of the nervous system. The original silver stains were designed for the visualization of normal fibers, but techniques are also available for differentiating degenerated from normal fibers. Such a technique is the one recently introduced

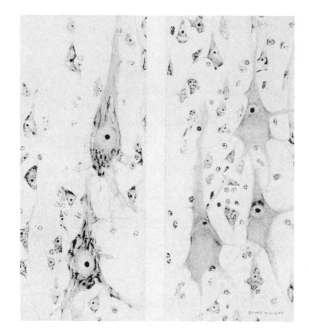

Neurons in the motor cortex of monkey. *Left,* normal cells; *right,* cells undergoing chromatolysis as a consequence of transection of the spinal cord (retrograde degeneration). (From Polyak. *The vertebrate visual system.* The University of Chicago Press, 1957)

by Nauta and Gygax (1954). With it the fiber projection of a brain area can be determined by tracing the degenerated fibers issuing from it after the area has been removed or coagulated. This and other related approaches depend on the phenomenon of *anterograde* or *Wallerian degeneration,* which designates the degeneration of fibers issuing from a cell body after the cell body is damaged or destroyed. Other fiber stains interact with the lipid of the myelin sheath and so stain the nerve fiber. The best known of these is *Weigert's technique,* which is useful particularly for normal brain material. *Marchi's method,* which uses osmium, is employed for demonstrating the fragments of degenerated fibers; this method is less reliable than a technique such as Nauta's. Myelin stains in general have the disadvantage of not staining nonmyelinated fibers or the collaterals and terminal branches of myelinated fibers (which lose their myelin sheath).

Attempts have also been made to stain the synaptic processes of nerve fibers, and to differentiate normal from abnormal synaptic endings in order to determine the exact point of termination of fiber tracts (Glees, 1946). The techniques employed have not been, so far, very satisfactory.

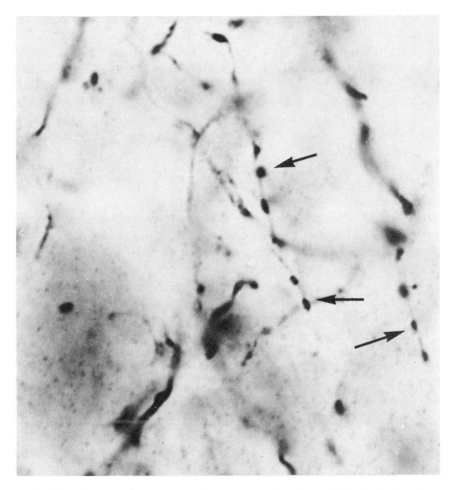

Droplike disintegration shown by degenerating axons (arrows) in the brain of a monkey stained with the Nauta technique. (Photo supplied by Dr. Walle Nauta) [unpublished]

Electron microscopy is becoming more and more useful for the study of the structural properties of such subcellular components as synaptic vesicles and nerve membranes (Palay and Palade, 1955; De Robertis, 1964).

**Production of Brain Lesions**   Staining and microscopic examination make possible the study of the fine structure of the brain under normal and pathological conditions. The study of the normal brain provides information about such regional characteristics as the distribution of different cell types in a given area and the course of major fiber tracts. More useful information is provided, however, by brains that had been experimentally manipulated before the death of the animal. With the multitude of fibers coursing in any region of the brain, it is difficult if not impossible to determine in normal material what specific fiber tracts connect with what specific structures. By cutting a fiber tract, however, one can investigate cell changes in the nuclei of their origin (retrograde degeneration); or by destroying selected nuclei one can trace the course of the degenerated fibers issuing from them (anterograde degeneration).

The production of *brain lesions* for this purpose is relatively easy in exposed brain areas, such as the surface of the cerebral cortex. After the skull is opened over the desired brain area, the brain may be removed, coagulated, or otherwise destroyed. The operation is performed under anesthesia, aseptic conditions are employed, and the animal is then permitted to live for a certain period, during which the degenerative process may take place. In the histological processing of the brain the location and extent of the damage are determined, and the degeneration produced by the lesion is evaluated.

Somewhat more difficult is the production of accurately placed lesions in unexposed, subcortical areas of the brain. For this purpose *stereotaxic instruments* are employed. The first stereotaxic instrument was designed by Horsley and Clarke (1908); improved instruments are now available, designed for use with small animals (rats, guinea pigs) or larger ones (cats, dogs, monkeys). All stereotaxic instruments consist of a head holder, which stabilizes the skull of the animal in a standard position, and a graduated frame to which all parts of the instrument are attached. Positioning of the skull vertically and laterally is carried out with two ear bars, which are placed inside the auditory meatus of the animal and then clamped to the frame of the apparatus. The horizontal positioning the head is achieved with bars that fit into the orbit of the eye or the upper teeth of the jaw. The frame of the instrument can accept graduated carriers into which are inserted electrodes that, connected with stimulators, pass electric current; or it can accept hypodermic needles for the injection of chemicals, and so on. With the use of the three-dimensional coordinate system provided by the stereotaxic instrument, into which the skull of the animal is placed in an arbitrary but standard position, the electrodes or probes can be inserted into any point of the brain with the help of an atlas.

*Stereotaxic atlases* are available for the brains of the rat (Krieg, 1946; De Groot, 1959; Massopust, 1961), the cat (Jasper and Ajmone-Marsan, 1954; Snider and Niemer, 1961), the dog (Lim et al., 1960), the macaque monkey (Snider and Lee, 1961), and the squirrel monkey (Emmers and Akert, 1963). Because there are variations in the size and shape of individual animals and because the placement of probes and the extent

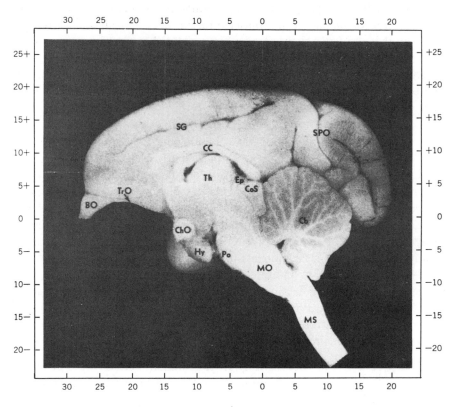

Projected position of the brain of squirrel monkey in the coordinates of a stereo-taxic instrument. Numbers on abcissa and ordinate in millimeters; O position corresponds to the ear bar placed into the auditory meatus. (From Emmers and Akert. *A stereotaxic atlas of the brain of the squirrel monkey,* The University of Wisconsin Press, 1963. Reprinted with the permission of the copyright owners, the Regents of The University of Wisconsin)

of destruction produced are subject to experimental error, stereotaxic placements have to be verified histologically.

In this context we may refer to recent attempts to produce reversible rather than permanent brain lesions. The definition of a *reversible lesion* is the temporary inactivation of, or interference with, the functioning of a selected brain region that, after a specifiable period, can return to its normal mode and level of functioning. The advantages of such a procedure over permanent surgical lesions are obvious; for instance, animals can serve as their own controls, or different sites can be inactivated successively. Among the many attempts, we may mention the *irritative electrical stimulation* of selected brain structures during testing procedures (Delgado and Rosvold, 1953); the production of *spreading depression* in the cortex (Bureš and Burešova, 1959); and such techniques as the insertion of *cold probes* into brain regions, *ultrasonic stimulation* of brain structures, and the *injection of metabolic inhibitors* into the brain. In all such attempts there must be evidence that indeed a "lesion" had been produced for a temporary interval and also that the effect was reversible—a task that requires careful control of stimulus parameters, reliable independent indices of the presence of a "lesion," and adequate means of determining the presence or absence of permanent damage.

**Behavioral Applications**    Lesion and ablation procedures are particularly well suited for the investigation of the problem of *localization of functions* in the central nervous system. The gross behavioral effects of ablation of such structures as the cerebellum or cerebral cortex have been studied by anatomists for some time. Systematic investigation of changes in specific aspects of behavior as a consequence of removal of circumscribed regions of the brain is of relatively recent origin. As pioneers in this field we may mention Fluorens (1824), Munk (1890), Goltz (1892), and Sherrington (1906). The modern era in this field began with the extensive investigations of Lashley (1929; see Beach et al., 1960).

Appropriately controlled modern ablation studies usually meet all or most of the following requirements:

1. *Adequate testing* or training of the animal before the operation. Alternatively, the testing or training is performed on a matched group of control animals.
2. The surgical procedure is performed under *aseptic conditions*, and care is taken to produce damage only to the brain structure selected. The animal must remain in good health and free of infection.
3. If feasible, *control operations* should be performed in other brain areas to determine the degree of specificity of the deficit produced.
4. The *retesting* has to be performed under conditions as nearly similar to the original testing conditions as possible.
5. The location and extent of the brain lesion produced must be *verified* histologically.

The problems that can be investigated with these techniques are practically unlimited. Examples are the following:

1. Effects of brain lesions on the gratification of basic needs, such as feeding, drinking, and sexual and reproductive processes;
2. Investigation of sensory losses produced by the removal of selected brain structures, including "sensory" and nonsensory regions;
3. Motor deficits produced by lesions in various "motor" and unspecific regions;

4. Changes in the animal's ability to solve new problems in an adaptive manner;

5. Deficits produced by different brain lesions on standard tests, such as maze running, alimentary and aversive conditioning, object discrimination, lever pressing, delayed response, and so forth.

Interpretation of behavioral alterations produced by brain lesions faces all the difficulties that characterize reliable analyses of behavior. For instance, failure of performance on a "sensory" task need not be caused by a specific sensory deficit produced by the brain lesion but may be the consequence, instead, of motivational change (the animal may no longer work for the original reward), of motor disability (the animal may be reluctant or no longer able to perform the "response"), and of several other specific or nonspecific factors. Evidently, good experiments in this area require sophistication in the production of brain lesions, in determining the behavioral alterations produced, and in the interpretation of the results.

**NEUROPHYSIOLOGICAL** The electrical activity of the brain
**TECHNIQUES** is an important source of informa-
**Gross Electrode Recording** tion regarding the nature of brain
functioning. The earliest attempts
in this field, employing string galvanometers, were restricted to recording brain potentials from the skull of animals (Caton, 1875).

EEG ACTIVITY. The first successful recording of "brain waves" from the skull of man was accomplished by Berger (1929), who named the technique *electroencephalography* (*EEG*). (If the recording of brain waves is made directly on the exposed surface of the cortex, it is sometimes referred to as electrocorticography, or *ECG*; no specific name has been given to recording EEG from subcortical structures.) In modern investigations of EEG activity specially designed *EEG machines* are used. The brain potentials are registered with needle *electrodes* thrust into the skin overlying the skull, with disk electrodes pasted to the skin, or with probe electrodes touching the surface of, or penetrating into, the brain. The electrodes are made of various metals (silver, stainless steel) or cotton soaked in saline. The electrodes are connected with the EEG apparatus, which consists of electronic differential amplifiers, and with ink-writing galvanometers. The latter leave a permanent record of the brain potentials on a paper chart that is moved past the ink writers at a constant speed. The electrical *potential differences* are usually recorded with two electrodes between two points, either between the ear, neck, or other "indifferent" source and a selected brain region, or between two brain regions. Modern EEG machines may have more than a dozen channels, which permit simultaneous recording of brain potentials from as many different areas

GUINEA PIG

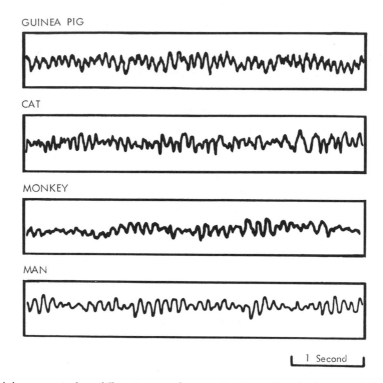

CAT

MONKEY

MAN

|___ 1 Second ___|

Alpha waves in four different mammalian species. Recordings in the animals from the cortex (ECG); in man, from the scalp (EEG). (Reprinted with the permission of The Macmillan Company from Brazier, *The electrical activity of the nervous system.* 2d ed., 1960. Published in North America by The Macmillan Company, New York)

of the brain. The apparatus may also be equipped with automatic wave analyzers and/or coupled with computers to provide information of the summated and *averaged* characteristics of waves over selected periods (Brazier, 1961).

The description and analysis of brain waves are usually made in terms of amplitude, frequency, and synchrony or asynchrony. The typical low-frequency (10–12 cycles per second), high-amplitude, and well-synchronized waves recorded from the occipital cortex in the resting individual with eyes closed is called the *alpha* wave. Opening of the eye or any sudden stimulation ("arousal") changes this synchronized pattern into a desynchronized, lower-amplitude and higher-frequency pattern, which is called the *beta* wave. During sleep the frequency and amplitude of the brain waves decrease, with occasional spindle bursts. Under abnormal conditions, as in epilepsy, high-amplitude spike bursts may predominate.

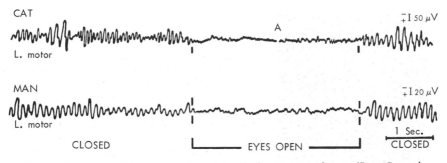

CAT
$\bar{+}$I 50 μV

L. motor

A

MAN
$\bar{+}$I 20 μV

L. motor

1 Sec.

CLOSED      EYES OPEN      CLOSED

Effects of opening of the eyes on the alpha rhythm in cat and man. (From Rempel and Gibbs. The Berger rhythm in cats. *Science*, October 9, 1936, **84**, 334–335.

Ink-writing EEG machines can record only low-frequency brain activity (up to 100 cycles per second). Recording of high-frequency activity requires the use of a cathode-ray oscilloscope, which is used almost exclusively when evoked potentials are recorded.

EVOKED POTENTIALS. When peripheral receptors are stimulated by their adequate stimuli, or when their afferents are stimulated electrically, the transmission of the afferent signals may be recorded from the appropriate subcortical relay nuclei and from the projection areas of the cortex in the form of *evoked potentials*. Similarly, when a brain structure is stimulated electrically or chemically (for example, by strychnine), evoked potentials may be recorded from all other brain structures with which it is directly or indirectly connected. For instance, photic stimulation of the eye, or electric stimulation of the optic nerve or optic tract, produces evoked potentials in the superior colliculus, the lateral geniculate body, the striate cortex, and other brain structures associated with vision. Evoked potentials may also be recorded from the striate cortex when the lateral geniculate body is stimulated.

Cathode-ray oscilloscopes are used most commonly for recording of evoked potentials. *Oscilloscopes* consist of a cathode-ray tube and of electronic amplifying and control circuits. The cathode-ray tube houses a cathode that emits an electron beam, accelerating and focusing anodes, a pair of horizontal and vertical deflection plates, and a fluorescing face at the end of the tube, which lights up wherever the electron beam strikes it. As a rule, the horizontal deflection plates are used, in conjunction with an oscillator, to sweep the electron beam from left to right with a predetermined speed—in bioelectric work with a range of a few milliseconds to several seconds; this gives the time base of the response. The potentials recorded by the brain electrodes are fed, after amplification by separate differential preamplifiers, to the vertical deflection plates, which then display the shape, amplitude, latency, and duration of the evoked poten-

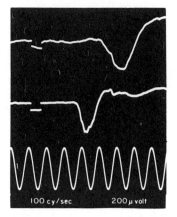

Simultaneous recordings with a dual-beam oscilloscope of evoked potentials to a light flash from the superior colliculus (upper trace) and visual cortex (middle trace). Application and duration of light flash are indicated by the break in traces on the left side. Lower trace gives the time base (in frequency) and voltage (amplitude) of the responses. The cortical evoked potential shows a shorter latency than does the collicular potential. (From Altman and Malis. An electrophysiological study of the superior colliculus and visual cortex. *Exp. Neurol.*, 1962, **5**, 236)

tials. For permanent records, photographs are taken of the events displayed on the oscilloscope face.

The pioneering work of applying modern amplifying and recording techniques to the study of evoked potentials is associated with the names of Adrian (1928), Erlanger and Gasser (1937), and their associates. Credit is due, particularly, for utilizing the evoked potential technique for tracing afferent pathways and intracerebral connections (*mapping* the brain) to Bremer (1953), Marshall (Marshall et al., 1937), and Woolsey (1947). In classical evoked potential studies, *deeply anesthetized* animals (rabbits, cats, monkeys) are used. In such preparations the "noise" caused by the ongoing EEG activity is greatly reduced or eliminated, and the latency, amplitude, duration, and shape of the "signal" (evoked potential) are easily determined. The *latency* of the evoked potential reveals the conduction velocity and, if there is any, the synaptic delay in the afferent pathway tested, whereas the *amplitude* of the response is presumed to reflect summatively the number of fibers activated. As a rule, evoked potentials consist of positive and negative components; they may persist for several milliseconds. Evoked potentials may be recorded at the onset of the stimulus (for example, when a light source is turned on), which is called the *on-response*. Termination of the stimulus may produce a similar potential, called the *off-response*.

On-response and off-response recorded in the superior colliculus to a light flash. The first break in the trace indicates when the light was turned on; the second break, when the light was turned off. (From Altman, unpublished record)

**Microelectrode Recording** Gross electrodes, the tip of which may range from about 0.1 millimeters to several millimeters in diameter, record responses from areas of comparable size. That is, they "average" the responses of a large population of neurons and fibers. To record events taking place in a single nerve cell or fiber, microelectrodes are required. Microelectrodes are made either of micropipettes or metal wire. The tips of micropipettes are drawn (by hand or with an instrument) to a diameter of about 0.1–1 micron; the pipettes are then filled with a conducting saline solution. Such microelectrodes are suitable for use near the surface of the brain or spinal cord. An alternative solution is to insert a fine metal wire through the bore of the pipette, or fill it with a metal, like indium, that has a low melting point (Dowben and Rose, 1953). The sturdiest microelectrodes with which the brain can easily be penetrated are made of rigid metal wires, such as tungsten (Hubel, 1957) or stainless steel (Grundfest et al., 1950). The tips of these are polished electrolytically to a diameter in the range of about 1 micron. The entire wire, the tip excepted, is then coated with an insulating cement. Owing to the small size of the tip, microelectrodes have a very high electric resistance. For this reason, microelectrodes are usually first connected with cathode followers (which are essentially current amplifiers) and then fed to conventional amplifiers (which amplify the voltage of the signal).

With microelectrodes, discharges from single nerve cells or fibers may be recorded either *extracellularly* or *intracellularly*. (For intracellular re-

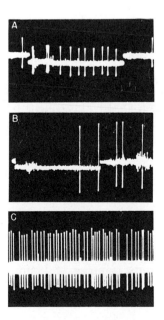

A few types of units isolated in the superior colliculus. A, the frequency of discharge of this unit is increased during illumination of the eye (indicated by downward drop of the trace). B, an off-unit, discharge inhibited at the onset of illumination. C, a rhythmically discharging "spontaneous" unit which could not be affected by light or other types of peripheral stimuli. (From Altman and Malis. An electrophysiological study of the superior colliculus and visual cortex. *Exp. Neurol.*, 1962, **5**, 246)

cording the tip has to be very small to prevent serious injury to the pierced cell.) Microelectrode recordings have been carried out in the spinal cord and in virtually all major subdivisions of the brain, and these studies have made considerable contribution to the effort of understanding of the functioning of isolated fibers or cells, called *units*, in the nervous system. In general, unit discharge has been found to be less predictable and more variable than evoked responses. Recently, computer techniques have been introduced to evaluate the results of single unit studies.

**Stimulation Techniques**    Electrical stimulation of nerve and brain antedates historically the introduction of electrical recording. The systematic work of Du Bois-Reymond and Helmholtz with induction coils in the first part of the last century was designed to deal with the problems of nerve conduction in *nerve-muscle preparations*. Electrical stimulation of the brain was first successfully carried out by Fritsch and Hitzig (1870), who produced body movements upon stimulation of the motor area of the cortex. Considerable use was made subsequently of electrical stimulation by Sherrington (1906), who used spinal animals extensively in his studies of reflex action.

In modern *brain-stimulation* studies, investigators use electronic stimulators that permit control of the shape (such as square, sinusoidal, sawtooth), frequency, polarity, duration, and intensity of the stimulating pulses, and also the monitoring of the stimulator output. Electrical-stimulation studies are in many respects complementary to electrical recording. Whereas electrical recording (in conjunction with physiological or electric stimulation of peripheral receptors) provides information about afferent conduction and transmission in the central nervous system, electrical stimulation of the brain is a source of information of efferent transmission, as evidenced by induced motor manifestations. Among the many accomplishments made with this technique are the mapping of the motor regions of the brain in general, and the mapping of the topographic representation of the body in the motor cortex, cerebellum, and several other structures in particular. Electrical stimulation of the brain in conjunction with electrical recording (as in evoked-potential studies designed to test brain connections) was considered earlier.

In addition to electrical stimulation, various chemical stimulants have been used by some investigators to induce motor responses or recordable electrical discharges. The best-known of these attempts is the use of strychnine by Dusser de Barenne and McCulloch (1939). If small strips of filter paper soaked in strychnine solution are placed on localized parts of the brain, EEG discharges (strychnine spikes) can be recorded in areas connected with the stimulated brain regions. This technique, which permits mapping of brain connections, is called *strychnine neuronography*. However, severe shortcomings of the technique, caused by the spreading of the chemical from the site of application, were reported by several investigators.

**Behavioral Applications**     Electrical brain stimulation and recording are most easily carried out in anesthetized animals. Such preparations are useful for the tracing of afferent and efferent pathways, and for mapping of intracerebral connections. But anesthetized animals cannot be utilized in behavioral investigations. To study the brain activity of normal animals and, particularly, the behavioral effects of electrical stimulation and the electrical concomitants of behavioral manipulations, unanesthetized or *awake animals* are required. Electrical stimulation of, and recording from, the brain of awake animals is made possible by implanting electrodes permanently into the brain. The *implanted electrode technique* was introduced by Baer (1905)

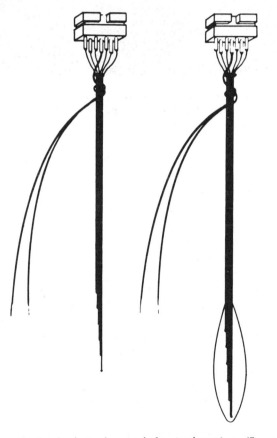

Diagram of multiple lead electrodes used for implantation. (From Delgado. Evaluation of permanent implantation of electrodes within the brain. *EEG clin. Neurophysiol.,* 1955, **7,** 638)

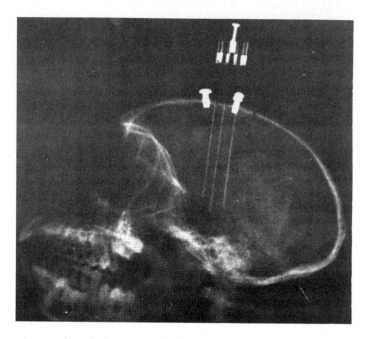

X-ray of an implanted electrode in the brain of a monkey. (From Sheer. *Electrical stimulation of the brain.* University of Texas Press, 1961. Reprinted with the permission of The Hogg Foundation)

and subsequently used systematically by Hess (1932, 1954). Recently, several modifications of the technique have been employed, including *multiple electrodes* that reach different depths of the brain (Delgado, 1952), the *implantation of microelectrodes* (Hubel, 1959), *telemetering devices* to transmit brain potentials to the recording instrument without the use of connecting wires (Hambrecht et al., 1963), and *miniaturized stimulating devices* that are attached to the body of the freely moving animal (Delgado, 1959).

There are many basic implantation techniques. The animal is first anesthetized; then the electrodes, attached to a plastic pedestal or nylon screws, are inserted into the brain. The device is cemented to the skull, and the electrode wires are collected together and attached to a plug. After the animal's recovery both stimulation and recording can be carried out in the freely moving animal.

The implanted electrode technique has provided a wealth of information on the relation of brain function and behavior. Hess's monumental studies revealed the essential role of the hypothalamus and adjacent diencephalic and rhinencephalic structures in feeding, and in aggressive, defensive, and sexual behavior—results that have been duly confirmed and extended by others. Most striking results were obtained recently with a modified technique by Olds (Olds and Milner, 1954; Olds, 1956, 1961). Olds found, with the use of a Skinner box and a lever connecting a microswitch to a stimulator, that an animal with implanted electrodes may stimulate its own brain by pressing on the lever. With this *self-stimulation technique*, Olds and others (Brady, 1958; Miller, 1957) identified brain regions in which electric stimulation apparently has a rewarding effect (shown by continuous high-rate of self-stimulation); they found other regions in which stimulation has no effects; and still other regions in which stimulation produces an aversive effect (shown by absence of self-stimulation after initial trials, or work performed by the animal to turn off the stimulating current, if such a setup is provided). In addition to these varied types of stimulation studies, the implanted-electrode technique has also been used for recording electrical activity in different brain regions during different types of induced behavior. An example of such an application is the study of EEG changes during habituation and learning (Chapter 13).

**NEUROCHEMICAL TECHNIQUES**   It is reasonable to assume that the structural properties of the nervous system are products of its specific molecular composition, and that neural functioning is dependent on underlying chemical processes. Nevertheless, the chemical analysis of nervous structure and function has lagged considerably behind anatomical and physiological investigations. Apart from sporadic attempts at the turn of the century (Thudichum, 1884), neurochemistry as a separate discipline did not emerge until late in the second quarter of this century, and its great achievements are of quite recent origin. The earliest biochemical studies dealt with analyses of the composition of the brain as a whole. Subsequently, investigations were made of the composition of different regions under both normal and pathological conditions (Elliott et al., 1962). Of quite recent origin is the attempt to study, with microchemical, histochemical, and radiochemical techniques, the composition of single nerve and glia cells both at "rest" and following their physiological "activation."

**Gross Neurochemical Techniques**   The composition of brain matter as a whole is studied with conventional biochemical techniques. The brain is removed rapidly after the animal's death, drained of blood, and quickly frozen to prevent autolytic changes. The desired parts of the brain are then homogenized; the soluble, particulate, and nuclear fractions are separated by differential centrifugation; and the composition is analyzed with standard techniques. Such studies have shown that the major biochemical constituents of brain matter are lipids, nucleic acids, and proteins. Because the brain has only a minimal amount of glycogen storage, it is entirely dependent on the liver and blood supply for its glucose needs. (A possible noncarbohydrate energy source of the brain is glutamic acid—an amino acid present in the brain in larger concentration than in any other tissue.)

Lipids are found in highest concentration in fibrous areas, because nerve membrane and particularly myelin are very rich in fatty substances. The lipid turnover is relatively low. Nucleic acids are concentrated in cellular areas. The protein content of brain matter is unusually high: more than 50 percent of the dry weight of nerve cells may be made up of proteins. Also, the protein turnover is very high, as high as that of some glands engaged in enzyme secretion. The significance of the great protein turnover in brain tissue is not well understood, but we may justifiably assume that it is intimately associated with nervous functioning. Apart from fibrous proteins (which are localized mostly in nerve fibers), various enzymes are present in neural tissue. The latter include oxidative enzymes, which are concerned with energy metabolism; proteolytic enzymes, which regulate the utilization of amino acid; and some specific enzymes associated with such neural processes as impulse conduction and synaptic transmission (such as cholinesterase). One of the major biochemical problems that remain to be determined is the process (or processes) underlying the transmission and channeling of nervous signals and the storing of information.

**Histochemical and**
**Microchemical Techniques**

In such heterogenous tissue as the brain it is of great importance to analyze the differential biochemical composition of diverse brain regions and the single cells contained in them. For this purpose histochemical and cytochemical (including microchemical) techniques have been developed. In general, *histochemical* techniques are derived from conventional histological procedures in which the chemicals used interact in a nonspecific manner with such classes of substances as lipids (myelin stains) or nucleic acids (cell stains). Histochemical techniques are designed to visualize specific components, for example, enzymes like cholinesterases, ATPase, oxidases, phosphatases, and so on. Most histochemical procedures are qualitative. The only basis for gauging the amount of the demonstrated substance present is by the concentration of stains (recently photometric procedures have been devised in an attempt to quantify histochemical results). The great advantage of the histochemical technique is that it makes possible *in situ* localization of various chemicals. Microchemical techniques are better suited for quantitative work. With these techniques the concentration of RNA, proteins, and certain other substances may be measured in minute samples or even in dissected single cells. Such a procedure was used recently in studies measuring chemical changes in single cells in "resting" and "activated" brain regions (Hydén and Pigon, 1960; Hydén and Egyházi, 1962). Hydén, who pioneered in investigating protein and RNA changes in nerve cells during functioning has, in addition, employed the techniques of microincineration, and of x-ray and ultraviolet microspectroscopy (Hydén, 1955, 1962).

**Radiochemical and**   A related approach in studying
**Autoradiographic Techniques**   chemical processes in the brain is
the *radioactive tracer technique*. By tagging selected chemicals (amino acids, nucleotides, steroid hormones, and various nutrients) with such radioactive isotopes as carbon–14, sulphur–35, phosphorus–32, or hydrogen–3 (tritium), the fate of the administered chemical, its rate of incorporation, and its differential regional distribution may be determined with the aid of *radiation detection instruments* (Geiger counters, scintillation counters). It was by means of the radioactive tracer technique, for instance, that the high rate of protein turnover in nerve was established

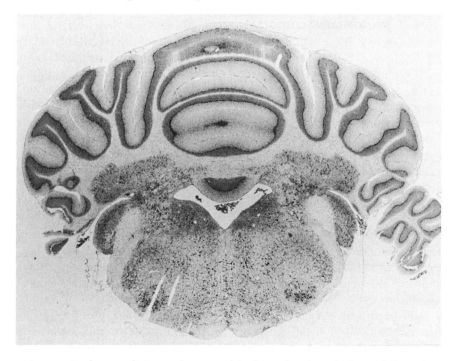

An unstained autoradiogram of a coronal brain section through the medulla and cerebellum of the rat. The animal was injected with a radioactively labeled amino acid and killed 2 hours after the injection. The differential uptake of the tagged amino acid (differing rates of protein metabolism) is indicated by the variable concentration of blackened photographic grain over different brain regions. (Photomicrograph from our laboratory)

(Waelsch, 1962; Richter, 1962). A more recent application of the radioactive tracer technique is *fine-resolution autoradiography*. Instead of extracting various substances from brain homogenates and measuring their radioactivity, the radioactive brain tissue is prepared histologically, coated with a photographic emulsion that is sensitive to radiation, exposed in the dark for a certain period, then developed according to usual photographic procedures. With this method the distribution of the tagged materials, which appear as dark grains overlying the tissue, can be determined *in situ*. Using a very weak beta-emitting isotope, such as tritium, the radioactive substance can be localized within single cells or even portions of the cell, and the rate of uptake or retention of the radiochemical can be determined quantitatively by *microdensitometry* (Altman, 1963 a). The technique permits preparation of regional maps of brain metabolism for such substances as proteins (Oehlert et al., 1958; Altman, 1963 c), and it is also useful for studying regional changes in brain metabolism during normal "activation" processes (Altman, 1963 b).

**NEUROPHARMACOLOGICAL**  Related to the biochemical ap-
**TECHNIQUES**  proach, but of divergent origin, is
the pharmacological study of brain
function and behavior. The use of certain substances (alcohol, opium, hashish, and mescaline) to ameliorate pain, induce euphoria, relaxation, or sleep, has long been a practice of mankind. The effects of some of these substances on perception, motor skill, and judgment have also been recognized. The systematic clinical and experimental use of *psychoactive drugs* (tranquilizers, sedatives, anesthetics, on the one hand, and "energizers" and stimulants, on the other) is of recent origin. In addition to the various "benevolent" drugs, several chemicals have also been identified, such as lysergic acid (LSD), which simulate pathological neural or mental states; these are called *psychotomimetic drugs*.

Though the accomplishments in this field have so far been largely of practical nature (the establishment of levels of dosage for various drugs, and the testing of their effects on various physiological and behavioral variables), neuropharmacology holds promise of contributing to neurological knowledge. Because psychoactive or neuroactive drugs can modify prevailing patterns of nervous activity (for example, produce EEG changes) and alter overt behavior, drug administration can serve as a useful tool in the experimental manipulation of the interrelation between brain and behavior. In fact, the application of such drugs in producing reversible *chemical lesions* offers some advantages over the more drastic surgical procedure, because the experimental subject's behavior can be tested not only before but after the experimental manipulation. Furthermore, the study of the *selective influence* of some drugs on specific brain regions could help to elucidate the differential chemical properties of different brain regions.

In the following pages a few examples of the achievements of neuro-pharmacological research will be mentioned.

**Techniques of Drug Administration**   Drugs can be administered systemically or intracranially. *Systemic routes* of administration are the intraperitoneal, intramuscular, subcutaneous, and oral routes. These routes are characterized by different rates of absorption and variable exposure to enzymatic action; therefore they are important variables in neuropharmacological research. Another method for studying the local action of drugs is the injection of chemicals directly into specified brain sites. As an example we may cite the study of Fisher (1956), who showed that sexual and maternal behavior can be induced by the injection of minute quantities of sex hormone into the region of the hypothalamus. A related method is the injection of chemicals into the ventricles through *implanted cannulae* (Feldberg and Sherwood, 1953). The assumption underlying the latter technique was that intraventricularly injected substances will be exchanged easily between the cerebrospinal fluid and the brain. However, a recent study using the autoradiographic technique revealed that the exchange of certain chemicals (radioactively labeled adenine, uracil, and thymidine) between the cerebrospinal fluid and brain is a very sluggish process; the study also revealed that the technique is not suitable for the uniform distribution of at least these chemicals over the brain (Altman and Chorover, 1963).

In addition to the routes of administration, there are several other important methodological variables in drug research. One of these is the *dose level*. Because different chemicals produce their effects at different concentrations, a common yardstick is required to permit standardization for comparative studies. Different quantities of two drugs that have the same effect on certain physiological and behavioral measures may be considered equivalent in their pharmaceutical potency. The *median lethal dose* (the concentration that produces death in half of the injected animals) has been used as such an index; an alternative measure is the *median effective dose*. The *temporal effectiveness* of a drug is another important factor. Some drugs have short-lasting, others long-lasting, effects; some achieve maximal effectiveness sooner than others. Associated variables are the *speed, frequency,* and *duration* of administration, the use of identical solvents, or *carriers,* and the *interaction* of different drugs. Only a few studies are as yet available in which all these variables are adequately standardized and controlled.

**Classification of Neuroactive Drugs**   One of the efforts of drug research has been the rational classification of the great variety of neuroactive chemicals. Such a classification could be based on anatomical considerations (in terms of specific sites of action), on a functional basis (in terms of specific physiological or behavioral effects), or on a chemical basis (in terms of the chemical composition of drugs). A variety of such classifications has been attempted (Berger, 1960). We lack knowledge of the site and mode of action of most drugs, and their chemistry is ill-understood; such attempts are therefore probably still immature.

As a preliminary classification it is justified to distinguish, first, between physiological and nonphysiological drugs. Adrenaline, histamine, serotonin, glutamic acid, or gamma aminobutyric acid are *physiological agents* that are present as normal humoral constituents or nutrients in the body and brain; they become "drugs" when administered from without and in a concentrated dose. Various other substances, such as reserpine, chlorpromazine, barbiturates, lysergic acid, or mescaline, on the other hand, are *foreign agents* that do not normally occur in the body and brain. The latter may, of course, interact physiologically with endogenous substances, by serving as competing *analogs, precursors,* or *antagonists.* In terms of their organic or cerebral effects, we may distinguish three major classes of neuroactive drugs: tranquilizers, energizers, and hypnotics. *Tranquilizers,* such as the various *Rauwolfia* derivatives (for example, chlorpromazine) decrease agitation, excitement, and emotionality. They do not seriously interfere with cognitive or motor performance, as determined by perceptual and motor tests. Among the *energizers,* or stimulants, are endogenous adrenergic substances, and such exogenous drugs as caffeine, amphetamine, and others. These substances tend to produce hyperexcitability and may facilitate sensory and motor performance. They also act as antidepressants in human application. Finally, *hypnotics,* such as barbiturates, are drugs that produce sensory and motor depression (sleep) and, in larger dose, anesthesia. Unless very large doses are administered, visceral reactions are not seriously impaired. In addition to these substances, there is a variety of drugs that act on selected organs (for example, muscle relaxants) or produce highly specific effects (such as psychomimetic drugs).

**Sites of Drug Action**     One of the most promising lines of investigation in neuropharmacology is the analysis of the site of action of various drugs. Such investigations can be carried out directly by studying the effects of a given drug on the electrical activity of different brain regions, or indirectly by relating physiological or behavioral processes produced by a drug to known brain structures controlling these functions. Thus it was found that administration of reserpine or chlorpromazine (which have a tranquilizing effect) produces seizurelike discharges in the rhinencephalon (amygdala, hippocampus, entorhinal cortex, and septum) without affecting neocortical regions (Killam and Killam, 1957; Preston, 1956; Sigg and Schneider, 1957). These studies suggest that activation of the rhinencephalon may be an important factor in the emotional relaxation produced by these tranquilizing drugs. Indeed, electrically produced hippocampal discharge (Andy and Akert, 1955) or hippocampal seizure produced by local application of carbachol (MacLean et al., 1955) induce behavioral effects analogous to those produced by tranquilizers. In contrast, hypnotics or anesthetics, such as barbiturates, are known to affect first the reticular formation and neocortical structures, producing the characteristic EEG patterns of sleep. They obviously do not seriously affect medullary structures that control breathing, blood circulation, and so on. The search for drugs more specific than these, drugs that can affect circumscribed brain regions, is one of the major tasks of experimental neuropharmacology.

### SELECTED READINGS

Altman, J. The use of fine-resolution autoradiography in neurological and psychobiological research. In T. J. Haley and R. S. Snider (Eds.), *Response of the nervous system to ionizing radiation*. Boston: Little, Brown, 1964.
————. Autoradiographic examination of behaviorally induced changes in the protein and nucleic acid metabolism of the brain. In J. Gaito (Ed.), *Macromolecules and behavior*. New York: Appleton, 1966.
Davenport, H. A. *Histological and histochemical technics*. Philadelphia: Saunders, 1960.
Elliott, K. A. C., I. H. Page, and J. H. Quastel. *Neurochemistry*. (2d ed.) Springfield, Ill.: Charles C Thomas, 1962.
Nastuk, W. L. (Ed.). *Physical techniques in biological research*. Electrophysiological methods. New York: Academic Press, 1963. Vol. 6.
Sheer, D. A. (Ed.). *Electrical stimulation of the brain*. Austin: University of Texas Press, 1961.
Uhr, L., and J. G. Miller. *Drugs and behavior*. New York: Wiley, 1960.
Votava, Z., M. Horvath, and O. Vinař (Eds.). *Psychopharmacological methods*. New York: Macmillan, 1963.

PART **III**

# NEURAL CONTROL
# OF ANIMATIVE ACTION

Having considered the basic structural organization of the nervous system, we shall now attempt to form a picture of its functional organization. We shall subdivide the mammalian nervous system into three functional components, the spinomedullary, paleocephalic, and neencephalic, and we shall try to show that these three divisions of the brain control three separate classes of animative functions.

The first of these, comprised of the intrinsic core of the spinal cord and its rostral extensions, represents the most ancient component of the chordate nervous system, which is present in such subvertebrate forms as *Amphioxus*. We shall present evidence to support the argument that the protochordate core of the spinal cord and medulla retains in all vertebrates the control of a single class of functions. This is the coordination of a large group of *routine maintenance* and *supporting activities*, which include such persistent visceral functions as the gastrointestinal, circulatory, and respiratory processes, and such stereotype relational activities as the maintenance of body posture and the coordination of the basic aspects of locomotion. The control of these activities, which represent the necessary background of all other neuromuscular animative functions, is dependent on morphogenetic processes; that is, the activities are *innate capacities* which are resistant to modification by experience. Furthermore, there is subjective human evidence that the performance of these functions does not depend on mental activity; they may therefore be referred to as *apsychic functions*.

The *paleocephalon* is composed of the nuclei of the mesencephalon (reticular formation, tectum, tegmentum), the more ancient components of the diencephalon (hypothalamus, paleothalamus, subthalamus), and the limbic system (rhinencephalon, hippocampus, allocortex). It is a system of structures that is present in the lowest forms of vertebrates, such as cyclostomes, and that receives afferents from the specialized head receptors, namely, the auditory, visual, and olfactory systems. We postulate, and will present evidence supporting the idea, that the protovertebrate paleocephalon controls one major class of activities, which we shall call *recurrent catering* or *servicing activities*. These are mainly relational activities, concerned with the direct gratification of the periodic existential needs of the body and performed by all members of a species in similar ways. They include the control of the recurrent task of satisfying the metabolic and reproductive needs of the organism (the appetitive aspects of food acquisition and of sexual and parental activities), the frequent task of protecting the integrity of the individual (defensive, aggressive, and affiliative activities), and the control of periodically or cyclically alternating energy-deployment processes (arousal and relaxation, sleeping and waking). Though the ends of these activities are set by inborn needs and dispositions, their mode of execution is guided and may be altered through interaction with the environment; accordingly, we shall

**TABLE 2**

TRIPARTITE ORGANIZATION OF ANIMATIVE ACTIVITIES AND OF THE MAMMALIAN CENTRAL NERVOUS SYSTEM

| | STRUCTURAL SUBDIVISIONS | | |
| --- | --- | --- | --- |
| | SPINOMEDULLARY | PALEOCEPHALIC | NEENCEPHALIC |
| Specific components | Segmental parts of spinal cord and medulla | Tectum, Reticular formation, Tegmentum, Hypothalamus, Rhinencephalon, Limbic system | Lemniscal pathway, Neothalamus, Neocortex, Pyramidal tract |
| Phylogenetic origin | Protochordate (Amphioxus) | Protovertebrate (Cyclostomes, Elasmobranchs, Teleosts, Amphibia) | Protomammalian (Mammals) |
| Subjective concomitants | Apsychic (None) ("Reflex") | Affective-emotional ("Instinctive") | Cognitive-volitional ("Intelligent") |
| Mode of organization | Stereotype, Innate, Impervious to modification | Species-specific, Modifiable | Personal, Unique, Acquired |
| Specific functions | Respiratory, Alimentary, Circulatory, Postural (Locomotor) | Appetitive, Consummatory, Agonistic, Affiliative | Discriminatory, Skilled, Exploratory |
| Activity classification | Persistent, Routine | Recurrent, Frequent | Singular, Occasional |
| FUNCTIONAL SUBDIVISIONS | MAINTENANCE | CATERING | INSTRUMENTAL |

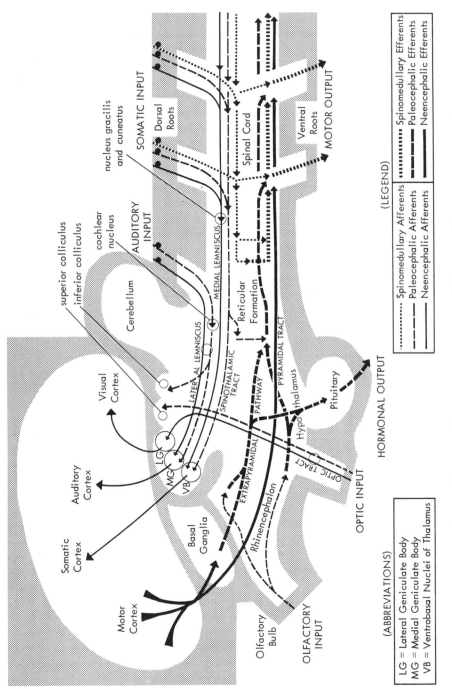

Simplified, schematic diagram of the tripartite organization of the mammalian nervous system.

(LEGEND)

................... Spinomedullary Afferents          ................... Spinomedullary Efferents
– – – – –  Paleocephalic Afferents          – – – – –  Paleocephalic Efferents
————— Neencephalic Afferents          ————— Neencephalic Efferents

(ABBREVIATIONS)

LG = Lateral Geniculate Body
MG = Medial Geniculate Body
VB = Ventrobasal Nuclei of Thalamus

refer to these activities as *modifiable capacities*. The activities controlled by the paleocephalon are often associated with a characteristic class of subjective or mental states, namely, feelings and emotions ("hunger," "thirst," "fear," "anger"), and may therefore be referred to as *affective functions*.

The *neencephalon* is comprised of the corticopetal lemniscal pathways, the neothalamic relay and association nuclei, the neocortex, and the corticofugal pyramidal pathway. It is a phylogenetically recent neural acquisition present in mammals only. We shall try to show that this proto-mammalian neural system is concerned with a third class of animative functions, which we shall call *singular instrumental activities*. These consist of novel, variable, and highly adaptive activities that individuals display in response to unique situations or new challenges encountered in their specific milieu. The adequate control of such activities requires the capacity to analyze different external situations with fidelity and accuracy, and also the ability to manipulate objects of the environment skillfully. Singular instrumental activities cannot be programed by inborn mechanisms but have to be developed by the individual in the course of its transactions with the environment; they are therefore considered *acquired capacities*. These neencephalic activities are often accompanied by a characteristic class of mental states, namely, knowing and willing, and are accordingly referred to as *cognitive functions*.

# 10

# Spinomedullary Control of Routine Maintenance Activities

*The Apsychic Integrative Level*

The spinomedullary system includes the spinal cord and its rostral extensions, the medulla and cerebellum. Because the spinal cord is a structure related in function to the segmental portions of the trunk and limbs, whereas the medulla and cerebellum are modified suprasegmental structures concerned with functions of the head and the body as a whole, we shall deal, in part, separately with these two components of the spinomedullary system.

**The Spinal Cord and Its** The spinal cord is composed partly **Segmental Control Functions** of cells and ascending fibers that project to, and of descending fibers that originate from, cortical and subcortical structures. One role of the spinal cord, accordingly, is to relay afferent information to, and transmit and execute the efferent commands of, higher suprasegmental brain structures. In this section we shall not be concerned with these phylogenetically more recent, superimposed components and functions of the spinal cord, but rather with its ancient, intrinsic components and functions.

A phylogenetically old and basic function of the spinal cord and of parts of the medulla is the mediation of local *segmental reflexes*. The concept of "reflex action," first popularized by Descartes, has been widely accepted as a functional as well as morphological entity ("reflex arc") ever since Bell and Magendie (Fearing, 1930) demonstrated the separation in the spinal cord of the dorsal, sensory and ventral, motor roots. The scientific study of spinal reflexes owes a great deal to the pioneering work of Sherrington, who successfully investigated various aspects of reflex activity in spinal animals, particularly spinal dogs. The *spinal animal* is a preparation in which the spinal cord is transected at the cervical level (*high spinal transection*) or some more caudal level (*low spinal transections*), and in which the cord is severed from rostral, or cephalic, influences. Although an abnormal preparation, because mammals cannot survive on their own in the absence of higher brain structures, the spinal animal is an adequate preparation for the study of reflexes controlled by local segmental mechanisms.

As described earlier, the spinal cord is a segmental structure, with the afferents and efferents of a given spinal nerve innervating restricted portions of the body. This segmental arrangement, which is quite distorted in quadruped vertebrates, is considered to be an ancient phylogenetic heritage, and it is reminiscent of the truly segmental organization of such chordates as *Amphioxus*. Spinal reflexes may be classified as intrasegmental and intersegmental reflexes. An example of an *intrasegmental reflex* is the myotatic, or stretch, reflex, considered briefly earlier (figure, page 224). Passively stretched muscle quickly develops active resistance, a response caused by compensatory contraction triggered by the stimulus of stretching. This response is mediated by the muscle spindles, which are sensitive to muscle stretching, and a monosynaptic reflex arc whose afferents and efferents are located in the spinal nerve of the same segment. Virtually all muscles show this response, but it is seen best developed in muscles that serve to counteract the force of gravity, the *extensor muscles*. However the stretch reflex, which is so important in supporting the quadruped standing stance, does not prevail under all circumstances. If the extended limb is stimulated by a nociceptive stimulus, it will withdraw quickly, a reflex response depending on the activation of *flexor muscles*. This protective response is another example of an intrasegmental spinal reflex, and it is *prepotent* over the postural stretch reflex (that is, it competitively displaces the stretch reflex).

Intrasegmental reflex activity is dependent on relatively complex regulatory processes. When the agonists of the stretch reflex, the extensors, contract in response to pulling, the antagonists of the activity, the flexors, relax. Conversely, when the flexor muscles contract in response to nociceptive stimulation, the response is accompanied by relaxation of the extensors, the antagonists of this reflex. (See figure on page 173.) *Reciprocal innervation* is one of the organizational principles underlying all reflex activities. It is based on an arrangement in which inhibitory impulses are sent to the antagonists of an action whenever its agonists are excited. A somewhat similar, though more complex, reciprocal arrangement underlies the *crossed extensor reflex*. When the flexors of a limb contract in response to stimulation, the response is accompanied by extension of the contralateral limb. A crossed intrasegmental reflex permits support of the posture of the body, one limb extending while the other flexes. Unlike the ipsilateral intrasegmental reflex, this reflex requires at least a 3-neuron reflex arc, with the axons of internuncials crossing to the opposite side.

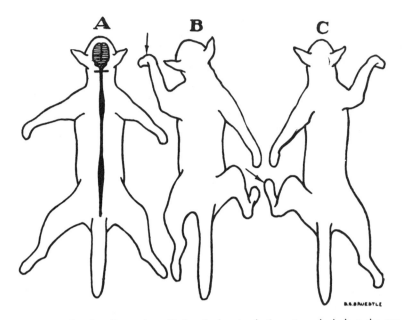

Intersegmental reflex figure in a high spinal animal. A, cut made below the medulla. B, response to stimulation of left forelimb. C, response to stimulation of left hindlimb. (After Sherrington. From Fulton, *Physiology of the nervous system*. Oxford University Press, 1951)

Intrasegmental reflex arcs can mediate such local activities as the posture-maintaining extension of a passively flexed limb or its protective withdrawal when injured or hurt. Indeed, such reflexes may be mediated by short pieces of the spinal cord, as in animals is which the cord is cut at both ends (Tower, 1937). More complex activities involving many segments of the body are mediated by *intersegmental reflexes*. An example of an intersegmental reflex is the coordination of the fore- and hindlimbs in the *maintenance of quadruped posture*, which is exhibited in a well-coordinated manner by spinal mammals. When, as a result of stimulation, one hindlimb flexes, we may observe not only the extension of the opposite hindlimb but the flexion of the contralateral forelimb and the extension of the ipsilateral forelimb. This pattern was called by Sherrington the *reflex figure*; regularly exhibited by spinal mammals, it prevents the animal from toppling. Obviously, intersegmental reflexes require functional circuits composed of a great number of neurons that coordinate the activity of a large number of segments.

Even more complex examples of an intersegmental reflex are the *tonic neck reflexes* shown by high spinal animals (Magnus, 1924). When the head of a spinal cat is turned to the right, its right limbs become immediately extended and its left limbs flexed. This response is interpreted as an adaptive preparatory posture permitting the animal to turn

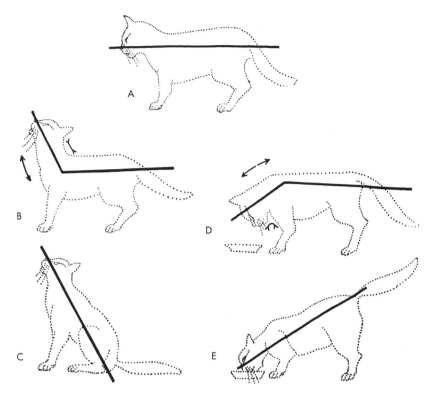

Tonic neck reflexes. Stimulation of the neck by turning head upward (B) produces extension of the forelimbs and flexion of the hindlimbs (C). The opposite effect (E) is produced by pushing the head downward (D). (After Llliott. *Textbook of anatomy.* J. B. Lippincott Company, 1963)

quickly to the right toward the object of its "attention." Similarly, when the cat's head (its gaze) is turned upward, there is an immediate extension of the forelimbs and flexion of the hindlimbs, as though to enable the animal to raise its body and reach for some object situated above ("cat looking at a bird"). Tilting the head downward produces flexion of the forelimbs and extension of the hindlimbs, apparently preparing the animal to lower its body and head ("cat looking for a mouse"). Through these reflexes the body is made to follow the movements of the head, a complex response that involves the cervical and many caudal segments of the body. Cutting the cervical spinal cord abolishes the tonic neck reflexes.

The spinal animal exhibits not only somatic reflexes (such as postural and protective reactions) but also a great variety of *visceral reflexes.* These include various *consummatory* sexual responses, and alimentary and excretory functions. In 1874 Goltz found in a female spinal dog that impregnation was followed by a normal period of gestation and the delivery of normal puppies. In the male spinal dog, erection of the penis and ejaculation may follow stimulation of the sexual zones of the body. This response is coupled with curving of the hind quarters downward, suggestive of the normal copulatory posture. Defecation, accompanied by lowering the hind-quarters of the body, and movements of the hindlimbs and tail resembling the normal defecatory action, is regularly seen in spinal dogs. Similarly, bladder contraction may occur as a reflex response in spinal animals after the bladder is sufficiently extended, although normal micturition requires the presence of suprasegmental centers. These are examples of local visceral reflexes at least partially controlled by reflex arcs localized at segmental spinal levels.

Can the spinal cord by itself control organized behavioral activities; that is, does the spinal cord have any functional autonomy? At least some degree of *spinal autonomy* is seen in lower vertebrates, such as elasmo-branchs, fish, and amphibia. The spinal hagfish, though inactive when left alone, can swim normally when stimulated (Prosser and Brown, 1961, p. 629). The neural programing of the rhythmic undulatory movements of swimming appears to be "built into" the spinal gray matter and does not even require afferent control. This fact was demonstrated in eels that were skinned and thus deafferented (Gray, 1936). Normal locomotion may also persist in spinal fish that use their fins in swimming, as in minnows, and also in primitive quadrupeds, such as frogs. Though usually inactive, the stimulated spinal frog can jump in a well-coordinated manner (Gray and Lissmann, 1946). Unlike the eel, however, the frog needs some afferent input from the body; following total deafferentation, loco-motor activity is abolished in the toad (Gray, 1950).

This relative autonomy seen in some spinal vertebrates is absent in mammals. Few if any of the activities exhibited by spinal mammals have the characteristics of integrated, total behavior patterns. Spinal mammals show the basic rhythmicity of quadruped locomotion, but they cannot really stand or move about, let alone cater for their various needs. The functions exhibited by spinal mammals are *supporting activities* essential for the execution of more complex behavior patterns; but these latter require the control action of suprasegmental brain structures. As the coordination of all trunk and limb activities is necessarily carried out by way of the spinal cord, in which the final motor neurons are located, the presence of subordinated reflex circuits in this region is of strategic advantage. Higher brain centers can thus easily utilize the built-in reflex patterns and modify them through descending effects.

**The Medulla and Its**             The medulla is the modified, rostral
**Suprasegmental Control Functions**    extension of the spinal cord. It re-
                                       ceives and sends fibers to a special-
ized part of the body, the head, by way of 10 cranial nerves (the olfactory nerve and optic "nerve" excepted). The caudal portions of the medulla

retain signs of their derivation from the segmental spinal cord; its more rostral portions (including the pons and some brain stem nuclei), which are related to the specific organs of the head, may be considered suprasegmental structures. In addition to the great ascending and descending fiber tracts that funnel through it, the medulla contains several nuclei concerned with visceral and somatic maintenance functions. These include nuclei controlling the maintenance of body posture, of respiratory and circulatory activities, and several alimentary and excretory functions.

CONTROL OF BODY POSTURE. Integrated *postural* and *righting reactions* depend on medullary control, in particular on the functioning of the *vestibular nuclei*. The chronic decerebrate and labyrinthectomized mammal can stand, in the sense that, when placed upright, it can support its weight. This is a performance dependent on the so-called *positive supporting reaction:* contact with the skin of the foot (and separation of the toe pads in the dog) produces a static response by means of which the limbs are turned into rigid pillars. However, in the absence of the vestibular system such an animal will topple when its balance is disturbed. The maintenance of postural equilibrium depends on the sensory processes of the vestibular sensory apparatus and on the integrative functions of the vestibular nuclei of the medulla.

The *righting reflexes* are initiated by afferent impulses set up in the fibers of the vestibular component of the eighth nerve by the otoliths of the utricle and saccule, which register changes in the position of the head with relation to gravity. These vestibular impulses are transmitted to the vestibular nuclei. Descending fibers of the vestibular nuclei, which form the *medial longitudinal fasciculus*, reach various motor nuclei of the brain stem, medulla, and the spinal cord, and influence the motor activities of the head, trunk, and limbs. The righting reactions can be easily demonstrated in *blindfolded* animals (and in animals in which, in addition to blindfolding, the cervical roots are cut to eliminate the tonic neck reflexes). The blindfolded animal, as long as it has an intact vestibular system, maintains its head in a horizontal position no matter what orientation is imposed on its body. Because the tonic neck reflexes take care of aligning the body with the head, the vestibular head-righting reflex also controls the righting of the body as a whole. This function is demonstrated dramatically when a blindfolded rabbit or cat is dropped in an upside down position to the ground. The animal quickly rights itself in mid-air, and lands safely on its feet.

In addition to the righting reflexes, which are guided by afferent impulses coming from the otoliths, the vestibular apparatus is also responsible for controlling various postural and oculomotor reactions related to *acceleration* or *rotation* of the head and body in space. These functions are mediated by the semicircular canals. A simple postural response is seen when a blindfolded cat is quickly lowered from a height, an instance

Vestibular righting reactions of a cat in midair after it was dropped upside down. (After Marey. In W. H. Howell, *Textbook of physiology,* John F. Fulton et al. [Eds.]. [17th ed.] W. B. Saunders Company, 1955, p. 221)

of linear acceleration. The animal's forelegs become immediately extended and the toes spread; this reflex is the *vestibular placing reaction.* A more complex set of reactions is associated with angular acceleration or rotation. A familiar reflex of this type is the *nystagmus* of the eyes. When the head of an animal is turned, the ocular muscles rotate the eyes automatically in the opposite direction. This is the *slow phase* of nystagmus, which permits the animal to maintain the direction of its gaze while the head turns. When the rotation of the head continues, the eyes quickly swing in the direction of rotation and become realigned with the orientation of the head. This is the *quick phase* of nystagmus. The labyrinthine control of nystagmus is well illustrated when this reflex is evoked by electric or caloric stimulation of the inner ear (squirting of warm water into the meatus). Nystagmus can also be evoked by visual stimulation; the reaction is produced in an animal when a striped drum is rotated in front of its eyes.

The vestibular nuclei and associated medullary structures may be considered suprasegmental centers that control the maintenance of body posture. At this level of the neuraxis are integrated various postural activities that enable the animal to resist interference with its normal posture (antigravity and related reactions) and allow it to respond with compensatory activities (righting reactions) when its balance is upset. It is owing to the integrative mechanisms located in this region that chronic low-mesencephalic cats (in which truncation passes rostral to the third nerve nucleus) can stand and right themselves, whereas low-pontine cats (in which parts of the pons and some cranial nuclei have been extirpated) remain passively in the position in which they are placed (Bard and Macht, 1958). Standardized body posture is of course an essential requirement for all sensory and motor activities.

It is not known whether *quadruped locomotion* is adequately organized in the medulla. Low mesencephalic cats do not walk spontaneously (Bard and Macht, 1958); however, when intensely stimulated, such an animal may take a few steps in an unsteady way. Normal and spontaneous quadruped locomotion in mammals requires the presence of certain forebrain structures.

CONTROL OF RESPIRATION. Because the oxygen store of the body, and its carbon-dioxide buffering capacity, is limited, there is continual need for the acquisition of $O_2$ and the elimination of $CO_2$. This function is achieved in land vertebrates by *pulmonary respiration*. Through the mouth and nose, air is drawn into and expelled from the lungs by the mechanical action exerted on the thoracic cavity by the ribs, chest muscles, and diaphragm. Oxygen and carbon dioxide are then exchanged between the blood and lungs in the capillaries of the alveoli (Chapter 3).

Adequate control of respiration requires not only a continuous rhythmic alternation of *inspiration* and *expiration* but also a regulation of the rates of these activities in harmony with the changing needs of the body. This persistent maintenance activity is controlled by the *respiratory centers* in the medulla. That a circumscribed region in the medulla is vitally involved in respiration was established by Legallois in 1812. He showed that breathing in the rabbit continued after removal of almost the entire brain, but ceased immediately after extirpation of the region of the medulla near the entrance of the eighth nerve.

Recent work (Young, 1960) suggests that there are in the medulla separate *inspiratory* and *expiratory* "centers," supplied by afferents from the lungs by way of the *vagus* nerve. In addition, there are other centers in the pons that exert modulatory effects on the medullary respiratory structures. The basic respiratory rhythm is controlled in a homeostatic manner: when the lungs are collapsed, inspiration is commenced; when the lungs are inflated, inspiration is terminated. This background rhythmicity is mediated by mechanoreceptors in the trachea and bronchi; unit discharges from their afferents in the vagus have been recorded. There is also evidence that this rhythmicity may be endogenous, the respiratory centers of the medulla being capable of maintaining it after deafferentation and separation from the pontine centers (Hoff and Breckenridge, 1949). However, this respiratory rhythm, whether endogeneous or peripherally controlled, can be modulated by varied afferent sources and also by superimposed brain structures in the pons and in more rostral regions. The control is essential for making respiratory adjustments to changing demands of the body or altered gaseous composition of the air. Also, breathing has to be coordinated with various other ongoing processes, particularly those carried out by the mouth, such as salivation, chewing, swallowing, and vocalization. Finally, when noxious substances are inspired, it may be necessary to occlude the air passages or initiate other protective reflexes, such as sneezing, coughing, and spitting.

All these reactions are controlled basically by the medullary and pontine respiratory centers, but there is also evidence of higher influences from paleocephalic and neencephalic levels. We may add at this point that the presence of redundant or superordinated cephalic centers capable of modulating the various maintenance and supporting activities is a principle of central nervous organization. This does not violate the assertion that such types of animal activities are primarily under spinomedullary control.

CONTROL OF CIRCULATORY ACTIVITIES. The transportation of oxygen and various nutrients to the needy cells of the body is the task of the cardiovascular system. Through the biomechanical action of the heart, oxygen-rich arterial blood is pumped to the various organs of the body, and the oxygen-poor venous blood is returned to the lungs, restored, and then recirculated. The fundamental rhythmicity of the heart is controlled by *cardiac pacemakers*; the pumping of the heart therefore persists after deafferentation.

In addition to the endogenous pulsatile activity of the heart, continual adjustments are made in the rate of blood flow that homeostatically compensate for the variable rates of metabolic activity in the body as a whole (as during strenuous exercise) or in discrete parts of it. The maintenance of standard concentration of oxygen and other substances carried by the blood stream is made possible by cardiac reflexes, which change the pumping rate of the heart, and by vascular reflexes, which dilate or constrict the blood vessels and thus affect blood pressure and blood flow. Local vasomotor reflexes may be controlled segmentally; they are seen in spinal animals. However, the integration of cardiac and vascular responses depends on the control functions of *vasomotor* and *cardioregulatory* "centers" in the medulla (Barron, 1960; Rushmer, 1960), which discharge through preganglionic sympathetic and parasympathetic efferents.

In the medullary vasomotor center two distinct areas have been identified by stimulation and lesion studies. Stimulation of one region, which was called the "pressor center," produces cardioacceleration and vasodilation; stimulation of the other medullary region, called the "depressor center," produces cardiodeceleration and vasodilation (not vasoconstriction). These "centers" appear to be endogenously active; that is, they discharge in a rhythmic fashion after deafferentation; presumably the rhythmic activity of neurons in these regions is sustained by chemical stimulants in the blood. But in the normal animal the rate of activity of these neurons, among others, is affected by afferents of the *carotid* and *aortic bodies* in the glossopharyngeal and vagus nerves. In addition to these medullary centers, powerful influences on cardiovascular activity emanate from the hypothalamus and some other brain structures.

CONTROL OF ALIMENTARY ACTIVITIES. Medullary centers also control a few routine alimentary processes. Decerebrate animals, for instance, can swallow food placed into the pharynx (Bazett and Penfield, 1922). *Swallowing* is a relatively complex muscular activity requiring the cooperation of about 20 different muscles. *Vomiting*, which is an even more complex act involving the coordination of respiratory, gastric, and other activities, is also controlled by the medulla. The *vomiting* "center" has been localized by means of stimulation and ablation techniques in the dorsolateral region of the medullary reticular formation (Borison and Wang, 1949). Similarly, *micturition*, which depends on the reciprocal action of muscles that contract the bladder and others that relax and open the orifice to the urethra, is controlled by pontine centers. The pontine influence on micturition is a facilitatory one (Barrington, 1921), lowering the threshold of bladder tension required to elicit the micturition reflex. Destruction of this region abolishes the micturition reflex (Tang and Ruch, 1956). Micturition, as all the other activities considered, is also controlled from higher levels of the neuraxis.

**Organization of Reflex Action** Although studied extensively for some time, the exact neural processes underlying reflex activity are still unknown. The use of the microelectrode recording technique promises to uncover the elementary properties of spinal reflex organization (Eccles, 1957; Lloyd, 1960), but to this day most of our information on the nature of reflex action derives from the type of studies introduced by Sherrington, who was able to demonstrate several principles of reflex organization in spinal animals. Reflexes are generally assumed to be subserved by synaptically connected neuron chains, or reflex arcs, that channel afferent impulses through internuncials to specific efferents innervating selected sets of muscles. We do not know whether this relaying function is dependent on *structural linkages* among specific neurons or on an unknown *functional affinity* that activates some neurons and eliminates others in the programing and execution of an action.

There is good evidence that the neural "*programs*" controlling reflexes are dependent on developmental mechanisms; that is, they are "inborn," and their organization does not require prior "experience" or learning. In other words, spinal and medullary reflexes, like so many other morphological and functional characteristics of the organism, are determined by *heredity* and *morphogenetic processes*. This is indicated by the fact that at least some of the spinal and medullary reflexes appear immediately after birth, where the possibility of prenatal experience may be excluded. An example would be respiration, which cannot occur intrauterally in mammals but which is exhibited in a normal fashion immediately after parturition. Other reflexes may mature after birth but are exhibited by animals in which the possibility of learning is experimentally eliminated. An example is the classic study of Carmichael (1926, 1927). Frog and salamander eggs were separated into two groups: one was reared normally, the other was anesthetized so that the developing larvae did not exhibit locomotion. When the narcotized animals reached maturity, they were transferred to a normal medium; as soon as they recovered from the anesthesia, they swam about practically like their normally developing mates. (As we may recall, locomotion in amphibia is to a large extent controlled at the spinal level.)

Not only can the organization of spinal and medullary reflexes occur without learning, but there is evidence that reflex activities may in fact be impervious to modification by the adaptive needs of the organism or the availability of experience. As an example, we may mention here the experiments of Weiss (1950) involving the *transplantation* or *reversal* of *limb buds* in amphibia. As a consequence of such experimental manipulations, the reversed limbs of the developing animal persist in moving in the wrong direction, propelling the animal backward when it attempts to pursue an object and move forward. Apparently, the muscles involved in locomotion are well coordinated by built-in patterning mechanisms, but the sequences of reciprocal contraction and relaxation of agonists,

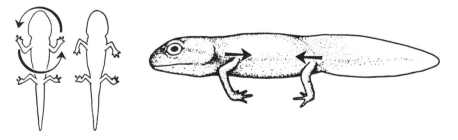

Reversed locomotion in the salamander after surgical interchange of right and left forelimb, as indicated on the left side. (After Weiss. Self-differentiation of the basic patterns of coordination. *Comp. Psychol. Monogr.* 1941, **17**, 1–96)

antagonists, and synergists are fixed with respect to the normal arrangement of the muscles and their skeletal attachments ("myotypic" neuromuscular organization) and fail to show the *adaptive reorganization*
necessitated by the reversed position of the limbs.

Whether reflexes mediated by the isolated spinal cord of mammals can
be modified by learning (Prosser and Hunter, 1936) was studied by several
investigators. In these experiments limb flexion (or contraction of a limb
muscle) was elicited with electric shocks. This "unconditional" stimulus
was paired then with another stimulus that initially failed to produce the
response in order to test for conditioning. Kellogg et al. (1946, 1947)
failed to establish conditioning in spinal dogs. In contrast, Shurrager and
Culler (1940) reported successful conditioning in spinal dogs, but the
results obtained by them do not give unambiguous evidence of true conditioning (Morgan and Stellar, 1950, pages 440–446. These findings would
therefore indicate that spinal and medullary reflexes are inborn, stereotype
processes which are not easily modified by the opportunities of individual
experience.

### SELECTED READINGS

Creed, R. S., D. Denny-Brown, J. C. Eccles, E. G. T. Liddell, and C. S.
  Sherrington. *Reflex activity of the spinal cord.* New York: Oxford, 1932.
Eccles, J. C. *The physiology of nerve cells.* Baltimore: The Johns Hopkins
  Press, 1957.
Fulton, J. F. *Physiology of the nervous system.* (3d ed.) New York: Oxford,
  1949.
Lloyd, D. P. C. Principles of spinal reflex activity. In J. F. Fulton (Ed.),
  *Textbook of physiology.* (17th ed.) Philadelphia: Saunders, 1955.
Ruch, T. C., and J. F. Fulton (Eds.). *Medical physiology and biophysics.*
  Philadelphia: Saunders, 1960.
Sherrington, C. S. *The integrative action of the nervous system.* London: Con-
  stable, 1906 (2d ed., Cambridge, 1947).
Walsh, E. G. *Physiology of the nervous system.* (2d ed.) London: Longmans,
  1964.

# 11

## Paleocephalic Control of Recurrent Catering Activities

### The Affective Integrative Level

The paleocephalon is a phylogenetically old, suprasegmental system of structures present in all vertebrates, including cyclostomes. It consists of parts of the mesencephalon (tectum, tegmentum, and reticular formation), diencephalon (paleothalamus, hypothalamus, and subthalamus), and the limbic system (hippocampus, amygdala, septal nuclei, and certain allocortical structures). The thesis of this chapter is that the protovertebrate paleocephalon represents a neural system that coordinates relational activities immediately and directly in the *service* of the *existential needs* of the organism. These activities are characterized by their *frequent recurrence* in the life of the animal, and by the *species-specific* (though modifiable) manner in which they are performed by the individual. These existential activities may be grouped into three major classes:

1. Cyclically or aperiodically alternating *energy-deployment processes*, which include sleep and wakefulness and, in the waking state, relaxation and arousal;

2. Periodically recurring gratificational or *need-satisfying* processes, which are concerned with the *appetitive* aspects of nutritional, sexual, and parental needs;

3. Frequently aroused social activities concerned with the *safeguarding of the integrity of the individual*, manifested as defensive, aggressive, and affiliative activities. Unlike spinomedullary activities, which are apsychic reflex functions, paleocephalic activities may be associated with *affective mental states* (feelings and emotions).

**Functions of the Mesencephalon, Including the Reticular Formation**  The mesencephalon is the "highest" suprasegmental coordinating center of lower vertebrates, such as fish and amphibia. Its major intrinsic components are the tectum, tegmentum, and the reticular formation. The *tectum* is the afferent terminal station of a variety of receptor systems, the optic and auditory included, which in mammals is represented by the inferior and superior colliculi. The major efferent outflow of the mesencephalon is from the *tegmentum*, a diffuse structure with ill-defined boundaries extending rostrally into the diencephalon and caudally into the medulla. Intermediate between the dorsal tectum and the ventral tegmentum is another structure with ill-defined boundaries, the reticular formation. The *reticular formation* may be considered to be composed largely of "internuncials," which mediate between the afferent input to, and efferent outflow from the mesencephalon.

Until recently it was believed that the afferent supply of the reticular formation was made up largely of *collaterals* of the large afferent of the "lemniscal" pathways. This theory was based mainly on physiological studies that showed long latency electric potentials in the reticular formation in response to stimulation of the somesthetic, vestibular, auditory, visual, and olfactory systems (Magoun, 1950). Evidence has recently accumulated indicating that the reticular formation has its own afferent supply, made up of small-diameter fibers, which course separately from the large diameter lemniscal fibers. It was shown by Collins and O'Leary (1954), for instance, that reticular evoked potentials have a much higher threshold than have evoked potentials in the ventral nucleus of the thalamus. Moreover, the reticular responses survived sectioning of the *dorsal columns*, which are composed of the bulk of the ascending "lemniscal" afferents, but were reduced to a trace after sectioning the *lateral columns*. Studies with silver staining suggest in a similar way (Bishop, 1959; Nauta and Kuypers, 1958; Russell, 1961) that many fibers of the "spinothalamic" tract terminate in the mesencephalic reticular formation; others terminate in the intralaminar nuclei of the thalamus which are conceived of as diencephalic extensions of the reticular formation. Because somesthetic fibers of the lateral columns transmit mainly *protopathic* impulses (nociceptive and related signals), the reticular formation may be selectively activated by this type of stimuli.

That collaterals to the reticular formation from the main lemniscal pathways may be altogether absent was demonstrated for at least two afferent systems. Using the Nauta staining technique, Bowsher (1958) showed that all fibers of the dorsal column terminate in the posterior ventral nucleus of the thalamus, and that no collaterals are given off to the reticular formation. Similarly, in another study employing the Nauta technique, we found (Altman, 1962) that after sectioning of the optic nerve or destruction of the lateral geniculate nucleus no degenerated preterminal fibers were present in the reticular formation. However, following destruction of the superior colliculus (Altman and Carpenter, 1961), the reticular formation was full of degenerated fibers. These latter findings suggested that the optic input to the reticular formation is an indirect one, relayed to it by the superior colliculus.

The reticular formation also receives fibers from the cerebellum, as well as from various diencephalic nuclei (the hypothalamus included), from rhinencephalic structures, and from various regions of the cortex. The efferents of the reticular formation pass to the adjacent tegmental nuclei and also in rostral and caudal directions. Caudally, the reticular efferents reach the cranial and spinal motor nuclei, synapsing in all probability with internuncials. Rostrally, reticular fibers reach the intralaminar nuclei of the thalamus, the subthalamic nuclei, and the hypothalamus. The reticular nuclear group of the thalamus is believed also to receive fibers from the reticular formation. The reticular nuclei, in turn, may be connected with the neocortex (Rose, 1952). The connections of the reticular formation, accordingly, are extensive. This fact, and additional observations, have led to the hypothesis that the reticular formation has important *integrative functions*.

Recent physiological investigations have revealed that the mesencephalic reticular formation is involved in regulating the tonic state of the nervous system (and through it the state of the organism as a whole) by exerting inhibitory and facilitatory effects both in caudal and rostral directions (Magoun, 1950). The caudal or spinal influences affect the afferent relay nuclei (modulating sensory transmission) and the motor nuclei (influencing the efferent discharge of motor neurons). The rostral, or cephalic, influences of the reticular formation are manifested physiologically as modifications of the "spontaneous" electrical activity of various brain structures, the neocortex included.

THE RETICULAR FORMATION IN SLEEPING, WAKING, AND AROUSAL. That the mesencephalon is vitally involved in the maintenance of the waking state was first shown by Bremer (1935). Transection of the brain stem at midcollicular level (referred to as the *cerveau isolé* preparation) produces EEG patterns in the cortex characteristic of somnolence or sleep. Bremer interpreted this result to be the consequence of interruption of the lemniscal pathways, which carry afferent impulses to the thalamus and neocortex. Moruzzi and Magoun (1949) found later that stimulation of the reticular formation produced *electrocortical activation*, changing the synchronized, low-frequency and high-voltage EEG characteristic of the relaxed state to a desynchronized, high-frequency, and low-voltage activity indicative of arousal. Subsequently, Lindsley et al. (1949) showed that severing the direct lemniscal pathways in the cat did not interfere with periodic wakefulness, whereas lesions placed in the reticular formation, sparing the lemniscal system, produced persistent somnolence with some irregular EEG waves and occasional spindle bursts. Conversely, stimulation with implanted electrodes in the reticular formation (Segundo et al., 1955; and others) produces immediate arousal in the sleeping animal,

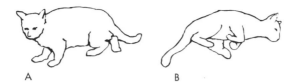

A                                    B

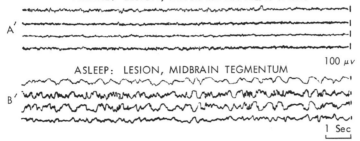

AWAKE: LESION, MIDBRAIN AFFERENT PATHS

A'

100 μv

ASLEEP: LESION, MIDBRAIN TEGMENTUM

B'

1 Sec

A, cat in which the lemniscal pathways were cut but the reticular extralemniscal pathway spared. This animal shows normal waking EEG (A'). B, animal in which the lemniscal pathways were spared but the reticular formation destroyed. This animal shows somnolence and a sleeping EEG pattern (B'). (From Lindsley. Attention, consciousness, sleep and wakefulness. *Handb. Physiol.*, Sec. 1, **3**, 1563)

accompanied by alteration of the electrocortical activity from the sleeping to the waking pattern. These experiments demonstrated the importance of the reticular formation in EEG activation and behavioral arousal.

Not only *ascending*, or rostral, but also *descending*, or caudal, influences were demonstrated from the reticular formation. Magoun and Rhines (1946) found in anesthetized preparations that electrically evoked cortical motor activities were diminished or enhanced as a consequence of concurrent reticular stimulation. In general, *inhibitory* effects were obtained from the medullary portion, and *facilitation* from the more rostral parts of the reticular formation. The latter structures included not only the mesencephalic reticular formation but also the subthalamus, hypothalamus, midline and intralaminar nuclei of the thalamus, and parts of the rhinencephalon (that is, most parts of the paleocephalon).

In addition to the mesencephalic reticular formation, some paleothalamic structures are also involved in the control of the "spontaneous" electrical activity of the brain. This conclusion was originally suggested by the work of Morrison and Dempsey (1942), who found that stimulation of the *intralaminar nuclei* of the thalamus produced rhythmic cortical activity, which was mediated through a slow conducting "diffuse" pathway, distinct from the main thalamocortical projection system. In the anesthetized animal a single electric pulse delivered to the intralaminar nuclei produced a burst of discharges resembling the spindle waves seen during sleep.

*Neural Control of Animative Action*

Repetitive stimulation produced the *recruiting response*, a synchronized wave discharge resembling the spontaneous EEG of the awake, resting brain. Later it was shown that repetitive stimulation of intralaminar nuclei with implanted electrodes produces sleep when the stimulus frequency is low, and arousal if the stimulus frequency is more rapid (Akimoto et al., 1956). The intralaminar nuclei, apparently, have electrocortical effects that are in many respects similar to those of the brain-stem reticular formation. On this basis, the intralaminar nuclei are sometimes considered to constitute the thalamic reticular system (Jasper, 1954), that is, the diencephalic extension of the reticular formation.

Both the mesencephalic and diencephalic portions of the reticular formation are under the influence of *centrifugal fibers* of the paleo- and neo-cortex. Efferent fibers to the reticular formation have been demonstrated from the rhinencephalon (Adey et al., 1956, 1957) and from various parts of the neocortex (Rossi and Brodal, 1956). These findings are in agreement with electrophysiological studies, which showed that following stimulation of various cortical areas, evoked responses could be recorded from the entire extent of the mesen- and diencephalic reticular formation (French et al., 1955). Also, EEG desynchronization and behavioral

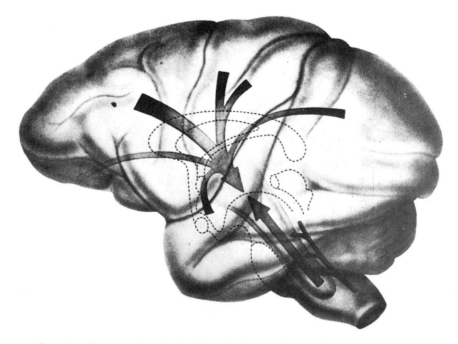

Schematic diagram of corticofugal projection to the reticular formation. (From French et al. Projections from cortex to cephalic brain stem [reticular formation] in monkeys. *J. Neurophysiol.,* 1955, **18,** 74–95 )

arousal can be produced from all cortical areas that project to the reticular formation (Segundo et al., 1955). The projection of the cortex to the reticular formation appears to be diffuse, as is suggested by the fact that single reticular units can be made to discharge from multiple cortical loci (Amassian and De Vito, 1954; Baumgarten et al., 1954; Scheibel et al., 1955).

Reticular activation of the caudal and rostral portions of the nervous system is mediated by a relatively slow-conducting, "diffuse" pathway. There is good evidence, however, that in addition to neuronal transmission, *humoral agents* can affect reticular activity. It is well known that intravenous administration of adrenaline and related substances (sympathetomimetic agents) has an activating effect on EEG and behavior. The reticular formation itself, together with the hypothalamus, was shown to have a high concentration of noradrenaline (Vogt, 1954). Bonvallet et al. (1954) and Rothballer (1956) have further demonstrated that the activating effect of sympathetomimetic drugs is mediated by the reticular formation. They found that sectioning of the brain stem, or lesions placed in such a way that they interrupted the connection between the reticular formation and cortex, abolished the dramatic arousal effect of adrenaline. That is, adrenaline cannot directly affect the EEG activity of the cortex; it can affect the EEG activity only by way of the reticular formation. That reticular neurons respond directly to adrenaline was shown in experiments in which the mesencephalic reticular formation was isolated from the rest of the brain both caudally and rostrally. In these preparations the discharge of reticular neurons is either accelerated or inhibited for a short period following injection of adrenaline. Bonvallet suggested that neural activation of the reticular formation is responsible for the rapid desynchronization of electrocortical activity, and that the slower, more sustained effect is dependent on the release of adrenaline. There is also good evidence that drugs capable of antagonizing adrenaline produce somnolence and sleep; in contrast, other drugs with adrenaline-like properties produce activation and arousal.

Accordingly, the maintenance of the waking state, as well as relaxation and sleep, is dependent on ascending influences that emanate from the brain-stem reticular formation and its diencephalic extensions. The *waking state* may be considered a sustained, tonic, energizing process that permits the animal to maintain a vigilant attitude and attend to its surroundings. It may be observed in exaggerated form, as "excitement," when the animal is engaged in vital interrelational activities, as when it is pursuing a prey, defending its territory, or engaged in sexual activity. These states, which require enhanced interaction with the environment, represent one phase in the cyclic deployment of organic energy resources. The opposite state, characterized by *relaxation* and *drowsiness*, leads to reduced contact with the environment and to the deployment of energy resources for the furtherance of internal maintenance processes. This state predominates following feeding or sexual satiation, or when danger or threat to the individual has been overcome.

There is, in fact, ample evidence that *afferent input* (which is the basis of contact with the environment) can be actively *facilitated* or *inhibited* by the reticular formation. That is, depending on reticular activity, the same physicochemical stimulus may be enhanced, or attenuated, or altogether rejected before it is relayed to higher centers. These effects are produced mostly by *centrifugal fibers*, many of which originate in the region of the reticular formation and terminate either in the first-order sensory relay nuclei or within the sense organs themselves.

Thus Granit and Kaada (1952) found that stimulation of the facilitatory portion of the reticular formation produced increased muscle-spindle discharge; stimulation of the inhibitory region, on the other hand, led to decreased rate of muscle-spindle activity. These findings suggested that the gamma efferent system represents a centrifugal mechanism through which the sensitivity of the muscle spindle to proprioceptive stimuli is controlled. These effects could also be produced from more rostral levels of the brain (Eldred et al., 1953). Transmission of somatosensory postsynaptic impulses at the first relay nucleus, evoked by stimulation of the dorsal roots, was blocked by concurrent stimulation of the reticular formation (Hagbarth and Kerr, 1954). Similar effects were observed in the spinal trigeminal sensory nucleus (Hernández-Peón and Hagbarth, 1955) and in the nucleus gracilis and cuneatus (Hernández-Peón et al., 1956) following stimulation of the reticular formation. Reticular effects on sensory transmission were also demonstrated in the visual and auditory systems. Granit (1955) and Dodt (1956) showed that stimulation of the reticular formation could facilitate or inhibit the unit discharge of single retinal ganglion cells. Similarly, stimulation in the region of the olivocochlear bundle (Galambos, 1956) or in the reticular formation (Brust-Carmona et al., 1960) may lead to reduction of the cochlear evoked potential to auditory stimuli.

That these effects may be related to behaviorally observed alterations in vigilance, arousal, or "attention" was suggested by investigations which showed comparable attenuation of retinal potentials to photic stimuli (Hernández-Peón, 1961), or of cochlear potentials to auditory stimuli (Hernández-Peón et al., 1956), in animals that were made to "attend" to other stimuli. Ascending reticular effects may also participate in the control of afferent transmission. Geniculate and cortical evoked responses to photic stimuli are altered by concurrent reticular stimulation (Bremer and Stoupel, 1959; Dumont and Dell, 1958). Unit discharges in these structures are also affected by reticular stimulation (Akimoto and Creutzfeldt, 1958; Arden and Söderberg, 1961). These effects may be both facilitatory or inhibitory in nature.

**Functions of the Hypothalamus** THE ROLE OF THE HYPOTHALAMUS
**and the Pituitary Gland** IN ENERGY DEPLOYMENT, IN SLEEP-
ING AND WAKING. In addition to
the reticular formation, the midline nuclei, and the intralaminar nuclei
of the thalamus, the hypothalamus also plays an important role in the
control of relaxation and arousal, and in particular in sleeping and waking.
(The hypothalamus, as we shall presently see, has many other regulatory
functions.)

Adequate deployment of the material and energy resources of the body
has two requirements: (1) homeostatic maintenance of the internal milieu,
and (2) support of excessive energy expenditure during strenuous enter-
prises, such as fighting, fleeing, repairing injuries, and so on. To maintain homeostasis and permit periodic energy mobilization, the body
utilizes a complex regulatory system involving the visceral organs, various
exocrine and endocrine glands, and nervous mechanisms, particularly the
sympathetic outflow. Let us consider an example of such a process. The
maintenance of constant glucose concentration of the blood (which is the
main energy source of the body) is dependent, first, on the liver, which
can store and release sugar, and, second, on the pancreas, which produces
insulin, the hormone required for utilization of glucose. It was shown
experimentally that, depending on the glucose level of the perfusate, the
liver may become a donor or recipient of glucose, and that insulin is secreted at a higher rate when the sugar concentration of the perfusate is
increased and at a lower rate when the sugar concentration is decreased
(Anderson and Long, 1947). This interplay between the organ storing
sugar and the organ controlling sugar utilization makes possible the maintenance of a standard blood-sugar level under "normal" conditions. This
regulatory function, however, cannot cope with emergency situations during which the sugar requirements of the body are greatly increased. In
emergency situations the adrenergic sympathetic outflow is activitated.
Sympathetic activation produces hyperglycemia and also contraction of the
spleen, which make available increased numbers of red blood cells and
thus more oxygen. It also produces increased cardiac and respiratory activity, and various other responses, which combine to make possible increased expenditure of energy.

The sympathetic outflow is under the control of the hypothalamus.
This fact was first demonstrated in 1909 by Karplus and Kreidl, who
showed that electric stimulation of the hypothalamus was followed by
sympathetic discharge. Later investigations revealed that sympathetic effects can be most readily obtained by stimulating the *posterior hypothalamic* areas. Stimulating this region of the hypothalamus in awake animals
(Hess, 1954) can reproduce practically all the characteristic sympathetic
effects, such as dilatation of the pupils, piloerection, increased blood pressure and respiratory activity, facilitation of spinal reflexes, EEG activa-

tion, and so on. According to Hess, the posterior areas of the hypothalamus are "dynamogenic centers" that make possible energy mobilization during "emergency" situations.

As the hypothalamus is vitally involved in regulating the somatic aspects of various emergency activities (pursuing, fighting, fleeing, and the like), the utility of its control of energy-mobilizing mechanisms is obvious. The involvement of the hypothalamus and adjacent regions in the regulation of sleeping and waking was deduced by von Economo (1929) from a clinical and pathological study of *encephalitis lethargica* (sleeping sickness) patients whose main symptom is chronic sleeping. Later, Ranson (1939) found that *destruction* of the posterior hypothalamus in the cat produced somnolence. *Stimulation* of the same area produces wakefulness, arousal, and activation of the cortical EEG (Gellhorn, 1953). Presumably, the hypothalamus interacts with the reticular formation in regulating these energy-deployment functions.

In summary, the reticular formation, together with the intralaminar thalamic nuclei and the hypothalamus, control the deployment of "nervous energy," manifested behaviorally as relaxation and arousal, and as decreased and increased contact with (or awareness of) the environment. Hess (1954) has referred to these opposite types of energy-deployment processes as the ergotropic (dynamogenic) and trophotropic (hypnogenic) phases, respectively. The two extreme manifestations of these energy-deployment processes are excessive excitement or emotionality, on the one hand, and sleep or coma on the other.

The hypothalamus is distinguished from most other essentially motor structures by the sparseness of its neuroefferent outflow and its intimate association with the three large neuroendocrine systems, the sympathetic and parasympathetic systems, and the pituitary gland. We have just referred to the role of the hypothalamus in regulating sympathetic activity, and we may recall our previous discussion of the intimate connection it has with the pituitary gland, particularly the neurohypophysis. These facts would indicate that the hypothalamus is primarily concerned with the regulation of visceral activities. There is, indeed, a wealth of data suggesting that the hypothalamus is a suprasegmental center controlling a variety of activities concerned with the satisfaction of the basic needs of the body. The hypothalamus plays a central role not only in the deployment of "nervous energy," but also in various aspects of feeding, drinking, sexual, and parental activities, and, beyond these, in agonistic and defensive activities.

THE ROLE OF THE HYPOTHALAMUS IN FEEDING. It has been known for a long time that lesions involving the region of the pituitary gland are often associated with weight increase or *obesity*. This effect (Fröhlich's syndrome in clinical medicine) was originally attributed to damage to the pituitary gland. However, it was shown by P. E. Smith (1930) that, as long as the hypothalamus remains unharmed, removal of the pituitary in rats does not produce obesity. Subsequently Hetherington (1941) showed that bilateral destruction of the *ventromedial hypothalamic nuclei* alone produces obesity. This obesity, it was found (Brobeck et al., 1943), is not due primarily to a metabolic disturbance (increased fat storage) but rather to voracious overeating, or *hyperphagia.* Anand and Brobeck (1951) suggested that the region of the ventromedial nuclei acts as a *"satiety center,"* which tends to inhibit food intake. This presumed inhibitory effect is believed to be exercised over the *lateral hypothalamic nuclei.* The latter act as a *"feeding center"* that facilitates food intake. This function is suggested by the observation that stimulation of the lateral hypothalamic nuclei and adjacent areas in cats (Brügger, 1943; Delgado and Anand, 1953) and goats (Larsson, 1954) produces, immediately or after some delay, increased food intake.

According to a recent report of Anand et al. (1962), the unit activity of single neurons in the "satiety center" of the hypothalamus increases with increased glucose availability or glucose utilization, whereas there is a slight decrease under such conditions in the unit activity of neurons of the "feeding center." Similarly, it was shown with Olds' technique of self-stimulation that rats with electrode placements in the lateral hypothalamus show a high rate of self-stimulation (Margules and Olds, 1962; Hoebel and Teitelbaum, 1962). Self-stimulation is inhibited by feeding and augmented by food deprivation; this indicates that self-stimulation in this area produces a "reward" effect associated with feeding.

Stimulation of the lateral hypothalamus also produces motor responses related to feeding, such as swallowing, chewing, licking, and the like (Hess, 1954). Conversely, bilateral destruction of the lateral hypothalamic nuclei in rats produces *aphagia* (Anand and Brobeck, 1951). After such destruction, the animals die of starvation if they are not tube-fed; however, if they are tube-fed for several days following operation they eventually start to eat and drink of their own accord (Teitelbaum and Stellar, 1954; Morrison and Mayer, 1957; Teitelbaum and Epstein, 1962).

THE ROLE OF THE HYPOTHALAMUS IN DRINKING BEHAVIOR. The involvement of the hypothalamus in water metabolism has been well established. The antidiuretic hormone of the posterior lobe of the pituitary, the substance that promotes water conservation by facilitating reabsorption of water from the kidneys, is under the control of the *supraoptic nucleus* of the hypothalamus. This is suggested by the findings that lesions destroying the supraoptic nucleus bilaterally abolish normal water metabolism (Ranson and Magoun, 1939), whereas stimulation of this region produces antidiuresis in unanesthetized animals (Harris, 1947). Indeed, it was suggested that "osmoreceptors" (Verney, 1947) in the supraoptic nuclei respond to changes in the osmotic pressure of the blood, and that the antidiuretic hormone is actually produced by neurons in this hypothalamic nucleus (Scharrer and Scharrer, 1954).

There is also good evidence that a circumscribed hypothalamic area, distinct from the region that releases the antidiuretic hormone, controls water intake in drinking or eating. Andersson (1953; Andersson and Mc-Cann, 1955) found that electric *stimulation* of the *dorsomedial region* of the hypothalamus produces excessive *drinking* in water-satiated goats. The same effect was also obtained when a small amount of hypertonic saline solution was injected into the same area, suggesting the presence of "osmo-receptors" in this region. The stimulated animals could even be induced to drink adulterated water, which they normally refuse. As Andersson and Wyrwicka (1957) have further shown, goats will perform a relatively complex learned act to obtain water during hypothalamic stimulation. *Destruction* of the same hypothalamic area results in transient (Andersson and McCann, 1956) or permanent (Witt et al., 1952) refusal to drink (*adipsia*).

Recent studies appear to indicate that the "drinking center" in the hypothalamus is closely associated with the "feeding" and "satiety centers" or that these two nutritive functions may have common representations in the hypothalamus. The association of these two functions is indicated by the observation (Teitelbaum and Epstein, 1962) that refusal to ingest food after lateral hypothalamic lesions is always combined with adipsia. In the early phases of recovery, aphagia slowly disappears, but

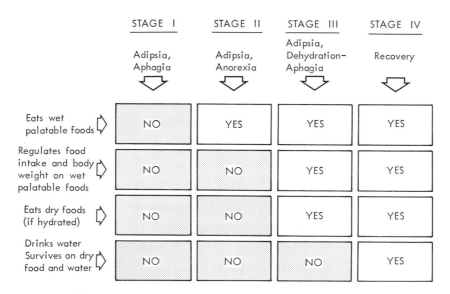

|  | STAGE I | STAGE II | STAGE III | STAGE IV |
|---|---|---|---|---|
|  | Adipsia, Aphagia | Adipsia, Anorexia | Adipsia, Dehydration–Aphagia | Recovery |
| Eats wet palatable foods | NO | YES | YES | YES |
| Regulates food intake and body weight on wet palatable foods | NO | NO | YES | YES |
| Eats dry foods (if hydrated) | NO | NO | YES | YES |
| Drinks water Survives on dry food and water | NO | NO | NO | YES |

Stages in the recovery from aphagia and adipsia following lateral hypothalamic lesions. (Teitelbaum and Epstein. The lateral hypothalamic syndrome. *Psychol. Rev.*, 1962, **69**, 83 )

adipsia remains; during this period the animal tends to eat wet but not dry food. Later the animal may accept dry food also, provided it is artificially hydrated. If complete recovery is achieved, the animal may also drink water; but unlike aphagia, adipsia can be a permanent deficit produced by lateral hypothalamic lesions in the rat. The intimate association between the feeding and drinking "centers" is also suggested by the investigations of Grossman (1960, 1962), who found that either eating or drinking can be elicited from the same hypothalamic site by injection of different chemicals (adrenergic drugs elicit drinking, whereas cholinergic drugs produce eating).

THE ROLE OF THE HYPOTHALAMUS IN SEXUAL AND REPRODUCTIVE BEHAVIOR. As we may recall, the pituitary gland secretes several trophic hormones concerned with the regulation of sexual and reproductive processes. The gonadotrophic hormone stimulates the development of the ovaries and the secretion of estrogens in the female, and it triggers spermatogenesis and the secretion of androgens in the male. Other related hormones of the pituitary are the luteinizing and lactogenic hormones, which are involved in the regulation of certain visceral aspects of maternal activities. It is not surprising, therefore, that destruction of the hypophysis is followed by atrophy of the gonads and accessory sex organs, and deficient sexual behavior. It might also be expected that the hypothalamus, which controls pituitary activity, exerts regulatory influences on procreative activities. Indeed, Fisher et al. (1938) observed that female cats with *anterior hypothalamic lesions* do not mate; this observation was confirmed subsequently in female guinea pigs (Brookhart et al., 1940, 1941). Furthermore, it was shown by Brookhart that in such animals systemic estrogen treatment does not induce receptivity, even though administration of estrogen restores mating in hypophysectomized female guinea pigs. This result was confirmed in female cats with anterior hypothalamic lesions (Sawyer and Robinson, 1956). These latter findings would suggest that the role played by the hypothalamus in regulating sexual behavior is not restricted to its regulation of pituitary secretion.

Fisher (1956) observed patterns of female sexual behavior in male rats after *injection* of testosterone into the *preoptic region*; Harris (1958) produced estrus in female cats with injection of very small doses of estrogen into the hypothalamus. Evidence of the presence of *estrogen-sensitive neurons* in the hypothalamus was obtained histologically (Lisk and Newlon, 1963) and by means of autoradiography (Michael, 1961). In female rabbits with implanted electrodes, EEG signs of altered activity were seen in the *anterior hypothalamic* area during courtship and mating (Green, 1954). The same was observed in the anterior (but not in the posterior) hypothalamus of estrus cats during vaginal stimulation and after-reaction (Porter et al., 1957). *Stimulation* studies with implanted electrodes in the squirrel monkey (MacLean and Ploog, 1962; MacLean et al., 1963) revealed various paleocephalic sites from which penile erection was obtained; these sites included various hypothalamic nuclei, such as the mammillary bodies and the preoptic nuclei. According to Vaughan and Fisher (1962), electric stimulation of the preoptic area in the rat may induce copulation. Whereas in the studies of MacLean penile erection was usually not accompanied by seminal ejaculation when the hypothalamus was stimulated, stimulation in the region of the *medial forebrain bundle* (which is the major pathway from the limbic system to the hypothalamus) was reported to produce seminal ejaculation without penile erection in the rat (Herberg, 1963).

The exact role of the anterior hypothalamus in controlling female sexual behavior does not emerge from these studies. The tentative assumption is that cells in the anterior hypothalamus respond to estrogen in the blood by activating brain-stem and spinal-motor centers involved in sexual behavior, as well as by releasing gonadotrophic and possibly other hormones from the pituitary. The latter assumption is supported by the finding that, in the female rabbit, ovulation in response to mating does not occur when the pituitary stalk is severed (Brooks, 1938). Similarly, ovulation in response to electrical stimulation of the *tuberal region* of the hypothalamus occurs only when the pituitary stalk is intact (Harris, 1955). As we shall see later, other brain regions, in particular the rhinencephalon, are also vitally involved in the regulation of sexual and reproductive behavior.

THE ROLE OF THE HYPOTHALAMUS IN INDUCING AGONISTIC BEHAVIOR. Agonistic activities (aggressive and defensive functions like fighting, threat posturing, fleeing, freezing) are intimately associated with activation of the sympathetic and parasympathetic systems. The involvement of the hypothalamus in the coordination of agonistic activities is therefore not surprising.

That subcortical structures are sufficient for the mediation of at least some aspects of *aggressive behavior* was demonstrated toward the end of the last century by Goltz (1892). He observed in the decerebrate dog that nociceptive stimulation elicited barking, growling, snapping of the jaws, lowering of the head, and other aggressive displays. Woodworth and Sherrington (1904) confirmed these findings in cats; they termed the manifestations *pseudaffective* responses, insofar as they resembled the "rage" displayed by normal animals. The investigations of Bard (1928), and of Bard and Rioch (1937), established that in the cat the caudal hypothalamus and midbrain had to remain intact to elicit *sham rage*. Hess (1928) found, similarly, that electric stimulation of the hypothalamus with relatively weak currents produced a "defensive reaction" in the cat. At the onset of stimulation the animal assumed a defensive posture, retracted its ears, began to vocalize, and then hissed and spat. During stimulation the animal would attack in a well-directed manner, but the aggressive display tended to subside as soon as stimulation was discontinued. The extensive investigations of Hess (1954), using the implanted electrode technique, revealed that in particular the *lateral* and *caudal* portions of the hypothalamus are involved in producing aggressive and defensive behavior. Destruction of this region produces placid, unresponsive animals (Ingram et al., 1936; Ranson, 1939). In contrast, destruction of the *medial* hypothalamic region (including the ventromedial nuclei) was reported to produce chronically savage cats (Wheatley, 1944). These latter findings suggest some differentiation within the hypothalamus of areas that either facilitate or inhibit the display of aggressive and defensive behavior. In a recent study (de Molina and Hunsperger, 1959) evidence was obtained of the presence of two sites in the hypothalamus and midbrain tegmentum, stimulation of which differentially produces anger or flight reactions in the unanesthestized cat.

THE ROLE OF THE HYPOTHALAMUS IN EMOTIONAL BEHAVIOR. Are the defensive, aggressive, nutritive, and sexual activities displayed by decerebrate animals, or by animals during stimulation of the hypothalamus, accompanied by emotions, in the way (one presumes) the normal expressions of fear, anger, hunger, and sexual desire are? Or are these "pseudaffective," "sham" responses, motor expressions devoid of their subjective, affective concomitants? Although there is a fundamental uncertainty about inferences made of the subjective states or experiences of animals, attempts have been made by some experimenters to throw light on this question.

Masserman (1941) reported that during hypothalamic stimulation cats showing autonomic and somatic signs of rage continued to drink their milk, groom themselves, and respond to fondling by purring. He concluded on the basis of this finding that the hypothalamus is merely a motor center, and that the expressions of "emotions" seen in these animals are truly pseudaffective states, not incompatible with simultaneous expression of basically different kinds of emotions. In contrast, Hess has argued that the fear and anger displayed by his stimulated cats were in no way distinguishable from such displays seen in normal animals (Hess and Akert, 1955). For instance, the stimulated cat would attack the observer under the slightest provocation. Cohen et al. (1957) reported that animals will learn to cross hurdles in relatively few trials to avoid hypothalamic stimulation. Further, the recent findings of Olds (1961) and others (Brady, 1958; Miller, 1957) with the self-stimulation technique suggest that stimulation of different regions of the hypothalamus may act as "positive" or "negative" reinforcers that resemble in their efficacy the "reward" or "punishment" effects of such natural motivational conditions as feeding or noxious stimulation.

THE HYPOTHALAMUS AND NONEMOTIONAL ACTIVITIES. In addition to controlling various aspects of such emotion-linked processes as arousal and relaxation, feeding and drinking, aggression and defense, sex and maternal behavior, the hypothalamus is vitally involved in the regulation of various homeostatic processes, which are best characterized as persistent domestic rather than recurrent relational activities. Among these functions is the hypothalamic regulation of body temperature. No explanation can be offered why temperature regulation (which is present only in phylogenetically higher, "warm-blooded" vertebrates) is shared with the other functions of the hypothalamus, except that this function is intimately connected with the activities of the sympathetic and parasympathetic systems, which in turn are regulated to a large extent by the hypothalamus.

Warm-blooded animals keep their body temperature constant by *dissipating heat* if the temperature rises above the standard level (about 37°C) and *generating heat* when the temperature falls. Heat dissipation is achieved by sweating, panting, vasodilation, salivation, and other processes, some of which are known parasympathetic responses. Heat production is dependent on such responses as shivering, piloerection, vasoconstriction, and increased skeletal motor activities—responses usually associated with sympathetic activation. Adequate temperature regulation requires afferent input from external and internal thermal receptors, which supply information relating to environmental and bodily temperatures, and efferent output to the various visceral and somatic organs that make possible heat dissipation, conservation, and generation.

There is good evidence that the coordination of thermal homeostasis is to a large extent dependent on the hypothalamus. Magoun et al. (1938) showed that heating of the *preoptic region* of the hypothalamus in cats produces panting and sweating. The same was also observed in monkeys (Beaton et al., 1943). Electric stimulation of the same area with implanted electrodes was likewise reported to produce panting and sweating in the cat (Hess, 1954) and goat (Andersson et al., 1956). These findings suggested the existence in the hypothalamus of "*thermoreceptors*," which directly respond to heat. Additional evidence for this assumption was obtained by von Euler (1950) in a study in which heating of the hypothalamus was combined with electrical recording. In the preoptic area slow potential changes were observed that correlated well with rises in local brain temperature—no such relation was observed in other brain structures tested.

In studies utilizing small stereotaxic lesions (Ranson, 1940) it was found that damage to the *anterior* hypothalamus interfered with heat dissipation processes, whereas lesions in the *posterior* hypothalamus abolished both heat-dissipating and heat-generating processes. These investigations suggested the existence of two "centers" controlling the normal maintenance of body temperature. When the entire hypothalamus is destroyed in mammals (cat or dog), a cold-blooded preparation is produced whose body temperature rises and falls with the temperature of the environment. Removal of structures rostral to the hypothalamus, the cerebral cortex included, do not interfere with temperature regulation (Bard, 1961).

**The Limbic System and Its Functions** The "limbic system" is a vaguely defined term consisting of the proto-vertebrate components of the forebrain, including such subcortical structures as the hippocampus, amygdala, septal nuclei, and some olfactory areas; such allocortical structures as the cingulate gyrus, hippocampal gyrus, and uncus; and possibly also such juxtallocortical structures as the orbitofrontal, insular, and temporal pole cortices. The entire system is sometimes also called the "rhinencephalon," even though only some of its components have direct olfactory connections (Pribram and Kruger, 1954). The latter term, however, has some functional justification, because the functions mediated by this system (regulation of interrelation with prey, enemy, sex partners) depend to a large extent in many vertebrates on olfaction. Owing to the involvement of the limbic system in need-gratifying activities with strong emotional concomitants, Papez (1937) postulated that some of its components represent the cerebral mechanism of emotion; on the basis of similar considerations MacLean (1949) coined the term *visceral brain*.

The limbic system is often considered to include not only the above structures but also the hypothalamus and the midbrain tegmentum (Nauta,

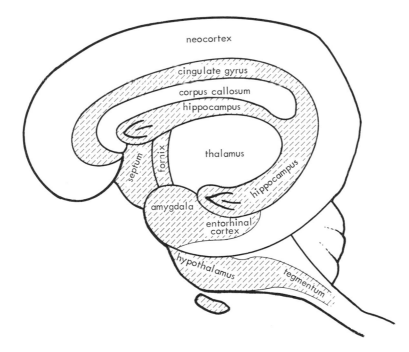

Schematic diagram of the limbic system in monkeys. The relative extent of the limbic system with respect to the neocortex is somewhat exaggerated.

1958), which represent the motor discharge centers of the Papez circuit. So conceived, the term "limbic system" is essentially synonymous with the term "paleocephalon" as used in this study.

**Hippocampus**   The hippocampus forms the bulk of the cerebral hemispheres of lower vertebrates (Green, 1960). It remains a considerable structure in lower mammals, where it is found interposed between the brain stem and the posterior neocortex. The major connections of the hippocampus are by way of its fimbrium and the fornix. Afferent fibers are believed to reach the hippocampus from the midbrain, midline nuclei of the thalamus, septal nuclei, entorhinal cortex, and gyrus cinguli. (These connections are not well established.) Efferent fibers of the hippocampus reach the mammillary bodies and other parts of the hypothalamus, the anterior and mediodorsal thalamic nuclei, the septal region, and also tegmental nuclei. For some time it was believed that the hippocampus mediated olfactory functions. This conception was abandoned, as there is no evidence of direct olfactory projection to the hippocampus. Further, well-developed hippocampus (Ammon's horn) is present in such an anosmatic animal as the porpoise (Breathnach and Goldby, 1954), which has no olfactory nerves. Indeed, partial removal of the hippocampus does not interfere with olfactory discrimination (Swann, 1934, 1935) or olfactory conditioning (Allen, 1940, 1941).

The characteristic EEG pattern of the hippocampus is the theta rhythm (4 to 7 waves per second), which is evoked by peripheral sensory stimulation in the awake rabbit, guinea pig, and cat (Green, 1960). This rhythm may be produced also by stimulation of the reticular formation, by behavioral arousal or by emotional excitement. There are some observations that implicate the hippocampus in the regulation of emotional behavior in general and sexual behavior in particular. For instance, stimulation of various paleocephalic structures that produce penile erection are accompanied by hippocampal after-discharges and spiking, and the erection may be maximal during (and depend on the build-up of) these abnormal hippocampal electrical discharges (MacLean and Ploog, 1962). That the hippocampus has a role in the regulation of sexual behavior is suggested by some of our recent autoradiographic studies (Altman and Das, 1965). By injecting thymidine-$H^3$ into rats to label the chromosomal DNA of multiplying cell nuclei, we found that a large proportion of the granule cells in the dentate gyrus of the hippocampus are formed postnatally. The rate of neurogenesis is high in the neonate and declines to a low level at a period that could be associated with sexual maturation. This rise and fall suggested that the delayed neurogenesis of the hippocampus may be related to delayed sexual maturation. Supporting this hypothesis, we found

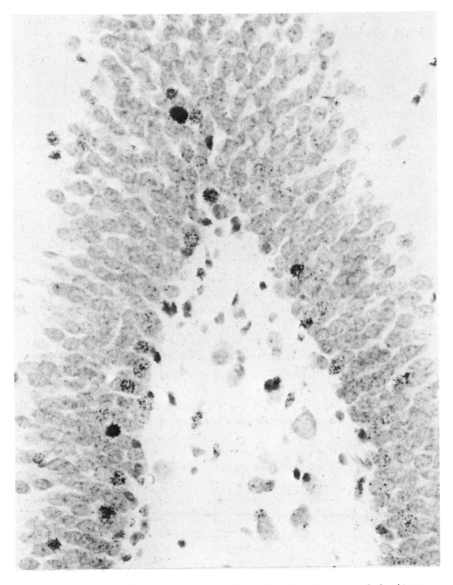

Autoradiographic labeling of granule cells in the dentate gyrus of the hippo-campus in adult rat. The animal was injected postnatally with tritiated thymidine to label cells preparing for multiplication. The labeled neurons in this region were all formed after birth. (Photomicrograph from our laboratory)

that systematically injected testosterone-H³, a radioactively labeled male sex hormone, is bound preferentially by cells of the hippocampus in adult male rats. Similar results were obtained with estradiol-H³ injected into adult female rats (Pfaff, 1965). These findings suggest that cells of the hippocampus may act as gonadal receptors and influence sexual behavior through efferent outflow to the hypothalamus.

**Amygdala** The amygdaloid complex in mammals is composed of the basolateral and corticomedial nuclei. The *corticomedial nuclei* are believed to be the phylogenetically older components, which can be traced back to cyclostomes. The *basolateral complex* becomes differentiated in higher mammals (Gloor, 1960). The corticomedial nuclei receive olfactory fibers from the lateral olfactory tract. In this region short-latency responses can be recorded to olfactory stimulation. In spite of obvious olfactory connections, the amygdala remains a well-differentiated structure in microsmatic species (higher primates) and anosmatic species (porpoise). Apparently the amygdala subserves functions that transcend the mediation of direct olfactory functions. Indeed, long-latency evoked potentials may be recorded in the amygdala in response to several types of peripheral stimuli (Dell, 1952). Likewise, impulses originating from different sense modalities and different parts of the body surface may converge on single amygdaloid cells, but there is no evidence of topographic representation (Machne and Segundo, 1956). The major afferent connections of the amygdala are with the reticular formation, pyriform cortex, and hippocampus. It also has connections with the insular, temporal pole, and posterior orbital cortices, and such neocortical structures as the motor cortex and temporal lobe. The major efferent outflow is by way of the stria terminalis. These fibers reach the septal nuclei, various nuclei of the hypothalamus, and possibly the subthalamus and some tegmental nuclei (Gloor, 1960).

*Stimulation* of the amygdala produces a variety of visceral and somatic responses. Pupillary dilatation or constriction, piloerection, salivation, and gastrointestinal, cardiovascular, and respiratory changes were frequently reported. More specific amygdaloid responses are sniffing, sneezing, coughing, micturition, and defecation. In anesthetized animals amygdaloid stimulation arrests smooth and skeletal muscle movements (Kaada, 1951). In the awake animal, turning movements of the head, licking, chewing, gagging, and retching were observed. In pregnant animals, amygdaloid stimulation may produce uterus contraction. Some of these responses are obviously dependent on sympathetic, parasympathetic, or pituitary activation (Koikegami, 1954); almost all can be seen on stimulation of the hypothalamus.

In awake animals amygdaloid stimulation may produce eating (Gastaut, 1952), which may or may not lead to a transient increase in food intake (Delgado and Anand, 1953; Green et al., 1957). More recently, amygdaloid stimulation was reported to produce inhibition of alimentary conditioned responses, and refusal to eat for varying periods (Fonberg and Delgado, 1961). Amygdaloid stimulation also produces a variety of emotional responses, such as a vigilant posture, expressions of fear and rage, occasionally with well-directed attacks (MacLean and Delgado, 1953). Amygdaloid stimulation was also reported to produce the opposite effect, relaxation and sleep (Anand and Dua, 1955). Self-stimulation studies have shown that amygdaloid stimulation has a rewarding effect, producing a high bar-pressing rate in rats (Olds, 1956, 1958).

*Ablation* studies suggest that the visceral effects described are transient, but that there are more profound and lasting emotional changes. The involvement of the amygdala in the regulation of emotional behavior was first suggested by the classical study of Klüver and Bucy (1938) in monkeys. Following bilateral anterior temporal lobectomy, which destroyed the amygdala, parts of the pyriform lobe and hippocampus, the "personality" of the operated monkeys underwent radical changes. The formerly wild and intractable macaques became tame and docile, showing no sign of fear or anger when provoked. These animals also developed a compulsive oral tendency (putting everything in the mouth) and hypersexuality (masturbation, mounting of every object). In addition, the animals showed "psychic blindness," that is, could no longer recognize familiar objects. Subsequent studies suggested that the "psychic blindness" was attributable to the neocortical damage, whereas the emotional changes could be produced by bilateral destruction of the amygdala alone (Smith, 1950; Walker et al., 1953; Mishkin and Pribram, 1954). (More recently, Akert et al. [1961] reinvestigated the effect of temporal-lobe ablation, producing little or no damage to paleocortical structures. They found transient oral tendencies and tameness, and permanent psychic blindness.)

Schreiner and Kling (1953, 1954, 1956) studied the effects of amygdalectomy in cats, agoutis, and lynx. All these animals became *tame* and showed increased oral tendencies and hypersexuality. Hypersexuality could be abolished by castration and restored with hormone treatment. Rosvold et al. (1954) found that, in a social situation, amygdalectomized rhesus monkeys became more submissive. In line with these taming effects, Weiskrantz and Pribram (1954, 1955, 1956), and Brady et al. (1954) observed impaired avoidance conditioning in amygdalectomized cats, though retention of previously learned avoidance responses was not affected by the operation. In contrast to these reports of taming, Bard and Mountcastle (1948) found that the rage threshold of amygdalectomized cats was raised, tame animals being turned into *savage* ones. In spite of disagreement on this point, there is consensus that the amygdaloid nuclei are intimately involved in the regulation of such emotional activities as feeding, sex, and self-defense (Goddard, 1964).

**Septal Nuclei**   The septal nuclei are anterior midline structures continuous with the
preoptic region of the hypothalamus. Anatomical and physiological studies
suggest that the septal region is connected with the hypothalamus, on the
one hand, and with olfactory and limbic structures on the other. Septal
lesions in the cat produce lowered fear and anger thresholds (Brady and
Nauta, 1953, 1955), suggesting that the septal nuclei exert an inhibitory
effect on the evocation of these emotions. Compatible with these findings
is the observation of Olds (Olds and Milner, 1954; Olds, 1955) of a
"reward" effect obtained in self-stimulating rats with electrodes placed
in the septal region. These effects are presumably largely dependent on
the adjacent fornix, which is one of the major fiber tracts of the limbic
system. Septal stimulation in man is reported to interfere seriously with
consciousness (Scoville, 1959; Heath and Mickle, 1960).

**Other Limbic Structures**   In addition to the hippocampus and
amygdala, the cingulate, insular, or-
bito-frontal and temporal-polar regions are also often classified with the
limbic system. These are paleocortical (allo- and juxtallocortical) structures connected with one another and also with some neocortical regions,
particularly the motor areas. *Stimulation of the cingulate gyrus* and some
of the other areas mentioned produces in cat, dog, monkey, and man
inhibition of respiration and a variety of visceral effects, such as changes
in blood pressure, inhibition of gastric motility, and bladder contraction. These effects resemble those obtained on direct stimulation of the
vagus—suggesting intimate connection with this nerve (Kaada, 1960).
In the awake animal, stimulation in these regions produces an *arrest
reaction*, during which the ongoing activities of the animal come to a halt.
The animal also shows some signs of "arousal," raising its head, with eyes
opened and pupils dilated. Stimulation of the cingulate cortex (Sloan and
Jasper, 1950), and of the orbitofrontal, insular, and temporal-polar cortex
(Kaada, 1951), also produces EEG desynchronization similar to that
obtained on stimulation of the reticular formation.

*Ablation* of these structures is not followed by permanent visceral or
somatic abnormalities. The major changes are motor restlessness and
emotional alterations. Some investigators (Smith, 1944; Ward, 1948)
reported that bilateral ablation of the cingulate gyrus in monkeys produces
tameness and a lowered rage threshold, though these changes may be
transient (Glees et al., 1950). Others (Pribram and Fulton, 1954; Mirsky
et al., 1957) failed to observe radical alterations in the emotional characteristics of monkeys after bilateral cingulectomy. In contrast, Kennard (1955)
reported emotional and related changes in cats. No clear-cut picture
emerges from these studies of the role of these latter limbic structures in

behavior, but they do suggest the involvement of the structures in integrative processes of emotional nature.

In summary, we may say that the evidence presented supports the contention that the paleocephalon controls a group of activities characterized by their intimate connection with the basic needs of the organism, their recurrence in the life of the animal, and by considerable energy mobilization and bodily exertion. Energy mobilization, that is, the deployment of the resources of the body, is primarily under the control of the reticular formation and its diencephalic extensions. Arousal and relaxation, ranging from frenzied excitement to sleep and coma, depend on ascending and descending influences emanating from these structures. The regulation of feeding and drinking, of some aspects of sexual and maternal activities, and of such self-preserving functions as fighting and fleeing, are controlled by the hypothalamus and several superordinated limbic structures, such as the amygdala, hippocampus, cingulate gyrus, septal nuclei, and the extrapyramidal motor pathway. The activities of these paleocephalic structures are largely species-specific (though modifiable, see Chapter 13) behavior patterns that are evoked whenever the needs of the organism remain unsatisfied or the integrity of the individual is threatened. Such functions are usually accompanied by emotion and may be characterized as *affective activities*.

## SELECTED READINGS

Brady, J. V. Emotional behavior. *Handb. Physiol.*, 1960, Sec. 1, **3**, 1529–1552.

Brobeck, J. B. Regulation of feeding and drinking. *Handb. Physiol.*, 1960, Sec. 1, **2**, 1197–1206.

Henry Ford Hospital International Symposium. *Reticular formation of the brain.* Boston: Little, Brown, 1958.

Hess, W. R. *Diencephalon: autonomic and extrapyramidal functions.* New York: Grune & Stratton, 1954.

Lindsley, D. B. Emotion. In S. S. Stevens (Ed.), *Handbook of experimental psychology.* New York: Wiley, 1951, Pp. 473–516.

MacLean, P. D. The limbic system ("visceral brain") in relation to central gray and reticulum of brain stem. *Psychosom. Med.*, 1955, **17**, 355–366.

Magoun, H. Caudal and cephalic influences on the brain stem reticular formation. *Physiol. Rev.*, 1950, **30**, 459–474.

Ruch, T. C. Neurophysiology of emotion and motivation. In T. C. Ruch and J. F. Fulton (Eds.), *Medical physiology and biophysics.* Philadelphia: Saunders, 1960. Pp. 483–499.

Sawyer, C. H. Reproductive behavior. *Handb. Physiol.*, 1960, Sec. 1, **2**, 1225–1240.

Teitelbaum, P. Disturbances in feeding and drinking behavior after hypothalamic lesions. In M. R. Jones (Ed.), *Nebraska symposium on motivation, 1961.* Lincoln: University of Nebraska Press, 1961.

# 12

# Neencephalic Control of Singular Instrumental Activities

*The Cognitive Integrative Level*

The term "neencephalon," as used here, designates a complex of neural pathways and centers acquired relatively late in vertebrate evolution. It is a protomammalian neural system consisting of the lemniscal afferent pathways, several neothalamic relay and association nuclei, an expanse of neocortical projection and association areas, and the pyramidal efferent pathway. The thesis of this chapter is that this mammalian neural system is concerned with the control of a third class of animative activities, which we call "singular, instrumental activities." These terms imply occasional adaptive activities exhibited by individuals in their specific milieu in response to unique conditions or events for which no provision is made (or could be made) by the individual's inherited repertoire of behavior. The formation and execution of such adaptive instrumental activities presuppose highly evolved receptor and afferent systems, which can provide an accurate, detailed, and "objective" representation of the external world. They also necessitate highly evolved memory and learning mechanisms, which make possible the acquisition of new sensory and motor schemata, or programs of behavior, and the extinction of old schemata. Finally, they require an ability to execute highly articulated, skilled activities, to permit manipulation and mastery of the environment. These neencephalic activities appear associated in man with the subjective experiences of knowing and willing, and are accordingly referred to as *cognitive* and *volitional* activities.

**Functions of the Neencephalic Pathways and Centers**    As we have seen earlier, the "lemniscal" or direct corticopetal pathways of the different sensory systems share several common characteristics. All of them are composed of at least three sets of neurons. The axons of the primary, unipolar or bipolar cells terminate ipsilaterally and synapse with second-order neurons of the local segmental, extralemniscal or lemniscal fiber systems. Of these, the second-order lemniscal fibers decussate and terminate in various thalamic relay nuclei. Here synaptic relations are established with third-order neurons, the axons of which pass ipsilaterally through the cortical radiation and terminate in projection areas of the posterior neocortex. These direct pathways are composed of well-myelinated fibers of large diameter, which conduct nerve impulses at a high velocity. The pathways are composed of a large number of afferent fibers, a characteristic suggesting the presence of channels for the transmission of detailed sensory information. They are also distinguished by accurate topographic organization, which permits the transmission of spatially accurate sensory messages. Three major sensory systems have direct corticopetal projections: the somatic, visual, and auditory.

SOME PROPERTIES OF THE DIRECT CORTICOPETAL SOMATIC PATHWAY. According to Herrick and Bishop (1958), the dorsal column and medial lemniscus, which are made up of the first- and second-order fibers of the somesthetic system, respectively, are mammalian acquisitions, which are absent in lower vertebrates without a neocortex. This direct two-neuron pathway is channeled to the ventrobasal nuclear complex of the thalamus, whence the somesthetic impulses are relayed by a third set of neurons to the somesthetic cortex. Microelectrode recordings have shown that single neurons in the ventrobasal nuclear complex respond to stimulation applied to circumscribed receptive fields in the skin, which may vary in size from a few square millimeters in the distal parts of the limbs to several centimeters in the trunk region (Rose and Mountcastle, 1959). Recordings made in this region also suggest that the fibers reaching the neurons bring modality-specific messages. At least, there is evidence of separate transmission of cutaneous (somesthetic) and subcutaneous (kinesthetic) impulses. Unlike the somatic fibers of the spinothalamic tract, which have a high stimulus threshold, the majority of cells in the ventrobasal complex can be fired by low-threshold stimuli (Mountcastle, 1961).

Electrophysiological mapping studies suggest an interesting phylogenetic trend in body representation in the ventrobasal nuclear complex in various mammalian species (Rose and Mountcastle, 1959). In rabbits, lemniscal representation is almost entirely restricted to the face (and particularly mouth) area, with minimal representation of the trunk and limbs. In cats, there is better representation of the limbs, and, in primates and raccoons, the limbs (and particularly digits) have extended representation. As will be stressed later, this observation lends support to the interpretation that the direct somatic corticopetal pathway is concerned with tactile discriminatory functions and the regulation of skilled manipulatory activities. The preferential representation of the face region in lower mammals may be associated with the fact that the mouth region is the main organ of

Schematic outlines of body representation in the ventrobasal thalamic nuclei in the rabbit, cat, and monkey. Note the increasing relative representation of the digits from rabbit to monkey. (From Rose and Mountcastle. Touch and kinesthesis. *Handb. Physiol.*, 1959. Sec. 1, **1**, 401)

manipulation in most lower mammals, whereas the growing areal representation of the limbs and digits in primates may be connected with the increasing importance of these organs in tactile discrimination and in object manipulation.

Third-order neurons located in the ventrobasal nuclear complex of the thalamus give rise to fibers that terminate in the *somatic areas* of the *cortex* (postcentral gyrus in primates). The connection between these two structures is again a direct and largely exclusive one, as indicated by anatomical studies revealing that cells in this thalamic relay region degenerate totally following ablation of the postcentral gyrus. Anatomical and electrophysiological investigations have further shown the presence of a topographic representation of the body surface on the somatic areas of the cortex.

The form of cortical body representation differs in different species, and it is "distorted" in accordance with the importance of specific body parts or organs in tactile and manipulatory functions. Thus, according to Adrian (1943), in sheep, cortical representation is restricted to the lip region; in pigs, to the snout, with no representation of the legs in either species. In goats, the representation of the legs is small in comparison with that of the mouth and snout, and the representation of the nostrils, in horses, is almost as extensive as that of the contralateral legs. In primates, cortical body representation is more evolved, with large areas being dedicated to the face and limbs, and also to the digits of the limbs. In spider monkeys, which have a prehensile tail, this specialized manipulatory organ also has considerable cortical representation (Chang et al., 1947). The extent of representation of peripheral structures in the cortex may be related to their role in tactile and manipulatory functions. Presumably, the larger number of cortical neurons available for a given structure improves the "graininess" of the projection "mosaic," or its resolving power, and permits better point-to-point localization and increased discriminatory articulation of the transmitted "image."

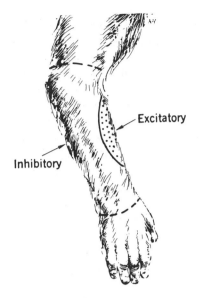

The discharge frequency of a neuron in the somatic cortex of a monkey was greatly increased when the "excitatory" region of its receptive field was lightly touched; similar stimulation of the surrounding "inhibitory" region caused a decrease in the discharge of the neuron. (From Mountcastle. Some functional properties of the somatic afferent system. In Rosenblith, Ed., *Sensory communication*. John Wiley & Sons, 1961)

Individual neurons in the somesthetic cortex, as in the ventrobasal nuclei of the thalamus, respond to stimulation of a circumscribed receptive field on the surface of the body. Such a receptive field is associated with an inhibitory surround in the skin, stimulation of which inhibits firing of the neuron (Mountcastle, 1961). It was also shown that stimulation of a skin area that produces inhibition of a given neuron may have an excitatory effect on an adjacent neuron. This system of reciprocal organization (which is dependent on lateral inhibition, see page 164) may be of some importance in coding the topographic locus and spatial attributes of the transmitted signal.

In addition to the postcentral gyrus (or its homologue in nonprimates) electrophysiological studies (Adrian, 1941; Woolsey, 1943) have revealed the existence of a *second somatic* cortical *projection area*. There is also anatomical (Walker, 1944) and electrophysiological evidence (Woolsey et al., 1947; Malis et al., 1953) of somesthetic projection to the motor area of the cortex (precentral gyrus in primates) and of motor outflow from the somatic areas. Accordingly, Woolsey (1958) suggested that we may distinguish the following cortical structures concerned directly with somesthetic functions: (1) *somatic sensory-motor area I*, such as the postcentral gyrus in primates (SmI); (2) *somatic sensory-motor area II* (SmII); (3) *somatic motor-sensory area I*, namely, the precentral motor area (MsI); and (4) *somatic motor-sensory area II*, also called the supplementary motor area (MsII). There is some evidence that the receptive fields in most neurons in the second somatic sensory-motor area are larger (which, therefore, give poorer resolution) than those in the primary somatic sensory-motor area, and that at least some of these fire to nociceptive stimuli only (Mountcastle, 1961). In the second somatic area there is also a convergence of somatic and auditory impulses (Mickle and Ades, 1952; Berman, 1961), a finding that suggests the existence of *intersensory interaction* at this region.

In summary, anatomical and electrophysiological studies imply that the direct corticopetal, lemniscal somatic pathway can transmit to the cortex, directly and with little delay, messages generated by low-threshold stimuli. These messages are modality-specific, show good spatial resolution, and preserve faithfully the topographic source of stimuli. This pathway, accordingly, may be responsible for the transmission of *object-centered* (cognitive), low-threshold *epicritic* messages, in contrast to the extra-lemniscal spinothalamic pathway, which appears to transmit *subject-centered* (affective), high-threshold *protopathic* messages (Head, 1920; Rose and Mountcastle, 1959).

The relatively few recent *ablation* studies, in which both somatic areas I and II were removed, have provided ambiguous data on their exact role in somesthesis. Zubek (1951 a, b, 1952) reported that in the rat tactual form discrimination may be retained after bilateral ablation of the somatic areas. In contrast, serious impairment in tactile discrimination was obtained in the cat (Zubek, 1951) and the dog (Allen, 1947). Benjamin and Thompson (1959) reported impairment in roughness discrimination after removal of the somatic areas in adult cats, with less serious deficit if the same areas were removed in infant cats. Monkeys after unilateral ablation of somatic areas I and II could, with some retraining, solve a somesthetic form-discrimination problem with the contralateral hand, but they displayed severe signs of tactile impairment (Kruger and Porter, 1958). In another study, Orbach and Chow (1959) found serious losses in tactile discrimination habits in monkeys after ablation of somatic area I. These animals, however, could relearn the task. Removal of somatic area II alone produced little deficit. Because tactile projection is also present in the motor cortex (MsI and MsII), removal of the somesthetic areas alone may not be sufficient to abolish tactile discrimination totally. This proposition, however, is difficult to test because added removal of the motor cortex would interfere with the motor performance of a task. In most of the available experiments of this type relatively simple form-discrimination tasks were presented to the animals, and simple response patterns (leg lifting, reaching, and so on) were required from them in response. It is not inconceivable that more complex tactile and manipulatory functions are mediated by the somesthetic projection areas.

SOME PROPERTIES OF THE DIRECT CORTICOPETAL VISUAL PATHWAY. The rods and cones of the retina form the photosensitive receptor surface on which a relatively accurate optic image of the external world is projected. The first-order neurons of this system are represented by the bipolar cells, which synapse in the retina with the second-order ganglion cells. The axons of the latter form the optic nerve and tract. The fiber components of small diameter, which are of phylogenetically more ancient derivation (Bishop, 1959), terminate in the superior colliculus. These high-threshold optic fibers represent the "extralemniscal" pathway of the visual system, with no direct projection to the striate cortex but a major outflow to the reticular formation (Altman and Carpenter, 1961). In contrast, the phylogenetically more recent, large-diameter, fast-conducting fibers of the optic tract terminate in the lateral geniculate nucleus, whence they are relayed to the striate area of the occipital lobe.

Anatomical (Minkowski, 1913) and electrophysiological (Talbot and Marshall, 1941) studies have established the existence of a topographic representation of the retina in the lateral geniculate nucleus and over the surface of the striate cortex. The cortical representation of the central portion of the retina (the area centralis, or fovea) is exaggerated relative to the peripheral parts of the retina. In the lateral geniculate nucleus of higher mammals, the optic fibers coming from the ipsilateral and contralateral eyes terminate in segregated laminae. In carnivores, the lateral geniculate nucleus is composed of three layers, the two outer layers (the dorsal and ventral layers) receiving fibers from the *nasal half* of the contralateral retina, the inner layer from the *temporal half* of the ipsilateral retina. In higher primates (Walls, 1953) there is a six-layered lateral geniculate nucleus. The two ventral layers contain many large cells; they are therefore called the magnocellular layers. The four dorsal layers are composed of smaller cells and are referred to as the parvocellular layers. The alternate layers of the primate lateral geniculate nucleus come from opposite eyes.

Granit (1947), using microelectrodes inserted into the retina, found that if the eye is stimulated with diffuse light, some retinal neurons fire at the beginning of stimulation ("on" units); others fire at the end of stimulation ("off" units); and still others fire at both the onset and the termination of illumination ("on-and-off" units). Kuffler (1953), using small reflected light spots as a stimulus, showed subsequently that there are only two types of retinal neurons, or "units," namely, "on" and "off" units. "On," or *center-on*, units fire (or are excited) when the center of their visual receptive field is stimulated, and stop firing (or are inhibited) when the concentric periphery of their visual receptive field is stimulated. The reverse holds for "off," or *center-off*, units. The "on-and-off" response of units observed with diffuse illumination is presumably attributable to simultaneous stimulation of the center and periphery of an "on" unit. The "on" units have also been described as *brightness-signaling*, or B units; the "off" units, as *darkness-signaling*, or D units (Jung, 1961). Such "on" and "off" units with *circular receptive* fields and antagonistic *concentric peripheries* have been observed not only in the retina but also in the lateral geniculate nucleus of the cat (Hubel and Wiesel, 1961). These investigators found that cells in the external (dorsal and ventral) layers were influenced exclusively by the contralateral eye, those of the middle layer by receptive fields in the ipsilateral eye. The receptive fields of cells influenced from the area centralis were smaller (permitting better spatial resolution) than those from the peripheral parts of the retina.

In contrast to the retina and the lateral geniculate nucleus, the receptive fields of single neurons in the striate cortex are of *varying shapes,* and with or without an antagonistic surround (Hubel and Wiesel, 1959, 1962). These receptive fields are usually *bar-shaped,* with parallel straight-line, rather than circular, boundaries and are oriented vertically, horizontally, or obliquely. Cortical units cannot be influenced easily by circular light spots but are best driven by stimuli of specific size, shape, orientation, or movement. Hubel and Wiesel distinguished between cortical units that have "simple" or "complex" receptive fields. Cells with simple fields have, like retinal and lateral geniculate units, excitatory and inhibitory parts. Light spots different in shape from the entire receptive field have

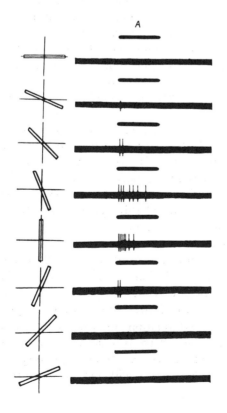

A

Response of a single neuron in the striate cortex to a bar-shaped visual image. Orientation of the bar determines the rate of discharge of this cell. (Hubel and Wiesel. Preceptive fields, binocular interaction and functional architecture in the cat's visual cortex. *J. Physiol.* [London], 1962, **160,** 106–154)

less effect than do spots of the appropriate size and shape; spots falling on the excitatory region alone have greater effect than those that fall on both excitatory and inhibitory regions. The response of "simple" units to moving objects can be predicted on the basis of stimulation of both the excitatory and inhibitory portions of their receptive fields. The most effective stimulus configurations are appropriately oriented slits (narrow rectangles of light), edges (lines between areas of different brightness), and rectangular bars. Cells with "complex" fields have no clear-cut excitatory and inhibitory portions, and their configuration is not easy to determine, because "complex" cells are not easy to "drive" with circular light spots. Some cells with complex fields can be driven by a properly oriented stimulus even when projected onto different parts of the retinal field.

Accordingly, a single cortical neuron can detect (or respond optimally to) a particular visual configuration or direction of movement. It is not understood how, at the level of the cortex, the circular receptive fields of the retina and lateral geniculate nucleus are transformed into specific shapes. Hubel and Wiesel found that all cells in a single vertical column of the cortex had the same receptive fields, and they postulated that the integrative process leading to the identification of shapes may occur at successive "levels" of such columns. They also found that, unlike cells in the lateral geniculate nucleus, the great majority of cortical cells representing the area centralis were influenced by stimuli from both eyes. In *binocularly* affected cells the two receptive fields tended to have the same shapes and orientation. These recent findings of integrative functions mediated by single cortical neurons contrast with older concepts of "mosaic" representation of pattern, movement, and other attributes in the visual cortex.

These results suggest that the direct corticopetal pathway, with its terminal station in the striate cortex, is involved in the mediation of the visual discrimination of such attributes as shape, size, and movement. Another approach designed to elucidate the role of the striate cortex in vision is the *surgical removal* of this area combined with a behavioral study of subsequent visual deficits. Pioneering work of this type was carried out by Lashley (1920), who usually employed rats in his extensive series of experiments. He found (Lashley, 1933) that rats trained to discriminate an illuminated alley from a darkened one showed amnesia for the habit if the striate cortex was removed bilaterally. However, the animals required no more trials to relearn the task than did normal animals. Similarly, prior removal of the striate cortex did not affect the learning of this task in naive animals. This finding suggested that *brightness discrimination* can be mastered in the absence of the visual cortex (although rats without a striate cortex showed a considerable deficit in discriminating two alleys with minimal brightness difference). In contrast, destruction of the striate cortex produced permanent deficits in the ability of rats to perform pattern-discrimination tasks. However, Lashley found later (1939) that sparing small remnants of the striate cortex may be sufficient to retain a learned visual-pattern discrimination. These findings of Lashley in the rat were found to hold also for other species. Brightness discrimination is not interfered with by bilateral removal of the striate cortex in dogs (Marquis, 1934) and monkeys (Klüver, 1941), but after removal of the striate cortex primates cannot learn a visual pattern discrimination (Klüver, 1941).

SOME PROPERTIES OF THE DIRECT CORTICOPETAL AUDITORY PATHWAY. The auditory system has a phylogenetic history different from that of the visual system. Unlike the visual system, which is of suprasegmental origin, the auditory system is derived from a segmental structure, the lateral line organ of fish. Presumably because of this circumstance, there is a complex auditory representation in the segmental nervous system (medulla). In the course of vertebrate phylogeny, however, the auditory system has acquired suprasegmental representations paralleling those of the visual system. The *toris semicircularis* of fish and amphibia (buried under the optic tectum) became differentiated into the inferior colliculus and, in mammals, a thalamic relay nucleus (the medial geniculate body) evolved to send fibers to the auditory projection areas in the temporal cortex. In spite of these parallels, no satisfactory evidence is available at present to suggest that the inferior colliculus represents an "extralemniscal" pathway (paralleling the role of the superior colliculus). Nevertheless, there is some evidence that the role of the medial geniculate body and of the auditory projection areas may be similar in audition to that of the lateral geniculate body and striate cortex in vision.

Recording evoked potentials in response to electric stimulation of small bundles of the cochlear nerve, Woolsey and Walsh (1942) established the existence of two auditory projection areas in the cat (AI, AII). This finding was subsequently confirmed by Tunturi (1944) in the dog. In all these areas there is an orderly representation of localized portions of the cochlea, with corresponding frequency-specific (tonotopic) organization (for example, Hind, 1953). In a combined anatomical and physiological study, Rose and Woolsey (1949) found that only destruction of the primary auditory area leads to widespread degeneration of the pars principalis of the medial geniculate body; the suggestion is then that the supplementary auditory areas receive their inputs from other sources. (For further details, see Ades, 1959; Woolsey, 1958, 1961.)

What is the contribution of the neencephalic auditory system to auditory functions? Girden et al. (1936) found that a decorticate dog could acquire a conditioned response to a sound, although the animal exhibited a considerable rise in absolute auditory threshold. Subsequently Girden (1942) showed that with continued testing the auditory threshold of such an animal returned to normal. This characteristic was confirmed by Kryter and Ades (1943) in the cat; they found that cats exhibited no change in the auditory intensity threshold after removal of the auditory cortex. Allen (1945) investigated the effects of removal of the auditory areas in dogs on frequency discrimination. He trained normal dogs to flex a leg in response to presentation of one tone and to withold this response when another tone was presented. After removal of the auditory areas (as defined by Tunturi), the animals showed no difficulty in relearning the leg flexion to the "positive" sound but were unable to inhibit responding when the negative tone was sounded. After repeated punishments for responding to the negative stimulus, the animal ceased responding to either the positive or the negative tone.

In a similarly designed experiment, Meyer and Woolsey (1952) studied in cats the effects of removal of the auditory areas I, II, together with removal of the second somatic area (SmII) on frequency discrimination. In animals in which parts of AI and AII escaped damage, frequency discrimination was unaffected; however, following total destruction of all the areas mentioned, auditory frequency discrimination of this type (responding to one tone and not responding to another) was abolished. In contrast, when discrimination is required between a continuous, neutral background tone and a subsequent tone of different frequency, which represents a "warning" of imminent punishment, as in the experiments of Diamond and Neff (1957), removal of area I and surrounding regions produces no appreciable deficit in frequency discrimination.

These results would suggest that frequency discrimination as such need not depend on cortical mediation but that the learning of a differential auditory discrimination (rather than merely a conditioned response to a change in frequency) is dependent on the auditory areas of the cortex. Of some interest in this connection is the finding of Diamond and Neff (1957) that cats trained to discriminate *auditory patterns* (for example, "low, high, low" tone being the pattern for the neutral stimulus, and "high, low, high" the pattern of the warning stimulus) lose the habit, and cannot relearn it, after removal of area I and the surrounding region. Whether this loss is comparable to the inability to discriminate visual patterns after removal of the striate cortex has not been adequately resolved (Diamond and Chow, 1962).

In summary, the available evidence seems to indicate that the somatic, visual, and auditory neencephalic pathways are not essential for the mediation of such basic sensory functions as roughness, brightness, or loudness discrimination. In contrast, removal of the respective cortical projection area seriously interferes with or permanently abolishes visual, auditory, and possibly somesthetic pattern recognition. Because pattern discrimination is the basis of *object recognition* (the majority of objects can be discriminated only on the basis of such configurational cues as shape, size, and details), the deficit produced by removal of cortical projection areas may be interpreted as interfering seriously with the ability of the animal to acquire a detailed and accurate representation of its physical environment.

CORTICAL PROJECTION OF OTHER AFFERENT SYSTEMS. There are several major afferent systems that lack direct pathways to the cortex or that have only ill-defined neencephalic representation. For example, there is no direct projection from the large olfactory system to the neocortex, although indirect connections may exist by way of rhinencephalic structures. It was believed for a long time that the vestibular mechanism lacks afferent pathways to the cortex. Some recent electrophysiological studies, however, suggest that vestibular impulses can reach the cortex (Walzl and Mountcastle, 1949; Andersson and Gernandt, 1954; Mickle and Ades, 1954). Likewise, it was believed for a long time that there is no cortical representation of gustation. But there is electrophysiological evidence of gustatory representation in the thalamic and cortical somesthetic face area (Patton and Amassian, 1952; Benjamin and Akert, 1959), and conflicting evidence whether ablation of the cortical taste area does (Benjamin and Pfaffmann, 1955; Benjamin and Akert, 1959) or does not (Börnstein, 1940; Patton et al., 1946) produce deficits in taste discrimination. Removal of an adjacent paleocephalic region, the insular cortex, was reported to produce changes in the preference threshold for quinine in the monkey (Ruch and Patton, 1946; Bagshaw and Pribram, 1953).

It is tentatively justified to conclude that the "lower" senses not concerned with gathering information about the objective or physical properties of the environment have only indirect or sparse representation in the neocortex. (Olfaction, as described earlier, provides information mostly about such subject-centered aspects of organic stimuli as the proximity of foe, friend, or mate; in contrast, gustation is concerned with the palatability of detected food substances. Similarly, the vestibular apparatus, which responds to such physical forces as gravity or acceleration, is concerned with the maintenance of body posture rather than the gathering of information about the environment.) There is no reason to assume, however, that impulses from these "lower" senses (which can be extremely complex in many respects) cannot reach the cortex to modify the organization of perceptual and manipulatory activities.

**Neencephalic Association Areas**  Flechsig (1876) coined the term "association centers" for the large expanse of cortical areas that do not receive major thalamic projections and that, in terms of myelin formation (*myelogenesis*), mature relatively late in postnatal development. The association areas also differ cytoarchitectonically from the granular sensory projection areas and the agranular motor projection areas, and are thus distinguishable from the latter by at least three morphological criteria. To these criteria may be added a phylogenetic one,

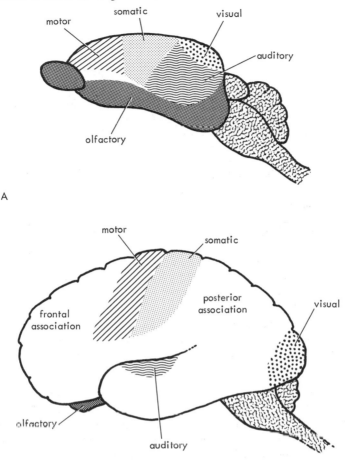

Comparison of the cortex of an insectivore, A (after G. Elliott Smith) with that of man, B. Almost the entire cortex of the shrew is occupied by projection fields of the various sensory systems and the motor area. In contrast, there is a wide expanse of frontal and posterior association fields in man. Figures are not drawn to scale.

namely, that the association areas show a progressive growth in mammalian phylogeny: the *posterior association field* surrounding the sensory projection areas and the *frontal association field* anterior to the motor region are virtually nonexistent in lowest mammals (insectivores) and become increasingly larger as we ascend from lower to higher forms.

The phrase "association areas" also implies, in terms of older psychological concepts, that these structures are involved in "higher" associative or integrative functions. Considerable research has gone into this problem in the last half century; although the accumulated evidence does not

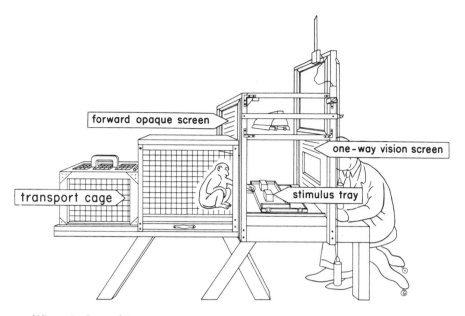

Wisconsin General Testing Apparatus for testing sensory discrimination, conditional reaction, learning set in monkeys. (After Harlow. From Leuba, *Man: a general psychology.* Holt, Rinehart and Winston, 1961. Courtesy of Dr. Harry F. Harlow)

support the older concept of associative functions as a distinctive property of these areas, it does suggest that these areas are involved in not easily specifiable "higher" or intellective perceptual and manipulatory functions.

We should mention at this point that the association areas in the cortex are not entirely devoid of thalamic projections, though these connections are much less bulky than those received by the projection areas. The posterior association areas have two-way connections with the pulvinar and posterolateral nucleus of the thalamus, and possibly also with some of the relay nuclei, whereas the frontal association areas receive and send fibers to the mediodorsal nucleus. Data, furthermore, suggest that the connections between the cortical projection and association areas are dependent at least partly on indirect cortico-subcortical pathways (Lashley, 1944; Sperry et al., 1955).

SOME COMMON TESTS OF "HIGHER" FUNCTIONS. In accordance with the assumption that the association areas are implicated in higher behavioral processes, several tests have been designed to probe losses in "intelligent" behavior as a consequence of ablation of these areas. In *sensory discrimination tests* the animal is confronted with two or more objects, and is rewarded (usually with food or water) for choosing the arbitrarily selected "correct" one. With the aid of such tests the sensory acuity and learning ability of the animal are assessed. In *conditional*

## DISCRIMINATION LEARNING CURVES

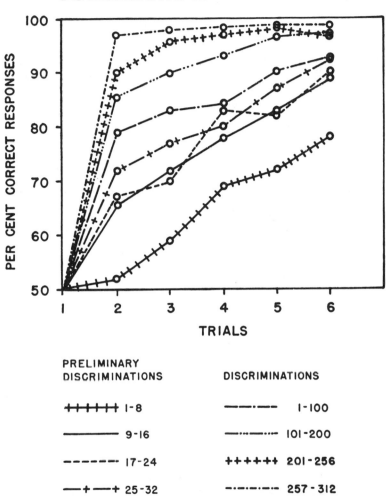

Learning curves of rhesus monkeys, plotted for successive blocks of discrimination trials. Learning is slow and gradual on the initial set of discrimination tasks but becomes fast and direct as the animal acquires a "learning set." (From Harlow. The formation of learning sets. *Psychol. Rev.,* 1949, **56,** 51–65) *Compare this with the following illustration.*

reaction tests the "correct" or rewarded choice between two stimulus objects is made dependent on a third condition. For instance, in the choice between a triangle and a square, the former is the correct one if it appears on a red background, whereas the latter is correct when the background is green.

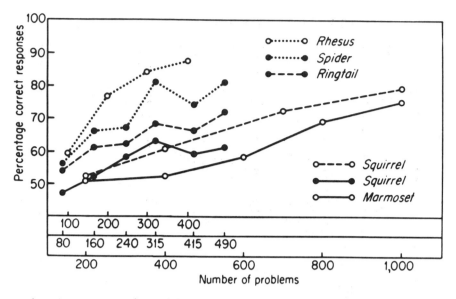

Learning-set curves obtained for a variety of species of monkeys. (From Riopelle, Complex processes. In Waters et al., Eds., *Principles of comparative psychology.* McGraw-Hill, 1960, page 220)

When animals are repeatedly presented with learning problems, they tend to solve the new problems faster; this is the *learning set task* (Harlow, 1949), which is believed to represent a "higher" capacity. In *matching tests* the animal is required to select among objects the one similar to that displayed by the experimenter or by the automatic testing apparatus. This test, instead of requiring the formation of a fixed choice, is probing the animal's ability to perceive changing relations. In the *oddity test* the animal has to select from several choice objects one that is in some respect different from the others. This, like the previous test, is testing the animal's capacity to perceive a relation among many objects. In the *delayed reaction test* food is hidden beneath a choice object in front of the animal. A screen is then lowered between the animal and the choice object for a certain period, the delay interval, and then the animal is permitted to make its choice (Hunter, 1913). In the *delayed alternation test* the placement of the reward is alternated from trial to trial (Carr, 1917). In these two latter tests, it was originally believed, an ideational process is involved, because the animal has to retain vicariously in its "memory" a preceding event. In the various *manipulation tests* the animal is required to turn levers, open latches, pull strings, or otherwise manipulate objects in order to receive a reward. With these tests the animal's ability to perform skilled acts and perceive relations among objects is investigated.

SOME FUNCTIONS OF THE POSTERIOR ASSOCIATION AREAS. On the basis of the proximity of the *prestriate areas* (areas 18 and 19 in the occipital lobe of primates) to the striate cortex, it was postulated a long time ago that these association areas mediate higher visual or "visuo-psychic" functions. Several investigators (Lashley, 1948; Chow, 1951, 1952; Riopelle et al., 1951; Meyer et al., 1951) tested this theory by re-moving bilaterally the prestriate areas in monkeys; they found that the operation produced little or no deficit on brightness, color, and pattern discrimination, or on the oddity problem. In contrast, other investigators (Ades, 1946; Ades and Raab, 1949) reported deficits on color and pattern discrimination in monkeys that underwent operations of this nature. Similarly, removal of the prestriate cortex (middle suprasylvian gyrus) in cats was recently reported to produce mild to severe impairment in visual size and shape discrimination and in solving detour problems (Warren and Sinha, 1957; Warren et al., 1961; Hara, 1962). The evidence about the role of prestriate regions in the mediation of complex visual learning tasks is, accordingly, ambiguous at present.

A better substantiated and more surprising finding is the involvement of the *infratemporal association areas* in visual discrimination functions. As mentioned earlier, Klüver and Bucy (1938) found that removal of the temporal lobe in monkeys produces, among other deficits, "psychic blind-ness" or loss of visual object recognition, without producing a field defect or losses in acuity. In subsequent studies it was shown that this deficit can be produced by bilateral removal of the *middle* and *inferior temporal gyri* (Chow, 1951, 1952; Riopelle et al., 1953; Pribram and Mishkin, 1955). Infratemporal ablations produce amnesia for learned color and pattern discriminations, though the animals can relearn these tasks. The deficit appears to be specifically visual; somesthetic discrimination and delayed response performance are not affected by the same operation (Pribram and Barry, 1956; Wilson, 1957; Pasik et al., 1960; Bates and Ettlinger, 1960). Furthermore, such visual deficits do not occur following ablation of several other association regions of the cortex, such as the parietal cortex or the medial surface of the temporal lobe (Chow, 1952; Mishkin, 1954; Wilson, 1957), a finding that suggests an instance of *double dissociation* (Teuber, 1955) of functions. Similar results were obtained recently by producing focal epileptic discharges in the occipital (Kraft et al., 1960) or infratemporal cortex (Stamm and Pribram, 1961) by placing a chemical irritant (alumina cream) over these areas. This procedure, unlike ablation, produced a deficit in learning but not in retention of tasks already mastered.

In an attempt to delineate further the deficit produced by infratemporal lesions, Orbach and Fantz (1958) and Chow and Survis (1958) showed that amnesia did not occur for visual tasks on which the animals were overtrained. In a similar vein, Pasik et al. (1958) found that the deficit following infratemporal lesions was greatly reduced if the visual patterns presented to the animals were large. Wilson and Mishkin (1959) compared the effects of striate and infratemporal ablations. No strict dissociation could be demonstrated; nevertheless, the monkeys with striate lesions showed, as expected, visual deficits attributable to acuity loss and field defects (these animals were most deficient on a patterned string task), whereas the animals with infratemporal lesions showed greatest deficit on complex learning tasks, specifically on the learning set problem (Riopelle et al., 1953).

The recent attempts to parcellate the "higher" functions of the posterior association areas have brought evidence of the existence of regions specifically concerned with somesthetic functions. It was found, for example (Blum, 1951; Blum et al., 1950; Pribram and Barry, 1956), that lesions in the *parietal association cortex* (sparing the somesthetic projection areas) produce in monkeys impairment in the performance of complex tactile discrimination tasks. Little or no deficit was found when tested on "simpler" somesthetic tasks, such as temperature and roughness discrimination, but there were considerable losses in pattern discrimination. If the parietal lesion extended to the *posterior temporal area* (Blum, 1951), the somesthetic deficit became even more pronounced. With parietal association cortex lesions the degree of tactile deficit was correlated with the difficulty of the test, as defined by the number of trials the animals required to learn the task preoperatively (Wilson, 1957). Similar results were obtained in another experiment (Stamm and Warren, 1961) in which, instead of ablation, the functioning of the posterior parietal cortex was interfered with by epileptogenic implants (alumina cream) placed over this area. This procedure interfered specifically with the acquisition (but not the retention) of more complex roughness-discrimination tasks.

Paralleling the deficits produced in visual and tactile discriminations after removal of the infratemporal and parietal association areas, respectively, deficits were reported in auditory "pattern" discrimination following ablation of the *insular-temporal cortex* (Diamond and Neff, 1957). A somewhat more surprising, and unresolved, finding is the severe deficit in simple auditory discrimination as a consequence of lesions in the lateral frontal association areas in monkeys (R. A. Blum, 1952; Weiskrantz and Mishkin, 1958).

The posterior association areas are, accordingly, implicated in discriminatory functions. Discriminatory losses are most pronounced in the visual modality (following prestriate and infratemporal lesions) but may also be produced in somesthesis (parietal lesions) and audition (insular-temporal lesions). In agreement with these findings, massive ablations of the *parieto-temporo-preoccipital areas* ("PTO cortex"), sparing the primary projection areas, produce amnesia and acquisition deficits in visual and somesthetic discrimination problems. These deficits are most severe for such tasks as conditional reactions, serial discriminations, mirror-image discrimination, and similar complex tasks (Blum et al., 1950; Blum, 1951; Harlow et al., 1951; Meyer et al., 1951; Riopelle et al., 1951; Harlow et al., 1952). Frequently these deficits are clearly not caused by primary sensory deficits (such as scotoma) but appear to represent *amnestic* (deficits in recall) and *agnostic* (deficits in "cognition") syndromes. Thus an operated animal that shows a preference for red over green (suggesting that it can perceive color) cannot learn a red-green discrimination, which is easily solved by normal animals (Semmes, 1953).

SOME FUNCTIONS OF THE FRONTAL ASSOCIATION AREAS. It was held for a long time that the frontal, or anterior, cortex mediates "higher" psychic functions. This belief was based, not on experimental evidence, but on phylogenetic considerations: that the frontal cortex is virtually nonexistent in lower mammals and is most highly developed in man. An extensive, systematic investigation of the functions of the frontal association field, the region anterior to the precentral motor and premotor areas, was carried out by Jacobsen. Jacobsen (1931, 1935) reported that bilateral removal of the frontal cortex in monkeys did not produce amnesia for previously learned visual discrimination tasks or for preoperatively acquired simpler manipulatory skills, such as opening latch boxes. However, such an operation produced deficits in the performance of serial tasks (the opening of boxes with several independent latches), on the delayed-reaction test (Jacobsen et al., 1935), and delayed-alternation test (Jacobsen and Nissen, 1937). Jacobsen also noted an increase in activity level, and marked distractability and stereotypy in behavior. These deficits or symptoms were not obtained after bilateral removal of the premotor, temporal, or parietal regions (Jacobsen and Haselrud, 1936; Jacobsen, 1936).

Impairment on the *delayed response task* has been confirmed by a number of investigators as an invariable consequence of bilateral frontal ablations. More recent studies with partial frontal ablations suggest (R. A. Blum, 1952; Pribram et al., 1952; Pribram and Bagshaw, 1953; Mishkin, 1957) that this deficit may be produced by removal of the midlateral frontal areas alone (banks of *sulcus principalis*). Lesions in the ventromedial and ventrolateral frontal regions produce little or no deficit on the delayed response test. Though deficit on the delayed reaction test is a consistent symptom after frontal ablations, a few investigators (Blum et al., 1951; Campbell and Harlow, 1945) reported slight recovery of the function if the animals were tested from 2 to 3 years after the operation. Also, improvement could be demonstrated in performance of this task when the level of external stimulation (which presumably produces distraction during the delay) was reduced (Malmo, 1942) or when the inter-trial period was lengthened (Spaet and Harlow, 1943).

Jacobsen's finding of an absence of deficits in visual discrimination tasks following ablation of the frontal cortex was also confirmed by several investigators (Harlow et al., 1951, 1952; Pribram et al., 1952).

However, others (Harlow and Dagnon, 1943; Blum, 1952; Ettlinger and Wegener, 1958; Weiskrantz and Mishkin, 1958; Orbach and Fischer, 1959) reported amnesia in some of their frontal or prefrontal animals for preoperatively acquired visual, somesthetic, and auditory discriminations, and an increase in the number of trials required to learn or relearn such tasks. In an attempt to resolve these contradictory findings, Rosvold and Mishkin (1961) undertook experiments designed to determine whether the deficits of frontal animals in visual discrimination are "sensory" or "nonsensory." They found that the same "frontal animal" may or may not show a visual-discrimination deficit, depending on the training procedure. If a *baited method* is used, in which the first choice of the animal is made consistently the correct one, so that the animal does not have to reverse its initial preference, the frontal animal does not show a deficit. If, on the other hand, an *unbaited procedure* is used, in which the animal's first choice is made the incorrect response, so that the animal has to inhibit and reverse its initial preference, the frontal animal shows considerable deficit in performance.

This result would suggest that frontal animals may be retarded on a discrimination task but that the loss is of "nonsensory" origin. Unlike the frontal animals, animals with posterior cortical lesions show a deficit irrespective of whether the baited or unbaited procedure was used—an indication that their loss is truly of "sensory" origin. This nonsensory deficit is also shown in *go no-go discrimination tasks,* in which the animal is rewarded for responding to the correct choice as well as for *not* responding to the incorrect one. Frontal animals display an inability to refrain from responding to the unrewarded stimulus (Rosvold et al., 1961). Similar deficit is seen in habit-reversal where the animal is required to respond to a previously negative stimulus (Settlage et al., 1948).

What is the common denominator of the behavior deficits produced by frontal ablation, or, to express it differently, what may be the inferred function of the anterior association areas? The delayed-reaction test, on which frontal animals are invariably deficient, was originally believed to test "higher" *ideational processes,* because the animal is required to make its choice on the basis of cues no longer available at the time of responding (Hunter, 1913). This interpretation was largely abandoned when it was found that virtually all species tested, such as rodents (Honzik, 1931), could solve the problem. The subsequent interpretation was that the delayed-response procedure tests *immediate memory.* Accordingly, Jacobsen interpreted the impairment of frontal animals subjected to this task as an immediate-memory deficit. The subsequent finding of impairment on the delayed-alternation and double-alternation tests could be interpreted in the same fashion. This hypothesis, however, cannot adequately explain other common (although not invariable) frontal-lesion symptoms, such as hyperactivity, distractability, and the inability to inhibit natural preferences or acquired habits.

An alternative hypotheses of the frontal-lobe deficit is an impairment of *cortical inhibition* (Stanley and Jaynes, 1949; Konorski, 1961; Rosvold and Mishkin, 1961). That is, according to this theory, the primary function of the frontal lobe is to inhibit responses initiated by subordinated neural systems. Indeed, this theory can explain the majority of frontal deficits. For instance, impairment found on the delayed-response test may be interpreted as an inability to inhibit competing, distractive activities during the delay period, and impairment on delayed or double alternation as the inability to inhibit a previously exhibited response. Hyperactivity, distractability, failure of withholding response to the no-go stimulus, inability to perform serial acts in their proper sequence, and inability to reverse a natural preference or an acquired habit, may be similarly interpreted as disinhibitory "release" phenomena (Jackson, 1888) caused by destruction of superordinated gating mechanisms.

If this interpretation is correct, the anterior association areas may be conceived of as being concerned with the coordination of adaptive instrumental activities by supervising, with the aid of inhibitory mechanisms, the performance of circumstantially inappropriate response tendencies. Evidence is available that the frontal-lobe inhibitory functions are, at least partly, mediated by way of the *caudate nucleus*, destruction of which produces symptoms similar to the frontal-lobe deficits (Rosvold and Delgado, 1956; Battig et al., 1960). But these inhibitory effects may also be exercised by way of the adjacent premotor and motor areas.

**Neencephalic Efferent Pathways and Centers**  In mammals there is a direct efferent pathway from the cortex to the bulbar and spinal motor nuclei, the pyramidal (or corticospinal) tract. There is no motor cortex or pyramidal tract in reptiles and birds (Kappers, 1920). In monotremes (platypus) there is an ill-defined cortical motor area with representation of the face and forelimbs but not of the hindlimbs; in marsupials, such as the wallaby, though, there is an amalgamated sensorimotor cortex with major projection to and from the face area, and a much smaller representation of the rest of the body (Lende, 1963). Even in some placental mammals, such as ungulates, in which there is an extending cortical representation of the face in the anterior cortex, limb responses are unstable, with a higher threshold for hindlimb responses. In higher mammals such as carnivores there is a better differentiation of the cortical motor area, and stable limb responses are obtainable. Differentiation of the motor cortex reaches its peak in primates, where the motor cortex is situated in front of the central fissure. Here there is an orderly, inverted representation of the body musculature, similar to that present in the sensory cortex for the

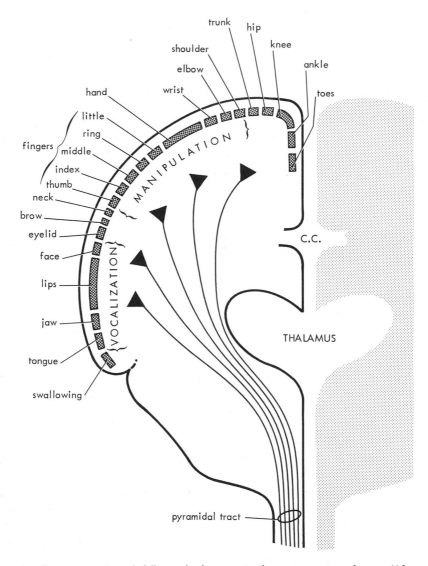

Areal representation of different body parts in the motor cortex of man. (After Penfield and Jasper. *Epilepsy and the functional anatomy of the human brain.* Little, Brown, 1954). Note that a large proportion of the motor cortex controls body structures concerned with two skilled functions, vocalization and manipulation.

somatic receptors. In addition to a representation of the limbs in general, there is in primates a discrete representation of the digits of the limbs.

The pyramidal tract shows a gradual evolution similar to the progressive growth of the excitable motor cortex. Bregmann (Kappers, 1920) found that, of the total area of the cervical cord, the pyramidal tract occupies

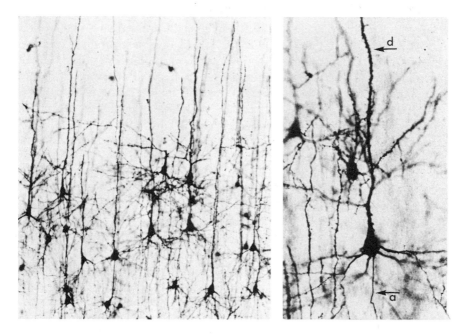

*Left, A,* pyramidal cells in the motor cortex of a monkey, stained with the Golgi technique. Note the long apical dendrites, projecting into the dorsal layers of the cortex. The pyramidal cells stained in this preparation represent only a small proportion of the total population of pyramidal cells in this region. *Right,* high-power photomicrograph of a single pyramidal cell. a, the axon (smooth surface without splnes); d, apical dendrite with spines. (Photomicrographs of material prepared by Dr. Enrique Ramón-Moliner)

3.6 percent in the opossum; 4.8 percent in the elephant; 6.7 percent in the dog; 20.1 percent in the cebus monkey, and 30 percent in man. There are about 32,000 pyramidal tract fibers in the mouse and 1 million in man (Lassek, 1954).

The motor area is histologically differentiated from other areas of the cortex by the enlargement of the pyramidal layers (III, V), which produces an agranular cortex. It is also characterized by the presence of giant pyramidal cells (Betz cells) in the fifth layer. The Betz cells are motor cells in which antidromic discharges can be produced by stimulation of the pyramid in the medulla (Phillips, 1956; Patton and Amassian, 1960). They are also the only cortical cells that, like the spinal motoneurons, are attacked by the poliomyelitis virus—a characteristic suggesting that these motor cells share a common biochemical property (Bodian and Howe, 1940).

It was believed in the past that the pyramidal fibers are formed exclusively of axons of the Betz cells. The quantitative studies of Lassek (1954), however, showed clearly that this cannot be true. In man, for instance, there are 1 million pyramidal tract fibers but only about 34,000 Betz cells. Furthermore, removal of the motor area does not produce total degeneration of the pyramidal tract; only an estimated one third of the pyramidal tract fibers degenerate in the monkey after removal of the motor area. After combined removal of the motor and premotor areas (areas 4 and 6) about one half of the pyramidal tract fibers degenerate (Welch and Kennard, 1944). Indeed, there is both anatomical (Minkowski, 1923; Hoff, 1935; Verhaart and Kennard, 1940) and physiological (Woolsey and Chang, 1948; Lance and Manning, 1954; Porter, 1955) evidence indicating the existence of motor outflow from the premotor, somatic (postcentral), and other areas of the cortex.

The majority of corticospinal fibers that descend to the spinal cord (some terminate rostrally in the cranial motor nuclei) decussate in the medulla. A small proportion may descend ipsilaterally, but these ipsilateral fibers are restricted to the cervical segments of the body (Chambers and Liu, 1957). Conforming with this arrangement, the effects of stimulation (or ablation) of the motor cortex are essentially restricted to the contralateral side of the body. In the cat, the corticospinal tract fibers terminate in the region of the nucleus proprius in the dorsal horn of the spinal cord but do not come in direct contact with the motor neurons of the ventral horn (Chambers and Liu, 1957). In the monkey, some of the corticospinal fibers (or their collaterals) directly reach the motor neurons in the dorsal part of the ventral horn (Chambers and Liu, 1958; Kuypers, 1960). In the chimpanzee, an increased number of cortical efferents reaches the ventral horn motor neurons (Kuypers, 1962). Paralleling this phylogenetic trend of increasing direct synaptic contact between pyramidal tract fibers and final motor neurons, a comparable ontogenetic trend was recently observed in the monkey (Kuypers, 1962). In the infant rhesus monkey (4 days of age) the corticospinal fibers terminate in the zona intermedia and do not reach the ventral horn motor neurons; by the age of 8 months, however, the cortical efferents invade the region of the ventral horn in a pattern similar to that seen in the adult rhesus monkey.

This phylo- and ontogenetic trend presumably accounts for some of the differences observed in motor losses after severance of the pyramidal tract in different species, or at different ages within the same species. On the first postoperative day after hemidecortication, cats and dogs can move about, though they display initially abnormalities of posture and locomotion, most of which disappear subsequently (Walker and Fulton, 1938; Tower, 1940). However, cats with bilateral destruction of the pyramids may be seriously impaired in the execution of more *skilled* locomotor patterns such as climbing a ladder (Liddell and Phillips, 1943). Removal of the motor cortex has more serious consequences in the monkey. After a longer period of postoperative recovery the animal can use, in a coarse manner, its hand and feet in locomotion and for the grasping of objects, but it cannot use its fingers in skilled acts, such as in grooming and manipulating objects (Tower, 1940). This deficit in the skilled use of the digits was observed to persist for a very long period (up to 4 years) and is probably a *permanent deficit*. From the ontogenetic point of view, removal of the motor cortex in the infant monkey is less severe, and is marked by greater recovery, than in the adult (Kennard, 1942).

Accordingly, the motor cortex and its pyramidal outflow need not be seriously involved in the control of such routine quadruped functions as locomotion, but it is essential for the execution of skilled motor acts, in particular *manipulatory activities*. In fact, the degree of development of the motor cortex in different species (or the degree of deficit produced by its removal) may be related to the use made of the motor appendages of the body. The original function of the limbs in quadruped vertebrates is locomotion. Amphibia and reptiles use their forelimbs and hindlimbs for swimming, running, and jumping, and only occasionally (as by the male during the mating season) for grasping. The little manipulation of their physical environment that amphibia or reptiles are capable of is usually carried out with the aid of the tongue and jaws. In birds the hindlimbs are used for walking, hopping, or swimming, whereas the forelimbs are specialized for another locomotor function, namely, flying. The major organ of manipulation is the beak, with which birds reach for objects, build their nests, or fight their adversaries, and only minimal use is made in such tasks of the hindlimbs. Likewise, in terrestrial mammals (both herbivores and carnivores) the limbs are used almost exclusively for locomotion; the digits of the paws (which are present in amphibia) are generally atrophied. Certain terrestrial mammals, such as cats, make use of their forelimbs in manipulating objects and in fighting, but in general they are not capable of performing skilled acts.

In contrast, arboreal mammals, such as some marsupials (opossum) or rodents (squirrels), but particularly primates, use their limbs extensively in such skilled motor tasks as swinging from branches, jumping from tree to tree, and picking fruits or other objects with their fingers. Most of these arboreal mammals also show a tendency to free their forelimbs on occasion from the task of maintaining body posture, by sitting on their hindlegs and using the forelimbs and their digits for opening nuts, breaking objects, and carrying food to the mouth. It is in primates that the limbs (both fore- and hindlimbs, and in some species also the tail) became specialized organs of manipulation, and the progressive development of the cortex is presumably partially attributable to this process. Successful manipulation requires not only detailed tactile information about the properties of the objects handled, and continuous kinesthetic feedback to monitor the progress in the execution of manipulatory acts, but also simultaneous visual input for adequate *hand-eye coordination*.

The partial transformation of the limbs from a postural and locomotor organ to a manipulatory organ permitted primates to acquire an increasing technical or *instrumental control* of their environment (Paillard, 1960), with concomitant extension of their perceptual "grasp" of the world they live in. The evolution of the motor cortex and of the pyramidal tract in primates is well correlated with their increasing ability to manipulate their environments skillfully.

What is the exact role of the motor cortex in the execution of behavior? After sectioning of the pyramidal tract in primates, electrical stimulation of the motor cortex will still produce motor movements in the limbs (Tower, 1940). These movements, which involve many muscles and are well integrated, tend to occur in the *proximal* (arms, legs) rather than *distal* parts of the extremities (digits). Similar types of movements can also be elicited from the premotor area after ablation of the motor cortex or sectioning of the pyramids (Hines, 1940, 1944). These findings suggest the existence of an *extrapyramidal pathway* from the motor and premotor areas of the cortex. Hines (1947) applied the term *holokinesis* to these organized, extrapyramidal types of movements (rhythmic motor activities suggestive of locomotion, swallowing, chewing, and the like). These are apparently innate action patterns, because they can be elicited from the cortex of foetuses at the age of 66–125 days of gestation. Hines distinguished these extrapyramidal, holokinetic movements, which are presumably organized subcortically, from the pyramidal *idiokinetic* movements, which can be elicited on cortical stimulation only at 135–162 days of gestation. The term "idiokinesis" refers to a postulated, discrete, or articulated innervation of single muscles that makes possible the subsequent organization of postnatally acquired skilled acts.

The implication of Hines' concept of idiokinesis is that the motor cortex serves as a superordinated *motor keyboard* for the patterning of skilled manipulatory acts. This idea brings us to the old controversy whether motor representation in the cortex is "mosaic" or "functional." Many investigators have argued in favor of Hughlings Jackson's dictum that the motor cortex "thinks in movements, not in muscles." That is, synergistically organized functional acts rather than single muscle movements are represented in the cortex. Indeed, stimulation of localized points of the motor cortex with large electrodes and with intense current generally produces organized movements in selected parts of the body. However, with the use of small stimulating electrodes and a minimal current, single muscles (Chang et al., 1947), or even parts of a muscle (Phillips, 1956), can be made to contract in isolation. The contraction is most easily accomplished when the cortical loci of distal parts of the extremities are stimulated. Discrete movements are elicited less easily from proximal extremities, and they may be also very difficult to obtain from lower mammals. Because the cortex has a pyramidal as well as extrapyramidal outflow, the reasonable assumption is that it can initiate the execution of subcortically organized motor schemata as well as skilled acts, which may be partly produced by pyramidal innervation. The presence of this isolated throughway from cortex to spinal cord need not imply that cortically induced movements are carried out exclusively by way of this direct corticospinal efferent system.

In summary, we may say that there is satisfactory evidence that the neencephalon (comprised of the lemniscal corticopetal pathway, the thalamocortical association areas, and the pyramidal corticofugal pathway) is primarily implicated in two types of functions, namely, the gathering of detailed, accurate, and objective information about the external world, and the execution of skilled manipulatory acts. These two functions, furthermore, may be conceived of as the essential building blocks of a class of behavior that we referred to as *singular instrumental activities*, in other words, as unique, adaptive patterns of behavior that individuals develop in their attempt to handle novel objects or events in their specific environment. These unique intellective (cognitive and volitional) patterns of behavior differ considerably from the species-common emotional patterns of behavior controlled by the paleocephalon. But in its capacity of a "higher" or superordinated control system, the neencephalon also supervises and modulates the activities managed by the various subordinated divisions of the nervous system.

## SELECTED READINGS

Beach, F. A., D. O. Hebb, C. T. Morgan, and H. W. Nissen. *The neuropsychology of Lashley.* New York: McGraw-Hill, 1960.

Chow, K. L., and P. J. Hutt. The "association cortex" of *Macaca mulatta*: a review of recent contributions to its anatomy and functions. *Brain*, 1953, **76,** 625–677.

Diamond, I. T., and K. L. Chow. Biological psychology. In S. Koch (Ed.), *Psychology: a study of science.* New York: McGraw-Hill, 1962. Vol. 4, pp. 158–241.

Lassek, A. M. *The pyramidal tract.* Springfield, Ill.: Charles C Thomas, 1954.

Paillard, J. The patterning of skilled movements. *Handb. Physiol.,* Sec. 1, **3,** 1679–1708.

Rose, J. E., and V. B. Mountcastle. Touch and kinesthesis. *Handb. Physiol.,* 1959, Sec. 1, **1,** 387–429.

Warren, J. M., and K. Akert (Eds.). *The frontal agranular cortex and behavior.* New York: McGraw-Hill, 1964.

IV

# ORGANIZATION OF
# INTERACTION WITH
# THE ENVIRONMENT

Possibly a few of the simplest domestic functions of the animative action system can be carried out "autonomously," that is, without the utilization of information about conditions in other parts of the body and in the external world. However, no behavioral, or interrelational, function, could serve its ends if it were carried out *in vacuo*, without due regard to ongoing outside events. Interaction with the environment is essential, first, for the *unfolding* or *acquisition* of appropriate patterns of behavior. To cope with the threats, opportunities, and challenges presented by its environment, the animal has to gather information about conditions in its milieu and develop or acquire suitable neural programs of behavior. Interaction is also required for the proper timing of the *actualization* or *realization* of the animal's repertoire of behavior so that its activities are triggered by or synchronized with matching stimulus conditions, and are appropriately regulated or steered by external signals. Some of the characteristics of these two important aspects of interaction with the environment will be considered separately under the chapter headings, "Central Programing of Animative Activities," and "Afferent Steering of Animative Activities." Finally, the overt activities of the animal have to be related to its internal needs. This very important aspect of the organization of interaction with the environment will be discussed under the chapter heading, "Internal Motivation of Animative Activities." .

the paleocephalon have important inborn components, which determine the direction of action (such as food seeking and courtship behavior), but they are also modifiable, because the goal objects of the activities (food objects, sex partners) are often acquired or fixated on as a result of individual experience (Freud called this process *cathexis*). Finally, the instrumental activities controlled by the neencephalon are to a very large extent dependent on the individual's singular encounters and attempts to cope with specific problems and unique situations in its own niche. These are activities that cannot be adequately programed except through learning, and they are also functions that are easily extinguished (unlearned) if they become useless, obsolete, or inappropriate.

In the following pages we shall consider these different modes of programing of animal action. We shall describe a few studies concerned with the nature of morphogenetic organization of central nervous circuits or synaptic "connections." We shall then consider the modifiability of some action patterns, during critical periods of maturation, by imprinting or cathexis. Finally, we shall briefly review the types of transactional learning functions that have been identified and will discuss our present state of knowledge of the physiological basis of memory and learning.

**MORPHOGENETIC PROGRAMING**      The manifold properties of the or-
**OF INBORN ACTIVITIES**      ganism are transmitted from one
generation to the next by heredity. Each germ cell is endowed, as we have seen earlier, with a unique molecular coding system, with the potentiality of producing an individual that is genetically similar to its parents. This process of unfolding or development is dependent on the presence of an appropriate external medium from which energy and matter are drawn for the realization of the individual's hereditary potentialities. The hereditary transmission of genetic information and the developmental realization of latent potentialities in an appropriate milieu are referred to as the morphogenetic process, and all the characteristics so developed may be called inborn, or innate, properties.

Accordingly, morphogenetic developmental processes are guided by hereditary or internal factors and are conditioned by environmental or congenital factors. Although this environmental dependency could be a source of great variability regarding the outcome of the morphogenetic end-product, the normal milieu of the developing embryo is, in general, a fairly constant one. In many types of germ cells the nutrients essential for development are present in the form of yolk within the egg, or the eggs are deposited by the mother into a specific nutritive substrate. To ensure against undue variations in temperature, the eggs are laid in the appropriate season, and are buried in the ground or deposited in water

# 13

# Central Programing of Animative Activities

Organisms are endowed with the ability to execute a few action patterns immediately after birth; other behavior patterns make their appearance later in life. Behavior patterns that are elicitable before or immediately after birth, in the absence of opportunity to learn them through experience, are often referred to as *innate*, or *inborn*, capacities, and the assumption is made that their neural programs are organized by hereditary, or morphogenetic, variables. An obvious example of inborn behavior, which appears instantaneously after birth, is breathing, a complex function necessitating the coordinated action of the abdominal and chest muscles, of the mouth, tongue, and other organs. Of the behavior patterns that appear postnatally some may also be inborn properties, with a late or delayed postnatal maturation; others are obviously dependent on experience and learning. The latter type of programing or patterning of action may be said to be dependent to a considerable extent on the organism's act commerce or transactions with the environment.

In fact, we may distinguish three modes of neural programing or terning of behavior:

1. *Fixed morphogenetic programing*, which occurs without indiv experience and is, in general, impervious to alterations by experience

2. *Modifiable epigenetic programing*, which consists of essential components but which also necessitates individual experience proper realization.

3. *Acquired transactional programing*, in which new schemat havior are formed on the basis of individual experience, with min ployment of inborn elements.

These three types of programing of behavior are related to th system of animative functions postulated by us. The routine r activities controlled at the spinomedullary level are morph patterned and are, furthermore, highly resistant to modific perience. The recurrent, species-specific catering activities or other relatively constant media. In higher forms the eggs may be incubated by the parents or, as in mammals, carried in the uterus to further ensure environmental uniformity. That is, the specific milieu in which development takes place is to some extent characteristic of the species and may itself be considered at least partly genetically determined. The establishment of a standard milieu is, of course, vitally important if the genetic inheritance is to be properly realized. Embryonic development in varying environments (as under experimental conditions) produces deformed individuals that cannot adequately maintain themselves or propagate their species.

The inborn repertoire of the organism includes virtually all its morphological properties and many, though not all, of its functional characteristics. All individuals of a given species have comparable biochemical composition and morphological constitution, and share similar motor mechanisms and similar types of receptors and nervous systems. Although, obviously, the *mechanisms* of action are largely inherited endowments, the functional *utilization* of these action mechanisms may be inherited or acquired properties, or a combination of the two. It is generally conceded that the functioning of most or all the visceral organs are inborn capacities, although their activation may be dependent on environmental priming agents (for example, the functioning of the lungs is primed after birth by the presence of air). No organism could survive if it first had to "learn" how to inspire and expire air, or how to pump blood through the chambers of its heart. Evidently, the innately organized morphological maturation of these visceral organs is coupled with innate functional programing; they are thus ready to carry out their tasks prenatally (the heart, for example) or immediately after birth (as in breathing). Not only visceral but skeletal mechanisms can function prior to transactional experience, as suggested by the fact that the proper coordination of some visceral functions, such as breathing, is dependent on skeletal mechanisms. Also motor activities such as sucking, swallowing, vomiting, crying, and the like appear to be present immediately after birth, even in the most highly evolved mammals. Less well established and somewhat controversial is the claim that, at least in lower vertebrates (such as fish, amphibia, and precocial birds), standing, locomotion, pecking at food objects, and similar activities are also morphogenetically formed, inborn capacities.

SOME INBORN OR FIXED ACTION PATTERNS. Precocial birds, such as the domestic chick, can right themselves, stand, and walk immediately after hatching. Although leg movements occur within the egg before hatching (which could be a source of prenatal experience), the complex acts of maintaining body posture and biped locomotion are carried out by the newborn chick without the aid of previous experience. Similarly, the newly hatched chick will peck at glistening objects on the ground, giving evidence of the existence of morphogenetically formed action schemata for the coordination of such a relatively complex visuomotor task. It has been argued (Kuo, 1932; Maier and Schneirla, 1935) that because bending of the head is observable in chick embryos the possibility of prenatal learning cannot be excluded in the pecking activity of the chick. Head bending, however, cannot be equated with the complex function of visually guided pecking at objects, a sequence of movements that is followed, if the object is edible, by ingestion. It has been reported (Engelmann, 1942; Fantz, 1957), that the inexperienced chick may also show some initial object preferences in pecking (for instance, it may select round, in preference to angular, objects and respond least to triangular objects). Similarly, the young gosling placed in front of a receding object will display a following response within 60 seconds of exposure to such a stimulus, reacting to the object as if to a surrogate mother (Jaynes, 1957; Moltz, 1960).

It is very important to realize, however, that these innate action patterns are not impervious to modification by experience. In fact, without experiential modifications many of these action schemata would lead to useless, maladaptive behavior. The pecking of the young chick becomes better coordinated with time, and soon the chick displays discrimination by ceasing to peck at inedible or noxious objects (Spalding, 1873 [1954]). Similarly, after exposure to a moving object of a specified size (which is normally the mother), the animal becomes fixated or imprinted to the object and will, as a consequence of the initial experience, follow that object selectively.

The identification of neonatally displayed inborn action patterns is somewhat easier than the recognition of those innate behavior patterns the maturation of which is delayed. It is often claimed that behavior patterns displayed by all members of a species in a uniform manner are inborn properties. This criterion is not necessarily a sufficient one. It is not impossible that members of a species can acquire species-common behavior patterns through individual experience (because of common characteristics and dispositions and the sharing of uniform habitats) and through intragroup facilitation. Only if it can be shown that a given behavior pattern develops in individuals isolated from other members of the group is one justified in assuming that the behavior in question is attributable to inborn postnatal maturation.

Is the delayed appearance of flying in birds attributable to delayed neuromuscular maturation, or is it explained by a functional organization largely dependent on learning? Spalding (1873 [1954]) investigated this question by hand-rearing swallows in small cages. He found that once the deprived swallows were released they flew as efficiently as normal animals. Grohmann (1938) reared doves in narrow tubes that prevented the use of their wings. When the normal control doves displayed their ability in flying, the deprived experimental animals were also freed; they, too, flew quite efficiently, an observation suggesting that learning is not essential to the coordination of flying. A similar experiment was performed by Carmichael (1926, 1927), who prevented the swimming "exercise" of developing amphibia by raising them in water containing chloretone as an anesthetic. The mature narcotized animals were eventually transferred to normal water; after a brief period of recovery, they swam like their normal mates. This finding was confirmed by Matthews and Detwiler (1926). Evidently some behavior patterns that appear postnatally, particularly locomotor functions, may be slowly maturing inborn processes.

In a recent study (Konishi, 1963), it was found that deafening domestic chicks at 1 day of age (which prevents them not only from hearing the vocal communication of other chicks but also from hearing their own vocalization) did not interfere with the development and display of normal, species-specific vocal patterns. (These vocal patterns include a food call, aerial alarm call, distress call, alerting call, aggressive call, and others.) Similarly, a whitethroat, or garden warbler, reared from an egg in isolation in a soundproof chamber develops a song similar to that of other members of the species. The coordination and elicitation of singing, in this species, do not require interaction with the environment (the presence of other birds). In other birds, such as the chaffinch, the song of the isolated, hand-reared animal is much simpler than that of normal animals. When such an animal is brought into the company of another inexperienced bird, however, the competitive situation elicits the development of the normal song pattern (Thorpe, 1963); this finding suggests the presence of innate programing of the normal pattern.

Rats reared in isolation will, on first opportunity, engage in sexual behavior, build nests, and retrieve their young. To answer the question whether nest building and retrieving are innate or learned behavior patterns, Riess (1950) isolated female rats at the age of 14–21 days, and kept them thereafter in a wire-mesh cage, fed on powdered food, with no objects to manipulate. Subsequently the animals were mated, transferred to a wooden box, and provided with paper strips, and their nest building and parental behavior were investigated. The animals so reared did not build nests and did not care properly for their young, most of which failed to survive. Riess concluded from this study that nest building and retrieving are dependent on previous experience with the handling and carrying of food objects. Because even experienced rats may fail to build nests when placed in new cages, Eibl-Eibesfeldt (1961) repeated Riess' experiment with one important modification: the paper strips were made available to isolated virgin and mated rats in their own cages (their tails were also amputated to further ensure their manipulatory deprivation). Some of the *virgin rats* started to build nests as soon as the paper strips became available to them; others scattered the paper strips first but built nests within 5 hours. Only a few of the rats failed to build nests, but this failure could be attributed to the circumstance that these animals had not established permanent sleeping quarters in their cages. All the *impregnated rats* built nests, and most of them retrieved their young; however, some appeared inefficient in carrying the young to their nest. Eibl-Eibesfeldt concluded that previous experience with handling objects is not a prerequisite for nest building and retrieving behavior, though animals with normal manipulatory experience tend to be more efficient in retrieving.

GENETIC STUDIES OF THE INHERITANCE OF BEHAVIOR. Though the various studies dealing with the genetics of behavior are not primarily concerned with the problem of the morphogenetic organization of action, such studies are obviously relevant to the topic under discussion. If a behavior pattern is demonstrably determined by the inheritance of the individual, its organization or programing must be dependent on innate rather than experientially acquired variables. There are several approaches to the study of the inheritance of behavior patterns, such as selective breeding, the comparison of different strains, and the effects of induced mutations.

*Selective breeding* consists of the interbreeding for several generations of individuals with some outstanding behavioral trait to determine whether they "breed true," that is, whether the trait in question is attributable to genetic factors. A well-known example is Tryon's studies (1931) in which rats were separated in terms of their ability to master a maze, and the "maze-bright" and "maze-dull" rats were selectively interbred for many generations. Tryon found that "maze-brightness" and "maze-dullness" bred true. Subsequent studies revealed that the inherited variable was not a "general intelligence" factor, because the maze-bright rats were found superior only on certain tasks (Searles, 1949). With the aid of the selective-breeding technique the inheritance of several behavioral traits or abnormalities has been demonstrated, such as the degree of emotionality (fear) displayed in an open-field situation (Hall, 1938; Searles, 1949); level of spontaneous activity (Brody, 1941); susceptibility to audiogenic seizures, that is, the development of epileptic discharge when exposed to intense sound (Frings and Frings, 1953); and many others.

Related to this approach is the comparative study of *inbred strains.* Different strains represent the outcome of inbreeding produced either by natural causes favoring segregation (such as geographic isolation and social or sexual incompatibility) or by selective breeding designed by agriculturists or breeders. Behavioral differences displayed by different strains or breeds represent ideal material for the study of the genetics of behavior. Stamm (1954) reported different degrees of hoarding behavior in different strains of rats. In a similar way, differences were obtained in the exploratory behavior of black-hooded and albino rats (Carr and Williams, 1957), and in various measures of sexual behavior in different strains of guinea pigs (Valenstein et al., 1954) and mice (McGill, 1962).

NEURAL MECHANISMS OF MORPHOGENETIC PROGRAMING. The demonstration that a behavior pattern can develop in the absence of relevant experience raises the important question of the mechanism by which it is coordinated. We may reasonably assume that the coordinated execution of a morphogenetically programed action sequence is dependent on central nervous circuits connecting the participating peripheral receptor and effector elements into a single, spatially and temporally integrated functional unit. It is commonly assumed, though not actually proved, that such an integration is mediated by neural circuits in which the elements are tied together by structural or functional synapses. If we assume that such a conception of structural or functional synaptic circuits is correct, the first question that arises is how they are formed. How do the growing neurons of the differentiating nervous system establish appropriate connections with one another so that they can mediate specific inborn functions? Consider a function such as quadruped locomotor rhythmicity, a phenomenon easily elicited in newborn mammals and also in experimental spinal preparations. How is the central nervous program of such a complex action sequence formed? How are the efferents transmitting the motor signals connected with the appropriate muscles, and how are the proprioceptive afferents, supplying feedback information from the limbs, connected with the spinal centers guiding locomotion?

These questions cannot be answered at present. Beginnings in the investigation of the morphogenesis of such neural circuits were made by Weiss (1950, 1952) and Sperry (1951). In one type of experimental approach, Weiss investigated the mode of innervation of *supernumerary limbs* in amphibia. If an extra limb taken from a donor is transplanted into the region of the limb nerve plexus of the host, the supernumerary limb (which is useless or of actual hindrance in locomotion) becomes innervated by fibers growing out from the limb plexus. How does the supernumerary limb move when the adjacent normal limb, with which it shares the limb plexus, is moving? Weiss found that specific muscles of the supernumerary limb contract in harmony with corresponding muscles in the normal limb. This phenomenon he called *myotypic response*, meaning that all muscles of the same name respond in similar fashion to presumed efferent impulses coming from a common nerve plexus. If a contralateral forelimb is transplanted next to the normal forelimb, the effect of such a myotypic response is a mirror-image action of the normal limb, so that the supernumerary extremity counteracts all the movements of its normal neighbor. If the right and left limbs are exchanged, the effect of the transplantation is that whenever the

Diagram showing the mirror-image arrangement in a supernumerary limb transplanted in the vicinity of the normal forelimb. Identical muscles are indicated by
the same shading. (From Weiss. Patterns of organization in the central nervous
system. *Res. Publ. Ass. nerv. ment. Dis.,* 1952, **30**, 3–23)

animal "intends" to move forward its limbs move it backward. The
maladaptive response in such an amphibian is said to be permanent; thus
it is possible that the coordination of this action is entirely a centrally
organized morphogenetic process. Presumably, efferent impulses are dis-
patched in such an animal in the normal fashion, and no adaptive compensation is made for the exchange of limbs.

Weiss (1952) explained his findings as follows. If we assume that the
outgrowth of nerve fibers from the limb plexus to the supernumerary
limb is a *random growth process* (in other words, any nerve fiber may
establish connection with any muscle group), then the results indicate
that the specificity of the responses is determined by the muscles themselves (which selectively respond to certain types of impulses) and not
by the random efferents communicating certain central programs of
action. A different interpretation of his findings, however, is possible.
The specificity of responses could be attributed to the circumstance that the
outgrowth of fibers from the nerve plexus is *not* a random process; rather,
that specific nerves succeed in establishing connections with specific
muscles. That this type of *selective growth process* may be the basis of
morphogenetic patterning of action is suggested by the experiments of
Sperry.

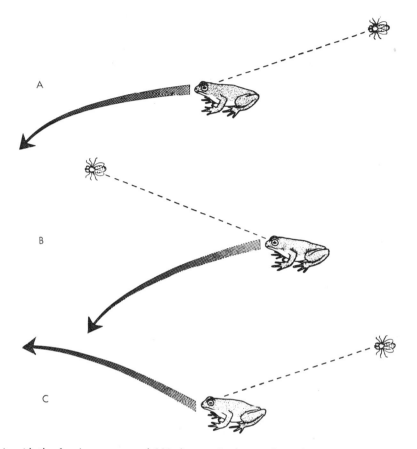

A, with the frog's eyes rotated 180 degrees in their sockets, the prey located behind and above the frog is struck in the opposite direction forward and downward.
B, with transplantation of the eyes to achieve a dorsoventral inversion, the animal
strikes the prey in front of it and above it, forward but downward. C, with naso-
temporal inversion of the eyes, the strike is directed appropriately upward but in
the opposite direction. (Sperry. Mechanisms of neural maturation. In Stevens, Ed.,
*Handbook of experimental psychology.* John Wiley & Sons, 1951, pp. 236–280)

If a quadrant of the amphibian optic lobe is destroyed, a blind area
(*scotoma*) is produced in the corresponding quadrant of the retina
(Stroer, 1939). This finding indicates that fibers originating in a specific
region of the retina pass to a specific region of the optic lobe. Such a
retinotopic projection (which is well established in the entire visual
system in a great variety of species) is an example of morphogenetic
patterning of central nervous connections. That selective connections
between specific regions of the retina and the optic lobe are indeed
essential for normal visual space localization in amphibia was shown by
Sperry (1942) and others. In amphibia the eyeballs can be rotated without

seriously damaging the optic nerves; thus the dorsal retinal half is displaced ventrally, and vice versa. As Sperry found, such animals display a reversal of their optic responses; when, for instance, a bait is displayed above the animal's head, the animal aims and strikes downward. This maladaptive visual response persists through the life of the animal. Similar results were obtained by Pfister (1955) in the domestic fowl. The birds were fitted with right-left reversing prisms, after which their visual aiming in pecking at grains was investigated. Two hens that wore the goggles for three months failed to learn to make allowances for the changed visual input. Hess (1956) found, likewise, that newly hatched chicks fitted with distorting lenses failed to make adaptive adjustments within 4 days of practice for the displacement of the visual world, and failed to learn to peck appropriately. It should be noted that, unlike lower vertebrates, higher mammals, such as the monkey (Foley, 1940) and man (Stratton, 1897; Kohler, 1951) can adjust to optically produced reversal or distortion of the visual world; this adjustment in higher mammals may be attributed to neocortical adaptive modification of visual spatial localization.

In amphibia the reversal of the eyeballs may be combined with severance of the optic nerves (Sperry, 1944, 1951). The optic fibers regenerate from the retinal stump and re-establish connections with the optic lobe. Superficially, the fibers in the regenerated optic nerve are in disarray. Behavioral examinations, however, showed that, functionally, central connections were established in an orderly, though maladaptive, manner. These animals, like those in which the eyes were merely rotated, showed a systematic reversal of their visuomotor responses. Apparently, fibers originating in a specified region of the retina establish connections with corresponding retinotopic areas of the optic lobe. This finding indicates that it is some specific property of nerve fibers coming from a certain region of the retina that predetermines their central terminations and not their position with respect to external space or any adaptive organizational factor.

What mechanism guides the outgrowing nerve fibers through specific pathways to their predestined end-station? Several theories have been proposed, but none can adequately account for this phenomenon. One of the oldest of these is the *theory of biotaxis* of Kappers (1932). His theory assumes that the direction of outgrowth of the axons and dedrites of a given neuron is determined by electric fields present in the region of development. Attempts to test this hypothesis, such as setting up artificial electric fields, have cast serious doubts on its validity (Weiss, 1941). Cajal (1928) advanced a *trophic theory*, according to which the growth of neuron appendages is primarily a random process, but fibers that can establish appropriate connections develop while others failing to do so atrophy and disappear eventually. This theory implies the existence of compatibility and incompatibility among neurons in establishing connections with one another. Not unrelated to this theory is the modern assumption that neurons with different functions are characterized by *biochemical specificities*, a factor that determines which other neurons they will establish contact with. According to this theory, neurons of a given system, for example, the visual, are endowed with some biochemical specificity that makes them compatible with one another and incompatible with neurons of other systems. Within such a single system further biochemical differentiation may exist so that neurons subserving some specific function may show preferential affinity to one another. It would be by such a mechanism that the randomly outgrowing optic fibers from the retina establish predetermined connections with corresponding retinotopic cells in the optic lobe. In conclusion, we must say that the mechanism of the morphogenetic formation of neural schemata of behavior is yet to be discovered.

**TRANSACTIONAL PROGRAMING** The development of the *mecha-*
**OF LEARNED ACTIVITIES** *nisms* of action is largely dependent on inborn, morphogenetic organizational processes. As we have argued in the previous section, the *functional* organization of these action mechanisms may also be in many instances based on inborn programing, irrespective of whether they are displayed prenatally, whether they are present at birth, or whether they mature postnatally.

In spite of the possibility of the inborn organization of some behavioral functions, such as breathing or locomotion, the organization of other activities is at least partly dependent on prior transaction with the environment. We are familiar with a large class of functions whose unfolding requires prior exercise or training, that is, individual "experience." The bird that initially pecks with relative indiscrimination at a large class of objects, whether nutritious, indigestible, or noxious, soon *learns* to restrict its pecking to a few specific objects in its environment that can satisfy its nutritional needs. Similarly, the newly hatched bird, which is potentially ready to follow and become attached to a large class of objects, soon becomes *fixated* on, or *imprinted* to, a specific object, which becomes its (natural or surrogate) mother. These are obvious examples of behavior patterns that, though having important innate components (the disposition to peck or follow), require experience and memory for adequate realization.

The biological advantages provided by the ability to modify or alter behavior patterns on the basis of experience are obvious. Morphogenetic organization provides ready-made programs of behavior, which permit the individual to handle situations in a stereotyped, species-specific manner. Such innate programs of action, by the nature and mode of their organization, are well suited to the control of generic tasks and to the handling

of situations that recur regularly in the habitat of the species. Morphogenetically programed activities, however, are not suitable for the adequate
handling of singular or unique problems that may be encountered by a
particular individual in its specific habitat. To deal with specific situations,
and also to make possible the mastering or conquering of species-alien
habitats for which morphogenetic programs of action were not evolved,
it is essential that the organism be endowed with the ability to modify
or reprogram its behavior on the basis of individual experience. Such
modifications of behavior are dependent on the capacity to store individual
experience by means of coded memory mechanisms, and also the ability
to retrieve and utilize these *memory traces* for the modification of old
behavior patterns or the formation of new actions.

The ability of animals to utilize experience makes possible (1) the
*modification* or alteration of inborn patterns of behavior and (2) the
*acquisition* of new action patterns in which relatively little use is made
of inborn behavior components. The best examples of the modification of
inborn responses are the phenomena of habituation, imprinting, and
classical (Pavlovian) conditioning. Experimental examples of the formation of new patterns of behavior are instrumental conditioning, trial-and-
error problem solving, and such acquired functions as complex sensory
discriminations, maze learning, and the acquisition of skills.

**Modification of Morphogenetic**     HABITUATION. If a "neutral" stimu-
**Action Patterns**     lus (that is, a stimulus that has
neither noxious nor beneficial con-
sequences) is repeatedly delivered to an organism, its response to the
stimulus tends to decrease gradually and may eventually cease altogether.
The habituation effect is distinguished from the phenomenon of *exhaustion* or *fatigue* insofar as it can be demonstrated with weak stimuli as
well as (or better than) strong stimuli, and it often occurs with very low
rates of repetition (with intervals of hours or even days). From the
biological point of view, habituation may be considered the abandonment
or elimination of unnecessary or useless responses; physiologically, it may
be dependent on some active *inhibitory process* that prevents the elicitation of a built-in response.

It has been argued (Humphrey, 1933; Thorpe, 1963) that habituation
is the simplest and most common form of learning in the animal world.
It has been demonstrated in all animal forms, including *Protozoa* lacking
a nervous system (Jennings, 1906). Habituation may be a component of
all higher forms of learning in which useless (unrewarded) responses
gradually disappear as new responses become strengthened. Habituation
may be restricted to a single sensory modality; it is often quality-specific
within a single modality. Furthermore, it is the only nonassociative type
of learning, because it consists of nothing more than the dropping out of

built-in responses. Finally, we may add, habituation is a phenomenon shown to occur at the lowest levels of the central nervous system, such as the spinal cord (Hernández-Peón and Brust-Carmona, 1961), and it is common at higher cephalic levels.

In recent neurophysiological investigations of habituation, a common procedure is to present the animal repetitively with a "neutral" stimulus, observe the behavior of the animal, and record changes in the electrical activity of its brain. When an animal is presented with a novel stimulus, say a metronome sound or a click delivered through a loudspeaker, a behavioral *orienting response* is usually elicited (pricking of ears, looking toward the source of the sound), accompanied by a generalized EEG arousal (blocking of the alpha rhythm) and recordable evoked potentials to each click from various way stations of the auditory system (Sokolov, 1963). As the clicks are repeated, the behavioral orienting response disappears, together with the EEG arousal response, and the evoked potentials to the click diminish in amplitude and may occasionally disappear altogether. This diminution of evoked potentials following repeated stimulation may occur at the first relay station of the auditory system, the

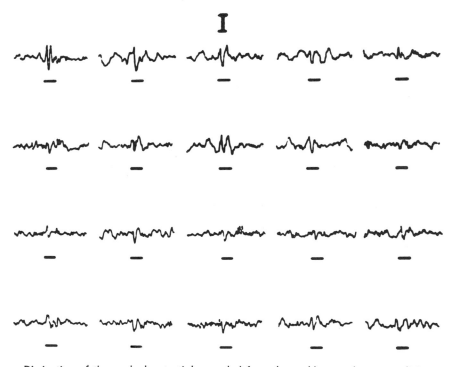

Diminution of the evoked potential recorded from the cochlear nucleus to a click (indicated by the bar below each trace) as a function of repetition. (Hernández-Peón et al. Auditory potentials at cochlear nucleus during acoustic habituation. *Acta Neurol, lat.-amer.* 1957, **3**, 144–156)

cochlear nucleus in the medulla (Hernández-Peón et al., 1956). That this habituation effect is indeed caused by the functional inconsequence or neutrality of the presented stimulus was shown by Galambos et al. (1956). If the habituated click is *reinforced* (that is, paired with a consequential stimulus such as an electric shock to the leg), the evoked potentials to the click reappear or increase in amplitude. The habituation to the click, furthermore, may be frequency-specific. For instance, when the frequency of the habituated click is altered, behavioral and EEG arousal effects are produced in sleeping cats (Sharpless and Jasper, 1956; Sokolov, 1963).

As Hernández-Peón and his collaborators have shown (Hernández-Peón and Brust-Carmona, 1961), such habituation effects may be obtained in several other sense modalities. In fact, it may also be demonstrated as low in the neuraxis as the transected spinal cord, in the absence of supraspinal influences from higher brain structures. This finding is in agreement with an early report of habituation of the arousal response in decorticate dogs (Lebidinskaia and Rosenthal, 1935).

IMPRINTING. Spalding (1872) and Heinroth (1910) reported that newborn geese isolated immediately after hatching tended to follow their human caretakers in the way naturally reared goslings follow their mother. This filial attachment on the basis of early experience was called by Heinroth *Prägung* (imprinting). Lorenz (1935), who called attention to the importance of imprinting, reported that a short but early association

Hess's apparatus for imprinting ducklings. The duckling follows the decoy around the circular runway. (From Hess. Ethology. In Barron, *New directions in psychology*. Holt, Rinehart and Winston, 1964, Vol. 2. With the permission of *Science*)

of isolated young ducklings with man is sufficient to establish a lifelong attachment. Such animals may ignore altogether individuals of their own species when they are later exposed to them, to the extent of transferring their sexual attraction (courtship, mating attempts) to man. Such imprinting effects may be established with other animal species, with inanimate objects that are artificially moved about (Ramsay, 1951), and even with a stationary flickering light (James, 1959).

Among the many characteristics of imprinting, Lorenz stressed the ease with which imprinting is formed: the requirement that the imprinted object share at least some properties with the *built-in releaser*, or signal, of that response; the dependence of imprinting on a *critical period* of the animal's maturational history; and, finally, the *irreversible* bond produced by imprinting. These and additional characteristics, according to Lorenz, distinguish imprinting from other types of associative learning. Recent investigations confirmed some but not all of these presumed differential characteristics of imprinting. It is now known that in many species of birds the young may be imprinted to a wide variety of objects that share few if any common properties. For instance, Fabricius (1951) found that in ducklings the shape and movement, as well as the size of the model (within limits), were of no appreciable importance, though color and sound appeared to have some significance. The quacking of the mother, which seemed to promote the subsequent response, could be successfully replaced with a variety of rhythmically repeated sounds. Fabricius concluded that the initial release of the subsequent response is attributable to a simple stimulus configuration, which constitutes the *innate releasing mechanism* of Lorenz, but that the animal is rapidly imprinted to a specific object, namely, its natural or artificial surrogate mother.

In contrast, the original assertion of Lorenz that imprinting produces irreversible bonds has not been unequivocally substantiated. In some species, the animal imprinted on man may, after a shorter or longer period of association with those of its own kind, acquire a normal social and sexual relation with them (Thorpe, 1963). In other species, early fixation may be permanent. Cichlid fish normally confine their parental activities to the young of their own species. It was observed (Noble and Curtis, 1939; Baerends and Baerends, 1950), however, that if naive cichlid fish are given eggs of another species in exchange for their own, they will accept them and raise the hatching young. Moreover, henceforth they will rear only young of this alien species; when their own eggs hatch they kill their young. Thus the restriction of parental activity under normal conditions to young of their own kind must be attributed to fixation by imprinting. In birds such imprinting may extend to recognition of the young as individuals. For instance, sea gulls readily accept any young for a few days after hatching and will feed them by regurgitating food. However, after several days the strange young are driven away and the gulls feed

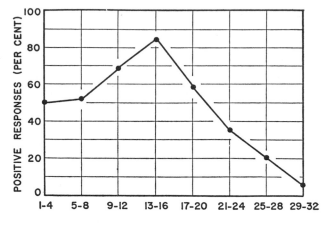

AGE   (HOURS)

The effect of age after hatching in ducklings on imprinting. (From Hess. Ethology. In Barron, *New directions in psychology.* Holt, Rinehart and Winston, 1964, Vol. 11. With the permission of *Science*)

only their own (Tinbergen, 1936). Recent investigations have shown that imprinting is not restricted to fish and birds; it may occur even in mammals, particularly ungulates (Scott, 1962).

The problem of *critical periods* has been intensively studied recently. In chicks, the optimal period of imprinting does not occur immediately after hatching but at the age of 13–16 hours (Hess, 1959). The investigations of Hess, furthermore, suggest that imprinting cannot be explained in terms of "primary need reduction," such as satisfaction of basic needs. Hess (1957) found that chicks that had to overcome hurdles when they were following a dummy became more strongly imprinted to it than did normal controls. Shocking the animal during its subsequent reaction, which in terms of the need-reduction theory (Hull, 1943) should have interfered with the establishment of the associative bond, strengthened imprinting (Hess, 1964). Similarly, the generation of an emotional state, such as fear, appears to strengthen the following-response. The establishment of such a bond is, in a general biological sense, of great utility to the young, because the mother provides it with food, protects it from predators, and in many ways supports its maturation. The opportunity of following an object is apparently by itself a rewarding or *self-reinforcing* process.

The ethologists (a group of zoologists, like Lorenz and Tinbergen, who are concerned with animal behavior, particularly its innate components) have shown great interest in the phenomenon of imprinting, because it represents an instance of learning which is at least in part innately de-

termined (for example, there is dependence on a critical period of maturation, and the imprinting is established with great ease). The following-
response is obviously an inborn tendency or disposition; gosling or chicks
of the right age will follow any moving object within a minute of their first
exposure to it. After a few minutes of following, which at the beginning is
largely nonspecific with regard to its object, the animal becomes firmly
attached to the specific object; thus, through transaction with the environment, the built-in following-response becomes fixated on, or channeled
toward, a specific object. Is this process, however, basically different from
the chick's pecking behavior, which is initially largely nonspecific but soon
becomes fixated on a few specific objects, that is, the few objects that are
edible? It is probable that the filial following-response is not the only example of imprinting. There is, indeed, some evidence of early imprinting
on food objects. In pecking, newly hatched chicks show a preference for
objects of a certain shape. Hess (1964) reported that this innate preference can be lastingly altered during the critical period of about 4 days of
age. When young chicks of this age are rewarded with food by pecking at
stimulus patterns for which they show low preference, they henceforth
shift their preference and persist in responding to the newly adopted
patterns even when they are no longer rewarded for it. We shall later discuss other instances of imprinting. In summary, imprinting may be described as a process of cathexis (fixation) in which an inborn response
tendency acquires its goal object and is thus modified from a diffuse or
general disposition to a response directed toward a specific object or class
of objects.

CLASSICAL CONDITIONING. In imprinting, a functional bond is
established between innate behavior tendencies (filial following or pecking) and goal objects that can *consummate* these tendencies (the maintenance of contact with the parent, ingestion of edible substances). Allied to this transactional channeling of response tendencies is the phenomenon called by Pavlov (1927) *conditioning*, and referred to by learning theorists as *classical conditioning*. There is, however, an obvious difference between imprinting and conditioning: in conditioning, the bond
established is not between the inborn response tendency and its goal object (for example, food substance) but with a signal that is spatially or
temporally *contiguous* with the goal object.

Pavlov's experiments originated with the physiological study of gastric
secretion and, later, of salivation in dogs. If meat powder is placed into
the mouth of a dog, the gustatory stimulus elicits salivation. If the duct
of the parotid gland is surgically brought into the open and a container
is attached to it to collect the secreted saliva, the magnitude of the salivation response can easily be determined. In Pavlov's terminology the taste
of food is an *unconditional stimulus* that elicits the *unconditional response*
of salivation by way of a presumed reflex pathway. Now, Pavlov found

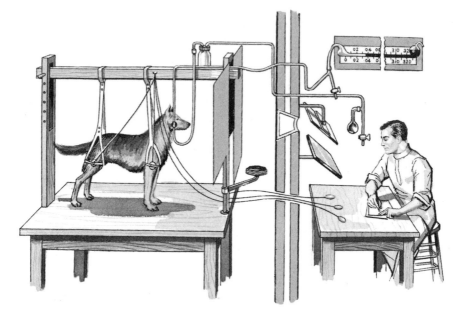

Experimental apparatus used by Pavlov to study conditioning of the salivary response. (From Leuba. *Man: a general psychology.* Holt, Rinehart and Winston, 1961. Redrawn from I. P. Pavlov, *Lectures on conditioned reflexes.* International Publishers, 1928)

that "psychic" causes may also produce salivation, and he undertook to investigate the physiological mechanisms of such "psychic secretions." If the presentation of meat powder to a dog is repeatedly paired with the beats of a metronome, the association of this arbitrary auditory *conditional stimulus* with the unconditional stimulus of food establishes some bond between the two events and the dog salivates to the presentation of the clicks alone. Pavlov observed that in order to preserve this *conditional response* (or conditioned response) to the clicks, the animal has to be given meat powder from time to time. In the absence of such a *reinforcement* the salivation response to sound is extinguished; this phenomenon of *extinction* was called by Pavlov *inhibition.* After a period of extinction, there may be a *spontaneous recovery* of the conditioned response, a phenomenon that he called *disinhibition.*

In the experimental situation set up by Pavlov the dog learns, on the basis of repeated associations between the click and the appearance of food, to "expect" food and to make *preparatory responses* associated with food acquisition and ingestion. Originally Pavlov thought that the dog learns to identify the conditional stimulus with food; that is, the conditional stimulus becomes a substitute for the unconditional stimulus and therefore elicits the same response. Indeed, it was observed in his laboratory that the dog, if conditioned to a light bulb, would occasionally lick it. However, the apparent identification of the unconditional and conditional responses is probably an artifact. The experimental setup in the usual conditioning experiment is a highly artificial one. For one thing, the association that is established is an arbitrary pairing of two unrelated events (the click and food). More importantly, the animal is placed in a harness, trained to remain motionless, and only a single response, salivation, is recorded. If the animal is tested under a freer condition, and all its responses are recorded, one discovers that the conditional stimulus does not represent food itself to the animal; it merely signals the food's coming and produces "expectation." In the presence of food the animal masticates, swallows, and engages in other aspects of the consummatory action of feeding; in contrast, when the conditional stimulus is presented, the freely moving animal looks at the bell, moves toward the food pan, and displays a variety of other signs of anticipatory behavior, including salivation (Zener, 1937).

The conditional stimulus in the situation described is a *reward signal* indicating the imminent appearance of food. Under more natural conditions, such a signal (for instance, noise made with the dog's dish) serves as a distal cue that guides the animal to food. The animal learns to appreciate such signals as "promises" of reward and it will "expect" the reward as long as the association tends to prevail. If the temporal or spatial contiguity between the signal and goal object is abolished, the animal "unlearns" the response and will cease to display the anticipatory and preparatory behavior (*extinction*). That is, in contrast to imprinting, where the distal stimulus originates directly from the goal object itself (sight or sound of parent, smell of food) and the response is *self-reinforcing*, because it leads to consummation, in conditioning the display of the anticipatory response is *contingent* on the persistence of a nonobligatory association between the conditional stimulus and the reinforcing goal object.

Conditioning of this type need not be restricted to food objects (*alimentary conditioning*) but may be established as readily when a distal signal is associated with other reward objects. Furthermore, it may also be formed with punishment as a reinforcement, called *aversive conditioning*. Under such situations, the conditioned stimulus serves as a *danger signal*. For example, the paired presentation of a sound with an electric shock to the limb soon produces anticipatory excitement, crouching, running, barking, defecation, and similar "fear" responses, which are displayed by the animal after a while in response to the sound even if the shock is omitted. Under natural conditions such distal cues can serve the animal as warning signals so that it may shun certain regions of its environment or avoid dangerous objects. In summary, the acquired recognition of "promising" or "threatening" anticipatory signals through conditioning permits the animal to orient itself appropriately toward propitious and obnoxious objects without the need of repeatedly establishing direct contact with them.

**Acquisition of New** INSTRUMENTAL CONDITIONING.    In
**Action Patterns** classical conditioning procedure the animal learns to appreciate signals associated with beneficial or aversive situations. The conditioned stimulus and the subsequent "reward" or "punishment" are contingent on a conditional external association, but they are not contingent on the behavior of the animal, which is not manipulating its environment and does not affect the situation itself. What the animal displays is therefore essentially an instance of *signal learning*. A somewhat different learning process underlies instrumental conditioning.

A simple example of instrumental conditioning is the procedure employed in the early work of Bekhterev (1913), a procedure widely used later by Liddell (1942). The dog (Liddell used sheep) is harnessed to a stand and habituated to the experimental setup. Then a signal, for example, the sound of a buzzer, is paired with the delivery of shock to the animal's leg. In this situation, however, unlike the classical aversive conditioning procedure, the animal may avoid the shock by making some response, such as lifting its leg (a response that the animal tends to display innately as a protective withdrawal from noxious stimulation). After a few such pairings of buzzer and leg shock, the animal displays a variety of fear responses when the buzzer is sounded (this phase represents essentially an instance of aversive conditioning), and when the animal lifts its leg, that response terminates the shock. As the trials continue, the animal's behavior changes insofar as it begins to show anticipatory withdrawal of the leg when the buzzer sounds, with the result that it does not get shocked. Thus the animal learns to avoid the shock whenever it hears the danger signal of the buzzer. This procedure is an instance of *avoidance conditioning*.

Leg withdrawal to prevent delivery of the shock is the simplest instance of instrumental learning, because the animal achieves mastery of the task by the mere anticipatory display of an innate protective reflex. A somewhat more complex example of instrumental conditioning is illustrated by the procedure designed by Thorndike (1898), in which the animal acquires a *new response pattern*. Thorndike put hungry cats into *problem boxes*, with food placed outside as an incentive to learn to open the door by turning a bar, pulling on a string, or some similar manipulation. The animals initially displayed random activity, such as moving about in the cage, scratching at the sides, and vocalizing, until finally, as though by accident, the latch was appropriately manipulated, the door opened, and the animal consumed the food. In the subsequent trials the random movements tended to diminish gradually, until finally the animals learned

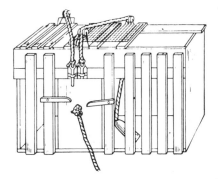

Thorndike's problem box with latches
and inside pedal to open the door.
(Thorndike, 1898. In H. I. Garrett,
*Great experiments in psychology.* Ap-
pleton-Century-Crofts, 1930)

to open the door immediately when placed in the box. The acquisition of a new skill of this sort, which is not part of the innate repertoire of the animal, was described by Thorndike as a *trial-and-error* process.

The slow and gradual, rather than sudden, acquisition of this skill, suggested to Thorndike that learning of skills in animals is a mechanical rather than "insightful" process, which is dependent on the formation of associative bonds rather than on "understanding" the problem and the appropriate solution to it. Thorndike formulated his *connectionist theory* according to which bonds are formed among those presumed neural schemata of the movements which are successful in producing the reward while the unsuccessful or useless ones are eliminated. This process occurs in conformity with the *principle of effect*, which says, "The greater the satisfaction or discomfort, the greater the strengthening or weakening of the bond" (Thorndike, 1911, p. 244).

But is it possible that the animals were overly excited and hungry and therefore incapable of gaining insight into the situation? Is it possible that the task was also difficult for the animals, who could not perceive the connection between the opening devices and the opening of the door, and that they therefore were forced to solve the problem in a "blind" mechanical manner? Adams (1929) repeated Thorndike's experiments with cats that were well adapted to the problem box and displayed little emotionality in the situation. The cats mastered the task quickly; the animals that used visual guidance in manipulating the opening devices, it was noted, were superior to those that did not. Indeed, cats and dogs, which make little use of limb-eye coordination in manipulatory processes, may be handicapped on such tasks because of lack of sensory cues. Primates, with good hand-eye coordination, learn such tasks with the greatest ease.

Instrumental conditioning tasks are easily presented to animals in a *Skinner box* (Skinner, 1938). The animal is placed in a box containing a lever and a food tray, together with some stimulus sources, such as a light bulb or buzzer. On pressing the lever, which through a microswitch activates the automatic food dispenser, the animal obtains a pellet of food as a reward. The animal (pigeon, rat, monkey) quickly learns to press the bar to obtain food. Subsequently the animal may be put on different "schedules of reinforcement" (Ferster and Skinner, 1957) by periodic or intermittent rewarding of lever pressing, or presented with discrimination tasks (that is, by being rewarded only for responses that coincide with or follow a specific signal). The ready mastery of such tasks illustrates the instrumental learning ability of animals, ranging from fish to primates, to obtain rewards or avoid punishment.

Related to these relatively simple examples of instrumental learning are other complex experimental tasks, such as *maze learning*. Maze learning in its simplest form is tested in a T or Y maze (Yerkes, 1912) in which the animal has to learn to turn to the right or left in order to obtain a reward. In more complex mazes (Small, 1899) there may be several blind alleys or delaying turns, and the animal's progress in mastering the task is scored by the gradual elimination of errors at *choice points*. Rats display an unusual capacity to learn their way through a complex maze, presumably because it is a task related to their natural mode of living. In a maze the animal is confronted with a serial learning task: it has to learn the correct turns at successive choice points on its way to the goal box.

Related to the problems faced by animals when they try to find their way through the tortuous path of a maze to a goal object are the various *discrimination tasks* by which animals are tested in sensory and perceptual experiments. In the simplest form of sensory discrimination task, the animal is presented with two dissimilar stimuli: when it selects the arbitrarily assigned "correct" ("positive") stimulus it is rewarded, but the reward is omitted or the animal is actually punished if it selects the "incorrect" ("negative") stimulus. The discriminanda may be presented to the animal successively or simultaneously. For instance, the stimulus objects may be attached to windows or openings in a box containing food, where the opening displaying the negative cue is locked and the one displaying the positive cue is open and permits access to the reward. With the use of such methods, animals (from fish to primates) were shown to be able to learn complex discriminations based on differences of pattern, size, color, pitch, loudness, and the like. Several more complex discrimination and manipulation tasks were described earlier (Chapter 12).

**Innate and Acquired Components in the Development of Behavior**    Though the morphogenetically and transactionally programed components of behavior differ radically in many respects, the two become intimately interwoven during development as the animal's potentialities and capacities are unfolded and realized. Most of the innately determined structural facilities of behavior, and many of its innately programed responses, acquire their functional utility only after a prolonged period of learning. For instance, the maturation of

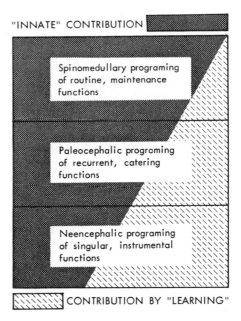

"INNATE" CONTRIBUTION

Spinomedullary programing of routine, maintenance functions

Paleocephalic programing of recurrent, catering functions

Neencephalic programing of singular, instrumental functions

Relative contributions of innate and acquired programing mechanisms to the different types of animative functions.

CONTRIBUTION BY "LEARNING"

the eye and its central nervous connections, and the display of such optic reflexes as the pupillary response, conjugate eye movements, accommodation, and the ocular following responses, become useful to the animal when it is provided with the opportunity of responding to and thus learning to discriminate the various visual objects of its environment. Even more significantly, what the animal learns is not determined entirely by exogenous factors or chance opportunities. Rather, the animal goes through phases of ontogenetic maturation during which it appears compelled to engage in specific activities and to interact with a selective class of objects, namely, those that are relevant to the momentary phases of its morphogenetic development. What we are referring to here are the *critical periods* of imprinting and learning during which the young animal learns to recognize its parent and the edible and inedible objects of its environment, and, somewhat later, its social and sexual mates. Most of these critical periods occur early in life, and this may be the basis of the crucial role of *early experience* in the development of behavior.

We have discussed earlier the phenomenon of imprinting with particular reference to the following-response of newly hatched precocial birds. Chicks and goslings become fixated on the first moving object that they happen to follow after hatching, and treat that object henceforth as their "mother." In that example the tendency to follow represents the innate component elicited initially in a diffuse manner by a large class of stimuli. But after first exposure to a followable object, the response becomes specific with respect to its goal object (this object under natural circumstances tends to be the true mother, who incubates the eggs and assists the young during and after hatching). Imprinting on a parent object declines rapidly as the animal grows older; that is, birds several days of age exposed for the first time to a moving object display a decreasing tendency to become attached permanently to that object. From a functional point of view this finding reflects the declining need of the young, as they grow older, for parental protection and guidance. In a similar manner, the recognition of water and of edible and inedible food objects occurs in precocial birds early in life, and the lasting food preferences and aversions that develop may also be considered examples of imprinting.

Although it is often stated that imprinting on a species-alien parent object also leads to sexual fixation, that is, to a transfer of sexual affection and of mating attempts to individuals of that species, this conclusion is based on observations in which the young remain with their foster parents for a prolonged period. Such studies therefore do not reveal the exact critical periods of early socialization and sexual fixation. In a recent study (Nicolai, 1956), evidence was obtained that in the bullfinch irreversible sexual fixation does not occur until after the young leave their nests, presumably when their sexual maturation begins. We shall later discuss several studies (Chapter 17) that deal with the great importance of early socialization and sexual play on the subsequent display of "normal" social and sexual behavior.

In the following paragraphs we shall deal briefly with investigations concerned with the problem of *early experience*. These studies have indicated that the environmental conditions to which an animal is exposed in the early phases of its development, particularly before weaning, have profound and lasting effects on various physiological and behavioral variables tested later on. The importance of early environmental variables on subsequent "psychic" development was originally stressed by Freud on the basis of studies of human patients, and the experimental investigation of the problem in animals was later advocated by Hebb (1949).

A popular experimental procedure for altering the early environment of animals is the *handling* of laboratory rodents. Mice or rats are customarily raised in the laboratory in small cages, that is, in a restricted environment in which the animal has little or no opportunity to establish intimate contact with the more varied extra-cage environment. The procedure of handling consists of removing the animal from its cage and transferring it somewhere else, where it is stroked, brushed, or otherwise stimulated by a person or an inanimate device (McClelland, 1956; Levine et al., 1956; Levine and Lewis, 1959).

In the early literature on these studies the term "gentling" was sometimes applied to this procedure; it is more likely, however, that the manipulation represents a stressful situation in which the unweaned animal raised in a restricted, familiar milieu is suddenly removed from its home cage, separated from its mother and siblings, and confronted with an unfamiliar, alien environment. Such a procedure, which may consist of a single episode of handling lasting for a few minutes, was reported to facilitate the early growth rate of animals (Ruegamer et al., 1954; Weininger et al., 1954; McClelland, 1956) and to increase the ability of rats to tolerate stressful situations (Weininger, 1956; Levine, 1956), or to withstand prolonged food and water deprivation (Levine and Otis, 1958; Denenberg and Karas, 1961). Handling also influences such physiological variables as maturation of the adrenal glands (Levine and Lewis, 1959), resistance to leukemia, and other factors (Levine, 1962). Handling also affects the learning ability of rodents (Levine, 1956; Levine et al., 1956; Bernstein, 1957). That the procedure is most effective between 10 and 20 days of age (Denenberg et al., 1962) suggests that it has a critical period. We may speculate that this is the critical period of "adjustment" during which exposure to an alien environment facilitates the development of as yet unknown adaptive mechanisms (adrenal-pituitary maturation?; Levine, 1962).

**THE PROBLEM OF MEMORY TRACE** Learning presupposes the storage, coded in some latent but retrievable form, of the programs or central schemata of acquired behavioral responses. The postulated storage entity is referred to as the memory trace, or engram. Considerable research and thought have gone into solving the problem of what the properties of the postulated memory traces are, where memory traces are or can be laid down, and what neural circuits are involved in producing and retrieving an engram. Because the problem is very far from having been resolved, the best we can do at present is to outline some of the experimental approaches dealing with the problem, describe some of the results obtained, and discuss the hypotheses that have been offered.

**Structures Involved in Memory Storage** It has been argued by philosophers and biologists that memory is a universal phenomenon in the living world, one that distinguishes living from inanimate things. This view is based on a broad concept of memory that includes not only individual memory but also "racial memory," the hereditary unfolding of ancestral characteristics during the development of the individual. If one restricts the term "memory," as we shall do here, to imply storage of *individually acquired experience*, the argument that memory is a universal phenomenon in the living world may not be appropriate. For instance, it is seldom claimed, and certainly it has never been demonstrated, that plants are capable of acquiring new response patterns through individual experience. Moreover, the other facet of the argument, namely that inanimate objects never manifest memory, no longer holds, because various engineering devices have recently been designed with immense storage and reliable retrieval capabilities.

LEARNING IN ANIMALS LACKING A NERVOUS SYSTEM. Another commonly voiced argument is that learning is dependent on the nervous system, with the implication that memory is always stored somewhere in the brain. Although this argument can be well defended by reference to studies in higher animal forms, in which ablations of brain structures were shown to produce amnesia for certain acquired functions, memory functions of the simpler kinds have been demonstrated in *Protozoa* lacking a nervous system. For example, the simplest form of learning, *habituation*, has been observed by many investigators in such acellular organisms as amebas, ciliates, and flagellates. For instance, Verworn (1889) observed that amebas that responded initially when exposed to a weak electric current, ceased to do so after a lapse of some time. The same was observed by Harrington and Leaming (1900) in amebas exposed to light. Jennings (1906), who studied the problem of habituation extensively in ciliates, observed clear effects of habituation to withdrawal and related protective responses when the animals were repeatedly stimulated with innocuous mechanical stimuli, such as a jet of water.

In addition to habituation, the occurrence of *associative learning* has also been claimed. Several investigators have, in fact, described the ability of *Paramecia* to learn to distinguish edible from inedible objects (Wichterman, 1953), to aggregate in regions where they were previously fed (Gelber, 1952; 1958), and to escape from capillary tubes (Smith, 1908; Day and Bentley, 1911) or mazes (French, 1940). Though these and several related claims were disputed by others (Thorpe, 1963), the available evidence does seem to suggest that at least some simple and transient forms of learning are possible in *Protozoa*. However, long-term learning effects were not described in *Protozoa* (Gelber claimed 3-hour retention); accordingly, it may be tentatively postulated that *long-term memory* necessitates a nervous system, possibly a well-developed centralized nervous system.

NERVOUS STRUCTURES INVOLVED IN LEARNING. There are three basic approaches that have been used profitably in studying localization of memory functions in the central nervous system. One of these is the *phylogenetic approach*, based on comparing the learning ability of animals with simpler and more complex nervous systems. Thus, by comparing the learning ability of protochordates, lower vertebrates, and mammals, one could theoretically adduce the role of spinomedullary, paleocephalic, and neencephalic structures in learning. A complementary negative approach is represented by *lesion studies*. These involve the removal or destruction of certain nervous structures, the severing of connections between various areas (including the two cerebral hemispheres), and the "functional ablation," or reversible interference, with the normal functioning of certain brain regions for the purpose of inferring from the learning deficits produced the role of the manipulated structures in memory functions. Finally, one can record the electrical activity of different brain structures or investigate local metabolic changes as *functional correlates* of learning.

THE SPINAL CORD AND LEARNING. The available experimental evidence indicates that the segmental nervous system can mediate learning in invertebrates. For instance, in *Planarians* not only long-term habituation (Westerman, 1963) but classical conditioning (Thompson and McConnell, 1955; Corning and John, 1961) and instrumental conditioning have recently been demonstrated (Best and Rubinstein, 1962). These studies have also shown that the cephalic portion of the nervous system is not essential to the preservation of the task learned, because *Planarians* regenerated from the cut tail-end may show savings in learning trials when retested.

We do not have comparable information on the role of the segmental nervous system in the order of chordates, such as *Amphioxus*, whose nervous system consists of little more than spinomedullary components. We have referred earlier to the finding of habituation effects in the transected spinal cord in mammals (Hernández-Péon and Brust-Carmona, 1961); this indicates that the simplest form of learning may be programed at this level of the neuraxis. In contrast, studies concerned with the ability of the *isolated spinal cord* to mediate simple conditioning have brought ambiguous evidence. Franzisket (1955) reported conditioning in spinal frogs. Similarly, Shurrager and Culler (1940) reported simple conditioning in spinal dogs. In this investigation the spinal cord was transected in the lumbar region; twitches in the dissected semitendinous muscle of the hindlimb were recorded in response to an unconditional stimulus (electric shock to the foot of the same limb) and a conditioned stimulus (light mechanical stimulation). In some of the animals tested, conditioned twitches could be demonstrated. These findings, however, could not be confirmed by Kellogg et al. (1946, 1947), who investigated the conditioned response of an entire limb, or by Pinto and Bromiley (1950), who used a technique similar to that used by Shurrager and Culler. Accordingly, *spinal conditioning* at best is possible, in mammals, when fragments of a response are investigated; in spinal mammals, integrated learned responses beyond habituation have not been shown thus far.

PALEOCEPHALON AND LEARNING. One approach to the study of the role of paleocephalic structures in learning is *phylogenetic*. Because spinomedullary structures appear to be only slightly involved in the mediation of learning, the learning ability of lower vertebrates, such as fish (which have a paleocephalon but no neencephalon), may be reasonably attributed to the mediating role of existing paleocephalic structures. Studies concerned with the learning ability of fish show that these animals not only may readily display habituation but can be conditioned, and can learn mazes, complex discrimination tasks, and the like.

Habituation in fish was shown by Triplett (1901), who found that perch ceased to attack minnows, on which they prey, when the minnows were separated in the aquarium by a glass partition. After bumping into the glass partition repeatedly, the perch refrained from attacking the minnows even when the glass partition was removed, though they did attack other prey, such as worms. In various species of fish, Frolov (1928) succeeded in establishing conditioned aversive reactions by pairing various neutral stimuli with intense light as the unconditional stimulus. These findings were confirmed and extended by Bull (1957). That some of the aversive conditioning demonstrated in fish may have been instances of *pseudo conditioning* was suggested by the experiments of Harlow (1939). Goldfish were first tested with mild shock and tactile stimulation, to which they failed to give a flight response. Then they were given stronger electric shocks, which elicited struggling and flight reactions. Subsequently they were retested with the original neutral stimuli, which were never paired with the unconditional stimulus, but these stimuli now elicited the flight response. This reaction is an instance of pseudo conditioning, an apparent generalized "sensitization" or "anxiety" produced by the previous experience of punishment.

However, the fact that fish can be conditioned and taught various complex tasks is beyond doubt. For instance, horned dace could be taught to select, by the attached color cues, the compartment baited with food (Reeves, 1919), and, as the extensive studies of Herter (1953) showed, various species of fish can master visual pattern-discrimination problems. Russell (1931) reported that three-spined sticklebacks can learn to obtain food by "*detour*" (taking an indirect route to the goal object), a learned performance which was remembered for at least 3 months. Successful detour performance in fish was also reported by others (Warden et al., 1936; Thorpe, 1963). Fish can learn to master mazes (Churchill, 1916; Welty, 1934), a laboratory task that may well be simpler than the well-documented homing ability of certain migrating fish, such as salmon. Recent studies have also shown that fish can learn to operate devices resembling Skinner boxes to obtain a reward (Haralson and Bitterman, 1950).

What specific paleocephalic structures mediate learning in fish? Sanders (1940) reported interference with visual and olfactory conditioning following removal of the optic tectum. Zunini (1941) found that removal of the forebrain in fish abolished a simple position habit but that the animals could relearn the task. In a more recent study, Bernstein (1961) reported transient loss of color discrimination following forebrain ablations in animals in which the optic lobes were not directly damaged. The available data, in general, are as yet insufficient to point to specific brain structures as mediators of learning in fish.

The evidence presented so far regarding learning in fish supports the argument that learning can be mediated by paleocephalic structures. Learning of various types (habituation, conditioning, instrumental learning, discrimination learning) has also been demonstrated in amphibians and reptiles (Thorpe, 1963). Finally, the learning ability of birds has been well established. Pigeons, for instance, can be taught as easily as can mammals to discriminate objects, operate puzzle boxes, or work on complex schedules of reinforcement in a Skinner box. However, because birds have highly evolved striatal and neostriatal brain structures not present in lower vertebrates, and because of doubts of the classification of these structures as paleocephalic, evidence of the bird's learning may not be relevant to the present argument.

That paleocephalic structures can mediate learning has also been established in mammals by the *ablation procedure*. For instance, it was shown in the laboratory of Pavlov, who himself originally advocated the idea that conditioning is mediated by the cerebral hemispheres, that conditioned responses can be established to visual and auditory signals in decorticated dogs (Poltyrew and Zeliony, 1930). Indeed, in an earlier study, Lashley (1922) found that rats, taught a visual brightness-discrimination task, exhibited amnesia when the visual cortex was removed in its entirety, but that the same animals could relearn the task at the same rate that normal rats learned it. If the rest of the cortex was then removed in such animals, the habit was retained; the inference is that subcortical structures mediated the habit. However, if removal of the visual cortex was combined with destruction of the superior colliculus and pretectal regions, the animals could not relearn the discrimination (Lashley, 1935). This finding suggests mediation of the habit by these latter structures. It is worth noting, though, that destruction of the superior colliculus in animals with intact cortex does not produce amnesia for brightness discrimination (Ghiselli, 1938); it may, in fact, improve the reliability of their performance (Altman, unpublished observations). The conclusion drawn from these findings, then, is that under normal conditions the visual cortex forms part of the circuit involved in retention of a brightness-discrimination habit, but in the absence of the visual cortex, subcortical visual structures can adequately mediate the habit. Furthermore, subcortical mediation is not restricted to such visual tasks. There is ample evidence that animals can acquire simpler auditory, tactile, and other types of discriminations after removal of the appropriate cortical areas (Chapter 12).

NEENCEPHALON AND LEARNING. It is obvious that even in mammals certain types of memory functions may be mediated by subcortical, presumably paleocephalic, structures. But, then, there are several types of learning functions that cannot be mastered by decorticate animals. As described in Chapter 12, rats cannot retain or master a visual pattern-discrimination problem after total extirpation of the striate cortex, a finding that holds for all mammalian species tested. Similarly, the retention or learning of more complex auditory, tactile, and manipulatory tasks may also be seriously interfered with following removal of various cortical projection or association areas. Although it is often ambiguous whether these losses are to be attributed to sensory impairment or memory deficits, one can justifiably state that without neocortical participation mammals cannot acquire complex discriminatory or manipulatory functions. The greater ease with which higher mammalian species acquire complex learning tasks may be attributed to the increasing size and complexity of the neocortical projection and, in particular, association areas. An instance of such a correlation in primates with more complex cortices is the increasing facility in forming *learning sets* (Harlow, 1949; see the figure on page 318). The neocortex may be considered the major memory mechanism of the central nervous system, and the greater modifiability and variability of behavior seen in mammals in general, when compared with lower vertebrates, may be attributed to the progressive evolution of the neencephalon.

**Circuits Involved**    ABLATION AND RELATED STUDIES.
**in Memory Functions**    The problem of identifying or localizing the circuits and mechanisms mediating memory has been approached recently with a variety of techniques. In discussing this problem we may perhaps begin by referring to some of the relevant studies of Lashley, who in fact came to doubt the existence of circumscribed memory circuits (1950). Lashley (1929) found that rats with cortical lesions are inferior to normal rats in maze-learning performance both in terms of rate of acquisition of the task and in retention of previously acquired habits. He found further that the more difficult the maze to be mastered, the greater the deficit of the operated animals. In addition, Lashley found that the amount of cortical tissue destroyed, irrespective of the regions involved, produced proportional deficits in maze-learning ability. For instance, destruction of from 5 to 10 percent of the cortex produced little learning or retention deficit. If the amount of destruction was as high as 50 percent, there was complete amnesia, and relearning was greatly protracted, irrespective of what specific areas were involved. This latter finding, which Lashley referred to as *mass action*, gave rise to the theory of *equipotentiality*. According to this theory, specific brain regions have, in addition to their specific functions (vision or audition, for example) also general or nonspecific functions, and these nonspecific functions give rise to the observed mass-action effects.

Critics of the theory have pointed out that because maze learning is a *multisensory* task also involving motor functions it is reasonable to expect such an apparent mass action irrespective of which sensory or motor-projection and association areas are destroyed. Lashley (1933), however, marshaled further evidence in favor of his theory of equipotentiality. 'I'sang (1934) reared blinded rats from birth, trained them on a maze task, and then removed their striate areas bilaterally. This operation produced as severe a deficit in retention of a maze habit in the blinded animals as it did in normal animals, even though the visual cortex in the blind animals could not subserve any specific visual functions. Similarly, Lashley (1943) found that removal of the visual cortex produces greater deficits in retention of learned tasks than does removal of the eyes; this again indicates that the visual cortex makes nonspecific contributions to behavior beyond its specific visual functions. This controversy, which has not been resolved, is of great importance, because the theory of equipotentiality implies that memory traces might be either *diffusely localized* or *replicated* over wide areas of the cortex, a theory that stands in contradiction to the simpler concept of *discrete loci* or *circuits* for specific memory functions.

Notwithstanding Lashley's findings, which suggest equipotentiality of different cortical areas in maze learning and at least some nonspecific contribution made by specific areas, the great bulk of experimental evidence supports the older idea that specific memory functions are mediated by discrete brain regions. We need only remember the evidence that the acquisition and retention of complex discrimination tasks are predictably interfered with or abolished by injury to or removal of the appropriate sensory projection and association areas. This being the situation, the next question that arises is what the properties of such circuits are and where they are localized in the brain.

The simplest hypothesis of neural circuits of memory functions is derived from the classical reflex theory. This theory asserts that the organization of the schemata of behavioral processes is dependent on synaptic connections between afferent elements that elicit, and efferent elements that execute, activities. If this model is correct, learning could be explained as the establishment of *new synaptic connections* between sensory and motor elements to form acquired "conditioned-reflex" circuits. The site of the "trace" is, then, the afferent-efferent juncture of the circuit, and no separate coding or storage mechanism is postulated. For instance, the circuit responsible for visual learning is conceived to consist of an afferent pathway from the eyes to various visual centers in the brain, connections from the visual centers by way of the association areas to the motor centers, and an efferent pathway discharging the response.

Although the circuit theory (to be described later as the interneuronal theory of memory trace) has not definitely been proved wrong, Lashley's studies cast serious doubts on the validity of such a simple conception of cortical memory circuits. Lashley (1942) showed that interruption of the intercortical connections between the sensory and motor areas in the rat does not interfere with learning, and that the animals can master at a normal rate a task as complex as conditional discrimination. This finding was recently confirmed in the dog by Adrianov (1960). Similarly, if rats are trained on a maze and then knife cuts are made throughout the cortex, severing the intracortical connections between the different areas that presumably mediate this multisensory task, no deficit in retention is produced (Lashley, 1944). A related finding was reported by Sperry et al. (1947) who found that crosshatching large parts of the surface of the cortex in monkeys, the sensory and motor areas included, produced no deficit in motor coordination. These and several other related results indicate that the original idea of learning as a process mediated by direct transcortical circuits is incorrect. These findings, however, do not eliminate the possibility that more complex pathways, involving subcortical loops, form the hypothesized memory circuits.

SPLIT-BRAIN PREPARATION. In addition to conventional studies of brain lesions, several other techniques have been introduced recently in an attempt to isolate some of the neural circuits involved in memory functions. One of these approaches requires transection of the corpus callosum, which produces a "split-brain" preparation. This method was first employed by Bykov (1926), who studied the effect on the conditioned salivary response of the transfer of the conditioned stimulus from the trained limb to the opposite, untrained limb. Although in normal dogs such a response is readily transferred from one limb to the other, the reaction did not occur in the animal with transected corpus callosum. The conclusion drawn from this finding was that the transfer of the function from one cerebral hemisphere to the other is dependent on a pathway passing through the corpus callosum.

Myers (1955) found more recently that in cats in which the optic chiasma was sectioned sagittally (so that visual input from one eye was restricted to the ipsilateral cortex) a visual pattern discrimination learned by one eye was easily transferred to the other, or "naive" eye (which was blindfolded during the training procedure). However, in animals with the corpus callosum sectioned such transfer did not take place (Myers, 1956; Sperry et al., 1956), and the second eye required as long a period of training as did the first. Interhemispheric transfer of this type could be abolished, when the sectioning was restricted to the posterior part of the corpus callosum; apparently the interhemispheric pathway of the visual system passes through this region (Myers, 1959). With the use of such split-brain preparations it was shown that each eye could be taught a different visual discrimination, even contradictory tasks, without interference (Trevarthen, 1962).

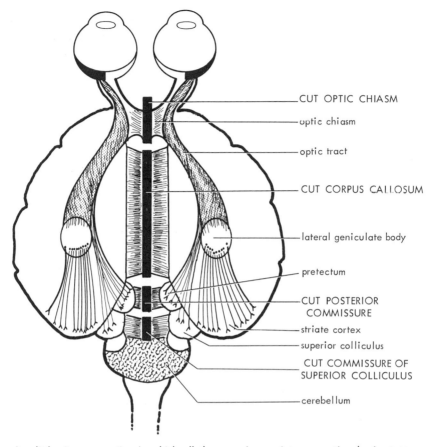

A split-brain preparation in which all the commissures interconnecting brain structures implicated in vision had been cut, together with the optic chiasm. (Based on work by Sperry, Myers, and others)

These findings established beyond doubt the importance of callosal commissural circuits for transmitting information from one cerebral hemisphere to the other. The next question that arose was whether information transmitted to one hemisphere is stored there alone, and merely transferred through the callosum during testing, or whether the callosum makes possible simultaneous recording of the memory trace during training. Chiasma-transected cats were taught monocularly "easy" and "difficult" visual discriminations; when the task was mastered, the "trained" hemisphere was removed (Myers, 1961). Postoperative testing indicated that easy discriminations were transferred during training from one hemisphere to the other, whereas difficult choices had to be "relearned" by the naive eye. This observation implies limited memory storage during unilateral training in the "untrained," contralateral hemisphere, which is not adequate for the mediation of more complex tasks.

A further interesting finding is the recent demonstration that the corpus callosum is essential only for the transfer of visual pattern discrimination; interocular transfer of a brightness discrimination task can occur when the callosum is cut (Meikle and Seichzer, 1960). This finding is in agreement with Lashley's original demonstration that brightness-discrimination habits can be mediated by subcortical structures. When the callosum is severed, the memory function can presumably be transferred to the opposite side by such fiber pathways as the commissure of the superior colliculus.

REVERSIBLE FUNCTIONAL ABLATION. A related technique for studying localization of memory functions (or the performance of learned behavior patterns) is the temporary disruption of the functioning of localized brain regions. Among the various techniques employed we may mention the implantation of *irritative chemicals* over selected areas of the brain and, the production of *spreading depression*. Because the effects produced by these techniques may be (at least partially) reversible, they are often referred to as functional ablation in contradistinction to the irreversible surgical ablation procedures. Chow and Obrist (1954) and Henry and Pribram (1954) showed that the placement of *aluminum hydroxide* cream over the surface of the cortex produces local epileptiform discharges. Later it was shown that when alumina cream is implanted over the visual cortex losses were produced in the rate of acquisition of visual discrimination problems but not in the mastering of a spatial alternation task (Kraft et al., 1960). Conversely, implantation of this irritative chemical over the lateral frontal cortex interfered with delayed alternation but not visual discrimination (Stamm and Pribram, 1960). Alumina cream placed over the posterior parietal cortex interfered with acquisition of somesthetic discriminations (Stamm and Warren, 1961); whereas placement over the infratemporal cortex interfered with both visual and somesthetic discriminations but not with an alternation task (Stamm and Pribram, 1961). Interestingly, this chemical irritant affects only the acquisition of a new learning problem; it does not interfere with the performance of a habit acquired before its application. Presumably, the procedure does not interfere with the *preservation* and *retrieval* of already formed memory traces, but with either the perceptual processes underlying acquisition of memory traces or their *consolidation*.

Another method of producing functional ablation is by provoking *spreading depression* over the cortex. If the cortex is irritated mechanically or chemically, an inhibitory process is produced (reduction of EEG activity, diminution of evoked potentials), which spreads slowly over the entire hemisphere. This effect, Leão's spreading depression, is not transmitted to the opposite hemisphere, a circumstance which makes possible the production of a *reversible hemidecortication*. The technique was utilized by Bureš and Burešova (1960), who injected potassium chloride unilaterally over the brains of rats and trained the animals on an avoidance problem. They found that if one hemisphere was depressed and the other spared on 2 successive days the animals showed considerable savings on the second day; but if one hemisphere was depressed on the first day and the opposite on the second day there was no apparent transfer of information during the period prior to testing from the normal, or "trained," to the depressed, or "untrained," hemisphere. In a more extensive study, Russell and Ochs (1963) confirmed the original findings of Bureš and Burešova that with unilateral training there is no transfer of stored information from one hemisphere to the other, even if the animals are permitted to survive for a longer period. However, if the animals were given a few trials with the untrained hemisphere, they showed considerable savings, indicating the occurrence of some active transfer under such circumstances. With bilateral training (that is, training without spreading depression) unilateral depression did not interfere with the performance of the task; seemingly, under normal circumstances both hemispheres store the acquired information.

Related to the previous techniques of reversible functional ablations is the attempt to interfere with normal functioning through direct *electric stimulation* of selected brain structures by means of implanted electrodes. Chiles (1954), for example, reported that rats trained in a Skinner box for food reward showed a slower and more variable rate of bar pressing when electric shocks were applied to certain thalamic and hypothalamic structures. Similarly, Rosvold and Delgado (1956) found that electric stimulation of the caudate nucleus interfered with the performance of monkeys on a delayed-alternation task, but it did not produce visual-discrimination deficits. In a more recent study (Weiskrantz et al., 1962) bilateral electrical stimulation in the region of the sulcus principalis of the frontal lobe was shown to produce chance performance in delayed alternation in trained monkeys. It may be noted that unlike epileptogenic chemical stimulation (alumina cream), which produces deficits in acquisition but not in retention, electrical stimulation appears to affect *retrieval* of the memory trace (the "trace" itself is not affected because the deficit is reversible).

A physiologically less well-controlled method, but one that permits investigation of the temporal course of the memory-consolidation process, is the technique of *electroconvulsive shock*. In this procedure high-voltage current is applied for a brief period across the head of the animal through electrodes attached to the ears; the current produces a generalized convulsion. From clinical practice it is known that electroconvulsive shock applied to patients (like traumatic brain concussion and anoxia) produces *retrograde amnesia*; that is, the patient shows a memory loss for events that occurred immediately before application of the shock, though memory for previous events may be unaffected (Russell and Nathan,

1946; Janis, 1950). These observations suggested that the procedure, which affects recent but not old memory, interferes somehow with the *consolidation* of the memory trace. In a systematic study with rats, Duncan (1949) showed that if rats were given convulsive shocks within seconds or minutes after training trials on an avoidance-conditioning task, the animals showed a decrement in learning. However, if the convulsive shock was applied one hour or longer after the training sessions, no interference with learning occurred. To rule out the possibility that the shock applied to the ears acted as negative reinforcement (that is, interfered with performance rather than with learning, as a result of punishment), Duncan also tested animals with electric shock applied to the legs. Except in animals that were so shocked within 20 seconds after the training session, this procedure did not affect retention. Thus the findings of Duncan suggested that electroconvulsive shock interferes directly with recent memory, presumably by preventing its consolidation into a more permanent form. These findings have since been at least partially confirmed with some modified techniques by others.

**Electrical Concomitants of Learning**    The studies that we have considered so far were designed to sever postulated neural circuits of memory functions or otherwise prevent the formation or consolidation of memory traces. A somewhat different approach is the attempt to record changes in regional brain activity during learning and thus localize the neural sites involved in the formation of memory traces and, if possible, make inferences about their physiological characteristics. This approach is a relatively new one, made possible by the introduction and refinement of the implanted-electrode technique for recording the brain activity of freely moving animals.

Historically, the oldest procedure of investigating changes in the electrical activity of the brain as a consequence of previous experience or training is the *conditioned blocking* of the alpha rhythm in man. The phenomenon of electrocortical conditioning was first reported by Durup and Fessard (1935), who observed that after repeated pairing of an auditory with a visual stimulus, the occipital alpha rhythm became blocked on presentation of the auditory stimulus by itself. This phenomenon of conditioned desynchronization of the EEG alpha rhythm was confirmed and extended in a study by Jasper and Shagass (1941). In this type of study the concern has been, not with overt or behavioral manifestations of learning and their electrical correlates, but with the demonstration of conditioning phenomena within the brain itself. At least partly related to this approach is another early attempt. Loucks (1935) stimulated the motor cortex of dogs to produce an unconditioned leg flexion, and then paired the cortically evoked motor activity with clicks. In this study Loucks failed to obtain conditioned leg flexion to the auditory stimulus after as many as 600 pairings. If the procedure was combined with food reward, such a conditioned response could be formed (Loucks, 1938). Later, Brogden and Gantt (1942) were able to establish a conditioned response to direct stimulation of the cerebellum without food reward. Subsequently, Giurgea (1955), and Doty and Giurgea (1961) succeeded in establishing conditioned responses not only by pairing a peripheral conditioned stimulus with a central unconditional stimulus but also by pairing stimuli applied to two cortical points. Thus *pairing* electrical stimulation of the *motor cortex*, which produces unconditional leg flexion, with stimulation of the *visual cortex* led rapidly to leg flexion as a consequence of stimulation of the visual cortex alone. The latter site could be isolated from the rest of the cortex by circumsection without affecting the conditioned response; however, undercutting the same area abolished the response. This observation suggested that cortico-subcortical rather than transcortical pathways mediated the response. The conditioned response established by central stimulation is easily transferred to direct peripheral stimulation (visual stimulation in this instance) of the sensory structures involved (Doty and Rutledge, 1959). This finding suggested that normal circuits may be utilized when central conditioning is established. In fact, the opposite procedure is also possible: a conditioned response to an auditory stimulus generalizes to electrical stimulation of the inferior colliculus (Nieder and Neff, 1961).

A more direct approach to the study of the electrical correlates of learning is the recording of brain activity in freely moving animals in the course of a normal training procedure. There are available at present studies that deal with changes in the electrical activity of the brain during habituation procedures, classical conditioning, instrumental conditioning, and discrimination learning.

We have referred earlier to the investigations of Galambos, Hernández-Peón, and others, which showed that overt *habituation* to repetitive stimuli (for instance, clicks) is accompanied by concomitant habituation effects in the electrical activities of the brain. This phenomenon consists of the failure of such repetitive stimuli to produce EEG desynchronization, combined with a gradual decrease in the amplitude of the evoked potential produced by the stimulus. It was also shown that if the habituated stimulus is associated with a reinforcing agent, say punishment, the stimulus reacquires its ability to desynchronize the EEG (Galambos et al., 1956; Beck et al., 1958). Though these findings regarding the central correlates of auditory habituation were replicated by many investigators and widely accepted, we must refer here to a recent study employing computer analysis (Worden and Marsh, 1963), which failed to confirm the claim of a reduction in the amplitude of cochlear, evoked potentials during habituation.

In studies employing *classical conditioning* procedures it was found that as the unconditional stimulus gradually acquires its conditional properties it shows an increasing tendency to produce an EEG arousal reaction in various brain sites (Beck et al., 1958; Yoshii and Hockaday, 1959). Significantly, these central arousal reactions *precede* the behavioral signs of the establishment of the conditioned response. However, whether this central arousal effect represents a correlate of the consolidation process or whether it merely reflects increased attention to the conditioned stimulus is debatable. The latter interpretation is supported by the observations of Beck et al. that as the training procedure continues (and presumably the consolidation process is more firmly established) the electrical arousal effect diminishes or may altogether disappear. The sequential changes in the electrical activity of different brain regions during conditioning procedures was studied by several investigators (Grastyán et al., 1959; John and Killam, 1959; Hearst et al., 1960).

In an extensive series of studies, Adey and his collaborators (Adey, 1961; Adey et al., 1961; Adey et al., 1962) found that during *instrumental conditioning*, with food as a reward for correct choices, synchronous slow waves (3–7 cycles per second) appeared in the hippocampus. These electrical changes were somewhat random during the initial phases of the

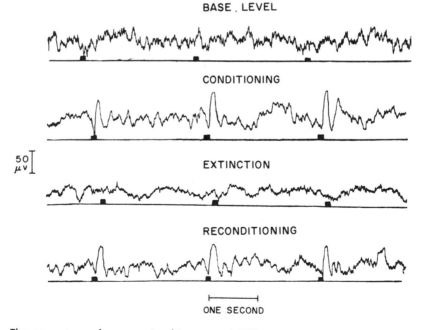

The upper trace shows ongoing hippocampal EEG activity in a monkey and the absence of a distinct response when a tone (black square) is repeatedly presented to the animal. When in an avoidance conditioning procedure the tone is used as a warning stimulus, it produces a large "conditioned" evoked potential. The response can be extinguished and reconditioned. (Hearst et al. *EEG. & clin. Neurophysiol.*, 1960, **12**, p. 140)

training procedure but became restricted later to the period when the animal made a correct choice. This synchronous electrical activity of the hippocampus did not disappear with overtraining. However, John and Killam (1959) and Lissák and Grastyán (1960) described a diminution or disappearance of the hippocampal slow waves after stabilization of the response.

An interesting approach to the problem of the electrical correlates of learning is the "tagging" procedure. Morrell and Jasper (1956) paired a frequency-specific flickering light, which produces *photic driving* of the same frequency in the visual cortex, with a neutral tone. After repeated pairings of the two stimuli, they found that the tone itself would evoke the frequency-specific photic potentials in the visual cortex. This electro-encephalographic effect was interpreted as the central nervous representation of the conditioned pairing of the stimuli. In a comparable experiment, John and Killam (1959) habituated cats to flickering light, which initially produced photic driving in the occipital cortex and other brain structures. When the flicker-evoked waves disappeared, the flickering light was paired with shock as a conditioned "warning" stimulus. John and Killam found that the frequency-specific rhythmic potentials gradually reappeared in the reticular formation and various visual centers before the conditioned response was established. As the conditioned response appeared overtly, the rhythmic potentials diminished in these brain structures and reappeared in the hippocampus and amygdala. These findings were at least partially confirmed by others (Wortis, 1960). Contrary to these results, Chow (1961) recorded the electrical activity of the infra-temporal cortex in monkeys trained on a visual discrimination in which flicker frequency was a cue to the solution of the problem. As we saw earlier, this region of the cortex is of importance for complex visual discrimination learning. Except for brief periods in the intermediate sessions of the training procedure, the frequency-specific rhythmic activity was absent in the infratemporal cortex.

Many of these studies implicated two brain structures, apart from the cortex, as components of the "memory circuit," namely, the reticular formation and the hippocampus. The involvement of the reticular formation was indicated by the results of Yoshii and Hockaday (1959), Gastaut (1958), and others, who observed that EEG signs of learning appeared first or most clearly in this structure. Other studies, such as those of John and Killam (1959), Lissák and Grastyán (1960), Adey et al. (1961), and McAdam et al. (1962), suggested that such early signs of conditioning may also appear in the hippocampus.

It is not possible to give at present a critical evaluation of the voluminous literature dealing with the problem of EEG signs of learning. The results of various investigators are to a large extent contradictory in details, and it is difficult to decide whether this discrepancy is due to different techniques and criteria employed or whether it reflects unreliability of the approach in general. Moreover, grave doubts have been expressed by some writers whether the presumed EEG signs of learning are indeed directly related to memory functions or, instead, reflect secondary effects due to changes in attentive and perceptual processes.

**Biochemical Concomitants of Learning**     It is reasonable to assume that changes in the structural and functional organization of the brain are accompanied by altered metabolic processes. The problem of the neural basis of memory and learning could therefore also be investigated with the aid of biochemical and related techniques. As an illustration of the biochemical approach to the problem we shall briefly consider three such recent attempts.

In the first type of experiments (Krech et al., 1960; Rosenzweig et al., 1962a) the concentration of cholinesterase, the enzyme that hydrolizes the neurochemical transmitter acetylcholine, was compared in the brains of rats reared in an *impoverished environment* with those that were reared in an *enriched environment*. These investigators found a *decrease* per unit volume in cholinesterase concentration in the cortex of the enriched animals and an *increased* concentration in the "subcortex." The investigators (Bennett et al., 1964) also noted an increase in the size of the cortex in the enriched animals that was positively correlated with the degree of environmental complexity to which the animals were exposed (see further page 376).

In another attempt, which has been pursued by Hydén and his collaborators, changes in the protein and RNA concentration of single nerve and glia cells, and changes in the base composition of RNA, were investigated as possible correlates of altered levels of neural activity. The studies of changes in protein and RNA concentration are predicated on the long-held belief that increased neuronal activity must be correlated with increased metabolism. The investigation of possible changes in the base ratios of RNA represents a test of the hypothesis that the neural storage of memory depends on changes in the *molecular configuration* of these macromolecules. Hydén and his collaborators (Hydén and Pigón, 1960; Hydén and Egyházi, 1962) have utilized vestibular stimulation (forced rotation and the learning of a rope-balancing task) and found evidence under certain conditions of changes in the concentration of protein and RNA, and also changes in the base ratios of RNA, in single cells of the Deiter's nucleus of experimental animals.

Finally, we may refer to a third attempt, carried out in our laboratory. The reasoning behind this project is similar to the experiments previously described, but a different technique is employed, namely, *autoradiography* (Chapter 9). If altered brain activity is accompanied by changed metabolism, this changed metabolism should be reflected by alterations in the rate

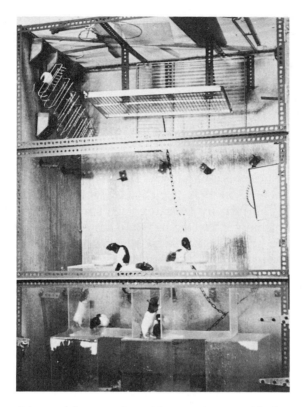

Setup used in our laboratory for raising rats in an enriched environment.

of utilization of various essential metabolic precursors. By administering to animals radioactively labeled precursors of proteins, RNA and DNA, we can investigate changes in the regional metabolism of these macromolecules at the cellular level over the entire brain. With this method we could show changes in the rate of uptake of leucine-$H^3$ by neurons in rats mildly exercised in an activity wheel and injected during exercise (Altman, 1963). No changes were seen in the animals injected after exercising. The differences observed in the protein and DNA metabolism in the brains of rats reared in enriched and impoverished environments are described and discussed on pages 376–377.

**Theories of Memory Trace** In the previous discussion we have entertained implicitly a variety of assumptions about the nature of the memory trace. We shall discuss here briefly some of the major neural theories of memory. First we may distinguish between functional and structural theories. An example of a *functional theory* is the concept that *reverberating electrical activity* through closed neuronal loops underlies the preservation of the memory trace. This theory is based on the histological observation by Lorente de Nó (1934) of the existence of such neuronal loops in the cortex. The assumption was made that sustained, electrical reverberatory activity among a set of neurons is responsible for the preservation of a newly established neural activity. It is now clear that such a functional theory cannot account for the *long-term* preservation of memory traces, because conditions that are bound to interfere with the ongoing electrical activity of the brain (such as sleep, coma, electroconvulsive shock, and freezing) do not interfere with long-term memory. Accordingly, Hebb (1949) suggested that such a functional reverberating process may underlie initial fixation of experience, or *short-term memory*, which may be followed by a structural consolidation of the memory trace for long-term preservation. The fact that short-term memory is affected by treatments such as electroconvulsive shock (retrograde amnesia) has been adduced to support a functional theory of short-term memory fixation. However, those who favor a morphological or molecular change in the brain as the basis of memory could argue for different stages of *structural consolidation*, with weaker bonds for short-term memory and stronger and longer-lasting bonds for long-term memory.

INTERNEURONAL THEORIES.   There are, we believe, three major *structural theories*, which might be called the interneuronal, intraneuronal, and extraneuronal theories. The interneuronal theory of learning is the oldest of the three; we have described it briefly earlier. The major assumption of the interneuronal theory is that as a consequence of transactions with the environment new connections are established between afferent, associative, and efferent pathways in the nervous system. Such theories involve postulation of the outgrowth of new fibers, collaterals, terminal boutons, or synaptic vesicles; the withdrawal, shrinking, or swelling of nerve processes; and similar structural alterations, which could bring neurons into new synaptic interrelation with one another. We refer to this theory as "interneuronal" because nothing more than a changed interrelation among neurons is postulated to underlie learning. In many respects this is the most parsimonious of all the structural theories: it does not imply the existence of separate sites of memory storage or any complex coding and retrieval mechanisms. The difficulty with this relatively simple circuit theory is that, occasional claims notwithstanding, there is no evidence at present of any synaptic change produced by learning. Furthermore, as we described earlier, Lashley's studies cast serious doubts on the existence of circumscribed discrete circuits; thus the assumption we have to make is that multiple circuits underlie learning, a proposition that is less parsimonious and more difficult to test than the original hypothesis.

In this context we may recall the observation of several neuroanatomists that the supragranular layer of the cortex (layer 2), which is composed of many short-axoned neurons, grows in relative width and cell density as we ascend the phylogenetic scale from, say, horse, cat, lemur, and chimpanzee to man (van't Hoog, 1920). On the basis of this and related observations it was suggested by Cajal and others that these short-axoned neurons, which have a restricted local output capacity, but can function as interconnecting elements, are concerned with "higher associative" functions. In a recent ontogenctic study employing Golgi staining (Scheibel and Scheibel, 1963) it was found that the granule cells in the cortex of kittens are the last cell types to develop their dendritic processes (as late as 2 months after birth), gradually becoming interposed between the afferent and efferent clements of the cortex. A new facet was added to these speculations by our recent finding with the use of thymidine-$H^3$ autoradiography that the majority of short-axoned neurons in the brains of rats is formed postnatally (Altman and Das, 1965b). In the brains of rats, the granular layer of the cortex is poorly developed, and the granular cells are found scattered among other cell types. Distinct and rich granular layers are present, however, in the olfactory bulb, in the dentate gyrus of the hippocampus, in the cerebellar cortex, and in the cochlear nucleus. In neonate and infant rats injected postnatally with thymidine-$H^3$ to label the multiplying cells, we found that the bulk of the cells forming these granular layers are formed during the infancy of the animals.

The postnatal origin of these cell types (a period during which the individual's interaction with its external environment begins), their slow postnatal growth, the increase in their number as we ascend the phylogenetic scale, and, finally, their strategic position between the long-axoned afferents and efferents, make it possible that these cells are the plastic, modulatory elements of the central nervous system.

INTRANEURONAL THEORIES. An obvious example of a biological "memory" mechanism is the coding of genetic information by the nucleotide or base sequence of DNA molecules in the chromosomes of cell nuclei. The information stored by DNA molecules is transferred to RNA in the nucleolus and cytoplasm, and the "instructions" are decoded when specific proteins are produced by enzymatic action inside the cell. Could a similar *molecular coding mechanism* underlie the preservation of individual experience? As we have described earlier, Hydén and his collaborators (Hydén and Pigón, 1960; Hydén and Egyházi, 1962) found some evidence of changes in the RNA composition in cells of Deiter's nucleus as a consequence of engagement of experimental animals in a task presumed to involve "learning." The idea that RNA may be specifically involved in learning processes was also tested by other investigators. Corning and John (1961) reported that the retention of an avoidance reaction by regenerating *Planaria* tails is seriously interfered with by treatment with ribonuclease (the enzyme that destroys RNA). Similarly, Dingman and Sporn (1961) found that the administration to rats of 8-azaguanine, an

RNA antimetabolite, interferes with the acquisition of a maze task, though not with the retention of a previously acquired task. Conversely, direct administration of RNA to rats was reported to reduce the period necessary for the learning of a conditioned avoidance task (Cook et al., 1963). However, because RNA is involved in all aspects of cell metabolism, the learning effects demonstrated by these treatments may more parsimoniously be considered nonspecific influences affecting cellular processes in general rather than memory functions in particular (Dingman and Sporn, 1964). Furthermore, in a recent study, Barondes and Jarvik (1964) were able to suppress cerebral RNA synthesis by intracerebral injection of actinomycin D, but they failed to observe any associated deficits in the acquisition or retention of a learning task. It may also be pointed out that the molecular theory is the least parsimonious of all neural theories of memory, because it calls for multineuronal circuits by means of which sensory information is transmitted and efferent messages are discharged, and requires in addition separate coding and decoding mechanisms.

EXTRANEURONAL THEORIES.    Nerve cells are embedded in the central nervous system in a virtually continuous matrix of tissue composed of the cytoplasm of various types of glia cells. It is generally accepted that the nourishing of nerve cells is dependent on glia cells, which surround both blood vessels and neurons and are thus assumed to control the passage of nutrients and waste products to and from the nerves. Because extracellular space is very scarce in central nervous tissue, the regulation of electrolyte movement may also be dependent on this glia-matrix. Glia cells are involved, too, in the myelinization of axons, and it is not inconceivable that satellite cells, which are now known to have an electric resting potential, could alter the excitability of neighboring neurons and thus bias their activity. The suggestion has therefore been made (Galambos, 1961) that glia cells, in their capacity to modify the activity of neurons, may be involved in memory functions. There is autoradiographic evidence that glia cells multiply in the brains of adult animals (Altman, 1963); therefore we undertook to study changes in the rate of glial multiplication in rats reared in enriched and impoverished environments (Altman and Das, 1964). We obtained evidence of significant increases in the number of glia cells (as indicated by labeling with thymidine-$H^3$) in the enriched group at various levels of the neocortex; small or no changes were observed in several subcortical structures investigated. These results would indicate that enrichment, a nonspecific behavioral treatment characterized by increased learning opportunities, leads to enhancement of glial multiplication in the cortex. This increased proliferative activity could be attributed to the heightened functional demands on neurons produced by increased behavioral activity, increased myelinization, due to the engagement of more pathways, or to increased rate of modifica-

**TABLE 3**

MEAN NUMBER OF LABELED GLIA CELLS IN CIRCULAR AREAS 310 MICRA IN DIAMETER IN THE BRAINS OF RATS REARED IN ENRICHED AND IMPOVERISHED ENVIRONMENTS

In all instances the designated structures were scanned in their entirety bilaterally.

| Structure | Enriched group | Impoverished group | Percentage of increase in enriched group | t-test P |
|---|---|---|---|---|
| Neocortex | 0.44 | 0.28 | 59 | <.001 |
| Amygdala and pyriform cortex | .38 | .34 | 12 | n.s. |
| "Dorsal thalamus" | .28 | .24 | 17 | n.s. |
| Hypothalamus | .25 | .25 | 0 | n.s. |
| Inferior colliculus | .34 | .28 | 21 | n.s. |
| Medulla | .20 | .18 | 11 | n.s. |

tion of the environs of specific neurons. At this point we may add that contrary to prediction, we obtained evidence of decreased protein metabolism in the cortex of rats reared in enriched environments, as indicated by the decreased utilization of leucine-$H^3$ (Altman and Das, in press).

In conclusion, evidence was presented in this chapter that programing at the segmental level is essentially an inborn or morphogenetic process. The routine activities controlled from this division of the nervous system, such as breathing, food ingestion, eliminative processes, maintenance of posture, and the like, can be executed by built-in coordinating mechanisms, which either appear immediately after birth or mature postnatally. Programing of behavior by paleocephalic mechanisms, which control food acquisition, courtship, agonistic behavior, and similar recurrent activities, requires important innate components, together with the opportunity of individual experience for imprinting on special goal objects and for the acquisition of conditioned distal signals of the goal objects. Finally, programing of behavior on the neencephalic level is largely dependent on experience and memory functions. The neencephlon, which is concerned with the coordination of cognitive and manipulative functions designed to deal with singular situations, is equipped with as yet ill-understood mechanisms that make possible the appreciation of complex signals and the elaboration of skilled instrumental acts. With the neencephalon, a mechanism was evolved that can dispense with the necessity of phylogenetic programing of behavior and lends an increasingly greater role to the molding of the schemata of behavior by individual experience. Various neural theories of memory have been discussed, but as yet no particular theory can be said to be adequately supported by experimental evidence.

## SELECTED READINGS

Beach, F. A., D. O. Hebb, and H. W. Nissen (Eds.). *The neuropsychology of Lashley.* New York: McGraw-Hill, 1962.

Chow, K. L. Brain functions. *Ann. Rev. Psychol.,* 1961, **12,** 281–310.

Delafresnaye, J. F. (Ed.). *Brain mechanisms and learning.* Oxford: Blackwell, 1961.

Deutsch, J. A. Higher nervous function: the physiological bases of memory. *Ann. Rev. Physiol.,* 1962, **24,** 259–286.

Hebb, D. O. *The organization of behavior.* New York: Wiley, 1949.

John, E. R. High nervous functions: brain functions and learning. *Ann. Rev. Physiol,* 1961, **23,** 451–484.

Kimble, G. A. *Hilgard and Marquis' conditioning and learning.* (2d ed.) New York: Appleton, 1961.

Lashley, K. S. In search of the engram. *Sympos. soc. exp. Biol.,* 1950, **4,** 454–482.

Mountcastle, V. B. (Ed.). *Interhemispheric relations and cerebral dominance.* Baltimore: Johns Hopkins Press, 1964.

Pavlov, I. P. *Conditioned reflexes.* New York: Oxford, 1927.

Sperry, R. W. Mechanisms of neural maturation. In S. S. Stevens (Ed.), *Handbook of experimental psychology.* New York: Wiley, 1951. Pp. 236–280.

———. Cerebral organization and behavior. *Science,* 1961, **133,** 1749–1757.

Thorpe, W. H. *Learning and instinct in animals.* (2d ed.) London: Methuen, 1963.

# 14

# Afferent Steering
# of Animative Activities

What is the role of receptors and afferent mechanisms in the organization of behavior? In line with our foregoing systematic presentation we may say that receptors can function in three major capacities: (1) as *regulators* and modulators of persistent routine activities or of routine aspects of ongoing complex activities; (2) as *releasers* and primers of already formed but inactive or latent programs of action; and (3) as *analyzers* for gathering information for the formation of new perceptual schemata and instrumental programs to permit adaptive modification, extension, and enrichment of the behavioral repertoire of the animal.

The term *afferent modulation* implies a rate setting or pacemaker function exercised over semiautonomous, persistent activities. An example may be the monitoring of $O_2$ or $CO_2$ concentration in the lungs and in the blood in order to modify the rate of persistent pulmonary and cardiac activity. The term *afferent regulation* implies a related activity in which feedback information is supplied to the efferent system about the magnitude, accuracy, and other aspects of a motor function, to make possible the comparison of the mode of execution of an action with its initiating central program. The term "afferent regulation" applies not only to feedback information supplied to *efferent* structures but also to feedback signals sent to *afferent* systems for compensations of body-generated or self-produced changes in external stimulus conditions. Thus the differentiation of the retinal displacement of a visual image due to eye movements from externally produced visual displacement (true object motion) can be accomplished if information is supplied to the central visual system about efferent outflow to, or actual movements of, the eyes, the head, or the body. As we shall see later, the stimulus conditions that can be utilized for such modulatory or regulatory functions are simple signals that may vary along a single dimension, for example, the concentration of a chemical, the amplitude of displacement, or the magnitude of mechanical pressure.

The term *afferent priming* refers to the activation or alerting of latent mechanisms through which their activities are synchronized with appropriate external conditions or events. An example of priming is the cyclical maturation of the gonads in many species, which was shown to be seasonally synchronized with increased daily illumination at the end of winter. *Afferent releasing* refers to the triggering function of stimuli that makes possible the timely execution of certain programed patterns of behavior. A simple example is the triggering of coughing when a chemical irritant reaches the mucous membranes of the respiratory passages. More complex examples are the release of appetitive behavior patterns (food seeking, courtship activities) or of aversive activities (defensive and offensive displays) by the presence of appropriate goal objects. Although the priming or triggering stimuli of some functions may be of simpler character (such as the presence or absence of a chemical), releaser stimuli often have more complex properties on the basis of which mate, foe, or prey may be identified appropriately.

The term *analyzer process* refers to the organization of new perceptual and instrumental schemata for the construction and reconstruction of representational "maps" or "blueprints" of the animal's environment. For this function animals need highly evolved proximal and distal receptors to register and evaluate changes in the conditions of their environment. This task often necessitates a multidimensional analysis of sensory messages and continued transaction with the environment.

### RECEPTORS AS REGULATORS OF ONGOING ROUTINE ACTIVITIES
#### The Importance of Afferentation

Although the coordinated execution of all complex activities requires peripheral guidance in the form of pacesetting control and feedback regulation, and is interfered with as a consequence of deafferentation, some visceral functions in all vertebrates and a few relational activities in lower vertebrates can be carried out under experimental conditions in the absence of afferent guidance. Sectioning of the afferent and efferent nerve supply of the stomach and intestines does not abolish their coordinated rhythmic activity. That is, the elementary regulation of gastrointestinal activity does not require a feedback loop passing through the central nervous system; this activity can be adequately guided by local nerve plexuses. Likewise, the severance of the vagal and sympathetic connections of the heart does not abolish rhythmic cardiac activity, which can be locally coordinated by the pacemakers of the sinoatrial node. These are examples of visceral organs whose activities can proceed autonomously without a feedback regulatory circuit, in fact, without central nervous efferent control. But even these organs, when conditions are normal, are under central nervous influence; the rate of their activity is modulated by varying body conditions and also by outside events, and regulated by feedback circuits. We know, for instance, that cardiac activity is affected by external temperature (heart rate plays a major role in the homeostatic regulation of body temperature), and we may assume that afferent signals generated by cutaneous thermal receptors are to some extent used for the modulation of cardiac activity. Cardiac activity is also regulated by homeostatic feedback mechanisms in which blood pressure and blood composition are monitored by mechanoreceptors in the aorta and by chemoreceptors in the aortic and carotid bodies.

Peripheral modulation and feedback regulation are, of course, more important for relational than for visceral activities. But even certain routine relational activities can be executed, at least in lower vertebrates, following deafferentation. Perhaps the first investigator to employ the method of *deafferentation* to study the role of peripheral guidance in the execution of motor movement was Hering (Gray, 1950). He showed that the coordinated execution of the scratch reflex in the spinal frog is not interfered with by deafferentation of the limbs executing the movement. Hering also found that deafferentation of two limbs does not interfere with coordinated walking, jumping, or swimming in the frog. The effect of deafferentation on the coordinated execution of locomotion was studied later by many investigators. Gray and Lissmann (1940) confirmed Hering's results and showed that, in the toad, sparing of the afferent supply of a single body segment was sufficient to maintain normal locomotor activity. Similar results were obtained by Lissmann (1946). The spinal tench (in which all dorsal roots except the two innervating the pectoral fins were cut) could swim normally. Likewise, spinal sharks showed normal locomotion after all the dorsal roots, with the exception of three innervating the pectoral fins, were cut, or when either all the anterior or all the posterior dorsal roots of the body were severed, or when all the dorsal roots of one side of the body were cut.

Do these findings indicate that locomotor activity in fish and amphibia can be guided autonomously by central "programs" without peripheral feedback? Gray (1950) argued that unequivocal support for such a claim would require the demonstration of survival of normal locomotor activity after elimination of *all* afferent input from the limbs of the body, a condition that is not displayed by the shark, tench, and frog, which cease their locomotion when totally deafferented. On this point it should be noted that, according to von Holst (1935), eels may continue with their undulatory swimming after total deafferentation (skinning), and a similar observation was made by Weiss (1936) in tadpoles. Moreover, because the retention of afferent input from a single body segment (which need not be from a limb but may be from a segment supplying the back or pelvic region [Gray and Lissmann, 1946]) is sufficient to maintain normal locomotion in the toad, this afferent input cannot represent an adequate feedback circuit. The input is more likely to provide a non-specific "activating" influence (Timbergen, 1951).

The limited influence exercised by afferents in modulating and regulating locomotor activity in amphibians is also suggested by the investigations of Weiss and Sperry (Chapter 10). Their studies showed that radical changes in the actual execution of locomotor patterns, such as those following transplantation or reversal of limbs, do not provide the central nervous system with sufficient feedback to produce adequate compensations or inhibit the maladaptive behavior. The studies of Sperry also suggested that the ability to produce adaptive compensations is also lacking in the visually guided snapping of amphibians when their eyes are rotated 180° or when the central connections of the optic tract are radically altered. That is, in the latter experiments we have instances of an activity elicited by a peripheral signal (the motion of a fly in front of the animal's eyes, for example) where the experimentally produced displacement of the input is not corrected adaptively even after repeated failures to reach the target. The conclusion we may draw from this is that feedback circuits are not sufficiently evolved in these instances to permit adaptive matching of the performance of an action with its program or goal.

**Modulation of Routine Activities**    It would be erroneous to conclude from the foregoing studies that feedback loops are not essential components of the regulatory mechanisms of lower vertebrates. Rather, it appears that many of the morphogenetically programed activities of lower vertebrates, because they are sufficiently rigid and insufficiently regulated, do not allow the development of adaptations to compensate for the radical alterations in afferent input or peripheral motor connections produced in these experiments. But under "normal" conditions the afferent and efferent activities of even the lowest vertebrates are modulated by exteroceptive signals and regulated by proprioceptive feedback.

Two descriptive examples of the modulation of a routine activity will suffice here. Animals at rest tend to assume a standard posture, the dorsal surface of the body up, the ventral surface down. As soon as the standard posture of the animal is disturbed by an external force, the animal immediately rights itself. As we saw earlier, righting reactions are displayed as obligatory reflexes, even in decerebrate animals, through the mediation of the vestibular apparatus. Notwithstanding the mandatory character of these righting reactions in the "passive" or resting animal, the "active" (or behaviorally engaged) animal continually changes its posture, which may come to deviate radically from the standard stance. For instance, in the course of its locomotion in pursuit of an object, an agile animal will point its head and body up or down, and will rotate its body in all directions. It would be erroneous to conclude from this observation that during locomotion the righting reactions are merely suspended or "inhibited," because interference with the animal's adopted stance during locomotion (such as the attempt to displace a rat hanging upside down from the ceiling of a cage) immediately elicits appropriate though atypical righting reactions. Apparently the schemata of righting reactions can be modulated in accordance with the changing functional engagements and stimulus conditions of the animal. Another example is provided by a recent observation of Harlow (1962). When a newborn monkey is placed on its back, it soon rights itself. However, if a cloth pad is placed on the belly of the infant, instead of righting itself it clasps the cloth. Functionally, the inhibition of the righting reaction in this example may be attributed to its replacement by the grasping reaction which infant monkeys display toward their mothers.

Similar modulatory effects are exhibited by animals when they adjust their patterns of locomotion to the properties of the terrain, when they avoid obstacles placed in their paths, when they suspend ongoing activities in face of insurmountable difficulties, when they adjust their chewing and swallowing movements to suit the consistency and resiliency of the ingested nutrient, and so forth. In essence, the function of afferent modulation is to make possible the control of behavior through multisensory channels so that ongoing activities are not performed "blindly" in a rigid automatic manner but are adapted to momentary conditions by appropriate stimulus conditions of the environment.

**Feedback Regulation of Activities** We have referred repeatedly to the major role played by feedback circuits in the preservation of homeostatic states and in correcting the deviation errors of goal-directed activities. Homeostasis is achieved by the initiation of corrective action (negative feedback) whenever conditions change from a pre-set standard. We do not know how these standards are represented in the central nervous system; in mechanical devices the standard may be a set level of voltage or temperature. Similarly, by setting the goal of an action, errors detected in aiming, tracking, and so forth, can be corrected through feedback loops; a mechanical example is the maintenance of a ship's course automatically by feedback devices connected with a direction-setting gyroscope.

Deviations from an established standard, and deflection from a set course, may be produced by a variety of factors; their correction may therefore necessitate different regulatory or compensatory functions. One source of error may be the *inaccuracy of the central program* itself, such as a tendency to overestimate or underestimate the magnitude or location of the target. Errors may also arise from a *discrepancy between the efferent commands* (motor outflow) *and the produced effector action.*

This discrepancy may itself arise from a variety of causes, such as inaccuracies at the myoneural junction in the translation of efferent commands into behavior, or differences in the magnitude and accuracy of the produced movements as a result of the variable inertia (such as weight and tension) of the external objects acted on.

There is some evidence that the nervous system can utilize three peripheral sources of feedback information in the regulation of behavior. These are (1) proprioceptive feedback, (2) reafferent feedback, and (3) exteroceptive feedback.

PROPRIOCEPTIVE FEEDBACK. Proprioceptive feedback is the most widely employed, and best known, of the peripheral regulatory mechanisms employed by animals. Proprioceptive feedback is mediated by specialized receptors (muscle spindle, Pacinian corpuscle, Golgi tendon organ) found in muscle, tendon, joints and surrounding cutaneous regions. Their function is to supply continual feedback information to the central nervous system about the state of the various muscles (the passive stretch, active contraction, and tension of muscle fibers) and the position of skeletal attachments near joints both at rest and during activity. In this capacity they can also monitor the mode of execution of efferent commands and thus make possible the correction of deviation errors in the execution of movements.

The role of proprioceptors in regulating behavior has been studied by two methods: by cutting the dorsal roots supplying certain body segments or by destroying central nervous structures that receive bulky input from the proprioceptors (cerebellum). As we have seen earlier, the execution of routine activities is not seriously affected in lower vertebrates by deafferentation. In contrast, the same procedure has the most serious consequences in all higher vertebrates, particularly on more complex motor activities. This was originally studied by Mott and Sherrington (1895), who found that after sectioning the dorsal root innervating the arm of a monkey, the animal ceased using its deafferented arm in its grasping and manipulatory activities, as though the arm were paralyzed.

What are the effects of removal of the cerebellum on the regulation of motor activity? As we have described earlier, the cerebellum is considered to be composed of two major components, the phylogenetically more ancient flocculonodular lobe receiving vestibular input, and the newer cerebellar hemispheres, which receive direct proprioceptive input and also have extensive two-way connections with the somatic and motor areas of the cortex. Destruction of the flocculonodular lobe in dogs or monkeys produces severe disturbances in the maintenance of the standing position and in equilibration. The deficit becomes less pronounced with time, but it can be made apparent by blindfolding the animal. The cerebellar hemispheres are concerned with the regulation of the tonus of the different muscles of the body and with the coordination and stabilization of motor activities.

Removal of the cerebellar hemispheres or parts of the cerebellar cortex does not interfere with the execution of motor action per se, but only with the mode of its execution. The cerebellum affects the stretch reflex, the major antigravity response of the body, by directly modulating muscle-spindle activity (Granit and Kaada, 1952). As a consequence of partial cerebellar ablation, the limbs may become permanently rigid, flexed, or extended. But even more pronounced is the effect of cerebellar lesions on the execution of skilled activities. The animal is not prevented by such lesions from engaging in skilled activities (which we believe to be initiated and controlled by the neocortex), but their execution appears ill-coordinated. The animal is *ataxic*, its movements are fragmented rather than synergistic and harmonious, and in reaching for objects the animal frequently misses the target. We do not at present know how the cerebellum regulates motor activity, but on the basis of its input characteristics, both from the peripheral proprioceptors and the sensorimotor areas of the cortex, and its restricted involvement in the regulation of motor activity, it may represent the *error detector* of a stabilizing feedback circuit.

REAFFERENT FEEDBACK. Whereas proprioceptive feedback is extensively utilized for the regulation of motor activities, reafferent feedback is essential to the control of sensory processes. In his studies of human vision, Helmholtz noted that *passive* displacement of the eye, as when it is forcibly moved by hand, is accompanied by an apparent motion of the visual world in the opposite direction, an illusory effect that may be attributed to the effective displacement of the image of the stationary visual world on the retina. This easily reproducible phenomenon poses a problem if we consider the fact that *active* ocular displacement does not produce apparent visual motion; when we move our eyes or heads around, the world does not appear to turn in the opposite direction. Helmholtz tried to resolve this paradox by postulating that the "volitional effort" that produces the active eye movement is taken into account or compensated for when the self-produced retinal displacement occurs; as a consequence, the displacement is not perceived consciously. During passive displacement of the eye there is no compensatory "volitional effort," and the consequent retinal displacement is perceived as the apparent movement of the external world.

Helmholtz's mentalistic interpretation has recently been rephrased by von Holst and Mittelstaedt (1950), who introduced two hypothetical concepts, which they called *efference copy* and *reafference*. The term "efference copy" connotes the postulated neural trace of the efferent outflow or command to action when a part of the body is moved. Reafference refers to the peripheral pattern of stimulation or afference induced by the movements of the body. Thus the movement of the image of a stationary object across the retina during eye movement represents a reafferent signal, which is distinguished from the *exafferent* stimulation of a moving object's shadow over the stationary eye. Von Holst and Mittelstaedt have further postulated that the trace of the efference copy of a movement persists in the nervous system until it is nullified by its complementary reafference, where the latter serves as a feedback report of the successful execution of the efferent command. Any discrepancy between the efference copy and reafference represents a mismatch and produces an illusion. Thus the reafferent visual signals of movement across the retina produced by passive eye motion, which are not matched by a complementary efference copy of eye movement, lead to the illusion of external movement.

We may note here that Helmholtz's observation of the illusory effects

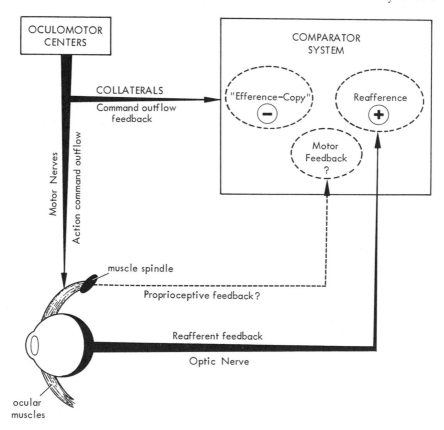

Hypothetical flow chart of the feedback loop of the visual system described in the text. (Modified after von Holst and Mittelstaedt. Das Reafferenzprinzip. *Naturwiss.,* 1950, **37,** 464–476; and Teuber. Perception. *Handb. Physiol.,* Sec. 1, **3,** 1648)

of passive displacement of the eye suggests that proprioceptive feedback is not utilized; otherwise information would be available to the nervous system about passive ocular movement, and compensations could be made for it. The absence of effective proprioceptive feedback is also suggested by the experiments of several investigators (for example, Mittelstaedt, 1949; von Holst et al., 1954), who found that permanent displacement of the eye in lower animals leads to the uncorrected misguidance of their visual aiming and righting reactions. This apparent absence of proprioceptive compensation was for a long time attributed to the reported absence of proprioceptors from the ocular muscles of the eye. It was recently established, however, that muscle spindles are present in the extraocular muscles (Cooper and Daniel, 1949; Merrillees et al., 1950), and also that stretching of these muscles produces increased afferent discharge in the oculomotor nerve (Cooper et al., 1951; Cooper and Fillenz, 1955). On the other hand, it remains true that stretching of the ocular muscles does not elicit the stretch reflex. Perhaps the functional neglect of proprioception emanating from the eye muscles may be attributed to the facts that (1) ocular muscles move a spherical organ that does not necessitate antigravitational reactions, and (2) inertia in this spherical organ tends to be invariant (the ocular muscles, unlike muscles of the trunk and limb, do not work against variable loads or weights). That is, the discrepancy between efferent command and effector action tends to be negligible in the eyes under normal conditions; therefore proprioceptive feedback loops are redundant.

The postulated reafference feedback appears to be utilized extensively in the organization and regulation of perceptual processes. Viewing an object through a wedge prism produces, as would be expected, displacement errors when one attempts to reach for it. However, Helmholtz (1867) found that, after repeated attempts, a perceptual reorganization occurs; objects can then be located with accuracy in spite of their optical displacement by the prism. Similar results were obtained by Stratton (1897), who wore reversing and inverting goggles on one eye for several days, with the other eye blindfolded. He found that after a few days an adaptation occurred to the distortion of the visual world; the perceived orientation of the legs in walking and of the arms in manipulating objects no longer appeared inverted. However, objects or scenes that were not interacted with, or were not previously traversed with the goggles, continued to appear inverted and disturbing. This finding suggested to Stratton that reorganization of visual perception required the "restoration of harmony" between the information gained from the body in the course of its interaction with the environment and the disarranged visual input. This conclusion of Stratton was subsequently confirmed by several investigators (Smith and Smith, 1962). Similar results were also reported by Foley (1940), who placed inverting and reversing goggles on a rhesus monkey. By the seventh day the animal became adapted to the sensory disarrangement and could locomote normally and locate objects with accuracy.

More recent studies (Held and Freedman, 1963) have indicated that the organization of normal visual perception during development, and its reorganization after such experimental manipulations as the wearing of prisms, necessitate active commerce with the environment, an interaction which cannot be replaced adequately by merely *exposing* the organism to, or transporting it *passively* through, its surrounding. Riesen (1961) observed that infant cats and a chimpanzee exposed to light periodically when their motor activity was severely restricted showed deficits in the development of their visual capacities. This dependence of visual development on active commerce with the visual environment was demonstrated recently by Held and Hein (1963). Dark-reared kittens were exposed to light periodically in such a way that an actively moving kitten carried another one passively over a visually patterned path. The passively transported kitten, unlike its active mate, was subsequently found to be deficient on certain visual tests in spite of its passive exposure to visual stimulation. The tentative conclusion we may draw from these studies is that the central decoding and organization of peripheral input is dependent to a large extent on active commerce with the sources of exteroceptive stimulation. Presumably, through such transaction the afferent signals from the objects interacted with are matched against the efference schemata of the nervous system, and the invariant properties of the external world are determined.

EXTEROCEPTIVE FEEDBACK.  Proprioceptive afferent signals provide feedback information about the translation of an efferent command into effector action. In contrast, exteroceptive feedback, such as tactual and visual monitoring of the performance of an action, gives information about the behavioral effectiveness of the performed action. Exteroceptive feedback is widely utilized by higher vertebrates in the regulation of skilled activities; as such, it belongs, strictly speaking, with the class of cognitive and manipulative activities. Presumably, exteroceptive feedback regulation is a higher nervous function, whereas proprioceptive and reafferent feedback regulation are medullary and cerebellar functions, which appear as unconscious processes in man. Furthermore, unlike proprioceptive feedback, which is involved essentially in regulating the execution of already programed actions, exteroceptive feedback is crucial for the programing of new action schemata. Exteroceptive feedback is best exemplified in the highly evolved *hand-eye coordination* seen in primates, where the manipulatory activities of the hands are guided not only by tactual feedback but by intermittent or continuous visual monitoring. We may consider here briefly one experimental approach designed to study the role of exteroceptive feedback in the regulation of behavior; this is the recently introduced technique of temporal delay of feedback.

The disrupting consequences of the *temporal delay* of exteroceptive feedback on the performance of skilled activities have so far been studied exclusively in man. Delaying the auditory feedback of a subject's own speech by means of a tape recorder with an extended tape loop was found to slow down speaking considerably, and it produced stuttering and other abnormalities of speech (Lee, 1950; Black, 1951). Maximal disturbances were obtained with a delay of about 0.2 seconds (Fairbanks, 1955). Whereas delayed auditory feedback slows down speech, acceleration of the feedback by electronic transmission of the vocal sounds through earphones (replacing the somewhat slower conduction of sound through air) accelerates speech (Peters, 1954). Similar results were obtained in studies in which the visual feedback of the subjects' writing, tracing, or drawing was delayed by means of an electronic telewriter (van Bergeijk and David, 1959) or an electromechanic telescriber (Kalmus et al., 1960). These skilled activities were slowed down progressively with increasing delay in visual feedback, with concomitant increases in errors and distortions in performance. More recently, television techniques were introduced to study the disrupting effects on a variety of behavioral activities of temporal delay in visual feedback (Smith and Smith, 1962). In general, the results obtained so far suggest that human subjects do not easily (if at all) adapt themselves to these distortions in the temporal characteristics of exteroceptive feedback and show little decrement in their ill-regulated behavior after prolonged exposure to such delays.

**RECEPTORS AS RELEASERS OF LATENT PROGRAMS OF ACTION** In the nineteenth century naturalists were impressed by the observation that immediately after hatching or metamorphosis insects are capable of performing various complex activities characteristic of their species without parental guidance or the apparent necessity of individual learning. Newborn insects may "recognize" prey and foe that they have never before encountered; build proper nests; identify, follow, and mate with opposite members of their own species; deposit their eggs in locations suitable for the maturation and hatching of the young; and often even provide for their offspring. These apparently purposive action patterns, which can be performed by animals without prior experience, were considered *instinctive acts*. Several of these descriptive, often anecdotal, accounts were later found to be exaggerated or incorrect, and with the emergence of the behavioristic movement, which attributed all complex activities to learning, the concept of instinct has been in disfavor for some time among many psychologists. However, the concept of instinctive activity was not entirely abandoned by zoologists. Ornithologists, in particular, persisted in pointing to the existence of behavior patterns that, like certain morphological traits, are characteristic of the species and may be used as taxonomic characters

(Whitman, 1898; Heinroth, 1910). Slowly, objective evidence was accumulated by the school of ethologists that in lower vertebrates, and to a lesser extent in mammals, innately programed action patterns are present, which can be triggered and guided by specific environmental signals. The postulated central mechanisms that can be activated by specific stimuli were called by Lorenz (1935, 1950) and Tinbergen (1951) *innate releasing mechanisms*, and the appropriate peripheral triggering stimuli were referred to as *innate releasers* or *signaling devices* (Tinbergen, 1963).

As an illustration of the mode of operation of innate signaling devices in the guidance of recurrent species-specific behavior patterns, we shall consider briefly studies concerned with the release and guidance of courtship and mating behavior in a few species of vertebrates. Tinbergen (1951) used the *dummy technique* to study the synchronization of sexual behavior in the three-spined stickleback. Sticklebacks are reared by the male parent, who ventilates the eggs in the nest and carries the young in its mouth when they are threatened. When the young reach a certain age they separate from the parent, join a school of their own age group, and forage for food together. Prior to the mating season the naive male thus never sees a pregnant female. When the mating season arrives, the males separate themselves from the school and make attempts to establish individual territories, which they defend from intruding rival males. The male then builds a nest on its territory. When the nest is finished, the stickleback begins to display its courtship behavior, a characteristic zigzag dance in the presence of visiting females. When the female is "enticed" she is led into the nest and induced to lay her eggs, which are then fertilized by the male.

Experiments with dummies have shown that the various steps in this complex pattern of activities are elicited by simple signaling devices to which individual sticklebacks respond appropriately without any prior experience, although their mode of responding may subsequently be slightly modified by differential experience. The male's zigzag dance is elicited by the approach of a female with swollen abdomen. A dummy lacking most of the characteristic traits of a stickleback but with a ventral swelling is courted more often and more frequently than is an exact replica of a stickleback without a swollen abdomen. This relatively simple signal, which in the normal female indicates her readiness to lay eggs, is the "key" that "unlocks" the courtship display. The female's *following-response* is elicited by the zigzag dance and the male's red color. Dummies that resemble a male but are not reddish in color are ignored, whereas a poor imitation of a male with red color, when moved about, is followed by the female. In this manner, because the execution of each step of the complex courtship behavior depends on appropriate releasers, the unfolding of the centrally programed behavior pattern is made conditional on the presence of suitable physical and social conditions.

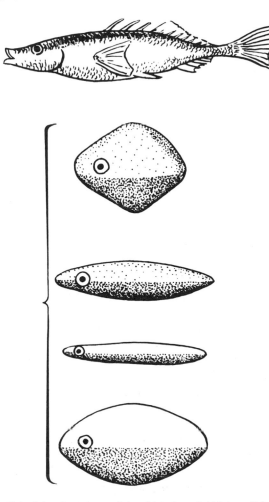

Fighting is not elicited by the top model, which is a faithful replica of a male stickleback, except that it lacks a red belly. In contrast, the four lower models, which do not resemble a stickleback but have red undersides, elicit territorial fighting. (After Tinbergen. *The study of instinct.* Oxford University Press, 1958)

The operation of releasers in triggering recurrent activities related to recognition of prey, foe, and mate, and in guiding nutritional, reproductive, and social behavior, has been established in various other vertebrates, including mammals. Eibl-Eibesfeldt (1962) reported that immediately after their metamorphosis from the larval stage, frogs and toads display their species-specific *prey-catching response* in the presence of simple dummies of prey. Such triggering may be seen in the clawed toad, which as a tadpole feeds on plankton and does not respond to prey; it appears, then, that this releaser is not acquired by earlier experience. Well known

A mounted, immature male robin with brown breast feathers (left) is seldom attacked in the breeding season, whereas a tuft of red feathers elicits fighting. (After Lack. *The life of the robin* [rev. ed.]. Penguin Books, 1953)

is the observation of Lack (1953) that the threat display of a male robin when its territory is approached by another red-breasted male can be elicited appropriately by a bundle of red feathers; in contrast, a mounted real robin that lacks the red breast is ignored. Examples of simple releasers in birds are many. Herring gull chicks, for example, "beg" for food by pecking at the bills of their mothers. The pecking response is elicited by the red color patch on the mothers' lower mandible. As Tinbergen and Perdeck (1950) have shown, the chicks' pecking response can, in fact, be intensified by exaggerating the appropriate releaser signals, for instance, when the chicks are presented with a thin, vertical stick with several red rings on it, in the total absence of the mother. Such releasers were called *supernormal stimuli* (Tinbergen, 1951). We may, finally, refer briefly to several innate releasers in mammals. Male rats reared in isolation "recognize" and respond appropriately by copulation when first encountering a female (Stone, 1922; Beach, 1942). Likewise, female rats presented the first time with nesting material build nests (Eibl-Eibesfeldt, 1961) and retrieve young placed in their cages (Wiesner and Sheard, 1933).

As we have seen earlier, persistent routine activities can be modulated or regulated by afferent signals representing changes along a single stimulus dimension, such as alterations in pH or osmotic pressure, variations in $CO_2$ or $O_2$ concentration, changes in the magnitude of mechanical displacement or shearing force, and the like. Such stimuli may be referred to as *unidimensional signals*. Preformed but latent behavior patterns may, in a few instances, be triggered by such unidimensional signals. Examples are the triggering of coughing by a chemical irritant or of withdrawal of a leg by a pinprick. However, the innate releasing schemata of typical recurrent activities, such as pecking at food objects or prey catching, courting and mating, of filial following and parental care, are commonly elicited by a combination of a limited number of cues or *oligodimensional signals*. An example of an oligodimensional signal is the combination of a simple movement pattern with a bright color, as in the releaser of the following-response in the female stickleback and in the releasers of courtship behavior in a great variety of fish, reptiles, and birds. Other examples are the combination of a color with a texture, as in the releaser of territorial fighting in the robin; the combination of a relatively simple sequence of sounds, as in the releasers of social behavior in birds, and so forth. Both the emission and "appreciation" of these oligodimensional signals are morphogenetically determined. The development of skin coloration or the appearance of colored and patterned feathers during the breeding season, the production and release of odorous substances, and the like are growth processes activated by internal humoral mechanisms (Chapter 17). Not only the mechanisms responsible for these signals but the receiver mechanisms as well are inborn; it is thus that effective communication among individuals of a species can be guaranteed without training or prior social encounters.

We may presume that in order to permit reliable intraspecies communication, uncommon and conspicuous signals have to be employed, signals that are not likely to be generated by random external events or used as signals by other species. We shall consider later (Chapter 17) the great variety of display patterns evolved by different species as signaling devices for the furtherance of intraspecies recognition and the synchronization of their reproductive and social activities. On the other hand, because the evocation of these signals is morphogenetically programed and their appreciation depends on inborn releasing schemata, there is a limitation to their possible complexity. As a consequence, inappropriate releasers, including supernormal stimuli, may occasionally trigger built-in activities. For instance, it was observed (Koehler and Zagarus, 1937) that ring plovers would sit on a white egg dummy with black dots in preference to their own eggs, which are light brown in color with darker brown spots. Contrariwise, appropriate conditions not accompanied by their releasers may fail to trigger the built-in response. An example is the report (Brückner, 1933) that a brooding hen will ignore its struggling chick placed under a glass, presumably because she cannot hear the chick's distress call, which is the releaser of the retrieval response.

We do not know how these releasers are programed. An attractive idea is the *password hypothesis* (Barlow, 1961), according to which one of the major functions of the afferent mechanisms of the central nervous system is the detection, or extraction, of certain stimulus configurations, the "passwords," from the great influx of stimuli. The operation of such a system requires eliminating most stimuli, called "noise," and *filtering* (that is, extracting and amplifying) as "signals" those stimuli that are of biological significance. Of course, the exclusive employment of such a filtering sensory mechanism has its limitations because it can detect only the presence of programed stimuli and cannot monitor novel occurrences and thus provide the animal with a blueprint of its singular environment.

The latter is the third function of the afferent system, one which necessitates complex coding, storage, retrieval, and comparator functions for the integration of complex *multidimensional signals* from the environment.

**RECEPTORS AS ANALYZERS: ORGANIZATION OF NEW PERCEPTUAL AND INSTRUMENTAL SCHEMATA** A considerable portion of the mammalian central nervous system is dedicated to the task of gathering information from the environment, both for the construction of blueprints, or representational maps, of the animal's environment, and for the organization of skilled activities to handle novel situations. We have considered previously the anatomy and physiology of the tactile, auditory, and visual "lemniscal" pathways, whose function is the accumulation of intelligence about the world surrounding the individual for the construction of an "objective" representation of its milieu. In a similar way, visual, tactile, and other sources of sensory information are utilized for the development of the motor schemata of skilled acts, which are carried out to a large extent under the control of the motor cortex through the pyramidal efferent pathway.

We shall not deal here in any detail with the problem of how animals succeed in constructing an empirically objective or valid representational system of their environments by extracting relevant and reliable information from the great influx of sensory input. We should point out only that the process requires continual interaction with the environment, the storage of acquired information, and the continual testing and revising of the various "hypotheses" (Krechevsky, 1932) formed about the nature and properties of environmental objects and events. That is, in opposition to the school of behaviorists (Watson, 1914; Thorndike, 1911) and neobehaviorists (Hull, 1943; Spence, 1956), who maintained that animal learning is a "mechanical" process, we *believe* that the building of perceptual schemata and instrumental programs is an ill-understood "cognitive" process in which the animal tries to "understand" and master its environment.

The controversy between behaviorists and cognitive theorists has been dealt with in detail in many articles and books (for instance, Kimble, 1961). As an illustration of this controversy let us very briefly consider the history of the argument concerning how a rat learns to master a maze. In an attempt to answer the question of the sensory contributions to maze learning, Watson (1907) eliminated different sense organs in rats and studied the effect of this procedure on trained and untrained rats. Running animals in the dark (or blinding them), depriving them of the sense of smell or hearing, or eliminating somesthetic input from the limbs, interfered little with the performance of trained rats or the learning ability of naive ones. Cutting the vibrissae produced slight transient detrimental effects, but the animals quickly adapted to their new state. Because elimination of these receptors did not interfere with the acquisition or retention of maze learning, Watson concluded that maze learning must be mediated by a sense modality that he did not interfere with, namely, kinesthesis.

If we may assume that in its attempt to master a maze the animal utilizes all available sensory cues, then the fact that the elimination of any one of these signal sources produces little or no deficit in the animal's performance need not mean that another, untested, receptor system guides the action. It was subsequently shown that cutting the dorsal columns of the cervical spinal cord in rats, which eliminates a good proportion of kinesthetic feedback from the forelimbs, and indeed impairs locomotion seriously, does not interfere with retention of maze learning (Lashley and Ball, 1929) or with the acquisition of the task (Ingebritsen, 1932). Moreover, Macfarlane (1930) showed that rats taught to wade through a maze would switch, if necessary, to swimming, or vice versa, although this change required different modes of locomotion which, in turn, generated different kinesthetic patterns of stimulation. The significance of sensory cues other than kinesthetic ones, at least in the course of acquisition of the task, was brought out by several subsequent experiments. Thus Dashiell (1930), using a checkerboard maze, found that after a few trials the animals would switch to shorter, unfamiliar paths in the direction of food, as though they were acquainted with the spatial location of the goal box. Familiarity with the spatial outlay of the maze is also suggested by the behavior of rats in a Hebb-Williams maze (Hebb and Williams, 1946) in which the animals quickly adjust to new partitions placed into the maze, and as rapidly abandon detours if partitions are removed. The importance of various sensory cues in maze learning was clearly shown, finally, in experiments in which more than one sense organ was eliminated in the same individual. Although merely blind, or anosmic,

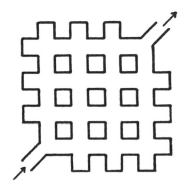

Checkerboard maze. (From Dashiell. Direction orientation in maze running by the white rat. *Comp. Psychol. Monogr.,* 1930, **7,** 1–72. In Woodworth and Schlosberg, *Experimental psychology.* Holt, Rinehart and Winston, 1938, 1954)

or deafened rats are not handicapped in maze tests, rats that are both blind and anosmic display great difficulty in mastering a maze (Lindley, 1930), and blind-deaf anosmic rats are totally helpless (Honzik, 1936).

What we are assuming is that in learning a maze the animal makes use of a variety of sensory cues. There is, indeed, evidence that the introduction of supplementary cue sources improves maze learning, whereas the elimination of sources of cues may retard it. Thus painting the correct alley of a T maze in one color, and the wrong one in a different color, greatly speeds maze learning (Snygg, 1935). If, on the other hand, the floor of a maze, from which the animal may presumably receive auditory and vibratory cues, is changed, previous mastery of the maze may be seriously interfered with (Shepard, 1935). Similarly, putting a dome over a maze, to eliminate extramaze cues, retards maze learning (Walthall, 1948).

In a series of experiments Tolman and his associates (1946 a, b) studied in a simple cross maze the role of *place learning* (learning the position of the goal box) and *response learning* (the tendency to turn "blindly" to the right or left, as postulated by the kinesthetic theory). The findings of these investigators suggested that the role of place learning is much more important than that of learning a specific response, though the latter may make some contribution to learning; learning a specific response is, indeed, the solution used by some animals. On the basis of these and other studies, Tolman (1932, 1948) postulated that in learning a maze the rat tries to form a blueprint or *cognitive map* of the outlay of the maze (the "means object") with respect to its expectation of the reward ("goal object"). If the animal fails to form a blueprint, it resorts to "mechanical" response learning. When the task is adequately mastered, however, the rat will, because of its possession of a blueprint of the maze, manifest "cognitive" place learning. In their attempt to acquire such cognitive maps, the animals tend initially to display "*hypotheses*" (Krechevsky, 1932), that is, systematic selection of certain cues in an effort to solve the maze problem.

Because perceptual and instrumental schemata are dependent on prolonged periods of learning, one of the most fruitful procedures for studying these processes is the ontogenetic or developmental one. We shall not be able to consider here in any detail the various studies concerned with the development of perceptual organization and the acquisition of motor skills, such as several current studies concerned with the genesis of space perception in various species of animals. These studies seem to indicate that perceptual organization depends (1) on innate organizational variables (such as certain Gestalt principles); (2) on morphogenetic factors that nevertheless require specific environmental conditions for their unfolding; and (3) continued exposure to a varied environment for opportunity to learn about the diverse properties of the external world. Let us consider here one type of experiment concerned with the problem of the development of space perception. In this study, an ingenious testing apparatus, the *visual cliff*, was used (Gibson and Walk, 1960; Walk and Gibson, 1961). The visual cliff consists essentially of a suspended glass plate over a well, one half of which is left transparent (this is the "deep" side), while the other side is made to appear "shallow" by a patterned material glued to the underside of the plate. The animal is placed over a pedestal dividing the "deep" and "shallow" sides, and its preference when stepping down is recorded. Dark-reared rats and cats as well as normal infants of various species show a statistically significant preference for stepping down on the shallow side, thus displaying an unlearned perception (and apparent fear) of depth.

As we have suggested before, perceptual organization is dependent to a large extent on early exposure to environmental stimuli and the continued availability of experience. Hebb (1949) reported that rats reared in an *enriched environment*, in which they could freely roam about and where a variety of objects was available to them, appeared superior in maze performance to rats reared under the normal restrictive conditions of the laboratory cage. Hebb's exploratory studies were subsequently confirmed by several investigators (Hymovitch, 1952; Bingham and Griffiths, 1952; Forgays and Forgays, 1952; and others). Hebb also postulated that infantile or *early experience* is of particular importance for the perceptual and intellectual development of the animal. The greater efficacy of early over later environmental enrichment on subsequent performance on learning tasks was experimentally confirmed (Hymovitch, 1952; Forgus, 1954, 1956).

Early sensory enrichment may have a variety of effects on perceptual development. First, exposure to physical and social stimulation can have a *nonspecific facilitatory* effect on perceptual and intellectual maturation. Second, exposure to a specific class of stimuli may promote the *biochemical* and *morphological maturation* of the sensory mechanisms of that particular modality. Finally, exposure to a specific class of stimuli may facilitate the *processing of perceptual information* in that modality.

We have discussed earlier several instances of *nonspecific facilitatory* effects arising from "early experience," when we dealt with the problem of handling during infancy. Cutaneous stimulation of rodents before weaning has a facilitatory effect on the learning ability of the animals when they are tested later in life. The type of stimulation often employed in these experiments (stroking with a brush, shaking the cage mechanically, or mild electric stimulation) cannot provide perceptual enrichment in the strict sense of the term, but presumably permits the animal's adaptation to exposure to an alien and threatening environment. Indeed, it was shown by several investigators that handled rats can withstand stress situations (such as food and water deprivation) better than unhandled ones.

The importance of sensory stimulation for the *biochemical* and *morphological maturation* of sensory structures was shown in studies in which the retinae of dark-reared animals were found to display signs of atrophy (Brattgård, 1952; Chow et al., 1957; Weiskrantz, 1958; Riesen, 1960; Rasch et al., 1961). Dark-rearing also affects the visual capacity of animals, particularly if the animal is deprived of visual stimulation early in infancy. Hebb (1937) reported that dark-reared rats were initially deficient on a visual pattern-discrimination task, although the animals quickly recovered and reached the performance level of normal controls. Dark-rearing from infancy, or rearing under conditions of diffuse illumination to prevent retinal atrophy, was found to have more serious and longer-lasting effects in higher mammals, such as cats (Riesen and Aarons, 1959) and chimpanzees (Riesen, 1958). The chimpanzee reared in darkness with periodic stimulation with diffuse light failed to show a simple blink response until almost a week after its emergence from the dark, and it took the animal even longer to display an ill-coordinated visual following-response. Similar results were obtained by Nissen et al. (1951) in a chimpanzee whose limbs were surrounded by cardboard tubes to prevent it from receiving normal tactual stimulation. The animal was found subsequently incapable of learning a simple tactual discrimination task.

We may finally refer briefly to experiments in which the opposite procedure of perceptual enrichment was employed in order to investigate the effects of early stimulation on subsequent *perceptual organization*. In mastering visual discrimination tasks, rats reared in cages provided with patterned visual stimuli were found superior to normal controls (Gibson and Walk, 1956; Gibson et al., 1958), and the facilitatory effect was found to be more pronounced when the animals were given this sensory "enrichment" early rather than later in life (Forgus, 1956).

### SELECTED READINGS

Gray, J. The role of peripheral sense organs during locomotion in the vertebrates. *Sympos. soc. exp. Biol.*, 1950, **4**, 112–126.

Holst, E. von. Relations between the central nervous system and the periphery. *Brit. J. Animal Behav.*, 1954, **2**, 89–94.

Riesen, A. Stimulation as a requirement for growth and function in behavioral development. In D. W. Fiske and S. R. Maddi (Eds.), *Functions of varied experience.* Homewood, Ill.: Dorsey, 1961. Pp. 57–80.

Smith, K. U., and W. M. Smith. *Perception and motion.* Philadelphia: Saunders, 1962.

Thompson, W. R., and T. Schaefer. Early environmental stimulation. In D. W. Fiske and S. R. Maddi (Eds.), *Functions of varied experience.* Homewood, Ill.: Dorsey, 1961. Pp. 81–105.

Tinbergen, N. *The study of instinct.* New York: Oxford, 1951.

Weiss, P. Experimental analysis of co-ordination by the disarrangement of central-peripheral relation. *Sympos. soc. exp. Biol.*, 1950, **4**, 92–111.

# 15

# Internal Motivation of Animative Activities

The organization of a behavioral act depends on the functioning of three processes. First, the coordination of action requires the existence and operation of a central nervous program that determines what component processes go into an action and their spatial and temporal sequences. Second, the adaptive performance of a central program necessitates peripheral guidance. This process is made possible by afferent mechanisms that trigger, guide, and regulate the execution of action sequences and thus synchronize central action commands with, and adapt them to, prevailing external conditions and ongoing events. Finally, it is our view that animative activities are not exercises that are performed by the organism autonomously or aimlessly; they are instead goal-directed or teleological processes that are initiated by certain needs or ends and terminated when the needs are satisfied or ends achieved. This third aspect of animative activities is called *motivation,* and the specific physiological processes (often hypothetical) that exercise these activating and goal-setting influences are called *drives.*

In this chapter we shall deal briefly with a few general aspects of motivation. We shall further pursue the problem of motivation in the final section of this book, where an attempt will be made to classify types of organized behavior, from a functional point of view, in terms of their motivational ends or goals.

**The Concept of Motivation and Drive**   In mechanical constructions, such as an automobile, the mechanism converting energy into work, the engine, is distinct from the source of energy, or fuel. Without fuel the engine of a car remains stationary and cannot perform the task for which it was constructed. The organism is different insofar as structure and function are inseparably tied together: the cells and organs of the body are dynamic entities whose steady-state existence presumes continued functioning. In spite of this intimate association of structure and function in organic systems, the animal body is to a large extent "mechanized," in the sense that various nonspecific and specific action mechanisms are available that can be utilized in the performance of different functions. For instance, the gratification of nutritive needs requires such nonspecific activities as exploration and locomotion, and such specific activities as responding selectively to food objects, chewing, swallowing, and alimentation. The engagement of animative mechanisms to perform a specific sequence of acts, such as is seen in food acquisition, is conceived of as an instance of motivation, where the conditions serving as instigators of food acquisition are considered the *motives*, or *drives*, of the specific actions observed.

All motivated acts consist of three common phases, which we shall refer to as (1) arousal, or activation, (2) engagement of specific mechanisms and activities, and (3) sustained and varied modes of pursuance of certain ends or goals. The "unmotivated" animal is presumably at rest— it may be lying on its side, relaxed and drowsy. The emergence of a motive state is first manifested in the arousal of the animal, in increase in vigilance and signs of restless overt activity. The second phase, varied in different motive states, is the initiation of, and engagement in, specific activities that can satisfy the organism's needs. Finally, if the end sought is not immediately achieved, the animal will persist in pursuing the goal of its motivated behavior and try different modes of attack until the goal is reached or the animal exhausted.

The specific activities produced by different motive states may also consist of different phases. For instance, food acquisitive activity may consist of (1) an *appetitive phase*, during which "hunger" is aroused, the search for food is initiated, and the animal engages in a variety of preparatory activities necessary for procuring food; (2) a *consummatory phase*, a sequence of processes concerned with the ingestion of the acquired food; and (3) a *satiation phase*, which terminates food-acquisitive activities. Similar phases may be observed during sexual motivation, which is initiated by an appetitive phase, sexual "desire" and courtship, and culminates in a consummatory phase, namely, copulation. Somewhat different phases are seen in aversive types of motivation, for example, when the animal is irritated or threatened. In such instances arousal is triggered by external stimuli, such as the appearance of a threatening object; this is the *aversive phase*. The consummatory phase is replaced by withdrawal, fleeing, or fighting; this is the *agonistic phase*. Successful withdrawal or victory in fighting leads to a *phase of relaxation*.

Terms such as "need," "want," and "drive" are loose descriptive concepts that refer to inferred general states rather than to concrete physiological processes. The animal running after food and vigorously ingesting it may be presumed to "need" or "want" the food, because the intensity and magnitude of food intake are correlated with the duration of food deprivation (up to a certain period). However, is the mere presence of a need (say, lowered glucose or amino acid concentration of the blood) sufficient to produce a drive? Or are specific mechanisms required to "translate bodily needs into behavior"? That need or want, on the one hand, and drive or motivation, on the other, are not synonymous is suggested by the absence of motivational states in certain need conditions (as when certain essential vitamins are lacking from the diet), and by the presence of "want" for substances that do not satisfy vegetative needs (such as saccharin) or may even be harmful to the organism (such as alcohol). Some information is available regarding the mechanisms that initiate drive states, gauge internal needs, and control the intensity or magnitude of acquisitive and consummatory activities. We shall consider this evidence in the following pages, together with a discussion of some of the characteristics and properties of certain types of motivated activities.

**Arousal and Activation** It is generally accepted that one
**Effects in Motivation** major aspect of motivation is behavioral arousal and activation. But
is motivation in this respect an "energizer" of behavior (a source of behavioral energy), or does it merely involve the channeling of available organic energy resources into specific directions? It is often explicitly claimed that drive is an energizing process; the term "drive," as originally used by Woodworth (1918), referred to this aspect of motivation. Indeed, Richter (1922) showed that, as measured in tambour-mounted activity cages or in activity wheels, rats show an *increase in overt activity* as food deprivation is prolonged, up to the third day of starvation (at that period, presumably as a result of declining energy resources, the animal becomes less and less active). Such increases in activity were found also in animals that were merely deprived of certain foodstuffs, such as proteins (Hitchcock, 1928) or vitamin B (Bloomfield and Tainter, 1943). Similarly, Wang (1923) found that mature female rats showed increases up to three times their normal level of activity at the height of their estrus cycle. These activity cycles, which begin at puberty, disappear after ovariectomy (Richter, 1927), and can be restored with estrogens (Young and Fish, 1945). These findings indicate that ovarian secretion induces increased activity. Although male rats do not show sexual activity cycles, castration does considerably reduce their activity level (Hoskins, 1925; Slonaker, 1930), a finding indicating that gonadal hormones also affect the activity level of the male.

However, evidence has accumulated over the years that the apparent increase in activity observed in hungry, thirsty, or sexually aroused animals may be restricted to *locomotor activity*, the type of activity that is measured in tambour-mounted activity cages or activity wheels, but that no over-all increase in *total energy output* is demonstrable when the more sensitive tilting cage or *stabilimeter* is employed. Using a stabilimeter,

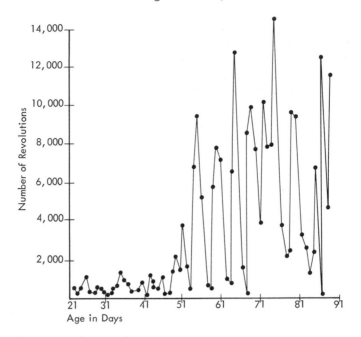

Onset of activity cycle in the female rat at puberty. (After Wang. The relation be-tween "spontaneous" activity and estrous cycle in the white rat. *Comp. Psychol. Monogr.*, 1923, **2**, No. 6. In Stone, *Comparative psychology*, 3d ed. Prentice-Hall, 1951, p. 65. Courtesy of Dr. Curt P. Richter)

Hunt and Schlosberg (1939) reported minimal decrease in the activity of castrated animals (9-percent reduction), though Slonaker (1930), using the less sensitive measuring instrument, found much greater activity reduction (98 percent). Similarly, Strong (1957), also using a sensitive stabili-meter, has found a decrease rather than an increase in total activity level as a function of increased food deprivation. Treichler and Hall (1962) compared the effect of decreased body weight, produced by food depriva-tion, on the activity of rats as measured both in activity wheels and stabilimeters. They obtained increased activity with increased food depriva-tion in activity wheels only, whereas stabilimetric measurements did not reveal a change in activity level.

These findings seem to suggest that the overt energy output of the animal is not significantly altered by drive states; only certain types of activity, such as locomotion, are increased. As locomotion is an aspect of the appetitive phase of such drives (search for food), the increase in locomotor activity may be taken as an indication of the onset of this phase. That food deprivation increases *searching* and *exploratory activity* has indeed been known for some time (Dashiell, 1925) and confirmed by many investigators. Of some interest in this connection is the study of

Campbell and Sheffield (1953), which suggests that situations capable of arousing or sustaining searching behavior may actually increase energy output in motivated animals. Using stabilimeters, they studied the activity level of hungry and satiated rats that were placed either in a "restricted" or "changing" environment. The activity level of food-deprived rats was the same as that of controls in the restricted environment; only in the changing environment did the hungry animals become more active than the controls. These considerations would suggest that during motive states the energy output of the organism is deployed and intensified in such a way that it promotes activities essential for the gratification of the prepotent needs. That is, motivation does not always have a net energizing effect, but it does have an activating effect.

The increased vigilance and random searching activity displayed by motivated animals are probably directly controlled by paleocephalic mechanisms (such as the reticular formation, hypothalamus, and others). There is some suggestive evidence of the mode of activation of the reticular formation by deprivation states and metabolic imbalance. It is known, for instance, that adrenaline secretion is increased considerably when the glucose level of the blood falls, or when $CO_2$ concentration increases or $O_2$ concentration decreases. In turn, adrenaline directly affects cells of the reticular formation, with resulting EEG activation characteristic of vigilance (Dell, 1958). Similar humoral effects could also be produced by gonadal hormones, but this reaction has not been established.

**Motivational Engagement of Specific Mechanisms** The initial phase of motivation, characterized by nonspecific arousal and random searching, is followed by a second phase of specific engagement, during which the animal shows *preferential attendance* to, and *selective interaction* with, objects that are goals of the motive state or means that further the attainment of such goals. The food-satiated animal does not respond to food; the immature or sexually satisfied male ignores the presence of a receptive female. The food-deprived animal, on the other hand, can detect the presence of well-hidden food sources and, if very hungry, responds to nutritive substances that it does not normally heed. Similarly, the sexually aroused animal (as best seen in periodically breeding species) can detect the location of a potential mate by the slightest of cues and will follow it over long distances, overcoming various obstacles. Two of the most obvious characteristics of motivated activity are the selective attendance to a restricted group of signals and intensified engagement in a selected class of motor activities at the expense of other potential signals and activities.

Lashley (1938) suggested some time ago that motivated (or "instinctive") behavior is based on chemical activation of specific neural centers that control such activities as courtship, mating, and caring for the young.

According to this view, which is also held by the ethologists (Lorenz, 1950; Tinbergen, 1951), the built-in neural coordination schemata of "instinctive" behavior (which we call recurrent catering activities) have normally a high excitatory threshold and remain inactive until some sensitizing substance, such as a hormone, lowers their threshold. When this sensitization occurs, the behavior pattern is easily elicited by external signals, such as the "innate releaser" of that action, or may even run off *in vacuo* in the absence of stimulation (Lorenz, 1937, 1950).

Numerous experiments support the view that motivational activities depend on *humoral sensitization* or activation of otherwise dormant specific animative mechanisms. For instance, Evans (1935) found that injecting males of the American chameleon with pituitary extracts in the winter (when they are normally very sluggish) produces territorial fighting and mating behavior, which is seen in normal animals only in the spring and early summer. Noble and Greenberg (1941) showed later that sub-cutaneous administration of testosterone produced characteristic male patterns of breeding behavior in immature males, adult castrated males, and even in females of this species. Male chicks injected with the same sex hormone exhibit the sexual patterns of adult cocks (Noble and Zitrin, 1942), whereas adult cocks injected with prolactin, the lactogenic hormone, display various aspects of maternal behavior. These, and similar studies (which will be considered in detail in Chapter 17), indicate clearly that humoral agents can activate the central programs of complex behavior sequences. The patterns, then, become elicitable by appropriate signals, such as those produced by mates, the young, and so forth. Humoral activation of neural programs of behavior may not be restricted to sexual and parental behavior. Feeding behavior, for instance, can be elicited in the satiated animal by injection of insulin into the blood stream (which promptly reduces the glucose concentration), and drinking behavior can be similarly provoked by injection of hypertonic saline. The production of feeding and drinking behavior by chemicals injected directly into the hypothalamus was considered earlier (Chapter 11).

**Motivational Pursuance of Specific Goals or Ends**  The idea that different visceral motive states lead to the activation of different sensorimotor programs is borne out by naturalistic observations. Young inexperienced fish and birds manifest in the spring a complex sequence of activities, such as migration, nest building, courtship displays, mating, brooding, and caring for the young, activities that they may never have engaged in before and that are apparently prompted by changing internal tissue conditions. Signals that they did not heed previously, such as a color patch on the skin or feather (the sex mark of a displaying sex partner or competitor), a leaf or a twig (materials suitable for nest building) become now major attractions, and strenuous acts, such as procuring food for the begging young, become their almost exclusive daily occupation. These are not "reflex" activities, in the sense of blindly performed forced movements, but neither can they be based on "foresight," because they are performed by inexperienced animals. They are obviously directed, goal-seeking activities, which persist until the unknown but sought-for end is reached. The courtship singing of the male bird persists until a female is attracted; nest building prevails until an adequate nest is completed; incubation of the eggs continues until the young emerge; and food is procured in increasing quantities as the begging of the growing young becomes intensified. The animal persists in pursuing these various ends in spite of numerous obstacles and the strenuous labor required. The energy expended on such efforts increases as difficulties are encountered, and the mode of attack is varied and becomes better adapted to the specific circumstances of the individual as the animal becomes more "experienced." Its capacities permitting, the animal may in the course of time learn new modes of attack to reach its goals.

**Measurement of Motivation**  We have considered previously some quantifiable indices of motive states, namely, the magnitude of locomotion and restless activity. Locomotor activity is most commonly measured in *activity wheels*, or rotating drums, which are coupled with mechanical counters. More recently, cages fitted with photoelectric cells have been used, in which the moving animal interrupts a light beam falling on a photocell, and this event is then registered by a counter or inkwriter. General restlessness has been commonly measured in tambour-mounted or spring-suspended cages; more recently, *tilting cages* (stabilimeters) supported by microswitches have been used (Campbell, 1954), and also cages connected with gramophone cartridges or sensitive microphones, which respond to the vibration produced by the animal's movements. An older method of measuring drive strength is the *obstruction-box* method (Jenkins et al., 1926), where obstacles are placed between the animal and the goal object. Most commonly, the obstruction is an electrified grid that the animal must cross. The frequency with which an animal crosses such a barrier in a given length of time, and the amount of shock or punishment that it is willing to take, are then regarded as indicators of the strength of the drive (Warner, 1927, 1928). This technique was also used for determining the relative strength of different drive states (Warden, 1931). With this technique, the highest rate of traversing an obstacle was recorded in lactating rats retrieving their young; the next highest, by thirsty animals crossing for water; and so on.

The measurement of drive strength on the basis of *work output* (rate of bar pressing in a Skinner box, speed and latency of running in a run-

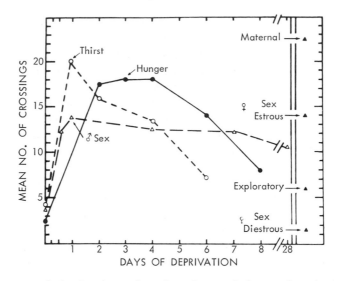

Summary graph showing the number of crossings made by rats through an electrified grid during a 20-minute period allowed for reaching different goal objects. (From Warden. *Animal motivation: experimental studies on the albino rat.* Columbia University Press, 1931.

way) is another common technique. A somewhat less direct, but no less popular, way of assessing drive strength is with such indices as speed of *learning* in a sensory discrimination task or in learning a maze; latency and magnitude of performance under such conditions are other measures of drive strength. Magnitude of *consummatory response* can also be used in assessing strength of motivation. The quantity of food or water ingested is a reliable index of need, because animals tend to eat and drink in proportion to their deficits. As far as the nutritive drives are concerned, length of deprivation and loss of body weight (which is a consequence of the former) can also be used for gauging drive strength in the first few days of deprivation in animals with regular feeding habits (in some species feeding is intermittent).

**Classification of Drives or Motives**   As described previously, we conceive of the animative action system as a mechanism primarily in the service of the vegetative needs of the individual and the species. Survival of the individual and species requires (1) the preservation of the individual through metabolic maintenance of the precarious steady-state of the organism, (2) the maintenance of the species through sexual propagation and parental assistance to the young, and (3) safeguarding the individual's integrity through social interaction. These are the conditions that permit vegetative existence, and the animative activities supporting these functions are considered to be in the service of, or motivated by, vegetative needs. The vegetative needs represent the first group or class of conditions that can engage or activate the animative system; the behavioral functions activated by such needs may be classified as *vegetogenic* or *viscerogenic functions.*

The metabolic *preservation of the organism* necessitates the continuous acquisition of oxygen, water, carbohydrates, amino acids, and other essential metabolic precursors of the body's structural and functional requirements. It also necessitates the maintenance of constant ionic composition of the blood, the maintenance of relatively constant temperature levels, the elimination of accumulating wastes and toxic by-products, and so on. These steady-state supporting processes have been subsumed under the name of *homeostasis* (Cannon, 1932). The various animative activities that service these homeostatic requirements, such as the seeking of food and water and the processes of ingestion, will be considered under the heading of metabolic or homeostatic activities. But homeostasis is not sufficient for organic survival. Homeostatic processes can ensure only the survival of the individual for a shorter or longer period representing its life span; *preservation of the species* over longer periods necessitates propagation. Propagation in higher animals depends on complex sexual and parental activities. These activities are considered to be motivated by a second group of vegetative drives; they will be considered under the heading of *sexual* and *parental functions.* Finally, both the individual and its offspring are surrounded by a hostile environment in which, for their safeguarding, a variety of defensive, offensive, and related social activities have to be performed: actual or potential friends have to be followed or adopted, enemies have to be fought or escaped from, and so on. Optimal survival conditions require cooperation with fellow members to *form* and *maintain social groups.*

The vegetogenic needs represent the first group of conditions that may engage or activate the animative action mechanism. There are also other sources of motivation. As stated before, the existence of organic mechanisms presupposes functioning; accordingly the animative system can be driven to action by its own functional states. The function of the sensory and motor mechanisms is to permit the animal to get to know and master its environment; it is not unnatural therefore that the neuromuscular system is also furnished with instigating mechanisms that make possible the realization of these tasks. The rested animal tends to exercise its limbs; the isolated animal tends to seek sensory stimulation. These *animative* or autochthonous sources of motivation give rise to *exploratory* and *manipulatory activities.* Activities motivated by vegetative and animative drives can be considered endogenous functions, because their mainsprings are internal "needs," "wants," or "tensions." Animals may also be driven to action by external objects in the absence of internal needs. Examples of externally motivated activities are acquired fears of, or attachments to, certain objects, the appearance of which evokes aversive or acquisitive activities. These types of activities may be referred to as *exogenous* or *autonomous functions* (Woodworth, 1947). Some of the characteristics of all these drive states are further discussed in the next, final section of this book.

**SELECTED READINGS**

Bindra, D. *Motivation: a systematic reinterpretation.* New York: Ronald, 1959.
Cofer, C. N. and M. H. Appley. *Motivation: theory and research.* New York: Wiley, 1964.
Hall, J. F. *Psychology of motivation.* Philadelphia: Lippincott, 1961.
Young, P. T. *Motivation and emotion.* New York: Wiley, 1961.

The structural and functional components of animal action that we have considered earlier are, in our view, the means, not the ends, of behavior. These mechanisms and capabilities are the essential building blocks, but not the functional units, of behavior. As an extension of this argument we may also say that some of the classical categories of human psychology, such as "sensation," "perception," and "remembering," do not represent functional entities but merely elements that may be present to varying degrees in most units of behavior. What, then, are the "units of behavior"? If our earlier thesis that animal action is primarily in the service of organic needs is correct, temporal and spatial sequences of animative action could be considered to be endowed with unity by the motive or drive states in the service of which they are engaged. Accordingly, we shall define as behavioral units, sequences of centrally coordinated and peripherally guided actions that are initiated by a drive state and terminated when the goal is achieved or when the pursuance of the goal is, for some reason, abandoned.

In the following chapter we shall deal briefly with the following four large classes of behavior.

1. *Economic types of behavior*. These include categories of behavior concerned with the homeostatic maintenance of the integrity of the individual. Examples are feeding and drinking, and the catering for nutritional needs through foraging, hunting, hoarding, migration, and so on. To this class also belong behavioral entities such as sleeping, hibernation, sanitary functions, building of shelters, and homing.

2. *Reproductive types of behavior*. These include a variety of behavioral activities concerned with the preservation of the species, such as courtship and mating, and ancillary activities, such as migration to breeding grounds, building of brooding nests, and various forms of parental behavior.

3. *Social types of behavior*. These include activities that make possible the formation and maintenance of collective groups. In different species social behavior may vary, depending on the interaction of two opposing tendencies, the affiliative and the agonistic dispositions of the individual members of the group.

4. *Educational types of behavior*. These include exploratory and manipulatory activities and juvenile play, forms of behavior that make possible the enrichment of the perceptual and operational repertoire of the individual and thus contribute to the individual's mastering of his environment.

# 16

# Preservation of the Individual

## Types of Economic Behavior

The preservation of the integrity of the individual necessitates, first, continual metabolic replenishment of the organism's energy losses and the unceasing repair of the tear and wear on its body structure. The energy and matter required for this are obtained through nutrition, that is, the acquisition and ingestion of suitable environmental substances. Nutrition, of course, requires a host of accessory activities, such as ranging over a foraging territory, the organization of hunting expeditions, the burying of surplus food for winter, and seasonal migration. Second, the preservation of the integrity of the individual also necessitates other types of economic behavior, such as the appropriate deployment of organic energy, with alternating periods of overt activity and inactivity in adaptation to the nocturnal-diurnal periodicity of the earth. This adjustment is best known as the sleeping-waking cycle, but it has been more recently identified as the more fundamental circadian rhythm (see below) displayed by all living organisms. Third, we may also classify as types of economic behavior the protection of the body from excessive temperature changes, sanitary functions, the acquisition and protection of a home territory, and certain related forms of behavior.

All these economic activities have one common property: they are homeostatic. The term *homeostasis* was introduced by Cannon (1932) to designate various feedback and regulatory processes whereby the body maintains the constancy of various internal conditions, such as the pH of the blood, and its water, mineral, and oxygen concentration. The homeostatic regulatory mechanisms were conceived by Cannon as depending primarily on humoral and visceral processes, though he recognized that skeletal activities, such as are involved in respiration, may also contribute to homeostasis. Subsequently, Richter (1942) further extended the principle of homeostasis to include behavioral activities. Richter found, for instance, that adrenalectomized rats, which would die within a week because they cannot maintain the constancy of the salt (NaCl) concentration of the blood, will remain in good health indefinitely by drinking large quantities of saline solution, if it is made available to them. Similarly, hypophysectomized rats compensate for their deficiency in heat conservation by using more nesting material and building larger nests.

All behavioral activities designed to satisfy the economic requirements of the body may be considered to be motivated by homeostatic needs. Some physiologists and psychologists have further extended the concept of homeostasis as an underlying principle of all organic drives. However, it appears farfetched to consider the sexual and maternal drives or the various animative drives, such as playing, or manipulative and exploratory activities, as homeostatic; and such an extension pre-empts the term of its more concrete meaning.

**Nutrition and Associated Functions**   *Nutrition* is the general term used for the various processes involved in the acquisition and incorporation of required substances from the external environment; the disposal of waste products is called *elimination*. In considering the nutritive and eliminative processes, it will be useful to distinguish the different mechanisms employed and functions displayed in the acquisition and elimination of gaseous, liquid, and solid substances. *Gaseous* chemicals are acquired mostly by respiration and eliminated by the same process. *Liquid* substances are ingested by drinking and eliminated by micturition. *Solid* substances are ingested by eating and eliminated by defecation. In general, the acquisitive processes, particularly those concerned with food and water, are more complex than the eliminative processes.

RESPIRATION.   The utilization of organic substances as sources of energy requires the availability of oxygen. Oxygen is obtained from the air or, by fish, from water. Oxygen is taken from the lungs or gills by the red blood corpuscles (erythrocytes) and carried through the cardiovascular system to the needy cells of the body. A considerable degree of autonomic regulation is achieved in oxygen uptake by changing the concentration of erythrocytes in the blood and by changes in the rate of breathing and circulation. In the habitat of land vertebrates, where oxygen is normally present in great abundance, the acquisition of oxygen is a routine process. Oxygen deficit (*air hunger*) may occur more commonly in fish, which are often seen surfacing or jumping out of the water, and particularly in aquatic mammals (such as seals, dolphins, or whales), which, having lungs but no gills, have to obtain oxygen from the air. Oxygen deprivation in terrestrial vertebrates occurs only under abnormal conditions, for example, in respiratory diseases, in higher altitudes, in closed polluted quarters, or when drowning. Under such conditions an acute air hunger arises, and the animal engages in violent activity in an effort to obtain oxygen.

FEEDING.   The process of food acquisition may be divided into several phases, the appetitive, consummatory, and satiation phases. The appetitive phase designates the period during which the animal exhibits behavior essential for the procurement of food. When food is acquired, the food-seeking activity is followed by the consummatory phase, or ingestion. If the obtained food is not sufficient (or is rejected), the cycle of food procuring and ingestion is repeated, until satiation is achieved. Satiation, the last phase, terminates the operation of the drive, though only temporarily.

*The appetitive phase*, a term introduced by Craig (1918) and popularized by the ethologists, usually begins with random activity, discussed earlier, combined with various expressions of "*hunger.*" It is not well understood what internal signals produce "hunger" and initiate feeding or, for that matter, what signals produce satiation and the cessation of food intake. Before the importance of the hypothalamus in the regulation of feeding was recognized, several *peripheral theories* were postulated. Cannon and Washburn (1912) showed in man that the subjective experience of hunger is associated with *stomach contractions*. Carlson (1924) postulated that decrease in the *blood-sugar level* produced the stomach contractions; he found that injection of glucose decreased the contractions, whereas injection of insulin increased them. More recently, Janowitz and Grossman (1951) suggested that the *oropharyngeal regions* can also record the volume of food ingested and may thus signal satiation. This conclusion was based on experiments in which it was found that prefeeding of dogs with a given amount of food produced a greater reduction in subsequent voluntary food intake than did the placement of the same amount of food directly into the stomach. The earlier results of the same investigators, however, suggested that the oropharyngeal afferent signals are supplemented by other peripheral sources of information, such as the rate of *nutrient utilization* by the body. This was suggested by *sham-feeding* experiments (Janowitz and Grossman, 1949), in which the ingested food is removed through an esophageal fistula; such animals tended to eat longer and more often than did normal animals. Furthermore, an inert substance placed in the stomach of animals produces a reduction in eating like that occurring after similar amounts of food have been placed there. Thus it appears that *stomach distension* also plays a role in registering food intake.

That the role of all these peripheral mechanisms cannot be a crucial one in regulating food intake was suggested by the early report of Sherrington (1900), later confirmed by Wangensteen and Carlson (1931), that removal of the entire stomach in man did not interfere with hunger and feeding. This observation was further confirmed in experiments in which the gastrointestinal tract was denervated in rats (Bash, 1939) and dogs (Harris et al., 1947).

Once the role of the hypothalamus in feeding was recognized, the peripheral theories of food intake were largely abandoned in favor of central theories. The best supported of the various central theories is the glucostatic theory, according to which glucose receptors in the hypothalamus register the concentration of blood glucose. Results obtained in normal and diabetic animals support this assumption: decreased utilizability or availability of glucose produces increased food intake (Mayer et al., 1955). Further supporting evidence is the finding that mice injected with goldthioglucose develop obesity (Marshall et al., 1955). Such animals show lesions in the ventromedial regions of the hypothalamus; the suggestion is that these cells selectively incorporate glucose (and are then destroyed by the gold attached to the glucose). More recently, Anand et al. (1962) reported that the production of hyper- or hypoglycemia in cats and monkeys provokes EEG changes in the "feeding" and "satiety" centers of the hypothalamus.

Critics have pointed out that neither of these findings supports the glucostatic theory. For one thing, the correlation between glucose availability and eating is not clear-cut (Janowitz and Grossman, 1951). For another, the lesion-producing effect of goldthioglucose is quite a general one, affecting several brain regions in which the "blood-brain barrier" is partially open. Indeed, the hypothalamus, which is richly supplied with blood and has gaps in its blood-brain barrier, could register the concentration not only of glucose but also of water, salts, carbohydrates, amino acids, and other constituents. Such an assumption could explain the phenomenon of specific hunger (Richter, 1942), the observation that animals will selectively feed on substances in which their diet has previously been made deficient (see further below).

An amalgamation of the peripheral and central theories is the multifactor theory of the regulation of food intake (Brobeck, 1960), supported by many investigators. Accordingly, both peripheral and central mechanisms cooperate in gauging the food need of the body. There is evidence that some of the peripheral signals referred to earlier may be registered and acted on by the hypothalamus. Sharma et al. (1961), for example, reported that distention of the stomach in a baboon produced increased EEG activity in the satiety center of the hypothalamus and no other regions.

In different species, different sensory mechanisms are utilized in the appetitive phase of food acquisition. In many surface-feeding fish, in most birds, and in such arboreal mammals as squirrels and primates, food detection may depend largely on vision. In bottom-feeding fish, or fish living in murky waters, and in terrestrial vertebrates, such as most rodents, ungulates, and carnivores, olfaction may be more important. As we know, animals can learn to respond to a variety of signals associated with food objects and can master complex instrumental acts that serve as means for the acquisition of food. Food acquisition may be a simple process if food is available in abundance; if food is scarce, however, acquisition may involve complex behavioral processes, such as hoarding, searching for pasture, foraging, hunting, struggling with prey, and seasonal migration.

Hoarding is widely practiced among rodents (rats, mice, hamsters, squirrels, beavers) and some carnivores (foxes, dogs). Hoarding consists of carrying food to the animal's home territory and hiding or burying it. Hoarding behavior, or components of it, is exhibited by inexperienced animals (Pitt, 1931; Wolfe, 1939), though its display may depend on experience. For example, laboratory rats raised under constant temperature and with an abundance of food do not normally hoard. Lowering of the temperature (McCleary and Morgan, 1946) or a period of food deprivation (Morgan et al., 1943; Bindra, 1947) elicit hoarding. Furthermore, feeding frustration early in life tends to lower the threshold for the elicitation of hoarding behavior in adulthood (Hunt, 1941; Hunt et al., 1947).

The *consummatory process* or food ingestion depends largely on gustatory control. The substances that reach the mouth are first "tasted" or screened for palatability. There is suggestive evidence that some instances of gustatory discrimination are based on built-in sensory control. For example, rats that have never before ingested a mild saline solution showed a preference for it over tap water on first exposure to it, in the same way "experienced" animals do (Weiner and Stellar, 1951). Similarly, rats show preference for all sweet substances, including saccharine, which has no nutritional value and which therefore cannot provide feedback information about the gratification of the food need. The consummatory act of feeding includes also such reflex processes as chewing, swallowing, and, in some grazing species, rumination.

Of great interest is the demonstration that, in addition to replenishing their daily caloric losses, animals show *specific hunger* for certain substances in which they are deficient. It has been known for a long time that domestic animals (chickens, pigs, dairy cattle) grow as well when they are given a *free choice* of nutrients as when they are fed on substances selected for their particular needs. In these earlier studies, because the free-choice substances were of natural origin, they contained a variety of nutrients. In subsequent, improved experiments, animals were presented with purified choice substances. In such an experiment, Richter (1942) found that rats selecting for themselves all their essential nutrients remained generally in good health, though their caloric intake was lower than that of control animals, which were fed on a standard laboratory diet. More recently it was reported (Scott, 1946; Pilgrim and Patton, 1947) that some rats may actually fail to maintain normal weight on such a "cafeteria" regime, though most of them are successful in satisfying their nutritional needs.

These investigations suggested that animals are to a large extent capable of selecting their diets in accordance with their nutritional requirements. This ability, and its limitations, were established in experimental deprivation studies. Richter et al. (1937) found that rats deficient in vitamin B consumed large quantities of this substance when it was presented to them in crystalline form. In another study, Richter (1939) found that adrenalectomized rats, which suffer from salt deficiency, not only consumed larger quantities of salt but also showed lower preference threshold than do normal rats to weak saline solutions. On the other hand, it was shown (Wilder, 1937) that rats deprived of vitamins A and D do not show a preference for nutrients that contain these substances.

Richter found that sectioning of the gustatory nerves abolishes the increased salt intake of adrenalectomized animals; thus, it seems, this compensatory reaction is dependent on gustation. Richter suggested that lowering of the gustatory threshold of adrenalectomized rats to salt is the basis of increased salt intake. Contradicting the theory that this "peripheral" factor causes increased salt intake is the finding of Pfaffmann and Bare (1950) that, as determined by direct recording of discharges from the chorda tympani nerve, the salt thresholds of normal and adrenalectomized animals are indistinguishable. Similarly, Carr (1952), and Harriman and McLeod (1953), using the conditioning technique, found no difference in the gustatory salt thresholds of normal and adrenalectomized rats. Though changes in *sensory threshold* cannot, therefore, explain the increased salt intake of the operated animals, the evidence obtained by Richter does suggest a change in their *preference threshold*.

The investigations of Epstein and Stellar (1955) suggest that the increased salt preference of adrenalectomized animals does not require learning or feedback from the beneficial effect of salt, for such animals, when deprived of salt for some time after the operation, will, on presentation of a saline solution, immediately ingest large quantities of the substance. However, in many other instances prior experience may be the basis of the preferential selection of specific food substances. For instance, rats that are deprived of vitamin B do not show preference for it when it is mixed with their common food source. However, if the food containing the vitamin is "tagged" with an artificial flavor, the animals slowly develop a preference for the flavored food and subsequently select the flavored substance even though the vitamin is removed (Harris et al., 1933). Conversely, food "habits" may often work against the mechanisms responsible for specific hungers. Young and Chaplin (1945), for instance, found that rats given a preference test in a particular apparatus between sugar and casein consistently chose sugar. When these rats were then deprived of casein for some time they stuck to their sugar preference and thus developed a protein deficiency. Only when these deprived animals were transferred to another type of preference-testing apparatus did they overcome their "habit" and chose adaptively casein over sugar.

DRINKING. Water is the essential medium of virtually all biochemical processes that go on within the organism. The amount of water is very high inside most cells, and there is a contant exchange of water between cells and the extracellular spaces (including the blood) surrounding them. A stable concentration of water is maintained inside cells and in the extracellular compartments, in spite of the fact that in terrestrial vertebrates the body's water loss is continuous and considerable: water is excreted in large quantities as urine, and lost through the lungs in breathing and through the skin in sweating. When dehydration occurs, the water loss is replenished by intake of water from external sources in the form of drinking.

What internal mechanisms signal water deficit or "*thirst*" and initiate drinking behavior? Cannon (1934) suggested that *dryness of the mucous membranes* of the mouth, tongue and throat, produced by tissue dehydration, is the peripheral signal that leads to the sensation of thirst and induces drinking. This "local" or *peripheral theory* was partially disproved by the finding of Montgomery (1931) that after removal of the salivary glands in dogs, which produced chronic dryness of the mouth, the operated animals drank no more (though more often) than controls. Though the sensation of thirst may depend on the dryness of the mouth, the regulation of water intake is obviously a more complex process.

In dogs, water intake is directly proportional to water loss (Robinson and Adolph, 1943). Bellows (1939) reported that dogs with implanted stomach fistulas, through which the water ingested by the animal could be immediately withdrawn, also drank in proportion to their deficit. As these animals did not utilize water, gauging of the intake must have occurred peripherally. Similarly, if a sufficient amount of water was placed through the fistula into the stomach, the animal still drank in proportion to its loss—provided that its drinking was tested immediately after the stomach loading. However, when the dogs were permitted to start drinking 15 minutes after stomach loading, they no longer ingested water. These experiments suggested the operation of both peripheral (esophageal) metering devices and internal gauging of water concentration. There is suggestive evidence that routine drinking is peripherally gauged, because normally animals stop drinking after a few minutes, presumably before the ingested water can reach all the dehydrated cells. If, in spite of drinking, dehydration is not removed (as when water loss is excessive), drinking is soon resumed; contrariwise, if hydration is achieved without ingestion (as in the artificial stomach-loading experiment, with drinking tested after the lapse of some time), drinking will not take place.

The *salinity* of the extracellular fluids was found to be a major indicator of water concentration and drinking. Stellar et al. (1954) found that when the stomach of rats was loaded through a fistula with hypertonic saline solution, the animals drank more water subsequently than without the load; whereas loading with hypotonic saline solution reduced their water intake. In a complementary experiment, O'Kelly and Falk (1958) found that when the stomach of rats was loaded with isotonic saline, their

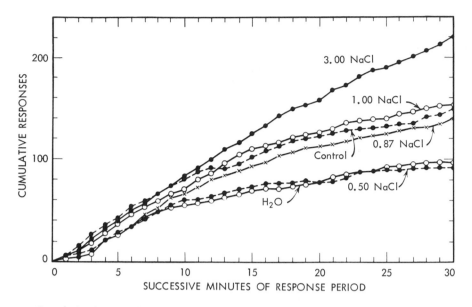

Cumulative bar-pressing responses in a Skinner box for water as a function of the salt concentration of the preload. (O'Kelly and Falk. Water regulation in the rat: II. *J. comp. physiol. Psychol.*, 1958, **51**, 22–25)

rate of bar pressing (which delivered drops of water) in a Skinner apparatus was comparable to the rate of normal rats. A hypertonic saline load increased the bar-pressing rate; a hypotonic load decreased it.

Apparently some mechanism in the body registers the salinity of the tissue fluids and regulates water intake. Evidence is available that central, hypothalamic mechanisms may be directly sensitive to the salinity of osmotic pressure of the blood. "Osmoreceptors," which presumably register directly the saline concentration of the blood, were postulated to exist in this region (see page 291).

ELIMINATION.    Elimination of gaseous waste products, such as $CO_2$, occurs by means of expiration. Soluble and liquid wastes are eliminated by micturition, the emptying of the bladder. Solid waste products are eliminated by defecation. As we have described earlier, urination and defecation are controlled by the nervous system, and such peripheral signals as the distension of the bladder or colon are utilized in the process. Urination and defecation are relatively simple animative processes. However, various animals require special conditions for their execution (such as the presence of dust for burying the excrement, a spot at some distance from home territory, and the like). Urination and defecation are also used by some animals in marking their territories, recognizing sexual mates, and in social communication.

**Circadian Activity Rhythms, Sleep and Wakefulness** Sleeping and waking, and a host of related processes to be considered, represent adaptations to the recurrent alternation of day and night produced by the rotation of the earth around its axis. Associated with this photoperiodicity are cyclic changes in temperature, humidity, the $O_2$ and $CO_2$ concentration of the air, the presence or absence of prey and foe, and a host of other important variables.

CIRCADIAN RHYTHMS. The alternation of waking and sleeping phases in the life of probably all animals may be said to represent an aspect of the ubiquitous *circadian* rhythm shown by all living things on earth. The term "circadian" (*circa* + *diem*) was recently coined (Halberg, 1959) to designate a variety of endogenous rhythmic processes with an approximate periodicity of 24 hours. Though the term is new, the phenomenon has been known and investigated for some time. In 1729, De Mairan found that plants raised in a dark room under relatively constant ambient temperature showed cyclic "sleep movements," the way they do when they are exposed to the normal alternation of light and dark (Bünning, 1960). This phenomenon was subsequently confirmed by several investigators, including Darwin (1880). There is good evidence that these circadian rhythms are *endogenous*. Hand-reared chickens (Aschoff and Meyer-Lohmann, 1954) and lizards (Hoffmann, 1959) raised under conditions of constant darkness or illumination, or lizards raised under artificial 18-hour or 36-hour days (Hoffmann, 1959) were found to show circadian rhythms similar to normally raised animals. Bünning (1960) found that exposure of *Drosophila* to constant light for 15 generations did not eliminate their circadian rhythm; the same was found in mice raised in constant light for 6 generations (Aschoff, 1960).

These diurnal rhythms, which encompass various visceral and behavioral functions, may vary in length from about 22 to 26 hours in different species or individuals, but they are resistant to modification by chemical interference or changes in temperature over a wide range. In any given individual the rhythm is very precise, with mean errors of at most a few minutes (Pittendrigh, 1960). Under free-running conditions (as in constant light), the endogenous circadian rhythm is not in phase with the external day-night cycle. The rhythm, however, can be easily "entrained" (Bruce, 1960), that is, synchronized with and reset by exogenous factors, particularly by light, which as a synchronizing agent or Zeitgeber adapts the endogenous rhythm to prevailing local conditions of photoperiodicity (Aschoff, 1960). The photic phase control of circadian rhythms may require several days of periodic alternation of light and dark, or the rhythm may be brought in phase with external conditions by a single perturbation of light or dark. (Unlike temperature, the duration and intensity of light may also affect the length of the circadian rhythm.) The transition periods of light and dark (under natural conditions these

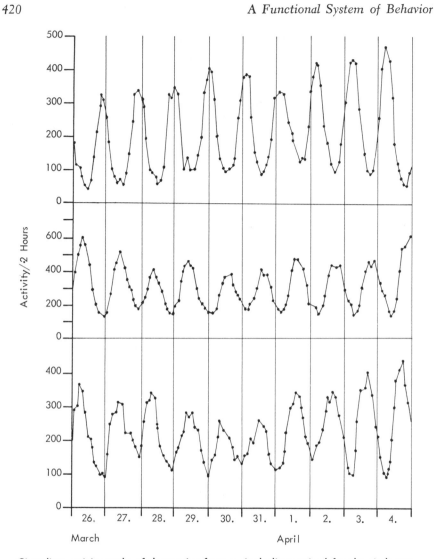

Circadian activity cycle of three mice from a single litter raised for the sixth generation in continuous illumination. (After Aschoff. *Exogenous* and endogenous components in circadian rhythms. *Cold Springs Harbor Sympos. quant. Biol.,* 1960, **25,** 11–28)

are dawn and dusk) are believed particularly effective in the phase control of circadian rhythms (Bruce, 1960). Dawn and dusk are, of course, the periods that mark the shifts in the activity phase of many diurnal and nocturnal animals.

In summary, the ubiquitous circadian rhythm may be said to represent an innate and self-sustained oscillation in the life of animals that, with the aid of Zeitgeber signals, can be easily synchronized with local and

**MAR. 29**

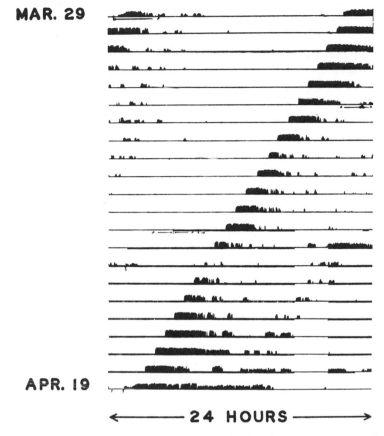

**APR. 19**

← ─────── **24 HOURS** ──────→

Twenty-two day record of the running activity of a female mouse in constant dark-ness. (Vertical bars for each daily record indicate number of revolutions of running wheel per minute.) Note the phase shift of the continuous circadian rhythm. (From Rawson. *Photoperiodism and related phenomena in plants and animals.* American Association for the Advancement of Science, 1959, pp. 791–800. Copyright 1959 by the American Association for the Advancement of Science)

seasonal day-night cycles. As we shall see later, this endogenous rhythm also serves as an *internal clock*, and makes possible, for instance, compass navigation by the sun or stars during seasonal migration or in homing. In addition to circadian rhythms, tidal rhythms have been described in various marine animals (Fingerman, 1960), and we shall later refer to annual breeding rhythms that may also depend to some extent on an internal timing mechanism. The physiological processes responsible for these rhythms in general and the circadian rhythm in particular are not known.

SLEEPING. Sleeping, representing the periodic cessation of the waking state, is easily identified by EEG changes and the great reduction of overt behavior and responsiveness to external stimuli. In most animals the reflexes responsible for the maintenance of upright stance are absent during sleep, and the animals assume a reclining posture. Most of the postural and locomotor muscles are relaxed during sleep, though some muscles (such as the sphincter of the bladder or the anus) are in a state of maximal contraction. Indeed, in spite of the over-all relaxation of body musculature, some animals maintain their upright posture during sleep (for instance, perching birds), and the human infant holds its fist tight when asleep, presumably as an atavistic display of a trait so important in young arboreal primates, which hold on tightly to their mother or the branch of a tree during sleep (Kleitman, 1963).

Szymanski (1919) used activity-recording cages for a comparative study of the sleeping-waking cycles of different animal species. He found that some species had a single prolonged resting period at night and were more or less continually active during the day. Szymanski called this sleeping-waking pattern *monocyclic*, and he postulated that this pattern was characteristic of animals (such as birds and primates) that rely heavily on vision in their behavior. Other species, like the rat, were found to have an alternating cycle of rest and activity both during the day and night; this pattern was named *dicyclic*. Finally, many species were found to have a large number of cycles within the 24-hour period; these he referred to as *polycyclic* species. Insofar as the bulk of the activity of some species is displayed during the day, and in others from dusk to dawn, animals may also be distinguished in this respect as *nocturnal* or *diurnal*. Visual animals (such as most birds and primates) tend to be diurnal; those relying on somesthesis (burrowing animals) or olfaction are often nocturnal. The nocturnal mode of existence represents an adaptation for protection against diurnal predators.

The differences in internal functions and overt behavior during sleep and wakefulness have been intensively studied for some time, and much of the relevant material was recently summarized by Kleitman (1963). It is well established that the level of metabolic activity, as indicated by decreased oxygen consumption and decreased heat production, is lowered during sleep. However, whether this is a fundamental aspect of sleep or merely a secondary consequence of resting and the concomitant decrease in muscular tension and body movements is still unresolved. At least some studies indicate that the difference in the rate of muscular activity is not the only variable, because after staying in bed for several months, human patients still show a 24-hour periodicity in the rise and fall of body temperature. We may also mention as an established fact the reduction of secretion and concentration in the blood of corticosteroid hormones during sleep in rats (Guillemin et al., 1959) and monkeys (Migeon et al., 1955). Again, we do not know whether the reduction of corticosteroids in the blood, which is under pituitary control, is a cause or consequence of reduced metabolism and overt behavioral activity.

Among the visceral functions that are altered during sleep we may mention changes in circulatory and respiratory processes. During sleep the heart rate is decreased, and there is also a fall in blood pressure. This slowing of the heart is a central nervous effect, because the denervated heart of the dog shows little change in activity during sleep (Samaan, 1934). The exact nature of changes occurring in respiration during sleep is still debated, but there is agreement that the net effect of these variable changes is lowered ventilation of the lungs during sleep. This change is indicated by many studies showing an increase in $CO_2$ concentration in alveolar air and an increase in $CO_2$ tension of the blood during sleep. The changes occurring in alimentary processes during sleep are not well established. There is evidence of decreased salivary secretion and of decreased secretion of some of the gastric juices. However, gastric motility does not seem to be affected, nor is there agreement about changes in the activity of the liver or in the concentration of blood sugar. An interesting finding is the increase in mitotic activity of epidermal cells at night in man (Cooper, 1939) and during the day in nocturnal rodents (Halberg et al., 1954). This would be one example of an increase in recuperative or regenerative functions during sleep.

Not only body temperature but also the temperature of the brain fall during sleep. This decrease was indicated in a study (Serota, 1939) in which thermocouples were implanted into the brain of cats; during sleep a fall in temperature was noted in the cortex, and an even more pronounced fall in the hypothalamus. These changes in temperature are possibly related to the radical changes in EEG activity during sleep, a finding we have considered previously. The change from the waking state to sleep (characterized by closure of the eyes, adoption of a sleeping posture, an increase in arousal threshold, and the like) is accompanied by a decrease in the frequency of the spontaneous EEG activity. This change, which is regulated by ascending influences from the reticular formation, has been interpreted to represent a decrease in the "facilitatory tonus" of brain structures responsible for the maintenance of the vigilant and mobilized state displayed by the awake animal.

From this point of view sleep may be conceived of as a process in which animals reduce their contact with their environments, and the associated EEG changes may represent the reduced activity of the central nervous structures responsible for the control of interrelation with the environment. A subjective aspect of this process, as known from human experience, is the reduction of consciousness or awareness during sleep. However, the state of suspended awareness during sleep is interrupted by episodes of dreaming. In this context it is interesting to mention that in sleeping cats the characteristic low-frequency EEG activity was found to be interrupted occasionally by low-voltage fast activity, often associated with rapid eye movements (Dement, 1958). This condition has been termed the "paradoxical phase" of the EEG sleep pattern, which may be elicited artificially in sleeping cats by low-level stimulation of the reticular formation (Grastyán, 1959). On the basis of similar findings in man, where the paradoxical phase of EEG and rapid eye movements appear to be associated with *dreaming*, it was postulated that also in animals this change in the electrical pattern of the brain reflects episodes of dreaming. That animals may occasionally dream has been suspected for a long time on the basis of everyday observations of growling, barking, twitching, and leg movements in sleeping dogs.

**Temperature Control and Hibernation**  The diurnal and seasonal fluctuations in the temperature of the environment are considerable, and animals have developed a variety of regulatory mechanisms to produce, conserve, and dissipate heat. Vertebrates are often distinguished as cold- and warm-blooded. Fish, amphibians, and reptiles are considered *cold-blooded*, birds and mammals *warm-blooded*. Indeed, under laboratory conditions, the body temperature of a frog or lizard will rise or fall as the ambient temperature of the room is raised or lowered, whereas the temperature of a pigeon or rat will remain constant over wide ranges of external temperature fluctuations. We should point out, however, that lizards, in their normal habitats, can maintain a relatively constant body temperature whether the air is cool or warm, by seeking warm sites, burrowing into the ground, and related behavioral processes.

In birds and mammals, the maintenance of a relatively constant body temperature depends, first, on a variety of visceral regulatory functions. When the body temperature falls, there is increased thyroid secretion (producing increased rate of metabolism), increased adrenalin secretion (leading to increased sugar release into the blood), and heightened cardiac activity; reactions that lead to increased *heat production*. Constriction of cutaneous blood vessels, inhibition of perspiration, and piloerection (fluffing of feathers or hair) contribute under such conditions to increased heat conservation. Some morphological changes may also aid heat conservation; among these are increased growth of hair or pelt during the cold season or a greater deposit of fat or blubber under the skin. When the body temperature rises above normal, various *heat dissipating* mechanisms may be activated, such as perspiration, vasodilation, and the like. The maintenance of a normal body temperature may also require various skeletal motor acts or behavioral processes. These include simpler processes such as shivering, panting, and stomping, or more complex behavioral acts, such as seeking protective shelters, nest building, or seasonal migrations.

Experimental studies dealing with activation of behavioral mechanisms to control body temperature are relatively few. Kinder (1927) has shown that the amount of paper strip used in nest building by rats correlated well with changes in ambient temperature: increasing the room temperature lowered the amount of paper used; decreasing the temperature raised it. Similarly, Richter and Eckert (1936) found that hypophysectomized rats, which suffer from lowered metabolic activity and decreased heat production, showed a compensatory increase in nest-building activity.

Before the arrival of winter, which is associated with the onset of cold weather and scarcity of food supply, some animals seek protective shelters, withdraw into their nests, and may nourish themselves on food hoarded during the summer. Other animal species *hibernate* during the winter months. Hibernation is a sleeplike, stuporous state during which the metabolism, body temperature, visceral functions, and overt activity of the animal are reduced to the barest minimum. Whereas the nonhibernator increases its food intake to maintain its body temperature, the hibernating animal changes its thermostatic standard to a low level. Thus the hedgehog (Herter, 1934), whose normal body temperature varies from 33.5° to 35.5° C, will hibernate if the ambient temperature falls below 14.5°; it then keeps its body temperature about 1° above the external temperature, down to 6° C. If the external temperature falls below this level, the animal will either maintain it at 6° or wake up. (The latter finding indicates that during hibernation the animal does not become "cold-blooded" but can retain some control over its temperature.)

The heart rate of the hibernating animal may be reduced to a few beats per minute, and the respiratory rate of some species to less than one per minute. The blood pressure becomes very low and the erythrocyte count decreases (Kleitman, 1963). The spontaneous EEG activity of the hibernating animal is retained (though its amplitude becomes very low), and the EEG rhythm may be desynchronized by peripheral stimuli (Strumwasser, 1959).

Out of season, hibernation may be induced in various hibernating species by the injection of insulin and terminated by the injection of glucose (Dworkin and Finney, 1922; Dische et al., 1931; Kayser, 1940). These findings indicate that lowered blood-sugar level, normally the consequence of food deprivation, can trigger hibernation. Likewise, hibernation may be induced on exposure of the animal to cold. Some species, such as the ground squirrel, hibernate within 24 hours after exposure to cold; others, like the golden hamster, first increase their food intake and store up fat, and will hibernate after some delay (Lyman and Chatfield, 1955). Notwithstanding this evidence of the external or environmental control of the triggering of hibernation, there are also findings indicating at least some degree of endogenous rhythmicity. Thus there is a report (Pengelley and Fisher, 1957) that ground squirrels kept in a warm room with an artificial 12-hour daylight regimen, and provided with ample food and water, hibernate from October to May. This endogenous rhythmicity may depend on rhythmic glandular changes, because chipmunks raised under constant temperature were found to show a regression of their pituitary, thyroid, and adrenal glands in the winter (Woodward and Condrin, 1945), changes associated with hibernation.

**Sheltering, Homing, and Migration**    In many species, individuals or small groups occupy for themselves *territories* of varying sizes, which they treat as their own property, as indicated by their aggressive displays toward, or attacks on intruders. Within such territories there may be a nook or den occupied by individuals, or a special nest built for their comfort and protection. The home or territory represents a preferred environment to which individuals withdraw not only for protection from inclement weather, but also as a place for hiding from predators, for storing hoarded food, for raising the young, or for merely resting during periods of inactivity.

*Homing*, the return of animals to a habitual nook, den, shelter, or nest after their foraging excursions or hunting expeditions, is quite common in a variety of species at all levels of the phylogenetic scale. To return to their home territory, animals will often cover long distances and negotiate difficult and tortuous paths. A few examples from vertebrates will suffice here. Fence lizards, according to Noble (1934) find their way home from a distance of 800 feet over a terrain that may be unfamiliar to them, a feat that may take the animals several days to accomplish. Tortoises return to their communal territory when displaced more than 1 mile (Cagle, 1944), and dogs find their way home over several miles of unknown territory (Schmid, 1932). That is, animals are capable not only of retracing their steps homeward but of finding their homes through unfamiliar territory. Most intriguing in this respect is the homing ability of certain birds, and particularly the migratory navigation of aquatic and arboreal vertebrates over distances of hundreds and thousands of miles.

Recent studies indicate that animals *navigating* over long distances use the sun, moon, or stars as a *compass* for orientation. The utilization of these apparently moving celestial objects requires, of course, that adequate compensation be made for local time. That is, the animal has to adjust continually (or sufficiently often) its angle of orientation toward these objects, a compensation that presupposes an internal timekeeping mechanism or clock. There is sufficient evidence that these abilities are displayed by inexperienced animals as innate capacities, though, as we shall see later, the experienced animal has the advantage of being able to utilize its familiarity with the topography of its home area or winter quarters.

Navigation with the aid of the sun as a compass was discovered independently in the bee by von Frisch (1950), and in starlings by Kramer (1950, 1952). Kramer observed that starlings kept in an outdoor aviary dis-

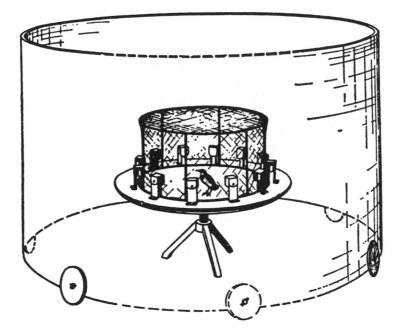

Training cage used by Kramer to study migratory orientation of birds under various natural and artificial conditions. (From Ursula von Saint Paul. Compass directional training of western meadowlarks [*Sturnella neglecta*]. *Auk*, **73**, 203–210. Credited to Kramer. In Dorst, *The migration of birds*. Houghton Mifflin, 1962, p. 355, Fig. 119. Copyright Houghton Mifflin)

played migratory fluttering in the direction taken by free starlings during migration. This observation made it possible to study migratory orientation under simple laboratory conditions. Starlings placed in a circular cage were found to retain their characteristic orientation after all view of the horizon was excluded or when the magnetic field around the cage was changed. In contrast, the birds showed disorientation when the sky was overcast, and their orientation could be modified with the aid of mirrors; apparently they used the sun for their orientation. Because the birds would retain their appropriate orientation in the direction of their migratory route for several hours, although the position of the sun had changed considerably, the assumption had to be made that the birds changed their angle to the azimuth of the sun (projection of the sun's position onto the horizontal plane) in accordance with the local time of the day. This supposition was confirmed experimentally.

Starlings trained to obtain food at a given time of the day from one of 12 circularly arranged hoppers, shifted their choice when tested another time of the day; thus they must have used the sun for the identification of the direction of the correct hopper and changed the angle in accordance with the time of testing. Similar results were obtained indoors

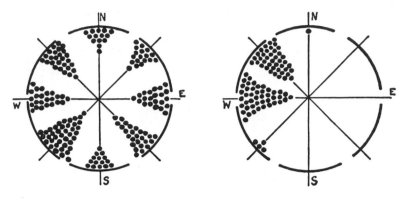

Influence of an overcast sky on the orienting ability of starlings. *Left,* random orientation when the sky is clouded (each dot represents one response). *Right,* immediate orientation in direction of the migratory path when the sky is clear. (From Kramer. Eine neue Methode zur Erforschung der Zugorientierung und die bisher damit erzielten Ergebnesse. *Proc. 10th Internat. Ornithol. Cong.,* Upsala, 1950, pp. 269–280. In Dorst, *The migration of birds.* Houghton Mifflin, 1962, p. 350, Fig. 115. Copyright Houghton Mifflin)

with the use of a bright light source as an artificial sun. Although some birds displayed a constant angle of orientation with respect to the artificial sun, others changed the angle counterclockwise in accordance with the time of the day.

These experiments established that starlings use the sun azimuth as a compass and that instead of maintaining a fixed angle, they change the angle in compensation for the movement of the sun over the sky. Because it was found that birds kept indoors in lightproof chambers showed normal compensation, it was assumed that the animals used some "internal clock" for the purpose, presumably a timekeeping mechanism dependent on the exact circadian rhythms of animals. Hoffmann (1960) tested this postulated dependence of time compensation on circadian rhythm in the following manner. After training starlings to select food from a hopper, as previously described, the synchrony of their circadian rhythm with respect to local time was shifted by 6 hours by an artificial day-night cycle. When retested at the usual time of day, the animals shifted their choice 90° from the original direction, confirming the dependence of their internal time keeping mechanism on a circadian rhythm entrained by the local light-dark cycle. The birds displayed their altered timekeeping until brought back to the natural day-and-night cycle. This finding was confirmed by Schmidt-Koenig (1960) in the pigeon.

Besides bees and starlings, sun-compass orientation was demonstrated in a variety of species of fish (Hasler et al., 1958), in turtles (Gould, 1957), and in other species of birds (Matthews, 1953 a; Perdeck, 1958). Sun-compass orientation, with appropriate compensations for the sun's movements, appears to be an innate capacity, because it could be seen in a hand-reared starling raised in a lightproof chamber and then tested with an artificial sun (Hoffmann, 1953). Depending on the geographic location of the habitat of the animal (Northern or Southern Hemisphere) and on its direction of migration (northward or southward), the compensation for sun movement is made clockwise or counterclockwise.

Although diurnally migrating fish or birds use the sun as a compass, Sauer and Sauer (1955, 1960) discovered that nocturnally migrating birds, like warblers, utilize the constellations of stars in their compass orientation. This was demonstrated by testing the birds at night with a technique similar to that designed by Kramer. The birds showed typical orientation in the direction of their migratory route when they could see a section of the clear or slightly overcast night sky. When the sky was heavily covered with clouds, the birds became disoriented. Subsequently these investigators found that the birds could appropriately orient themselves under the artificial starry sky of a planetarium, where they appeared to depend on the stars of greater magnitude. When the planetarium sky was shifted out of phase with local time, either the birds became disoriented or their orientation was altered in a manner indicating that they kept local time. When exposed under a starless dome, the birds remained motionless or showed an absence of directional preference in their orientation.

The migratory orientation displayed by birds is a fixed one, pointing in the direction of the route they normally take during migration. Experiments have been performed in which migratory birds were displaced before or during their migration to determine whether they maintain their fixed compass orientation, and follow a route paralleling their normal migratory path, or change their angle to compensate for the displacement (Matthews, 1955). Inexperienced juvenile birds were found to take a parallel route, an indication that they used exclusively their innate compass orientation. However, some of the experienced adult birds changed their path to head directly to their goal; they probably utilized their familiarity with the topography of the correct route. These experienced birds may be said to use *map orientation* in addition to the more fundamental fixed-direction, compass orientation. Variable angle orientation, and possibly the use of an acquired "map," may be the basis of homing in pigeons that, carried to distant places, immediately orient themselves appropriately and fly by the shortest route home.

### SELECTED READINGS

Anand, B. K. Nervous regulation of food intake. *Physiol. Rev.*, 1961, **41**, 677–708.

Autrum, H. (Ed.). *Animal orientation. Ergeb. der Biol.*, vol. 26. Berlin: Springer, 1963.

Brobeck, J. R. Regulation of feeding and drinking. *Handb. Physiol.*, 1960, Sec. 1, **2**, 1197–1206.

Cold Spring Harbor Symposia on Quantitative Biology. *Biological Clocks.* Vol. 25, 1960.
Dorst, J. *The migration of birds.* Boston: Houghton Mifflin, 1962.
Jones, M. R. (Ed.). *Nebraska symposia on motivation.* Lincoln: University of Nebraska Press (appears annually).
Kleitman, N. *Sleep and wakefulness.* (2d ed.) Chicago: University of Chicago Press, 1963.
Oswald, I. *Sleeping and waking.* Amsterdam: Elsevier, 1962.
Richter, C. P. Total self-regulatory functions in animals and human beings. *Harvey Lect.*, 1943, **38,** 63–103.
Wayner, M. J. (Ed.). *Thirst.* New York: Macmillan, 1964.
Wolf, A. V. *Thirst.* Springfield, Ill.: Charles C Thomas, 1958.

# 17

# Propagation of the Species

## Types of Reproductive Behavior

Nutritional gratification of the organism's metabolic requirements makes possible the survival of the individual. Survival of the species requires, in addition, sexual propagation and parental care of the offspring. Sexual and parental behavior, the function of which is fertilization of the ovum by a sperm and the furtherance of embryonic and postnatal development, is composed of a series of complex activities that differ considerably among the various classes of vertebrates and, to some extent, also among different species within the same class.

In most vertebrates sexual activity is a cyclic phenomenon, dependent on seasonal or, more frequently, recurrent maturation and atrophy of the sex organs and glands. This periodicity applies particularly to the female, in which the ova have to mature prior to fertilization by the male, and the reproductive organs must be prepared for carrying and supplying the eggs and the developing embryos. Because female sexual activity is cyclic rather than continuous, its synchronization with the sexual activity of the male, and with appropriate environmental conditions, is a primary requirement. This synchronization is partially achieved by the priming effects of external physical factors affecting both the male and female, such as increase in daily illumination and temperature in the spring, the arrival of the wet season in tropical regions, and so on. These external factors are particularly important for the synchronization, or phase matching, of the reproductive process with the optimal season for nurturing the young (the warm season in temperate climates, the wet season in tropical areas).

The synchronization of sexual maturation in males and females, and of their readiness to breed, is also dependent on complex courtship behavior. Courtship behavior may precede, follow, or be intimately associated with the establishment of a breeding site and nest-building activity. The next process is the fertilization of the ova by sperms, which is accomplished by spawning in most fish and by internal, coital fertilization in higher vertebrates. The coital mating process is followed by egg laying in reptiles and birds and, after a longer period of gestation, by parturition in mammals. The laying of eggs in birds is followed by brooding behavior. The care for the young includes, in some fish and in most birds and mammals, such *parental nurturing behavior* as feeding, cleaning, and providing the young with protection and optimal conditions for their growth and maturation.

**Internal or Hormonal Priming of**    Sexual and parental activities are
**Sexual and Parental Activities**    vegetogenic processes induced by
hormonal regulatory mechanisms. These hormones are produced primarily by the gonads and the pituitary. In no other vegetogenic activity is the regulatory effect of humoral agents so well established as in sexual and parental activities. Because sexual behavior, and its hormonal basis, are different in the male and female, we shall consider separately here the evidence of humoral effects in the two sexes. We shall subsequently consider some observational and experimental findings relating to the hormonal control of maternal and paternal behavior.

HORMONES AND MALE SEXUAL BEHAVIOR.    Removal of the gonads in males (castration) seriously affects sexual behavior in all vertebrates, although in sexually experienced animals various aspects of sexual behavior may survive for a long period after the operation. Castrated gobiid fish become nondiscriminatory in sexual behavior and court males as well as gravid (egg-carrying) and nongravid females (Tavolga, 1955). In castrated frogs, no signs of sexual behavior were observed at a time when the majority of normal frogs were mating (Shapiro, 1937a). In the rat, penile intromission is gradually reduced over a period of several months after castration (Stone, 1927; Nissen, 1929; Beach, 1942d), with the last ejaculation observed approximately 30 days after castration (Stone, 1939). The same reduction in sexual activity was also reported in male hamsters (Beach and Pauker, 1949), guinea pigs (Grunt and Young, 1952b, 1953), and cats (Green, Clemente, and de Groot, 1957; Rosenblatt and Aronson, 1958). Monkeys become sexually impotent 4 or 5 months after castration (Thorek, 1924). In dogs, sexual behavior may persist for several years after castration (Beach, 1958). In most species, individual differences have also been noted, some individuals being more affected by castration than were others.

Castration has the most serious effect on sexual behavior when it is performed before puberty. In *prepuberally castrated* animals such consummatory responses as erection and intromission do not normally occur, though the animals may display some appetitive behavior, such as running around the female and even jumping on her (Beach, 1944a). The failure in the development of normal sexual behavior after castration may be attributed to removal of sex hormones from the blood. This conclusion is borne out by the dramatic therapeutic effect of injecting male sex hormone into castrated males and by the development of *precocious sexual behavior* after androgen injection into immature males.

Injection of testosterone into immature male guppies produces normal patterns of mature sexual behavior (Eversole, 1941). The same was also observed in immature domestic fowl (Noble and Zitrin, 1942) and in many other species. Similarly, daily injections of testosterone re-establishes normal sexual behavior in adult castrated rats (Shapiro, 1937b; Stone, 1939; Beach, 1944) or guinea pigs (Moore and Price, 1938; Grunt and Young, 1952b). Beach and Holz-Tucker (1949) reported that, in the castrated rat, raising the dose levels of testosterone essential for restoring sexual behavior produces a proportional increase in sexual activity, exceeding the level of sexual activity shown by the animals before castration. In contrast, Grunt and Young (1952b, 1953) found in male guinea pigs injected with testosterone, and Goy and Young (1957b) in female guinea pigs injected with estradiol, that irrespective of the dose level, hormone injection leads to the *restoration* of the characteristic level of sexual activity displayed by the individual prior to castration. Thus animals that were scored low, medium, or high on sexual activity before castration, remained low, medium, or high after castration, irrespective of the daily dose of administered testosterone. These contradictory results may be due to species differences.

These studies employing the testosterone-replacement technique clearly suggest that androgens have a major role in regulating male sexual behavior. The survival of several aspects of sexual behavior even in some prepuberally castrated animals has been attributed by some investigators (Sollenberger and Hamilton, 1939; Spiegel, 1939) to androgens secreted by the *adrenal cortex*. However, this hypothesis was disproved by a recent study (Warren and Aronson, 1957), which showed that adrenalectomy did not abolish sexual manifestations that survived in prepuberally castrated hamsters. Similarly, adrenalectomy did not diminish the sexual activity displayed by postpuberally castrated male dogs (Schwartz and Beach, 1954). Another possibility, which will be considered later, is that some displays of sexual behavior are of neurogenic origin.

HORMONES AND FEMALE SEXUAL BEHAVIOR. Female sexual behavior, which is manifested in mammals in increased locomotion, running after the male, lordosis, malelike mounting activity, and receptivity, is a cyclic process that appears only during "heat" (the *estrus period*). Following *ovariectomy* in females, the estrus cycle and receptivity are immediately and permanently abolished. However, estrus behavior can be restored in the ovariectomized female, or elicited in the female during *anestrus*, by administration of estrogens. This has been established in the rat (Boling and Blandau, 1939; Beach, 1942 a), hamster (Frank and Fraps, 1945), cat (Bard, 1939), dog (Robson, 1938), and monkey (Ball, 1936; Hartman, 1938). Estrogen is particularly effective when it is followed by injection of progesterone (Dempsey et al., 1936). A single injection of estrogen, or estrogen and progesterone, is sufficient to produce increased activity, lordosis, and other behavioral signs of heat. As a rule, however, the female will not accept the male unless repeated injections are made, because without repeated injections vaginal changes (cornification) characteristic of normal heat will not be produced (Ford and Young, 1951). With administration of these sex hormones, precocious female behavior was also induced in immature guinea pigs (Wilson and Young, 1941) and rats (Beach, 1942c). These facts justify the conclusion that female sexual behavior is more dependent on humoral regulation than is male sexual behavior.

In summary, androgens are very effective in stimulating masculine behavior in males, and estrogens in producing feminine behavior in females. We should add that these hormones may also have other effects. Estrogen injected into males can produce hormone-alien, host-specific, masculine behavior or hormone-specific, host-alien feminine behavior. Similarly, androgen injected into the female may produce hormone-alien, host-specific feminine patterns of behavior or hormone-specific, host-alien masculine patterns (Young, 1961). No adequate explanation is available at present for this dual role of hormones (having specific and nonspecific sexual effects) or the bisexual capacity of the responding organism (manifesting the behavior of its own and of the opposite sex).

HORMONES IN PARENTAL BEHAVIOR.    Parental behavior is also dependent on hormonal activation, but our present knowledge of the role of humoral agents in nest building, egg laying, incubation, parturition, and rearing the young is extremely inadequate. In the night heron, in which these parental activities are performed jointly by the male and female, testosterone was found to initiate *nest building* in both sexes, whereas estrogen had no effect on either prospective parent. In general, nest building occurs in birds at the height of follicular activity, and, in species in which the male also participates in nest building, this behavior coincides with the height of testicular activity (Marshall and Coombs, 1957). In ring doves, pretreatment with estrogen induces immediate nest building (when nesting material is available) without the normal antecedent courtship behavior (Lehrman, 1958). Prolonged administration of stilbestrol also induces nest building in the ring dove (Lehrman, 1958).

Injection of posterior pituitary extract into domestic hens induces *egg laying* within a few minutes (Burrows and Byerly, 1942). Pituitary prolactin leads to *incubation* in broody strains of hens (Riddle, 1937), and normally incubating hens were shown to have high prolactin levels of the pituitary (Saeki and Tanabe, 1955). *Nurturing the young,* including brooding, guiding, and protecting them, is induced with prolactin in domestic hens (Nalbandov and Card, 1945) and other birds (Crispens, 1956, 1957). Even the domestic cock, which does not normally participate in caring for the young, is induced by prolactin to show some (though not all) patterns of broody behavior (Nalbandov and Card, 1945).

Injection of progesterone into intact or spayed female mice produces increased *nest-building* activity, but it has no such effect on the male (Koller, 1956). In contrast, estrogen was reported to have inhibitory effects on maternal behavior in the rat (Hain, 1935; Weichert and Kerrigan, 1942). Anterior pituitary extracts induce adult virgin rats to *retrieve* young rats (Wiesner and Sheard, 1933). Prolactin may have such an effect not only on virgin female rats but on males (Riddle et al., 1942). *Lactation* in females is also induced by prolactin, and the prolactin concentration of the pituitary is highest immediately before and a few days after parturition (Reece and Turner, 1937a). Suckled rabbits, which produce more milk than do the nonsuckled, have correspondingly higher pituitary concentration of prolactin (Meites, 1954).

**External Synchronization of Sexual and Parental Activities**  Internal conditions, communicated primarily by way of hormones released into the blood, are of major importance in regulating sexual and reproductive behavior. In addition, the cyclic maturation of the sex organs and of activation of sexual behavior is influenced by various external conditions, such as the length of daily illumination, increase in temperature, availability of a nesting territory and nesting materials, and the presence of other members of the species. The appropriate cycling of the various phases of sexual activity is of course necessary in order to permit synchronized activity between the mating partners and also for the accomplishment of the relatively lengthy nurturing process while optimal conditions (warm climate, abundance of food) prevail.

Both observational and experimental data indicate that the seasonal cycling of sexual activity is dependent on the length of day or duration of *illumination*. For instance, brook trout spawn in the middle of winter when daily illumination is *shortest*. That decreased amount of light is the controlling factor of sexual maturation in this species was shown by Hoover and Hubbard (1937), who induced fertile spawning at the height of summer by artificially decreasing the length of daily illumination. In most birds and mammals, courtship and sexual behavior begin early in the spring, when daily illumination is *increasing*. In conformity with expectation, sexual maturation is easily induced in a variety of species during any season by artificially altering the daily cycle of illumination (Beach, 1948, 1951).

Another factor in the seasonal synchronization of sexual activity is external *temperature*. Ground squirrels breed early in the spring; before their breeding, while the animals are still hibernating, a rise occurs in the concentration of pituitary gonadotrophic hormones (Wells, 1935). Because the animals are not exposed to light during their hibernation in underground nests, it was assumed that changes in external temperature might be a controlling factor. Indeed, sexual activity can be prolonged in the ground squirrel (it normally declines at the coming of the warmer season) by keeping the animals at about 4° C (Wells, 1936).

Mating in some species may require special environmental conditions. Thus amphibians have to return to water to breed, and it was found that frogs do not manifest mating behavior when water pools are absent in the dry season. As soon as rain falls and small puddles are formed, sexual behavior is promptly activated. In other species, sexual behavior is preceded by *migration*, often characterized by a return to "ancestral" breeding grounds. (The problem of migration to breeding grounds was considered before.)

In many species of fish, birds, and mammals, mating behavior is preceded by the establishment of a *mating territory* and the building of a *brooding nest*. The establishment of mating territories is often preceded by territorial fights or displays. Nest building on a territory may be performed by one sex; when it is finished, the other mate is "invited" or permitted to share the nest. Nest building may also be a part of the courtship behavior in which both male and female participate. Animals that cannot establish a territory or cannot build nests may not be able to participate in mating behavior. Whitman (1919) observed some time ago that ring doves and pigeons will not ovulate if nesting locations and nesting materials are not available. This finding was confirmed and extended by Lehrman et al. (1961), who found that female ring doves kept with males are retarded in ovulation when nesting bowls and nesting materials are not present in their cages. Marshall and Disney (1957) found in Weaver finches, which build their complex nests following rainfalls, that nest building is initiated by the availability of green grass. If this material is made available to them, Weaver finches will engage in nest building in the absence of a preceding rainfall.

The presence of other members of the species, of the same or opposite sex, may also be involved in the regulation of sexual behavior, particularly in the female. For instance, *visually isolated* pigeons do not lay eggs, but if other females are present, or even when a mirror is placed into the cage so that the female can see herself, egg laying may be induced (Matthews, 1939). In parakeets, an isolated female can be induced to lay eggs by auditory stimulation, when she is allowed to hear (but not see) a breeding pair (Vaugien, 1951). In house sparrows, the presence of females is not sufficient; a male must be present to initiate building by the female (Polikarpova; from Lehrman, 1961). The same was also observed in the domestic canary (Warren and Hinde, 1960). Lehrman (1958) found that when a pair of male and female ring doves are put together in a cage, they will use the available nesting material after a 1- to 3-day period of courtship. When they are kept together for such a period without nesting material, they begin building the nest as soon as nesting material is made available to them.

The maturational and activating influence produced by the presence of other members of the species may at least partially be attributed to their *sexual displays* during the breeding season. During this period males and females acquire secondary sex characteristics and display mutually appreciated signals by means of which they communicate to each other their state of sexual readiness (see below). Such signals may prime, accelerate, or release sexual behavior in potential mates.

**Aspects of Sexual Behavior**  BREEDING MIGRATION. The *fall migration* of birds to warmer climates is functionally associated with economic necessities, because it represents an escape from the climatic rigors and food shortage of the coming winter season. In contrast, the *spring migration* of birds, or the return of trout or salmon from the sea to fresh-water streams, is related to *reproductive* necessities. Spring migration is initiated by gonadal changes; it leads to the return of males and females to their ancestral breeding grounds, where they immediately engage in reproductive behavior. (We have dealt earlier with the navigational aspects of migration, which are presumably common to both types of migration and apply also, more generally, to homing behavior.)

Salmon and trout hatch in headwater streams where they stay until they are about 1 year old. Then they descend downstream to spend from 2 to 6 years in the open sea. When ready to breed, the fish return to the fresh-water stream from which they came, spawn there, and die. The studies of Shapovalov (1940) indicated that the majority of tagged trout and salmon that had returned found their way to the home stream; only a small proportion ended up in a headwater a few miles removed from their ancestral spawning grounds. The earlier investigations of Rich and Holmes (1928) showed that if the spawned eggs were transplanted to another stream, the salmon returned later to the stream in which they were brought up rather than to the stream in which they were spawned; thus an acquired discriminatory function may be involved in their ability to find their ancestral home. Of some interest in this connection is the experiment of Hasler and Wisby (1951), which indicates that fish show olfactory preference for water taken from the stream in which they were nurtured.

What visceral conditions necessitate the migration of these fish over long distances from fresh water to sea, and what are the capacities that make possible their return to their breeding grounds? It has been established experimentally that at the time of their seaward migration young salmon show a preference for salt water over fresh water (Houston, 1957). The changing water preference was studied more extensively by Baggerman (1959) in the three-spined stickleback. In the spring, stickleback migrate from the sea to fresh water; after spawning and nurturing the young, they return to the sea. Laboratory experiments showed that before the onset of the breeding season stickleback will select, if given a choice, fresh water in preference to salt water, although after the breeding season the preference changes to salt water, paralleling the seaward migration of the species under natural conditions. If gonadal maturation is induced out of season by increased duration of illumination, fresh-water preference accompanies this change. Thus gonadal maturation may be associated with fresh-water preference, gonadal atrophy with salt-water preference. However, there is also evidence of a built-in alternating cycle of preferences. If sticklebacks are continuously exposed to prolonged periods of illumination and warm water (simulating conditions in the spring), the fish will go through alternating cycles of gonadal maturation and atrophy, and the associated changes in salt- and fresh-water preference. Moreover, gonadectomy does not abolish the alternating cycles of water preference in sticklebacks.

Evidently, the control of gonadal cycles, and of changing salt- and fresh-water preference, depends on an endogenous rhythmicity that is phase-controlled by, but not entirely dependent on, exogenous synchronizing agents. (We shall see parallel findings in birds.) There is some evidence that thyroxine activity is high during migration, and that the administration of thyroxine induces fresh-water preference in sticklebacks, whereas the administration of thiourea, a thyroxine inhibitor, induces salt-water preference (Baggerman, 1959). It should be stressed at this point that the alternating fresh-water and salt-water preference cannot be the cause of seaward and homeward migration, because the salinity of the stream does not increase until the fish come close to the sea; there must be other variables that induce and guide the fish to migrate. As we have seen earlier, fish and birds can utilize the sun as a compass in migration, though the role of sun-compass orientation in the migration and homing of salmon, trout, and stickleback has not yet been investigated.

Breeding migration has been more extensively investigated in birds. Rowan (1925, 1938) found that a group of juncos (snowbirds) exposed to a schedule of lengthened daily illumination showed premature gonadal maturation, as well as a preseasonal urge to migrate to their northern breeding grounds. Another group of birds exposed to a schedule of short days did not show gonadal changes or a tendency to migrate. Subsequent studies showed that in addition to gonadal maturation there is a marked increase in fat deposition as a result of daily illumination (Wolfson, 1945), a condition that may have something to do with preparing the birds for their life in colder habitats.

Although the changing length of the day in spring and fall may be a factor regulating the migration of birds, the role of light cannot be a fundamental one. For one thing, birds that winter in lower latitudes (in the tropics or the Southern Hemisphere) are not exposed to lengthened illumination at the coming of the northern spring, a circumstance that led Bissonnette (1937) to conclude that the cyclic gonadal changes are based on an endogenous rhythm. Moreover, birds (drakes) kept in continued total darkness were found to show testicular cycles unrelated to changes in external illumination or temperature. Some light was thrown on this problem by the demonstration (Marshall, 1959; Wolfson, 1959) that, whereas increased illumination in the winter induces gonadal maturation, this effect is not obtained immediately after the breeding season in the fall. Evidence was obtained that after breeding there is a *refractory period*, during which illumination leaves the gonads unaffected. Indeed, during this period a schedule of "short days" will enhance the subsequent responsiveness to increased daily illumination. By appropriately alternating periods of "short days" with "long days" several cycles of gonadal maturation and fat deposition can be induced in birds (Wolfson, 1959). Apparently, the phase and rate of maturation rather than the rhythmicity itself are controlled by light schedules. The rhythmicity itself depends on endogenous mechanisms (alternating periods of responsiveness and refractoriness), which may be accelerated and phase-controlled by daily periods of illumination as exogenous *Zeitgeber*. In birds wintering in lower latitudes or in the tropics, changing conditions of humidity and rainfall, rather than light, may be the exogenous synchronizing signals.

We know at present very little about the physiological mechanisms that control the endogenous (circannual) gonadal rhythmicity, or the mechanisms by which light can entrain this rhythm. It is generally assumed that the action of light is mediated by the pituitary, which controls gonadal activity through gonadotrophins. The experiments of Benoit and Assenmacher (1959) showed that sectioning of the optic nerve in drakes reduced but did not abolish gonadal response to light. They also showed that direct photic stimulation of the hypothalamus induced gonadal maturation; this observation suggests that intracerebral photic receptors may respond directly to light. There is also some evidence that there is hormonal control of the responsive and refractory periods to light because prolactin was found to inhibit the photoperiodic gonadal response (Bailey, 1950; Lofts and Marshall, 1956).

COURTSHIP BEHAVIOR. Courtship behavior, which is preparatory to mating, differs in complexity and duration in different species. In some species, the meeting of a male and a female in heat leads to a brief *mutual examination*, followed by immediate copulation. In other species, days and weeks must elapse, during which the mates engage in various preparatory activities and perform *rituals* and *ceremonies* before the consummatory act of copulation can take place.

At the beginning of the breeding season the males of various species (and, in some species, the females) develop special *sexual markings* and ornaments and engage in various displays, the behavioral effects of which are the "threatening" or *repulsion* of competitors and the "excitement" or *attraction* of prospective mates. For instance, the male jewelfish (Noble and Curtis, 1939) acquires nuptial coloration at the beginning of the breeding season and establishes its territory in a corner of the aquarium. Intruding males, and at the beginning also females, are driven away. The egg-laden gravid females keep returning, as if attracted by the color display of the male, and finally a female is accepted. The acceptance is manifested by a mutual display of quivering together, following which they jointly build a nest. The importance of sex colors in such behavior was shown by Noble and Curtis (1939), who found that female jewelfish remained longer near brighter males than near paler males, and a greater proportion laid their eggs near the brighter males. A similar courtship pattern, considered earlier, was described in the three-spined stickleback by Tinbergen (1951).

The adoption of nuptial robes, the display of brilliant colors, the dancing and quivering, are correlated with, and may be interpreted as expressions of, *intense sexual motivation* and as signals by means of which this state or "mood" of the animal is communicated to other members of the species. Color display is only one of the several possible *means of communication* employed during courtship. For instance, breeding frogs locate and attract each other mainly by sex calls, whereas the marbled salamander (Noble and Bradley, 1933) ejects a chemical from a specialized gland, which attracts the female to the breeding ground. With the evolution of internal fertilization in higher vertebrates arose an increased need for mutual recognition and for the synchronization of sexual behavior. Most wild animals tend to avoid bodily contact because, as Tinbergen remarked, "being touched usually means being captured" (1953, p. 22). This aversion must be temporarily removed and a readiness for mutual contact established. The potential mating partners communicate with each other by means of signals, which also have "attraction" properties, so that they will tend to approach each other in spite of various obstacles. For instance, in the American chameleon (Greenberg and Noble, 1944) the male with brightest dewlaps has the greatest potentiality for attracting a female. Males whose dewlaps are tied down are approached less frequently by females than are those that can display normally their red throat fan.

It is in birds that courtship *displays* and *ceremonies* are most highly developed. In various species these actions may consist of singing, the display of colored feathers and ornaments, dancing, and aerial or aquatic acrobatics. We may consider here a single example. When the ruffs of

be subordinated to the males in the social hierarchy of the group to permit mating.

SPAWNING AND COPULATION. The ultimate organic function of sexual interaction between a male and a female is the fertilization of ova by sperms. In lower vertebrates, as in many species of fish, fertilization is an *external process,* referred to as *spawning.* Following a brief or long courtship period, the female releases its ova, and synchronously, or shortly thereafter, the male ejects its sperms. Then, in the water, the mobile sperms approach the ova, and the two become conjugated. External fertilization is also seen in some amphibia, as in the frog, where the male mounts and clasps the female and then they jointly release their germ cells into the water. A form of *internal fertilization* may be seen in the sexual behavior of salamanders (Noble, 1931). Following courtship activity, the male discharges a packet of sperms, which is picked up by the female and inserted into her cloaca. Internal fertilization with *copulation* is seen in some fish, and it is the common mode of sexual fertilization in reptiles, birds, and mammals. In mammals, the male mounts the female, which is then followed by penile intromission and ejaculation. Mounting does not always lead to intromission, and intromission is often performed without ejaculation. Rats, for instance, ejaculate only after several intromissions, and satiation is reached after several ejaculations (Stone and Ferguson, 1940; Beach and Jordan, 1956). Receptivity of the female is restricted to her estrus period, which does not recur during pregnancy, whereas males tend to remain sexually active for a longer period, in some species, throughout the entire year.

Prior *experience* is not essential for courtship and mating in lower vertebrates, as was shown experimentally in fish reared in isolation (Tinbergen, 1951; Shaw, 1962). Likewise, male and female rats reared in isolation may mate as soon as they are placed together in a cage (Stone, 1922). However, some inferiority in the mating patterns of isolated male rats was noted in terms of latency and frequency of copulation (Zimbardo, 1958). Male guinea pigs reared after their weaning in isolation were also found inferior in several aspects of sexual behavior to males reared in the company of females (Valenstein et al., 1955). However, males reared with other males were not distinguishable from males reared with females, whereas males reared with spayed (and therefore nonreceptive) females showed a low level of sexual activity. These results, which were also observed in females (Goy and Young, 1957 a), indicate that *juvenile social experience,* presumably involving sexual "play," facilitates the development of sexual behavior even in such lowly forms as rodents. Rosenblatt and Aronson (1958 a, b) studied sexual behavior in two groups of cats, one castrated after considerable sexual experience, the other castrated after only minimal sexual experience. In the sexually experienced cats, mating behavior persisted for some time after castration. Similarly, in prepuberally

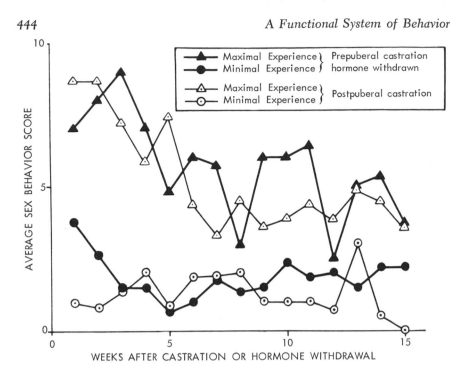

Sexual activity of experienced and inexperienced cats 15 weeks after post-
puberal castration or of withdrawal of androgen replacement therapy in prepuberally castrated cats. Under both conditions the experienced animals show a
higher level of sexual activity. (From Rosenblatt and Arsonson, The decline of
sexual behavior in male cats after castration. *Behaviour,* 1958, **12,** 285–388. In
Bliss, *Roots of behavior.* Harper & Row, 1962, p. 146, Fig. 9–2)

castrated cats that were given androgen-replacement therapy, and were
thus induced to engage in sexual behavior, sexual activity survived for
some time after discontinuation of the androgen treatment. In primates,
sexual experience is particularly important in the performance of normal
sexual behavior. Males and females reared in isolation display various aspects of sexual behavior but will not copulate for a long period (Yerkes
and Elder, 1936) or will altogether fail to do so (Harlow, 1962; Mason,
1963).

**Aspects of Parental Behavior**   NEST BUILDING.   As described ear-
                                    lier, nest building in birds may pre-
cede mating, or it may occur concurrently with courtship and mating. The
function of nest building is to provide a protected area for the deposition
of eggs, as well as to create a suitable environment for hatching the eggs
and rearing the immature young. As such, nest building is properly classified as a parental rather than a sexual behavior.

Different species of birds build different types of nests (Lehrman,
1961), but the variability in nest building within a species is usually negli-

gible. Some birds build their nests on the ground or in crevices in the ground; others build their nests in holes in trees or on the branches of trees; still others may build on rocks, on vegetation on the surface of water, in the chimneys of houses, and so on. In nest building, grass, leaves, twigs, mud, rotting vegetable materials, feathers, and other substances may be used. These may be put together haphazardly or worked into a solid, well-shaped structure with water and saliva. Most birds build single nests for themselves and their offspring, others (like the weaverbird) construct large communal nests in which each pair has a separate chamber. Nest building in birds may be the task of the male or female, or both parents may participate in at least some aspects of nest building (such as carrying nesting material).

Nest building is exhibited also by many mammals. This may occur all year round to provide the young and adults with shelter. Various rodents and carnivores burrow holes and underground passageways where they rest, sleep, and store their food; others occupy holes in trees, caves in rocks, or, like higher primates, build temporary shelters from twigs and leaves before retiring at night. (Many mammals, like ungulates, never build shelters or nests.) In addition to this year-round shelter-building activity, females may display increased nest-building behavior following pregnancy, before parturition, and during lactation. Kinder (1927), for example, measured in rats the amount of paper used in nest building. Males and nonpregnant females used a comparable amount, the females displaying a 5-day periodicity, with paper consumption being highest in the diestrus period. In pregnant females there was a sudden increase in the use of paper, which reached a maximum a few days prepartum. The increased nest-building activity continued during the entire period of lactation.

Koller (1956) found in mice that males and nonpregnant females build a small *sleeping nest*, which they may construct every night if it is removed during the day, whereas pregnant females build a much larger and heavier *brooding nest*. Injection of progesterone into nonpregnant females led to the building of large brooding nests, but this effect could not be obtained in males. The building of brooding nests could also be induced in nonpregnant females by placing young mice into their cages, provided that the young could be touched and retrieved by the "foster mothers." Removal of the young of true mothers following parturition had the effect of immediately halting the building of brooding nests.

Nest building appears to be essentially an unlearned behavior pattern in lower mammals. *Primiparous* rats (that is, rats giving birth for the first time) build nests and care for their young as well as do experienced rats (Wiesner and Sheard, 1933), though the technique of retrieving the young may improve in both primiparous and *multiparous* rats for a few days after parturition (Beach and Jaynes, 1956b). Similarly, primiparous golden hamsters, provided that they are at least 3 months old, build nests as skillfully as experienced females (Dieterlen, 1959). As Eibl-Eibesfeldt showed, nest building in rats does not even require previous experience with handling objects (see page 337). In contrast, the quality of nests built by inexperienced female rabbits was found to be inferior to that of the same rabbits after previous experience (Ross et al., 1956). The pregnant rabbit shows two phases of nest-building activity (Zarrow et al., 1962). The animal first builds a nest composed of any available material, for example, paper strips or straw. Such nests are built also by nonpregnant rabbits. Several days before parturition the animal adds hair from its own body and covers the nest with it; this structure may be considered the brooding nest. The building of a brooding nest was found to be associated with hair loosening at the same period (Sawin et al., 1960). Inducement of abortion, ceasarian operation, and in some animals treatment with prolactin were found to induce the building of brooding nests (Zarrow et al., 1962); such observations suggest an intimate association between this behavior pattern and internal changes associated with parturition.

EGG LAYING AND INCUBATION. The patterns of egg laying differ greatly in the animal world. Some animals, like turtles, bury their eggs in the sand; there is no incubation. After a period, the young hatch and find their way to the water without parental assistance. In other animals, from fish to birds, the parents ventilate, protect, or warm the eggs. *Incubation* behavior is most highly developed in birds. Most birds lay a clutch of eggs and begin incubation while still laying eggs or after egg laying is completed (Lehrman, 1961). Some birds, like the domestic hen, keep laying eggs until they have accumulated a sufficiently large number (because of this the domestic hen can be induced to lay eggs all year round). Others lay for a fixed period after which, irrespective of the number of eggs in the clutch, incubation begins. Incubation in some species of birds is the function of the female alone, which may be fed by her mate or go without food during the entire period. In a few species (like the phalarope) the task of incubation rests on the male alone. In many others, incubation is shared by both parents, who alternately sit on the eggs and feed themselves.

The function of incubation is to maintain a relatively high and constant level of temperature inside the eggs for the furtherence of the embryonic development of the chicks. During incubation the bird presses a featherless region of its breast, called the *incubation patch*, against the eggs. In song birds the feathers of the incubation patch are molted a few days before the first egg is laid, and the region becomes highly vascularized (Bailey, 1952). It is assumed that the high vascularization in this region leads to heat generation and that the incubating bird is cooling itself by transferring heat to the eggs. Depending on whether it is the male or female, or both sexes that participate in incubation, the incubation patch tends to be present in the animal partaking in this task. A few days after the young are born, the increased vascularity of the incubation patch disappears.

PARTURITION IN MAMMALS. Various mammals display different positions during parturition. In most species the usual posture is sitting or crouching, though in some (for example, in ungulates) the standing position is quite common. Before parturition the animal tends to lick the genital region, and when the young emerge they are licked off too. The assistance provided by the mother to the emerging young may be associated with this tendency of licking. Most females eat the placenta after delivery, a behavior which may be seen even in such strictly herbivorous animals as ungulates. The tendency to lick (and eat the placenta) may be related to the increased salt requirement developed by the mother during parturition (Barelare and Richter, 1938), and it may be the first manifestation of nurturing behavior displayed toward the young. It is during this early and brief critical period that the mother becomes imprinted on its own young. Kids and lambs separated from their mothers for a few hours after delivery may be subsequently rejected (Collias, 1956, Hersher et al., 1963).

NURTURING THE YOUNG. The young of some birds are covered with feathers and capable of locomotion immediately after hatching. Such neonates, referred to as *precocial young*, require much less parental care than do *altricial young*, which are featherless and incapable of locomotion for a long period after birth. Domestic chicks and ducklings belong to the first category; the parental behavior of the mother in these species consists of leading the young to food, going to their help when they emit distress calls, retrieving them when scattered, and brooding them (spreading her wings around them). Parental behavior toward the altricial young of other species is more complex. For example, pigeons feed their young for a long period by regurgitating the contents of their crops; other birds regurgitate partially digested food from their stomach or feed them with freshly acquired insects and other food substances. The feeding of young is guided in many species by special innate signaling devices; an example is the food-begging pecking of the herring gull chick at the color patch of the mother's mandible, studied by Tinbergen (1953). Feeding of altricial young may be the task of the female, the male, or both parents. In many species the parents may spend a good part of the day on the arduous task of collecting enough food for the growing family.

Like birds, mammals differ widely in their degree of maturation at birth. The young of ungulates can stand and walk within hours after birth, and the only task of the mother is to suckle and protect them. The young of other mammals, like most rodents, carnivores, and primates, may be quite helpless for some time after birth and require considerable parental assistance. All mammalian neonates are suckled by their mother for varying periods. Lactation begins before parturition, and its initiation is under humoral control, namely, the secretion of prolactin. But the maintenance of lactation is also dependent on the continued suckling of the young. For this reason removal of young rats from their mother is followed within a few days by the cessation of milk secretion (Selye, 1934), whereas repeated replacement of maturing rats by younger rats makes possible extension of lactation from the normal 20-day period to 70 days (Nicoll and Meites, 1959). Indeed, the continued milk production of milch cows is at least partly attributable to their continued milking.

The nursing of neonates capable of locomotion (kids, calves, colts) is essentially a passive process on the part of the mother, whereas the nursing of young that cannot move about adequately (young mice and rats, kittens, puppies) requires considerable parental assistance. Lactating mice, rats, cats, and dogs repeatedly return to their nests and assume a posture that facilitates suckling by the young. In many mammals the scattered young are gathered together in the nest before nursing. This behavior is related to *retrieving:* when young mice, rats, kittens, or puppies crawl away from their nests they are soon gathered and returned by their mother. Like lactation, retrieval is at least partly under the control of prolactin secretion (Riddle et al., 1935 b), but it is also dependent on the presence of young. Even virgin rats (Wiesner and Sheard, 1933) and mice (Leblond, 1938) will retrieve young with which they are confined, but this tendency is increased in the middle of pregnancy and is most pronounced after parturition (Rabaud, 1921 a, b). Young mice emit supersonic cries to which the mother responds from some distance, but young that are anesthetized (and therefore do not emit distress calls) may also be retrieved (Zippelius and Schleidt, 1956). The investigations of Beach and Jaynes (1956 a, c) suggest that olfactory, visual, and tactile sensory signals may all play a part in retrieval behavior in rats. Retrieval was found to be more pronounced while the offspring are still young, and lactating rats (Wiesner and Sheard, 1933), hamsters (Rowell, 1960), and dogs (Menzel and Menzel, 1953) may manifest heightened retrieval behavior when alien neonates are substituted for their own, older offspring. Lactating females may even retrieve young of different species; for instance, rats were observed to retrieve mice (Wiesner and Sheard, 1933); Beach and Jaynes, 1956 c).

MATERNAL-FILIAL AFFECTIONAL RELATIONS.   In addition to the direct satisfaction by the parent of the need of neonates for food, shelter, and protection from predators, infants appear to need the maintenance of periodic contact and certain forms of interaction with the parent or a surrogate. Levy (1934) fed young puppies with milk from bottles with small- or large-hole nipples and found that the duration of sucking was not a direct function of food need. The puppies that had obtained an adequate amount of milk after a short period of sucking through the bottles with large-holed nipples persevered in sucking for long periods after, and sometimes even displayed sucking movements during sleep. This finding was confirmed by Ross (1950).

The affectional need of the young and the consequences of its frustration were recently studied in monkeys by Harlow and his collaborators (Harlow, 1960, 1962 b). When the neonate monkey is removed from its mother it begins to whimper immediately and shows other signs of apparent distress. The animal appears to derive emotional comfort from contact with its mother, and when tested with a soft cloth pad it clings to it as it does to its mother; contact with a soft surface is apparently an important sensory variable. This type of observation led to the investigation of the development of affectional attachments and other social traits in monkeys raised with dummies or surrogate mothers. Harlow and his collaborators used two types of surrogate mothers, made either of cloth or wire, which were or were not furnished with milk bottles for nursing. The monkeys displayed a much greater preference for the cloth than for the wire surrogate; and the monkeys raised with a wire surrogate would spend more time, when given an opportunity, with the cloth model.

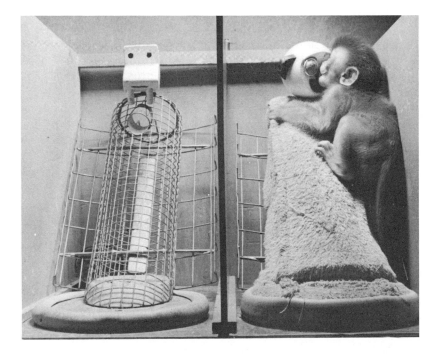

Infant monkeys raised with a wire or cloth surrogate mother. (Photo courtesy of Dr. H. F. Harlow)

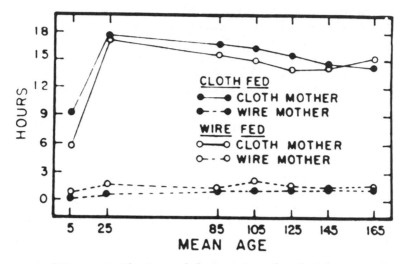

Amount of time spent with wire or cloth surrogate mothers by infants nursed on wire or cloth surrogates.(From Harlow. Development of affection in primates. In Bliss, Ed., *Roots of behavior. Harper & Row*, 1962, p. 161, Fig. 10–4)

When "threatened" in an open-field situation, the young raised with a nursing wire surrogate tended to run for protection or comfort to the nonnursing cloth dummy. When tested with nursing or nonnursing cloth models, the animals showed a preference for the former; they also tended to prefer rocking to stationary models, and surrogates with moderate inclines to models with a steep incline. In general, the young raised with a cloth surrogate displayed a more "normal" pattern of development than did the monkeys raised with a wire surrogate or in total isolation; yet none of these animals succeeded in establishing subsequently normal social and sexual relations with other monkeys.

**SELECTED READINGS**

Armstrong, E. A. *Bird display and bird behavior.* London: Drummond, 1947.

Beach, F. A. *Hormones and behavior.* New York: Hoeber, 1948.

Lehrman, D. Hormonal regulation of parental behavior in birds and infrahuman mammals. In W. C. Young (Ed.), *Sex and internal secretions.* (3d ed.) Baltimore: Williams & Wilkins, 1961. Vol. 2, pp. 1268–1382.

Rheingold, H. L. (Ed.). *Maternal behavior in mammals.* New York: Wiley, 1963.

Young, W. C. The hormones and mating behavior. In W. C. Young (Ed.), *Sex and internal secretions.* (3d ed.) Baltimore: Williams & Wilkins, 1961. Vol. 2, pp. 1173–1239.

# 18

# Formation and Maintenance of Groups

## Types of Social Behavior

Intraspecies social interaction may be seen in some or all phases of the individual's life. Two fundamental types of social interaction may be distinguished, namely, agonistic and affiliative relations. Agonistic behavior includes aggressive and defensive activities, such as is manifested in threat displays and fighting, on the one hand, and submissive acts and fleeing, on the other. Affiliative activities include the tendency of animals to join or form schools, flocks, herds, or packs, as well as cooperation among members of a group and the establishment of social hierarchies (the latter process is often based on prior agonistic behavior).

Unlike the vegetogenic activities considered before (nutritive, sheltering, sexual, and parental activities), which are directly induced by internal states, agonistic and affiliative activities are only indirectly influenced by endogenous conditions. Social interaction is to a large extent exogenous in nature; for it is the presence of an individual or group that directly evokes and regulates agonistic and affiliative interactions. The nature of interaction, however, is affected by internal needs. Thus aggressive behavior may be associated with competition for food or mate, and it may be minimal or absent when these drive states do not prevail.

**Agonistic Behavior** Agonistic behavior (Scott, 1962) refers to such interactions among individuals as fighting, fleeing, hiding, "freezing," and displays of hostility and submission. Because individuals of a single species tend to aggregate in common habitats, that is, in regions that provide optimal conditions for their existence, intraspecies competition for food, shelter, and mate is unavoidable. Invading the territory of another individual often provokes aggressive behavior, which sometimes takes the form of serious combat. More often, however, it consists of *threat displays*, that is, ritualized social signals by means of which the stronger (or more strongly motivated) individual tries to "frighten" its competitor, sends it fleeing, or forces it to accept a submissive role. (In contrast, the interspecies conflict between predators and their prey can be a life-and-death struggle in which all the energies of the contestants are engaged.)

Best-known examples of agonistic activities are the "fear," "anger," and "rage" reactions seen in cats, dogs, and monkeys. Both states are associated with a variety of humoral and visceral responses, and with *expressive movements* that are typical for the species. The humoral and visceral responses consist of sympathetic and parasympathetic activation (and the release of adrenaline and acetylcholine), with concomitant changes in the rate of breathing, in blood pressure, sugar metabolism, and EEG activity. The expressive movements consist of various "emotional displays," such as baring of teeth, hissing or barking (as in "anger"), freezing or crouching (as in "fear"), and general behavioral "arousal." Among animals living under natural field conditions, fighting and fleeing are commonly and frequently displayed behavior patterns.

By virtue of their mode of existence, some species are characterized by dominant aggressive traits, others by defensive traits. Carnivorous feline and canine species display aggression frequently while hunting for, stalking, pursuing, and attacking their prey, whereas herbivorous animals, like ungulates, commonly show such defensive behavior as fleeing when in the least threatened. Indeed, the body construction of carnivores permits successful aggressive behavior (large snout with strong "canine" teeth, powerful claws, and the like), whereas that of herbivores is well suited for defence (well-developed legs and hooves for running). This basic difference in mode of agonistic behavior is obviously primarily determined by structural properties adapted to the animal's basic mode of existence. Hereditary differences may also exist in this respect between different breeds of the same species. For example, certain domestically bred strains of fish (Siamese fighting fish), birds (gamecock), and dogs (terriers) are characterized by excessive combativeness. According to Scott (1942), inbred strains of mice may differ in aggressiveness, and the characteristic traits of their offspring, when interbred, follow hereditary principles (Fredericson, 1952).

Of course, all species are capable of both aggressive and defensive behavior; the overpowered carnivore may flee, and the cornered herbivore attack. Specific environmental situations and internal conditions can provoke appropriately either of these agonistic patterns of behavior. Aggressive behavior is characteristically seen in male ungulates during the breeding season when they are competing among themselves for dominance over the females of the herd. Similarly, aggression may arise among animals competing for food under conditions of scarcity. In a flock of goats (Scott, 1948), aggressive behavior was found to be low among dominant animals after they were fed, but delay in feeding increased their combativeness. When the animals were provided with sufficient food, and when the food was scattered over a large area to minimize crowding and competition during feeding, fighting and dominance were absent. No such relation was observed between hunger and aggressiveness among mice (Ginsburg and Allee, 1942), but in the chaffinch starvation was reported (Marler, 1955) to increase aggressiveness in subordinate members of the group.

The direct relation between agonistic behavior and sexual maturation is well established in many species. For instance, two normal male mice placed together into a cage will immediately engage in combat, and the fight will usually perist until one wins and the other assumes a submissive role. No fight ensues among castrated males, but when the castrated mice are injected with male sex hormone, they will fight like normal animals (Beaman, 1947). Fighting can become "habitual" in such castrated animals, because it may persist after cessation of hormone administration. This conclusion is also supported by the finding (Urich, 1938) that male mice castrated in adulthood continue to fight, but those castrated pre-puberally rarely fight. In general, among vertebrates, males are more aggressive than females, and the aggressive behavior of the male tends to increase as sexual maturation takes place, particularly during the breeding season. The aggressive traits of a ram, bull, or stallion are well known; for some time farmers have been reducing the combativeness of male domes-ticated animals by prepuberal castration.

These observations suggest that androgens released into the blood may induce combativeness. Indeed, female swordtails (both spayed and normal) became more combative and improved their social rank order after implantation of testosterone pellets (Noble and Borne, 1940). Similar changes in aggressive behavior or social rank were reported following androgen treatment in chickens (Allee et al., 1939), ring doves (Bennett, 1940), female rats (Ball, 1940; Beach, 1942), and other animals.

Females tend to be more defensive than males in conflict situations and, when in heat, are often submissive. In diestrus the female resists the male but becomes submissive during the estrus period. Spayed hamsters are aggressive when placed in a cage with a male (Kislack and Beach, 1955), but estrogen injection followed by progesterone reduces or eliminates aggression. However, no such effect was observed in hamsters when estrogen alone was injected. Estrogen injection alone was reported to leave essentially unaltered the social position of domestic hens (Allee and Collias, 1940), canaries (Shoemaker, 1939), and rhesus monkeys (Mirsky, 1955).

The aggressive behavior shown by males and the submissive behavior exhibited by females are intimately associated with sexual activity. In cichlid fish (Baerends and Baerends, 1950), a male that cannot defend and establish a nesting territory fails to develop its nuptial color markings.

However, when the dominant, territory-holding male is removed, the one next in rank order in the social hierarchy will develop nuptial colors. In chickens (Guhl et al., 1945), males low in rank order in the social hierarchy of the flock show total suppression of sexual behavior, even when the dominant males are removed. When put into another flock, such a male does mate with strange hens. In contrast to the male, hens highest in the rank order of the flock engage least frequently in sexual behavior, whereas hens low in the hierarchy are frequently mounted (Guhl, 1950). Submissive behavior in the female apparently is associated with sexual receptivity.

Intraspecies agonistic behavior is, accordingly, caused to a large extent by conflict among members of a group in their competition for food, a mate, and other essentials of life. These intraspecies conflicts seldom produce serious injury to the combatants. In many species such fights are *ceremonial*; they are a means by which the combatants dramatize their serious "intent." Fights are often tournaments in which the contestants test each other's strength, skill, and perseverance, but during which certain rules are adhered to so that the animals do not seriously harm each other. Fighting mice or rats push and kick each other, and occasionally they may even bite, but after a while the losing partner falls on its back, exposing its most vulnerable body parts in a sign of surrender, and the victor immediately stops the fight.

Through such combats animals living in a group establish a *social hierarchy* in which the weaker or less aggressive individuals abstain from competing with, and submit to, the stronger and more aggressive members. Social organization founded on antecedent agonistic behavior was first recognized in domestic chickens by Schjelderup-Ebbe in 1913 (1935) and named by him a *pecking order*. The top-ranking hen pecks all other members of the flock, the next in rank submits to the top-ranking hen but pecks at all others, but the lowest-ranking member in the hierarchy is pecked by all and submits to all. The establishment of such pecking hierarchies brings some order to the group with the result that conflicts arising from competition for food, shelter, and a mate are reduced. Social hierarchies like the above have been identified also in a variety of mammalian species, including primates.

**Affiliative Behavior**    Agonistic behavior serves the function of segregating individuals within a group or a territory in such a way that each can acquire, in accordance with its strength and dominance characteristics, a separate niche for itself. Agonistic behavior is intimately associated with the tendency of individuals to *aggregate* and form groups. Fish tend to aggregate in schools, birds in flocks, mammals in packs, troops, hordes, and herds. The aggregations of animals may be the result of external causes, such as a rich food supply in a given region, the presence of a water hole, or a well-protected shelter. In addition, however, most animals display a strong affiliative tendency in that they follow, join, and move with a group composed of other members of the species.

Affiliative behavior is furthered by a variety of conditions, and the sources of social aggregation may be different in different species. Sexual attraction between the male and female, the rituals of courtship, and the joint tasks of parenthood may produce affiliative bonds between the parents. Rearing of the young, and the varieties of parental-filial interaction, produce affiliative tendencies between the young and their parents. These sexual and parental-filial bonds may serve as the nucleus of group formation in some species, such as red deer (Darling, 1937) and sheep (Scott, 1945). In others, the affiliation of sex partners may be transient, restricted to the duration of the breeding season. Similarly, the affiliation between young and their parents may come to an abrupt end as the young reach maturity. In this type of species the formation of group life may be independent of sexual and reproductive bonds. Indeed, in many group-living species, the mating season produces a partial or total breakdown of the social organization, during which period the school, flock, or pack disintegrates, and individual males and females establish segregated territories from which other members of the original group are excluded.

Social behavior is seen in lower as well as higher forms of vertebrates, but the size and cohesion of the groups that are formed differ greatly in different species. Schools of fish, flocks of birds, and herds of mammals may have hundreds or thousands of members. But within these groups there is usually a loose association among the members. Stronger signs of cohesion may be seen in smaller groups, such as packs of carnivores or hordes of primates.

Group life offers various benefits to the individual, and these may contribute to sustaining the cohesion of the group. Feeding is frequently a group activity. Goldfish were found to eat more and grow better in groups than in isolation, even when ample food is available to the isolated individuals (Welty, 1934; Allee, 1938). More importantly, location of food sources is made easier when more individuals engage in the process. In many species, when an individual locates a food source it emits a feeding call, and soon the entire group hurries to the site (Tinbergen, 1953). Such an influence on the group is considered an instance of *social facilitation*, a phrase that refers to the observed phenomenon of the initiation or induction of the performance of an act as a result of its exhibition by others. For example, when one member of a flock suddenly flies off, all the others immediately follow it. Nice (1943) observed in song sparrows that as one ate, bathed, or preened, the others followed it, and thus the activity of the group as a whole became synchronized. A similar observation was made in aviaries of finches (Crook, 1961); as birds in one aviary began to wash themselves, birds in adjacent aviaries soon became engaged in the same activity. Very often the converse effect may also be observed. An individual may initiate an activity, for example, leave the group to feed, but if it fails to induce others to follow its example (that is, fails to obtain social facilitation) it immediately stops its deviant action and rejoins the group (Moynihan and Hall, 1954).

Collective action is particularly important in *defensive* behavior, and in some species it may also be exhibited in *aggressive* acts, as in the hunting of packs of wolves. For instance, the warning of other members of the group of the imminent danger of an approaching enemy is commonly seen in a variety of species. Injured minnows emit a substance from their skin that induces the others to seek cover. Diluted extracts of the skin were found to be effective in producing this *alarm reaction* (von Frisch, 1941); the chemical was subsequently identified as a purinelike compound (Hüttel, 1941). A substance ejected by and producing alarm reaction in top smelt was recently isolated (Skinner et al., 1962). The American antelope raises its white rump patch when it detects some danger, and the visual alarm signal is transmitted from one animal to another across the plains, and all of them quickly aggregate (Seton, 1953). By means of various signals of social communication the behavior of the group is thus synchronized. The advantages of such forms of social communication are obvious. When the distress call of a single individual can send the whole group fleeing, it is no longer necessary for each individual to be on continuous alert. The task is often assumed by the "leader" of the group, which is on guard while other members of the group browse or sleep. The alarmed group may then engage jointly in defence or attack. An example of joint defence is the *mobbing behavior* seen in various birds. Thus sparrows mob a sparrow hawk (which preys on them); if the latter is not excessively hungry, the sparrows may succeed in driving the predator away (Tinbergen, 1953).

The organization and size of groups may influence not only the overt behavior but also the physiological state of individuals. For instance, in mice the mean weight of the adrenal cortex increases linearly as the population is increased, with a subsequent fall as population density becomes supersaturated (Christian, 1964). The increase in the weight of the adrenal gland of individual mice was related to social rank. Mice with lowest rank showed highest weight increase; in contrast, the adrenals of dominant mice were comparable in weight to the adrenals of mice from small groups. This growth in the weight of the adrenal cortex may be related to increased secretion of adrenocortical hormones, which, as we saw earlier, is a component of the organism's response to stress. A direct or indirect consequence of these and related organic changes is the retardation in the growth and fertility of individuals, as a consequence of which the size of the population tends to fall (Thiessen and Rodgers, 1961).

**Forms of Social Organization**   In the following pages we shall describe briefly a few investigations concerned with social organization in some selected species of vertebrates.

In a recent study, Shaw (1960) observed that in fish (*Menidia*) schooling begins when the young reach a certain size. Newly hatched fry, 5–7 millimeters in length, approach each other from an angle; when they get too close, both of them swiftly dart away. When the fry reach about 10 millimeters in length, they approach each other in *parallel orientation*, and may then swim together, in parallel or in tandem, for a few seconds. When they reach about 15 millimeters in length, they are found to swim regularly together in parallel lines and with more or less equal spacing between them; soon they are joined by more and more fish and thus a

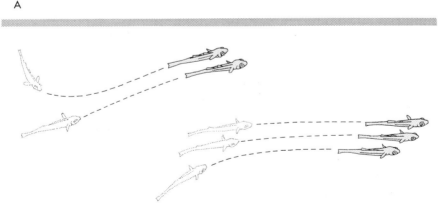

Schooling in juvenile fish. A, two newly hatched fry, 5–7 mm in length, approach each other sideways and, when a few mm apart, dart away. B, older fry, about 10 mm in length, tend to approach each other in a parallel fashion and then swim together. (After Shaw. *Sci. Amer.,* 1962, **206,** No. 2, 112)

school is formed. Apparently an affiliative tendency is present from the beginning, together with agonism generated by the inappropriate (sideways) orientation of the approaching animals. When the fish develop the parallel approach and orientation, the affiliative tendency is no longer brought into conflict with repulsion and the animals remain together in a relatively rigid formation. As the experiments of Shaw suggest, experience is not essential to developing the parallel approach and locomotion; fry reared in isolation until they reach the age of about 15 millimeters in body length will immediately approach appropriately the others and be accepted by the school. Schooling in these fish is primarily dependent on visual cues, as fish separated from one another by a glass partition display mutual approach and parallel orientation, whereas blinding of fish abolishes schooling.

Schooling in fish is an example of the formation of a large but relatively loose social group. The individuals forage, flee, and migrate in unison, but there is no evidence of mutual recognition, of a hierarchic order, or of any division of labor among them, aspects that characterize more complex forms of social organization. As we have seen earlier, in birds, such as the domestic chicken, a hierarchic pecking order is common, a social organization based on mutual recognition and on ordering individuals in accordance with their strength and ability. The individuals learn to recognize one another as members of the group, and even the lowest-ranking member acquires a permanent role in the flock or in-group from which other individuals are excluded. Hierarchic social organization in which individuals acquire specific roles has been identified in several species; we shall briefly consider here some recent studies concerning social organization in subhuman primates.

Following the classical studies of social organization in baboons by Zuckerman (1932) and in howling monkeys and gibbons by Carpenter (1934, 1940), there has been a resurgence of interest recently in the social organization of primates. As an example, we may briefly describe the findings of Washburn and De Vore (1961) about the social behavior of free-ranging baboons in Kenya. Baboons in zoos are known as aggressive animals, but under natural conditions in-group fighting is reduced to a minimum by a hierarchic social organization. In every troop there is a dominant male who is never molested by others, and whose right to food, females, or other objects of his choice is never disputed. The dominant male is usually surrounded by other mature males, who lend it support when conflicts arise, and so they jointly rule the entire troop. The organization of the troop is best seen when baboons are on the move. The front of the troop is made up of nondominant mature males and some larger adolescent males. They are followed by mature females and other juvenile males. The rear is occupied by nondominant males, and in the center, surrounded by the dominant males, are the females with their infants. In this way the adult males protect the females and the young; when actually attacked by a predator, the mature males form a defensive wall between the attacker and the weakest members of the group. Such a group organization has also been described recently in Japanese macaques (Imanishi, 1957).

The formation and maintenance of such a closely knit social group with coordinated social behavior require that the members be familiar with one another's traits and capacities, and also have an ability to communicate their moods, needs, or intentions. It has been established that baboons and macaques possess quite a large repertoire of communicative signals, which are appropriately appreciated by other members of the group (Kummer, 1957; Altmann, 1962). Very important also are the affectional attachment to and dependence on one another, which are developed early in life by socially raised monkeys. An important aspect of their group living is mutual grooming, the removal of dirt, loose skin, and parasites from the partner's hair. From infancy the young monkey is groomed by its mother; in addition to its hygienic aspect, the grooming represents the establishment of an affectional bond between them. Grooming, as a reciprocal activity, is also practiced by the growing youngsters and all the adults. The animal needing to be groomed presents itself to its partner, closes its eyes, and shows signs of relaxation; later the partner may reciprocate or, if a dominant member of the group, merely expect the service without returning it. Females often groom the males, and the dominant males are the favorite recipients of the females' attention.

The formation of social bonds in primates is based on a long period of learning, as indicated by the absence of normal social behavior in monkeys raised in isolation. Mason (1963) studied the social behavior of two groups of rhesus monkeys, one captured at about 20 months of age in the wild and another raised in isolation in the laboratory. The monkeys in the latter group were removed from their mothers shortly after birth and raised in individual cages in which they could see, but could not establish physical contact with, one another. Before the experiments were undertaken, when the animals were about 2½ years old, both groups were isolated; they were tested periodically in pairs to determine their modes of social interaction. The restricted monkeys showed very little mutual grooming, and they tended to fight frequently and bitterly; the wild monkeys groomed frequently and had only minor quarrels. In competition for food, the wild monkeys quickly established a hierarchic relation whereas the isolated monkeys kept fighting. This difference in social behavior was attributed to the inability of the isolated monkeys to communicate their intentions by gestures, postures, and vocalization, which substitute for fighting in the socially experienced animals. Finally, the isolated animals could not engage in normal sexual behavior, not even when an isolated male was paired with an experienced female. These latter findings are largely in agreement with those of Harlow described previously, which showed the sexual, and later parental, inadequacy of monkeys raised with surrogate mothers.

The imitative ability of monkeys and apes is well established experimentally. Naive primates will successfully imitate trained primates in the solution of test problems (Warden and Jackson, 1935; Crawford and Spence, 1939; Warden et al., 1940). In the wild, this trait of monkeys leads to the acquisition and "cultural" transmission of social traditions. Troops are known to have their own range, watering holes, and sleeping places. In several recent Japanese studies, the mode of transmission of newly acquired habits has been intensively studied. An example is Kawamura's (1963) study of the habit of washing sweet potatoes before eating them. The practice was first observed in an immature female, but it soon spread through the female's playmates and mother to all other members of the group, and later from this group to some others.

### SELECTED READINGS

Allee, W. C. *The social life of animals.* (2d ed.) Boston: Beacon Press, 1951.

Carpenter, C. R. *Naturalistic behavior of nonhuman primates.* University Park: Pennsylvania State University Press, 1964.

De Vore I. (Ed.). *Primate behavior; field studies of monkeys and apes.* New York: Holt, Rinehart and Winston, 1965.

Scott, J. P. *Aggression.* Chicago: University of Chicago Press, 1958.

Southwick, C. H. (Ed.). *Primate social behavior.* New York: Van Nostrand, 1963.

Tinbergen, N. *Social behavior in animals.* London: Methuen, 1953.

Zuckerman, S. *The social life of monkeys and apes.* London: Routledge, 1932.

# 19

# Mastering the Environment

*Types of Educational Behavior*

**Reactive versus Active** Behaviorists have considered animal
**Views of Behavior** action a reactive process and made
various attempts to construct a
stimulus-response model of behavior (Watson, 1919; Hull, 1943; Spence,
1956). This attempt is rooted in the Cartesian mechanistic tradition,
which, by analogy with the way motion is induced in inert substances,
views organic behavior as a *reaction* produced by external agents rather
than an *action* generated by internal forces.

As we have indicated before, we view organisms as primarily internally
programed, work-producing, open systems (Chapter 1) that must have
commerce with their external environments in order to satisfy their
"needs" and adapt their internally initiated processes to prevailing external conditions. This view does not deny the occurrence of externally
triggered reactions, such as reflexes, but it considers them to be subordinated components of more complex goal-seeking activities that serve organic
needs and functions. This active conception of behavior is supported by
the evidence of endogenous neural programing patterns, of spontaneous
receptor activity, of centrifugal modulation of signal transmission, and
the major role of internal, visceral drives in the functional organization of
behavior. Moreover, recent studies indicate that, apart from visceral drives,
animal action may be initiated and sustained also by such "neurogenic"
motives as the *exploratory* (Montgomery, 1954), or *curiosity* (Berlyne,
1955) drive, and by a postulated *manipulatory* drive (Harlow, 1954). That
is, animals may actively seek sensory stimulation and engage in overt
activity in the absence of vegetative needs. Analytically, these exploratory
and manipulatory activities may be considered to originate from the
tissue conditions of the animative action system itself (though evidence
for this is lacking). From the functional point of view, the exploratory
drive may be looked on as the need of higher animals to enlarge their
perceptual horizon and become familiar with objects in their surroundings;
in contrast, the manipulatory drive, which is dramatically exhibited in the

play of young, is a manifestation of their need and attempt to master their environments.

**Exploratory Activities**    Apparent exploratory activity is seen in rats placed in an unfamiliar surrounding, and what looks like "curiosity" is displayed by monkeys, particularly the young, which tend to inspect and manipulate all new objects placed in their cages. Nissen (1930) studied the urge of rats to explore an unfamiliar maze by placing them into an obstruction box in which they had to cross an electrified grid to get to the maze. He found that food- and water-satiated rats crossed the grid, and suffered the electric shock, for the sole reward of exploring the maze. In a similar manner, Tolman (1932) suggested that the common observation of *spontaneous alternation* of rats in a T maze (the animals' tendency to alternate their turns) is best explained in terms of an exploratory tendency.

In contrast to Tolman's idea, a more widely accepted explanation of this phenomenon was in terms of "reactive inhibition" (Hull, 1943), a postulated inhibitory force generated by the motor execution of an action. Montgomery (1952) undertook to resolve this controversy by placing rats in a cross maze in which alternation between the arms of the maze (*place alternation*) could be distinguished from a tendency to alternate turns to the right and left (*response alternation*). Montgomery obtained evidence favoring the idea that rats tend to alternate places or stimuli rather than responses in a maze. A similar result was obtained by Glanzer

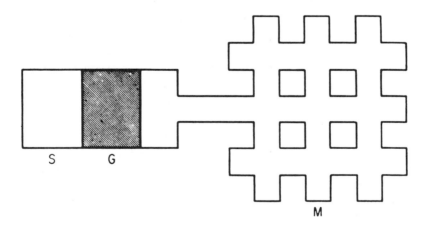

S        G

M

Obstruction box used by Nissen to study exploratory activity in rats. S, starting box; G, electrified grid; M, a maze representing the incentive for exploration. (From Nissen. A study of exploratory behavior in the white rat. *J. genet. Psychol.*, 1930, **37**, 361–376. In Waters et al., *Principles of comparative psychology.* Copyright © 1962, McGraw–Hill, Inc. Used by permission of the McGraw-Hill Book Company)

(1953), who, however, interpreted his findings in a somewhat different manner by postulating a "stimulus-satiation" effect, that is, reactive inhibition generated, not by the previous response, but by the previously encountered stimulus.

That rats may display a true exploratory tendency, something akin to curiosity, was shown in a different type of study by Berlyne (1950). He exposed rats to familiar and unfamiliar objects and found that rats sniffed and looked at unfamiliar objects longer than at familiar ones. Berlyne (1955) also found that the rats tended to scrutinize the new object for about a minute, after which their "curiosity" declined steeply. Berlyne (1955) compared the tendency of three groups of rats to enter from an experimental box into an adjacent alcove. One group was confronted with the alcove containing a novel object; a second group, with the alcove containing a familiar object; and the third group, with the alcove empty. The highest number of entries into the alcove was shown by the first group, and the least number of entries by the last group. Similar results were obtained by Thompson and Solomon (1954), who investigated the amount of time spent by rats in "sniffing" and "looking at" two visual patterns, one of which was displayed to them for some time before the test; the other was novel. The animals displayed their "curiosity," and thus the memory of the "familiar" pattern, by spending more time in front of the novel stimulus pattern. Similarly, Montgomery (1954) found that, in a maze, rats learned to enter preferentially the arm that led to the second complex maze; they ignored the arm that led to a small, empty box.

Exploratory activity is displayed more forcefully in primates than in rodents. Welker (1956a), investigating the exploratory behavior of chimpanzees, found that the animals showed a great interest in novel objects, but that within a given session the interest shown in an object tended to decline rapidly. Presented with the same objects on succeeding days, the chimpanzees showed an initial revival of interest, but if newer objects were then introduced, their exploratory behavior increased. These observations suggest a temporary (within-session) and permanent (day-to-day) decline in exploratory activity when the novelty of a stimulus wears off. Welker also found that chimpanzees spent more time with complex than with simple objects; they showed a preference for moving or changing objects, and for the larger, brighter, and more heterogeneous objects. In a study using animals of different ages (Welker, 1956b), it was found that young chimpanzees (3–4 years) were more responsive to novel objects than were the older animals (7–8 years), whereas infants (1–2 years) displayed an initial fear of novel objects.

In a somewhat different type of experiment, Butler (1953) studied learning in monkeys in which the incentive was the satisfaction of the animals' curiosity. Individual animals were put into an enclosed chamber supplied with two peepholes. The peepholes were covered with two different colored cards; the animal could use the color as a cue to tell it which of the two windows was open. The reward for solving this discrimination task, which they did successfully, was the opportunity to look through the peephole into an occupied laboratory. Then Butler (1954) investigated the reward value of different visual incentives. In this study the enclosed chamber had only one window, which could be opened for a limited period at a time; the frequency with which the animal opened the window was then taken as an index of the magnitude of the animal's motivation. The highest number of responses was made to the sight of another monkey as the incentive, and the animals also responded with great frequency for the reward of looking at an electric train. The lowest number of responses was made when the room was empty. In animals kept for different periods in the enclosed chamber without an opportunity to look out, the frequency of window openings increased with prolonged

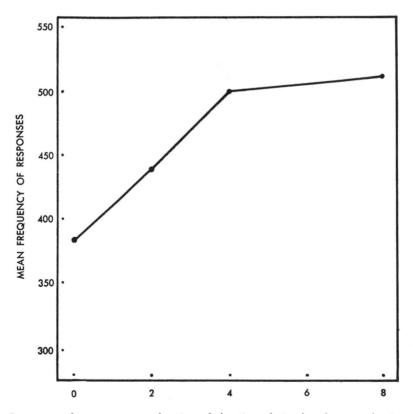

Frequency of responses as a function of duration of visual-exploratory deprivation. (From Butler. The effect of deprivation of visual incentives on visual motivation in monkeys. *J. comp. physiol. Psychol.*, 1957, **50**, 177–179)

stimulus deprivation up to 4 hours (Butler, 1957 a). Butler (1957 b) also found that monkeys placed in a soundproof chamber would learn to press one of two levers for the auditory reward of the transmitted noises of a monkey colony.

These and other related psychological studies established that mammals may engage in exploratory activity in the absence of any other motivation. Investigatory activity as an inherent property of mammalian behavior has also been studied physiologically. Pavlov (1927) observed in his conditioning studies that the introduction of a novel stimulus interfered with conditioning, producing an investigatory or orientation ("what-is-it") reflex. Extended studies of the *orientation reflex* (Sokolov, 1963) showed that this activity is associated with a variety of visceral and somatic responses. Among the visceral changes we may mention the alterations in cardiovascular and respiratory activity, changes in the galvanic skin response (GSR), and dilation of the pupil. Among the somatic responses are changes in muscle tonus, halting of ongoing overt activities, changes in EEG activity toward an arousal pattern, opening of the eyes, pricking of the ears, sniffing, turning of head, and so on. These orienting responses may be considered the routine components of *diffuse* or *nonspecific arousal*, which occurs before *specific investigatory responses* are introduced to deal specifically with the concrete objects or events arousing the animal's "attention."

On prolonged exposure to a stimulus, or if it is repeated monotonously, the orienting responses tend to decline and may subsequently disappear altogether. This phenomenon is referred to in Pavlovian terms as the "extinction of the orientation reaction," or *habituation*. The shorter the interval between repeated presentation of the stimulus, and the weaker and less changeable the stimulus, the faster habituation sets in. The habituated stimulus can reacquire its orientation-arousing properties when it is associated with a significant stimulus, such as food reward or punishment (Chapter 13).

Exploratory activity has been most widely investigated in mammals, although it has also been observed in lower vertebrates (Welker, 1961). The prevalence of exploratory activity in mammals, and its intensification in such higher forms as monkeys and apes, suggest the possible involvement of the neencephalon in the generation of exploratory behavior. Indeed, several investigators have described diminished visual exploratory activity in monkeys following cortical ablations (Butler and Harlow, 1954; Denny-Brown and Chambers, 1958). In a recent systematic study, Symmes (1963) found that ablations in the temporal lobe in monkeys produced a reduction in visual exploratory activity but that frontal ablations did not have this effect. As we may recall, the temporal association areas are implicated in complex discriminatory functions.

**Manipulatory Activities** Animals that have been immobilized
**and Playing** for a period tend to run around and
exercise their limbs. The supposi-
tion that there is a primary *need for activity* was tested by Hill (1956),
who confined rats from 5 to 46 hours in small cages in which they had
ample food and water but could not move about. After different periods
of enforced inactivity, the rats were placed into activity wheels to measure
their running activity. Hill found that the animals displayed an increased
rate of running with increased confinement, and he postulated that a
need for exercise is built up as a consequence of activity deprivation.

In a study by Harlow et al. (1950) monkeys were presented with
mechanical puzzles; it was found that the animals mastered the problems
and persisted in assembling the puzzles in the absence of any other

A mechanical puzzle, in which the animal is required to disengage different hooks
in a serial order, is solved by monkeys for the sole reward of mastering the task.
(Photo courtesy of Dr. H. F. Harlow)

reward except the opportunity to manipulate them. Harlow and his collaborators (Harlow et al., 1956; Mason et al., 1959) found that this *manipulatory tendency* appears in young monkeys from 20 to 30 days of age and then increases with age for some time as the animals acquire more experience with different objects. Harlow postulated that there is in monkeys a true manipulatory drive distinct from, but comparable to, the other drives of the organism.

*Playing* has never been satisfactorily defined; it is, in fact, the scientifically most neglected aspect of animal behavior. Loosely speaking, playing is evidenced by an animal when it is vigorously engaged in activity or exercising its skills in the absence of any extrinsic utility, as seen in the "aimless" running about, jumping, rolling, and wrestling of young animals. Playing is seldom if ever seen in lower vertebrates, although courtship and agonistic behavior is easily mistaken for play (Welker, 1961). Playing is very common in the young, and less frequently it may be displayed also by adults. The way animals play varies in different species, a fact that may be related to differing bodily constitution and mode of existence. Kittens pounce on moving objects and wrestle with each other, colts kick up their heels and gallop, and monkeys forever manipulate objects.

Groos (1915) postulated that playing has two aspects: (1) a *formal* one, that is, the activation or engagement of the "instincts" (or the innate behavioral repertoire of the animal) for the furtherance of their maturation, and (2) an *energetic* one, that is, the disposal of the *surplus energy* of the young, whose needs are largely catered to by the parents. To these two aspects may be added a third, that play is evidenced particularly by the young of mammals who have to acquire their skills through experience (Nissen, 1951). According to this view, play lacks immediate utility but may have an important educational function by providing young animals with the opportunity of acquiring and enriching their behavioral repertoire. When the animal grows up and develops its essential stores of behavioral schemata, and when its energies are engaged by the needs of everyday life, playful activity diminishes or disappears.

**Addendum: "Psychic" Motivation and Behavioral Autonomy** As we have seen, animal behavior is primarily motivated by visceral or somatic drives. There is suggestive evidence, however, that in addition to these drives, behavior may also be instigated by apparent "psychic" needs, such as the *affective* aspect, or concomitant, of actions. For example, rats were found to learn an instrumental task for the reward of a saccharine solution (Sheffield and Roby, 1950), a nonnutritive but (to us, at least) sweet-tasting substance. Sugar, which is of course a nutritive substance, was itself found to serve as a reward to satiated animals just as well as to hungry ones (Smith and Kinney, 1956), an observation indicating that the reinforcing property of sugar does not derive entirely from its nutritional qualities. Likewise, copulation without opportunity of ejaculation was found to serve as an incentive to rats (Sheffield et al., 1951). This result was obtained in naive rats in which copulation could not be secondarily associated with primary-need reduction through previous consummations of the sexual act. These findings suggest that animals will work and master new tasks for the opportunity to ingest pleasant-tasting substances or engage in erotic behavior, presumably for the affective or hedonic benefits derived from these acts. That *hedonic motivation* is a forceful determinant of animal behavior was stressed by Young (1961), who found that palatability, apart from nutritional quality, is a major factor in the food selection of rats.

Not only "pleasure," but its opposite on the hedonic scale, "fear" or "anxiety," may also motivate animal behavior. Miller (1948) placed rats in a shuttle box composed of two compartments, one painted black and the other white, with an open door between. When placed in the box, the animals displayed no preference for either compartment. Then the rats were shocked through the grid of the floor of the white compartment, from which they immediately escaped into the black compartment. Following a few trials, in which the animals were shocked after being placed in the white compartment, the rats would exhibit fear (defecate, urinate) and cross into the black compartment even when the shock was discontinued. Many of the animals so trained would subsequently learn to operate a mechanical device in order to open the door placed between the two compartments. This accomplishment was apparently reinforced by the animals' fear or anxiety in the absence of actual punishment. In a subsequent study (Miller, 1951), animals treated in a similar manner were required to press a bar to escape into the safe compartment. It was found that the animals originally shocked with an electric current of high voltage displayed a higher rate of bar pressing than did those shocked previously with a current of lower voltage.

Apparently, innate or acquired pleasures and fears can motivate behavior in animals. Prior to these findings, it was postulated by Allport (1937) that action schemata originally exhibited as a consequence of the satisfaction of some primary need could, through repeated performance, acquire *functional autonomy* and instigate behavior in the absence of the original need. A similar concept was developed by Anderson (1941), who found that satiated rats would continue to work for food; he referred to this effect as the "externalization of drive." Or we may refer to the studies by Rosenblatt and Aronson (1958 a, b), which indicated that experienced cats, but not inexperienced subjects, would continue to exhibit sexual behavior after castration. Established habits may under some circumstances, accordingly, motivate behavior; such habits may occasionally work even in opposition to tissue needs. To illustrate, we may recall the experiment of Young and Chaplin (1945), who found that rats that formed a habit of selecting a sugar solution in a choice apparatus continued to select this substance instead of casein when they were made protein-deficient. Only when they were transferred to a new apparatus did they give up their established habit and select the nutrient that they were deprived of. Hebb (1949) argued that various aspects of feeding behavior are based on learning and that hunger has an aspect of "addiction."

By referring to "psychic" drives we do not wish to imply that they are fundamentally different from other biogenic or neurogenic processes. As we have mentioned before, certain classes of animative activity are accompanied by manifestations that, from our human experience, we associate with subjective or conscious experiences, such as feeling, perceiving, and knowing. We do not know whether these subjective states are epiphenomenal concomitants of the objective aspects of affective and cognitive processes or whether they represent an important functional component of these processes. The advances made so far in the neurological study of behavior do not permit us to resolve the ancient *mind-body problem;* indeed, it is not inconceivable that the apparent psychophysical dualism is a metaphysical problem which cannot be resolved by the increased accumulation of experimental data in this field.

### SELECTED READINGS

Berlyne, D. E. *Conflict, arousal and curiosity.* New York: McGraw-Hill, 1960.
Welker, W. I. An analysis of exploratory and play behavior in animals. In D. W. Fiske and S. R. Maddi (Eds.), *Functions of varied experience.* Homewood, Ill.: Dorsey, 1961. Pp. 175–226.

# References

Adams, D. K. Experimental studies of adaptive behavior in cats. *Comp. Psychol. Monogr.*, 1929, **6**, 1–168.

Ades, H. W. Effect of extirpation of parastriate cortex on learned visual discrimination in monkeys. *J. Neuropath. exp. Neurol.*, 1946, **5**, 60–65.

————. Central auditory mechanisms. *Handb. Physiol.*, 1959, Sec. 1, **1**, 585–613.

————, and D. H. Raab. Effect of preoccipital and temporal decortication on learned visual discriminations in monkeys. *J. Neurophysiol.*, 1949, **12**, 101–108.

Adey, W. R. The sense of smell. *Handb. Physiol.*, 1959, Sec. 1, **1**, 535–548.

————, C. W. Dunlop, and C. E. Hendrix. Hippocampal slow waves: distribution and phase relationships in the course of approach learning. *Arch. Neurol.*, 1960, **3**, 74–90.

————, N. C. R. Merrillees, and S. Sunderland. The entorhinal area: behavioral, evoked potential and histological studies of its interrelationships with brain stem regions. *Brain*, 1956, **79**, 414–439.

————, J. P. Segundo, and R. B. Livingston. Corticifugal influences on intrinsic brain-stem conduction in cat and monkey. *J. Neurophysiol.*, 1957, **20**, 1–16.

————, S. Sunderland, and C. W. Dunlop. The entorhinal area: electrophysiological studies of its interrelations with rhinencephalic structures and the brain stem. *EEG clin. Neurophysiol.*, 1957, **9**, 309–324.

Adrian, E. D. The all-or-none principle in nerve. *J. Physiol. (London)*, 1914, **47**, 460–474.

————. *The basis of sensation*. London: Christophers, 1928.

————. Afferent discharges to the cerebral cortex from peripheral sense organs. *J. Physiol. (London)*, 1941, **100**, 159–191.

————. Afferent areas in the brain of ungulates. *Brain*, 1943, **66**, 89–103.

————. The electrical activity of the mammalian olfactory bulb. *EEG clin. Neurophysiol.*, 1950, **2**, 377–388.

————. Sensory messages and sensation; the response of the olfactory organs to different smells. *Acta physiol. scand.*, 1953, **29**, 5–14.

————, and R. Matthews. The action of light on the eye. III. The interaction of retinal neurones. *J. Physiol. (London)*, 1928, **65**, 273–298.

Adrianov, O. S. Motor defensive reflexes in dogs after disconnection of the cortical ends of the analyzers. *Pavlov J. Higher Nerv. Activity*, 1960, **10**, 401–410.

Akert, K., R. A. Gruesen, C. N. Woolsey, and D. R. Meyer. Klüver-Bucy syndrome in monkeys with neocortical ablations of temporal lobe. *Brain*, 1961, **84**, 480–498.

Akimoto, H., and O. Creutzfeldt. Reaktionen von Neuronen des optischen Cortex nach elektrischer Reizung unspezifischer Thalamuskerne. *Arch. Psychiat. Nervenkr.*, 1958, **196**, 494–519.

————, N. Yamagouchi, K. Okabe, T. Nakagawe, I. Nakamura, K. Abe, H. Torii, and K. Masahashi. On the sleep induced through electrical stimulation on dog thalamus. *Folia psychiat. neurol. Jap.*, 1956, **10**, 117–146.

Allee, W. C. *Cooperation among animals*. New York: Henry Schuman, 1938.

————, and N. E. Collias. The influence of estradiol on the social organziation of flocks of hens. *Endocrinology*, 1940, **27**, 87–94.

————, ————, and C. Z. Lutherman. Modification of the social order in flocks of hens by the injection of testosterone propionate. *Physiol. Zool.*, 1939, **12**, 412–440.

Allen, W. F. Effect of ablating the frontal lobes, hippocampi, and occipito-parieto-temporal (excepting pyriform

Allen, W. F. (*cont.*)
areas) lobes on positive and negative olfactory conditioned reflexes. *Amer. J. Physiol.*, 1940, 128, 754–771.

————. Effect of ablating the pyriform-amygdaloid areas and hippocampi on positive and negative olfactory conditioned reflexes and on conditioned olfactory differentiation. *Amer. J. Physiol.*, 1941, 132, 81–92.

————. Effects of destroying three localized cerebral cortical areas for sound on correct conditioned differential responses of the dog's foreleg. *Amer. J. Physiol.*, 1945, 144, 415–428.

————. Effect of partial and complete destruction of the tacticle cerebral cortex on conditioned differential foreleg responses from cutaneous stimulation. *Amer. J. Physiol.*, 1947, 151, 325–337.

Allison, A. C. The morphology of the olfactory system in vertebrates. *Biol. Rev.*, 1953, 28, 195–244.

Allport, G. W. *Personality: a psychological interpretation.* New York: Holt, Rinehart and Winston, 1937.

Altman, J. An electrophysiological study of the superior colliculus and visual cortex. *Exp. Neurol.*, 1962, 5, 233–249.

————. Some fiber projections to the superior colliculus in the cat. *J. comp. Neurol.*, 1962, 119, 77–95.

————. Autoradiographic investigation of cell proliferation in the brains of rats and cats. *Anat. Rec.*, 1963a, 145, 573–591.

————. Differences in the utilization of tritiated leucine by single neurones in normal and exercised rats: an autoradiographic investigation with microdensitometry. *Nature*, 1963b, 199, 777–780.

————. Regional utilization of leucine-H³ by normal rat brain: microdensitometric evaluation of autoradiograms. *J. Histochem. Cytochem.*, 1963c, 6, 741–750.

————, and M. B. Carpenter. Fiber projections of the superior colliculus in the cat. *J. comp. Neurol.*, 1961, 116, 157–177.

————, and S. L. Chorover. Autoradiographic investigation of the distribution and utilization of intraventricularly injected adenine-³H, uracil-³H and thymidine-³H in the brains of cats. *J. Physiol. (London)*, 1963, 169, 770–779.

————, and G. D. Das. Autoradiographic examination of the effects of enriched environment on the rate of glial multi-

plication in the adult rat brain. *Nature*, 1964, 204, 1161–1163.

————, and ————. Autoradiographic and histological evidence of postnatal hippocampal neurogenesis in rats. *J. comp. Neurol.*, 1965, 124, 319–336.

————, and ————. Post-natal origin of microneurones in the rat brain. *Nature*, 1965b, 207, 953–956.

Altmann, S. A. Social behavior of anthropoid primates: analysis of recent concepts. In E. L. Bliss (Ed.), *Roots of behavior.* New York: Hoeber, 1962. Pp. 277–285.

Amassian, V. E., and R. V. De Vito. Unit activity in reticular formation and nearby structures. *J. Neurophysiol.*, 1954, 17, 575–603.

Amberson, W. R., and D. C. Smith. *Outline of physiology.* (2d ed.) New York: Appleton, 1948.

Amoore, J. E. Current status of the steric theory of odor. *Ann. N.Y. Acad. Sci.*, 1964, 116, 457–476.

Anand, B. K. Nervous regulation of food intake. *Physiol. Rev.*, 1961, 41, 677–708.

————, and J. R. Brobeck. Hypothalamic control of food intake in rats and cats. *Yale J. Biol. Med.*, 1951, 24, 123–140.

————, G. S. Chhina, and B. Singh. Effect of glucose on the activity of hypothalamic "feeding centers." *Science*, 1962, 138, 597–598.

————, and S. Dua. Stimulation of limbic system of brain in waking animals. *Science*, 1955, 122, 1139.

Anderson, E., and J. A. Long. Effect of hyperglycemia on insulin secretion as determined with the isolated rat pancreas in a perfusion apparatus. *Endocrinology*, 1947, 40, 92–97.

Anderson, E. E. The externalization of drive. I: Theoretical considerations. *Psychol. Rev.*, 1941, 48, 204–224.

Andersson, B. The effect of injections of hypertonic NaCl solutions into different parts of the hypothalamus of goats. *Acta physiol. scand.*, 1953, 28, 188–201.

————, R. Grant, and S. Larsson. Central control of heat loss mechanisms in the goat. *Acta physiol. scand.*, 1956, 37, 261–279.

————, and S. M. McCann. Drinking, antidiuresis and milk ejection from electrical stimulation within the hypothalamus of the goat. *Acta physiol. scand.*, 1956a, 35, 191–201.

Andersson, B., and S. M. McCann (*cont.*)
———, and ———. The effect of hypo-thalamic lesions on the water intake of the dog. *Acta physiol. scand.*, 1956b, **35**, 312–320.
———, and W. Wyrwicka. The elicitation of a drinking motor conditioned reaction by electrical stimulation of the hypothalamic drinking area in the goat. *Acta physiol. scand.*, 1957, **41**, 194–198.
Andersson, S., and B. E. Gernandt. Cortical projection of vestibular nerve in cat. *Acta Oto-Laryng*, 1954, Suppl. 116, 10–18.
Andy, O. J., and K. Akert. Seizure patterns induced by electrical stimulation of hippocampal formation in the cat. *J. Neuropath.*, 1955, **14**, 198–213.
Anfinsen, C. B. *The molecular basis of evolution.* New York: Wiley, 1959.
Arden, G. B., and U. Söderberg. The transfer of optic information through the lateral geniculate body of the rabbit. In W. A. Rosenblith (Ed.), *Sensory communication*. New York: Wiley, 1961. Pp. 521–544.
Armstrong, E. A. *Bird display*. London: Cambridge, 1942.
Aschoff, J. Exogenous and endogenous components in circadian rhythms. *Cold Spring Harbor Sympos. quant. Biol.*, 1960, **25**, 11–28.
———, and J. Mever-Lohmann. Angeborene 24-Stunden-Periodik beim Kücken. *Pflüg. Arch. ges. Physiol.*, 1954, **260**, 170–176.
Astbury, W. T., E. Beighton, and C. Weibull. The structure of bacterial flagella. *Symp. Soc. exp. Biol.*, 1955, **9**, 282–305.
Audus, L. J. *Plant growth substances.* (2d ed.) New York: Wiley, 1960.

Baer, A. Über gleichzeitige elektrische Reizung zweier Grosshirnstellen am ungehemmten Hunde. *Pflüg. Arch. ges. Physiol.*, 1905, **106**, 523–567.
Baerends, G. P., and J. M. Baerends. An introduction to the study of the ethology of Cichlid fishes. *Behaviour*, 1950, Suppl. **1**, 1–242.
Baggerman, B. The role of external factors and hormones in migration of stickle-backs and juvenile salmon. In A. Gorbman (Ed.), *Comparative endocrinology*. New York: Wiley, 1959. Pp. 24–37.
Bagshaw, M., and K. H. Pribram. Cortical

organization in gustation (Macaca mulatta). *J. Neurophysiol.*, 1953, **16**, 499–508.
Bailey, R. E. Inhibition with prolactin of light-induced gonad increase in white-crowned sparrows. *Condor*, 1950, **52**, 247–251.
———. The incubation patch of passerine birds. *Condor*, 1952, **54**, 121–136.
Bajusz, E. "Red" skeletal muscle fibers: relative independence of neural control. *Science*, 1964, **145**, 938–939.
Ball, J. Sexual responsiveness in female monkeys after castration and subsequent estrin administration. *Psychol. Bull.*, 1936, **33**, 811.
———. The effect of testosterone on the sex behavior of female rats. *J. comp. Psychol.*, 1940, **29**, 151–165.
Bard, P. A diencephalic mechanism for the expression of rage, with special reference to the sympathetic nervous system. *Amer. J. Physiol.*, 1928, **84**, 490–515.
———. Central nervous mechanisms for emotional behavior patterns in animals. *Res. Publ. Ass. nerv. ment. Dis.*, 1939, **19**, 190–218.
——— (Ed.). *Medical physiology.* (11th ed.) St. Louis: Mosby, 1961. Pp. 544–553.
———, and M. B. Macht. The behavior of chronically decerebrate cats. In G. E. W. Wolstenholme and C. M. O'Connor (Eds.), Ciba Foundation Symposium, *Neurological basis of behavior*. Boston: Little, Brown, 1958.
———, and V. B. Mountcastle. Some forebrain mechanisms involved in the expression of rage with special reference to suppression of angry behavior. *Res. Publ. Ass. nerv. ment. Dis.*, 1948, **27**, 362–404.
———, and D. M. Rioch. A study of four cats deprived of neocortex and additional portions of the forebrain. *Johns Hopkins Hosp. Bull.*, 1937, **60**, 73–147.
Barelare, B., and C. P. Richter. Increased sodium chloride appetite in pregnant rats. *Amer. J. Physiol.*, 1938, **121**, 185–188.
Bargmann, W. Relationship between neurohypophysial structure and function. In H. Heller (Ed.), *The neurohypophysis*. London: Butterworth, 1957. Pp. 11–22.
Barlow, H. B. Possible principles underlying the transformations of sensory messages. In W. A. Rosenblith (Ed.),

Barlow, H. B. (*cont.*)
*Sensory communication.* New York: Wiley, 1961. Pp. 217–234.

Barnes, R. B., U. Liddell, and V. Z. Williams. Infrared spectroscopy, industrial applications. *Industr. Eng. Chem.,* 1943, **15**, 659–709.

Barondes, S. H., and M. E. Jarvik. The influence of actinomycin-D on brain RNA synthesis and on memory. *J. Neurochem.,* 1964, **11**, 187–195.

Barrington, F. J. F. The relation of the hind-brain to micturition. *Brain,* 1921, **44**, 23–53.

Barron, D. H. Vasomotor regulation. In T. C. Ruch and J. F. Fulton (Eds.), *Medical physiology and biophysics.* Philadelphia: Saunders, 1960. Pp. 691–707.

Bash, K. W. An investigation into a possible organic basis for the hunger drive. *J. comp. Psychol.,* 1939, **28**, 109–134.

Bates, J. A. V., and G. Ettlinger. Posterior biparietal ablations in the monkey. *Arch. Neurol.,* 1960, **3**, 177–192.

Batini, G., M. Palestini, G. F. Rossi, and A. Zanchetti. EEG activation patterns in the midpontine pretrigeminal cat following sensory deafferentation. *Arch. ital. Biol.,* 1959, **97**, 26–32.

Battig, K., H. F. Rosvold, and M. Mishkin. Comparison of the effects of frontal and caudate lesions on delayed response and alternation in monkeys. *J. comp. physiol. Psychol.,* 1960, **53**, 400–404.

Baumgarten, R. V., A. Mollica, and G. Moruzzi. Modulierung der Entladungsfrequenz einzelner Zellen der Substantia reticularis durch corticofugale und cerebelläre Impulse. *Pflüg. Arch. ges. Physiol.,* 1954, **259**, 56–78.

Bazett, C., and W. Penfield. A study of the Sherrington decerebrate animal in the chronic as well as the acute condition. *Brain,* 1922, **45**, 185–264.

Beach, F. A. Analysis of the stimuli adequate to elicit mating behavior in the sexually inexperienced male rat. *J. comp. Psychol.,* 1942a, **33**, 163–207.

———. Sexual behavior of prepuberal male and female rats treated with gonadal hormones. *J. comp. Psychol.,* 1942b, **34**, 285–292.

———. Relative effects of androgen upon the mating behavior of male rats subjected to forebrain injury or castration. *J. exp. Zool.,* 1944, **97**, 249–295.

———. *Hormones and behavior.* New York: Hoeber, 1948.

———. Instinctive behavior: reproductive activities. In S. S. Stevens (Ed.), *Handbook of experimental psychology.* New York: Wiley, 1951. Pp. 387–434.

———. Neural and chemical regulation of behavior. In H. F. Harlow and C. N. Woolsey (Eds.), *Biological and biochemical bases of behavior.* Madison: University of Wisconsin Press, 1958. Pp. 263–284.

———, D. O. Hebb, C. T. Morgan, and H. W. Nissen (Eds.). *The neuropsychology of Lashley.* New York: McGraw-Hill, 1960.

———, and A. M. Holz-Tucker. Effects of different concentrations of androgen upon sexual behavior in castrated male rats. *J. comp. physiol. Psychol.,* 1949, **42**, 433–453.

———, and J. Jaynes. Studies of maternal retrieving in rats: I. Recognition of young. *J. Mammal.,* 1956a, **37**, 177–180.

———, and ———. Studies of maternal retrieving in rats: II. Effects of practice and previous parturitions. *Amer. Naturalist,* 1956b, **90**, 103–109.

———, and ———. Studies of maternal retrieving in rats: III. Sensory cues involved in the lactating female's response to her young. *Behaviour,* 1956c, **10**, 104–125.

———, and L. Jordan. Effects of sexual reinforcement upon the performance of male rats in a straight runway. *J. comp. physiol. Psychol.,* 1956, **49**, 105–110.

———, and R. S. Pauker. Effects of castration and subsequent androgen administration upon mating behavior in the male hamster (*Cricetus anuratus*). *Endocrinology,* 1949, **45**, 211–221.

Beadle, G. W. Chemical genetics. In L. C. Dunn (Ed.), *Genetics in the 20th century.* New York: Macmillan, 1951. Pp. 221–239.

Beaman, E. A. The effect of the male hormone on the aggressive behavior in male mice. *Physiol. Zool.,* 1947, **20**, 373–405.

Beaton, L. E., C. Leininger, W. A. McKinley, H. W. Magoun, and S. W. Ranson. Neurogenic hyperthermia and its treatment with soluble pentobarbital in the monkey. *Arch. Neurol. Psychiat.,* 1943, **49**, 518–536.

Beck, E. C., R. W. Doty, and K. A. Kooi. Electrocortical reactions associated with conditioned flexion reflexes. *EEG clin. Neurophysiol.,* 1958, **10**, 279–289.

Beck, L. H. Osmics: theory and problems related to the initial events in olfaction. In O. Glasser (Ed.), *Medical physics*. Chicago: Year Book Publishers, 1950. Vol. 2, pp. 658–664.

Beidler, L. M. Taste receptor stimulation. *Progr. Biophys. Chem.*, 1961, **12**, 107–151.

Békésy, G. von. *Experiments in hearing*. New York: McGraw-Hill, 1960.

Bekhterev, V. M. *Objektive Psychologie oder Psychoreflexologie*. Leipzig: Teubner, 1913.

Bellows, R. T. Time factors in water drinking in dogs. *Amer. J. Physiol.*, 1939, **125**, 87–97.

Benjamin, F. B. Relationship between injury and pain in the human skin. *J. appl. Physiol.*, 1953, **5**, 740–745.

Benjamin, R. M., and K. Akert. Cortical and thalamic areas involved in taste discrimination in the albino rat. *J. comp. Neurol.*, 1959, **111**, 231–260.

———, and C. Pfaffmann. Cortical localization of taste in albino rat. *J. Neurophysiol.*, 1955, **18**, 56–64.

———, and R. F. Thompson. Differential effects of cortical lesions in infant and adult cats on roughness discrimination. *Exp. Neurol.*, 1959, **1**, 305–321.

Bennett, E. L., M. C. Diamond, D. Krech, and M. R. Rosenzweig. Chemical and anatomical plasticity of brain. *Science*, 1964, **146**, 610–619.

Bennett, M. A. The social hierarchy of ring doves: II. The effect of treatment with testosterone propionate. *Ecology*, 1940, **21**, 148–165.

Benoit, J., and I. Assenmacher. The control by visible radiations of the gonadotrophic activity of the duck hypophysis. *Recent Progr. Hormone Res.*, 1959, **15**, 143–164.

Benzinger, T. H. On physical heat regulation and the sense of temperature in man. *Proc. Nat. Acad. Sci., U.S.*, 1959, **45**, 645–659.

Bergeijk, W. A. van, and E. E. David. Delayed handwriting. *Percept. Mot. Skills*, 1959, **9**, 347–357.

Berger, F. M. Classification of psychoactive drugs according to their chemical structures and sites of action. In L. Uhr. and J. G. Miller (Eds.), *Drugs and behavior*. New York: Wiley, 1960. Pp. 86–105.

Berger, H. Über das Elektrenkephalogramm des Menschen. *Arch. Psychiat. Nervenkr.*, 1929, **87**, 527–570.

Berlyne, D. E. Novelty and curiosity as determinants of exploratory behaviour. *Brit. J. Psychol.*, 1950, **41**, 68–80.

———. The arousal and satiation of perceptual curiosity in the rat. *J. comp. physiol. Psychol.*, 1955, **48**, 238–246.

Berman, A. L. Overlap of somatic and auditory cortical response fields in anterior ectosylvian gyrus of cat. *J. Neurophysiol.*, 1961, **24**, 595–607.

Bernard, C. *Leçons sur le système nerveux*. Paris: Ballière, 1858.

Bernstein, J. J. Brightness discrimination following forebrain ablation in fish. *Exp. Neurol.*, 1961, **3**, 297–306.

Bernstein, L. The effects of variations in handling upon learning and retention. *J. comp. physiol. Psychol.*, 1957, **50**, 162–167.

Bertalanffy, L. von. *Problems of life*. London: Watts, 1952.

Best, J. B., and I. Rubinstein. Maze learning and associated behavior in Planaria. *J. comp. physiol. Psychol.*, 1962, **55**, 560–566.

Bindra, D. Water-hoarding in rats. *J. comp. physiol. Psychol.*, 1947, **40**, 149–156.

Bingham, W. E., and W. J. Griffiths. The effect of different environments during infancy on adult behavior in the rat. *J. comp. physiol. Psychol.*, 1952, **45**, 307–312.

Bishop, G. H. The relation between nerve fiber size and sensory modality: phylogenetic implications of the afferent innervation of cortex. *J. nerv. ment. Dis.* 1959, **128**, 89–114.

Bissonnette, T. H. Photoperiodicity in birds. *Wilson Bull.*, 1937, **49**, 241–270.

Black, J. W. The effect of delayed sidetone upon vocal rate and intensity. *J. Speech Hearing Dis.*, 1951, **16**, 56–60.

Bloomfield, A., and M. L. Tainter. The effects of Vitamin B deprivation on spontaneous activity of the rat. *J. lab. clin. Med.*, 1943, **28**, 1680–1690.

Blum, J. S. Cortical organization in somesthesis. *Comp. Psychol. Monog.*, 1951, **20**, 219–249.

———, K. L. Chow, and K. H. Pribram. A behavioral analysis of the organization of the parieto-temporo-preoccipital cortex. *J. comp. Neurol.*, 1950, **93**, 53–100.

Blum, R. A. Effects of subtotal lesions of frontal granular cortex on delayed reactions in monkeys. *Arch. Neurol. Psychiat.*, 1952, **67**, 375–386.

Bodian, D. The generalized vertebrate neuron. *Science*, 1962, **137**, 323–326.

―――, and H. A. Howe. An experimental study of the role of neurones in the dissemination of poliomyelitis virus in the nervous system. *Brain*, 1940, **63**, 135–162.

Börnstein, W. S. Cortical representation of taste in man and monkey. *Yale J. Biol. Med.*, 1940, **12**, 719–736.

Boling, J. L., and R. J. Blandau. The estrogen-progesterone induction of mating responses in the spayed female rat. *Endocrinology*, 1939, **25**, 359–364.

Bonvallet, M., A. Hugelin, and P. Dell. Tonus sympathique et activité électrique corticale. *EEG clin. Neurophysiol.*, 1954, **6**, 119–144.

Borison, H. L. and S. C. Wang. Functional localization of central coordinating mechanism for emesis in cat. *J. Neurophysiol.*, 1949, **12**, 305–314.

Bowsher, D. Projection of the gracile and cuneate nuclei in Macaca mulatta: an experimental degeneration study. *J. comp. Neurol.*, 1958, **110**, 135–155.

Brachet, J. *Chemical embryology*. New York: Interscience, 1950.

Brady, J. V. The paleocortex and behavioral motivation. In H. F. Harlow and C. N. Woolsey (Eds.), *Biological and biochemical bases of behavior*. Madison: University of Wisconsin Press, 1958. Pp. 193–235.

―――, and W. J. H. Nauta. Subcortical mechanisms in emotional behavior: affective changes following septal forebrain lesions in the albino rat. *J. comp. physiol. Psychol.*, 1953, **46**, 339–346.

―――, and ―――. Subcortical mechanisms in emotional behavior: the duration of affective changes following septal and habenular lesions in the albino rat. *J. comp. physiol. Psychol.*, 1955, **48**, 412–420.

―――, L. Schreiner, I. Geller, and A. Kling. Subcortical mechanisms in emotional behavior: the effect of rhinencephalic injury upon the acquisition and retention of a conditioned avoidance response in cats. *J. comp. physiol. Psychol.*, 1954, **47**, 179–186.

Brattgård, S.-O. The importance of adequate stimulation for the chemical composition of retinal ganglion cells during early post-natal development. *Acta Radiol. Suppl.*, 1952, **96**, 1–80.

Brazier, M. A. B. (Ed.). *Computer techniques in EEG analysis*. Amsterdam: Elsevier, 1961.

Breathnach, A. S., and F. Goldby. The amygdaloid nuclei, hippocampus, and other parts of the rhinencephalon in the porpoise (*Phocaena phocaena*). *J. comp. Neurol.*, 1954, **88**, 267–291.

Bremer, F. Cerveau "isolé" et physiologie du sommeil. *C. R. Soc. Biol. Paris*, 1935, **118**, 1235–1241.

―――. *Some problems in neurophysiology*. London: Athlone, 1953.

―――, and N. Stoupel. Facilitation et inhibition des potentiels évoqués corticaux dans l'éveil cérébral. *Arch. intern. Physiol. Biochem.*, 1959, **67**, 240–275.

Brindley, G. S. *Physiology of the retina and the visual pathway*. London: E. Arnold, 1960.

Brobeck, J. R. Regulation of feeding and drinking. *Handb. physiol.*, 1960, Sec. 1, **2**, 1197–1206.

―――, J. Tepperman, and C. N. H. Long. Experimental hypothalamic hyperphagia in the albino rat. *Yale J. Biol. Med.*, 1943, **15**, 831–853.

Brodal, A., T. Szabo, and A. Torvik. Corticofugal fibers to sensory trigeminal nuclei and nucleus of solitary tract. *J. comp. Neurol.*, 1956, **106**, 527–555.

Brodmann, K. *Vergleichende Lokalisationslehre der Grosshirnrinde*. Munich: Barth, 1909.

Brody, E. G. Genetic basis of spontaneous activity in the albino rat. *Comp. Psychol. Monogr.*, 1941, **17**, 1–23.

Brogden, W. J., and W. H. Gantt. Intraneural conditioning: cerebellar conditioned reflexes. *Arch. Neurol. Psychiat.*, 1942, **48**, 437–455.

Brookhart, J. M., and F. L. Dey. Reduction of sexual behavior in male guinea pigs by hypothalamic lesions. *Amer. J. Physiol.*, 1941 **133**, 551–554.

―――, ―――, and S. W. Ranson. Failure of ovarian hormones to cause mating reactions in spayed guinea pigs with hypothalamic lesions. *Proc. Soc. exp. Biol.*, 1940, **44**, 61–64.

Brooks, C. M. A study of the mechanism whereby coitus excites the ovulation-producing activity of the rabbit's pituitary. *Amer. J. Physiol.*, 1938, **121**, 157–177.

Brown, P. K. and G. Wald. Visual pigments in single rods and cones of the human retina. *Science*, 1964, **144**, 45–52.

Bruce, V. G. Environmental entrainment of circadian rhythms. *Cold Spring Harbor Sympos. quant. Biol.*, 1960, **25**, 29–48.

Brückner, G. H. Untersuchungen zur Tiersoziologie, insbesonders zur Auflösung der Familie. *Z. Psychol.*, 1933, **128**, 1–20.

Brügger, M. Fresstrieb als hypothalamisches Symptom. *Helvet. physiol. pharmacol. Acta*, 1943, **1**, 183–198.

Brust-Carmona, H., et al. Quoted from R. Hernández-Peón, Reticular mechanisms of sensory control. In W. A. Rosenblith (Ed.), *Sensory communication*. New York: Wiley, 1961. Pp. 497–520.

Bünning, E. Opening address: biological clocks. *Cold Harbor, Sympos. quant. Biol.*, 1960, **25**, 1–9.

Bull, H. O. Behavior: conditioned responses. In M. E. Brown (Ed.) *The physiology of fishes*. New York: Academic Press, 1957. Vol. 2.

Bullock, T. H. and F. P. J. Diecke. Properties of an infra-red receptor. *J. Physiol. (London)*, 1956, **134**, 47–87.

Bureš, J., and O. Burešova. The use of Leão's spreading cortical depression in research on conditioned reflexes. *EEG clin. Neurophysiol.*, 1960, Suppl. 13, 359–376.

Burrows, W. H. and T. C. Byerly. Premature expulsion of eggs by hens following injection of whole posterior pituitary preparations. *Poultry Sci.*, 1942, **21**, 416–421.

Butler, R. A. Incentive conditions which influence visual exploration. *J. exp. Psychol.*, 1954, **48**, 19–23.

———. The effect of deprivation of visual incentives on visual exploration motivation in monkeys. *J. comp. physiol. Psychol.*, 1957a, **50**, 177–179.

———. Discrimination learning by rhesus monkeys to auditory incentives. *J. comp. physiol. Psychol.*, 1957b, **50**, 239–241.

———, and H. F. Harlow. Persistence of visual exploration in monkeys. *J. comp. physiol. Psychol.*, 1954, **47**, 258–263.

Bykov, K. M. Conditioned reflexes on dogs with sectioned corpus callosum (1926). Quoted from K. M. Bykov, *The cerebral cortex and the internal organs*. Moscow: Foreign Languages Publishing House, 1959.

Cagle, F. R. Home range, homing behavior and migration in turtles. *Misc.*

*Publ. Mus. Zool. Univer. Mich.*, 1944, **61**, 1–38.

Cajal, S. Ramón y. *Degeneration and regeneration of the nervous system.* New York: Oxford, 1928.

Campbell, B. A. Design and reliability of a new activity-recording device. *J. comp. physiol. Psychol.*, 1954, **47**, 90–92.

———, and F. D. Sheffield. Relation of random activity to food deprivation. *J. comp. physiol. Psychol.*, 1953, **46**, 320–322.

Campbell, R. J., and H. F. Harlow. Problem solution by monkeys following bilateral removal of the prefrontal areas: V. Spatial delayed reactions. *J. exp. Psychol.*, 1945, **35**, 110–126.

Cannon, W. B. *Bodily changes in pain, hunger, fear and rage.* (2d ed.) New York: Appleton, 1929.

———. *The wisdom of the body.* New York: Norton, 1932.

———. Hunger and thirst. In C. Murchison (Ed.), *Handbook of general experimental psychology.* Worcester, Mass.: Clark University Press, 1934. Pp. 247–263.

———, and A. Rosenblueth. *Autonomic neuro-effector systems.* New York: Macmillan, 1937.

———, and A. L. Washburn. An explanation of hunger. *Amer. J. Physiol.*, 1912, **29**, 441–454.

Carlson, A. J. *The control of hunger in health and disease.* Chicago: University of Chicago Press, 1916.

Carmichael, L. The development of behavior in vertebrates experimentally removed from the influence of external stimulation. *Psychol. Rev.*, 1926, **33**, 51–58.

———. A further study of development of behavior in vertebrates experimentally removed from the influence of external stimulation. *Psychol. Rev.*, 1927, **34**, 34–47.

Carpenter, C. R. A field study of behavior and social relations in the howling monkeys (*Alouatta palliata*). *Comp. Psychol. Monogr.*, 1934, **10**, 1–168.

———. A field study in Siam of the behavior and social relations of the gibbon (*Hylobates lar*). *Comp. Psychol. Monogr.*, 1940, **16**, 1–212.

———. Characteristics of social behavior in non-human primates. *Trans. N.Y. Acad. Sci., Ser. II.*, 1942, **4**, 248–258.

Carr, H. A. The alternation problem; a

Carr, H. A. (cont.)
preliminary study. J. animal Behav., 1917, 7, 365–384.

——, and J. B. Watson. Orientation in the white rat. J. comp. neurol. Psychol., 1908, 18, 27–44.

Carr, R. M., and C. D. Williams. Exploratory behavior of three strains of rats. J. comp. physiol. Psychol., 1957, 50, 621–623.

Carr, W. J. The effect of adrenalectomy upon the NaCl taste threshold in rat. J. comp. physiol. Psychol., 1950, 45, 377–380.

Caton, R. The electric currents of the brain. Brit. med. J., 1875, 2, 278.

Cattell, M., and H. Hoagland. Response of tactile receptors to intermittent stimulation. J. Physiol. (London), 1931, 72, 392–404.

Chambers, W. W., and C.-N. Liu. Cortico-spinal tract of the cat. J. comp. Neurol., 1957, 108, 23–53.

——, and ——. Cortico-spinal tract in monkey. Federation Proc., 1958, 17, 24.

Chang, H. T., T. C. Ruch, and A. A. Ward. Topographical representation of muscles in motor cortex of monkeys. J. Neurophysiol., 1947, 10, 39–56.

Chapman, F. M. The courtship of Gould's manakin on Barro Colorado Island, Canal Zone. Bull. Amer. Mus. nat. Hist., 1935, 68, 471–525.

Chiles, W. D. Performance during stimulation of the diencephalic activating system. J. comp. physiol. Psychol., 1954, 47, 412–415.

Chow, K. L. Effects of partial extirpation of posterior association cortex on visually mediated behavior in monkeys. Comp. Psychol. Monogr., 1951, 20, 187–217.

——. Further studies on selective ablation of association cortex in relation to visually mediated behavior. J. comp. physiol. Psychol., 1952, 45, 109–118.

——. Anatomical and electrographical analysis of temporal neocortex in relation to visual discrimination learning in monkeys. In J. F. Delafresnaye (Ed.), Brain mechanisms and learning. Oxford: Blackwell, 1961. Pp. 507–525.

——, and W. D. Obrist. EEG and behavioral changes on application of Al(OH)₃ cream on preoccipital cortex of monkeys. Arch. Neurol. Psychiat., 1954, 72, 80–87.

——, and S. J. Survis. Retention of overlearned visual habit after cortical abla-

tion in monkey. Arch. Neurol. Psychiat., 1958, 79, 640–646.

——, A. H. Riesen, and F. W. Newell. Degeneration of retinal ganglion cells in infant chimpanzees reared in darkness. J. comp. Neurol., 1957, 107, 27–42.

Christian, J. J. Endocrine adaptive mechanisms and the physiologic regulation of population growth. In R. G. Van Gelder (Ed.), Physiological mammalogy. New York: Academic Press, 1964, Vol. 1.

Churchill, E. P. The learning of a maze by goldfish. J. animal Behav., 1916, 6, 247–255.

Cohen, B. D., G. W. Brown, and M. L. Brown. Avoidance learning motivated by hypothalamic stimulation. J. exp. Psychol., 1953, 53, 228–233.

Cole, L. J. Direction of locomotion in the starfish (Asterias forbesii). J. exp. Zool., 1913, 14, 1-32.

Collias, N. E. The analysis of socialization in sheep and goats. Ecology, 1956, 37, 228–239.

Collins, W. F., and J. L. O'Leary. Study of a somatic evoked response of midbrain reticular substance. EEG clin. Neurophysiol., 1954, 6, 619–628.

Cook, L., A. B. Davidson, D. J. Davis, H. Green, and E. J. Fellows. Ribonucleic acid: effect on conditioned behavior in rats. Science, 1963, 141, 268–269.

Cooper, S., and P. M. Daniel. Muscle spindles in human extrinsic eye muscles. Brain, 1949, 72, 1–24.

——, ——, and D. Whitteridge. Afferent impulses in the oculomotor nerve from the extrinsic eye muscles. J. Physiol. (London), 1951, 113, 463–474.

——, and M. Fillenz. Afferent discharges in response to stretch from the extraocular muscles of the cat and monkey and the innervation of these muscles. J. Physiol. (London), 1955, 127, 400–413.

Cooper, Z. K. Mitotic rhythm in human epidermis. J. invest. Dermatol., 1939, 2, 289–300.

Corning, W. C., and E. R. John. Effect of ribonuclease on retention of conditioned response in regenerated planarians. Science, 1961, 134, 1363–1365.

Costa, E., and M. H. Aprison. Studies on the 5-hydroxytryptamine (serotonin) content in human brain. J. nerv. ment. Dis., 1958, 126, 289–293.

Couteaux, R. Motor end plate structure. In G. H. Bourne (Ed.), The structure

Couteaux, R. (cont.)
and function of muscle. New York: Academic Press, 1960. Pp. 337–378.

Cragg, B. G. Centrifugal fibers to the retina and olfactory bulb, and composition of the supraoptic commissures in the rabbit. Exp. Neurol., 1962, 5, 406–427.

Craig, W. Appetites and aversions as constituents of instincts. Biol. Bull. Woods Hole, 1918, 34, 91–107.

Crawford, M. P., and K. W. Spence. Observational learning of discrimination problem by chimpanzees. J. comp. physiol. Psychol., 1939, 27, 133–147.

Crick, F. H. C. On the genetic code. Science, 1963, 139, 461–464.

Crispens, C. G. Prolactin: an evaluation of its use in ring-necked pheasant propagation. J. Wildlife Mgmt., 1956, 20, 453–455.

———. Use of prolactin to induce broodiness in two wild turkeys. J. Wildlife Mgmt., 1957, 21, 462.

Crook, J. H. The basis of flock organisation in birds. In W. H. Thorpe and O. L. Zangwill (Eds.), Current problems in animal behaviour. London: Cambridge, 1961. Pp. 125–149.

Dale, H. H. Transmission of nervous effects by acetylcholine. Bull. N.Y. Acad. Med., 1937, 13, 379–396.

———, and W. Feldberg. The chemical transmitter of effects of the gastric vagus. J. Physiol. (London), 1933, 80, 16P.

Dallenbach, K. M. The temperature spots and end-organs. Amer. J. Psychol., 1927, 39, 402–427.

———. In E. G. Boring, H. S. Langfeld, and H. P. Weld, Psychology. New York: Wiley, 1935.

Darling, F. F. A herd of red deer. New York: Oxford University Press, 1937.

Darwin, C. The power of movement in plants. New York: Appleton, 1881.

Dashiell, J. F. A quantitative demonstration of animal drive. J. comp. Psychol., 1925, 5, 205–208.

———. Direction orientation in maze running by the white rat. Comp. Psychol. Monogr., 1930, 7, 1–72.

Davis, H. Excitation of auditory receptors. Handb. Physiol., 1959, Sec. 1, 1, 585–613.

———. Some principles of sensory receptor action. Physiol. Rev., 1961, 41, 391–416.

Day, L. M., and M. Bentley. A note on

learning in Paramecium. J. animal Behav., 1911, 1, 67–73.

De Groot, J. The rat forebrain in stereotaxic coordinates. Amsterdam: Noord-Hollandsche Uitgevers, 1959.

Delgado, J. M. R. Permanent implantation of multilead electrodes in the brain. Yale J. Biol. Med., 1952, 24, 351–358.

———. A transistor-timed stimulator. EEG clin. Neurophysiol., 1959, 11, 591–593.

———, and B. K. Anand. Increase of food intake induced by electrical stimulation of the lateral hypothalamus. Amer. J. Physiol., 1953, 172, 162–168.

———, and H. E. Rosvold. Effect on intelligent behavior of stimulation or destruction of pathways in the frontal lobes of monkeys. Federation Proc., 1953, 12, 32.

Dell, P. C. Corrélations entre le système végétatif et le système de la vie de relation. J. Physiol. (Paris), 1952, 44, 471–557.

———. Some basic mechanisms of the translation of bodily needs into behaviour. In Ciba Foundation Symposium on the Neurological Basis of Behaviour. Boston: Little, Brown, 1958. Pp. 187–203.

Dement, W. C. The occurrence of low-voltage, fast electroencephalogram patterns during behavioral sleep in the cat. EEG clin. Neurophysiol., 1958, 10, 291–296.

De Molina, F. A., and R. W. Hunsperger. Central representation of affective reactions in forebrain and brain stem. J. Physiol. (London), 1959, 145, 251–265.

Dempsey, E. W., R. Hertz, and W. C. Young. The experimental induction of oestrus (sexual receptivity) in the normal and ovariectomized guinea pig. Amer. J. Physiol., 1936, 116, 201–209.

Denenberg, V. H., and G. G. Karas. Effects of differential infantile handling upon weight gain and mortality in the rat and mouse. Science, 1959, 130, 629–630.

———, and ———. Interactive effects of infantile and adult experiences upon weight gain and mortality in the rat. J. comp. physiol. Psychol., 1961, 54, 685–689.

———, J. R. C. Morton, N. J. Kline, and L. J. Grota. Effects of duration of infantile stimulation upon emotionality. Canad. J. Psychol., 1962, 16, 72–76.

Denny-Brown, D., and R. A. Chambers. The parietal lobe and behavior. *Res. Publ. Assoc. nerv. ment. Dis.*, 1958, **36**, 35–117.

De Robertis, E. D. Some observations on the ultrastructure and morphogenesis of photoreceptors. *J. gen. Physiol.*, 1960, **43**, Suppl. 2, 1–13.

———. *Histophysiology of synapses and neurosecretion.* New York: Macmillan, 1964.

De Vries, H., and M. Stuiver. The absolute sensitivity of the human sense of smell. In W. A. Rosenblith (Ed.), *Sensory communication.* New York: Wiley, 1961. Pp. 159–167.

Diamond, I. T., and K. L. Chow. Biological psychology. In S. Koch (Ed.), *Psychology: a study of a science.* New York: McGraw-Hill, 1962. Vol. 4, pp. 158–241.

———, and W. D. Neff. Ablation of temporal cortex and discrimination of auditory patterns. *J. Neurophysiol.*, 1957, **20**, 300–315.

Dieterlen, F. Das Verhalten des syrischen Goldhamsters. *Z. Tierpsychol.*, 1959, **16**, 47–103.

Dingman, W., and M. B. Sporn. The incorporation of 8-azaguanine into rat brain RNA and its effect on maze-learning by the rat: an inquiry into the biochemical bases of memory. *J. Psychiat. Res.*, 1961, **1**, 1–11.

———, and ———. Molecular theories of memory. *Science*, 1964, **144**, 26–29.

Dische, Z., W. Fleischmann, and E. Trevani. Zur Frages des Zusammenhanges zwischen Winterschlaf und Hypoglykaemie. *Pflüg. Arch. ges. Physiol.*, 1931, **227**, 235–238.

Dodt, E. Centrifugal impulses in rabbit's retina. *J. Neurophysiol.*, 1956, **19**, 301–307.

Dohlmann, G. Some practical and theoretical points in labyrinthology. *Proc. Roy. Soc. Med.*, 1935, **28**, 1371–1380.

Doty, R. W., and C. Giurgea. Conditioned reflexes established by coupling electrical excitation of two cortical areas. In J. Delafresnaye (Ed.), *Brain mechanisms and learning.* London: Blackwell, 1961.

———, and L. T. Rutledge. Generalization between cortically and peripherally applied stimuli eliciting conditioned reflexes. *J. Neurophysiol.*, 1959, **22**, 428–435.

Dowben, R. M., and J. E. Rose. A metal-filled microelectrode. *Science*, 1953, **118**, 22–24.

Dumont, S., and P. Dell. Facilitations spécifiques et non-spécifiques des réponses visuelles corticales. *J. Physiol. (Paris)*, 1958, **58**, 261–264.

Duncan, C. P. The retroactive effect of electroshock on learning. *J. comp. physiol. Psychol.*, 1949, **42**, 32–44.

Durup, G., and A. Fessard. L'électroencéphalogramme de l'homme. *Année psychol.*, 1935, **36**, 1–32.

Dusser de Barenne, J. G., and W. S. McCulloch. The direct functional interrelation of sensory cortex and optic thalamus. *J. Neurophysiol.*, 1938, **1**, 176–186.

Dworkin, S., and W. H. Finney. Artificial hibernation in the woodchuck (*Arctomys Monax*). *Amer. J. Physiol.*, 1927, **80**, 75–81.

Eccles, J. C. *The physiology of nerve cells.* Baltimore: The Johns Hopkins Press, 1957.

———. Neuron physiology: introduction. *Handb. Physiol.*, 1959, Sec. 1, **1**, 59–74.

———. *The physiology of synapses.* New York: Academic Press, 1964.

Economo, C. von. Schlaftheorie. *Ergebn. Physiol.*, 1929, **28**, 312–339.

Edinger, T. Evolution of the horse brain. *Geol. Soc. Amer.*, 1948, Memoir 25.

Eibl-Eibesfeldt, I. Angeborenes und Erworbenes im Nestbauverhalten der Wanderratte. *Naturwiss.*, 1955, **42**, 633–634.

———. Fortschritte der vergleichenden Verhaltensforschung. *Naturwiss. Rundschau.*, 1956. Pp. 86–90, 136–142.

———. The interactions of unlearned behavior patterns and learning in mammals. In J. F. Delafresnaye (Ed.), *Brain mechanisms and learning.* Oxford: Blackwell, 1961. Pp. 53–73.

———. Die Verhaltensentwicklung des Krallenfrosches (*Xenopus laevis*) und des Scheibenzünglers (*Discoglossus pictus*) unter besonderer Berücksichtigung der Beutefanghandlungen. *Z. Tierpsychol.*, 1962, **19**, 385–393.

Eldred, E., R. Granit, and P. A. Merton. Supraspinal control of the muscle spindles and its significance. *J. Physiol. (London)*, 1953, **122**, 498–523.

Elliott, K. A. C., I. H. Page, and J. H. Quastel. *Neurochemistry.* (2d. ed.) Springfield, Ill.: Charles C Thomas, 1962.

Emmers, R., and K. Akert. *A stereotaxic atlas of the brain of the squirrel monkey.* Madison: University of Wisconsin Press, 1963.

Engelmann, C. Versuche über den Geschmacksinn des Huhnes. VI: Über angeborenen Formverlieben bei Hühnern. *Z. Tierpsychol.,* 1942, **5**, 42–59.

Epstein, A. N., and E. Stellar. The control of salt preference in the adrenalectomized rat. *J. comp. physiol. Psychol.,* 1955, **48**, 167–172.

Erlanger, J., and H. S. Gasser. *Electrical signs of nervous activity.* Philadelphia: University of Pennsylvania Press, 1937.

Ettlinger, G., and J. Wegener. Somaesthetic alternation discrimination and orientation after frontal and parietal lesions in monkeys. *Quart. J. exp. Psychol.,* 1958, **10**, 177–186.

Euler, C. von. Temperature potentials in the hypothalamus. *J. cell. comp. Physiol.,* 1950, **36**, 333–350.

Evans, H. E. The correlation of brain pattern and feeding habits in four species of cyprinid fishes. *J. comp. Neurol.,* 1952, **97**, 133–142.

Evans, L. T. Winter mating and fighting behavior of *Anolis carolinensis* as induced by pituitary injections. *Copeia,* 1935, **1**, 3–6.

Eversole, W. J. The effects of pregneninolone and related steroids on sexual development in fish (*Lebistes reticulatus*). *Endocrinology,* 1941, **28**, 603–610.

Fabricius, E. Zur Ethologie junger Anatiden. *Acta zool. fenn.,* 1951, **68**, 1–175.

Fairbanks, G. Selective vocal effects of delayed auditory feedback. *J. Speech Hearing Dis.,* 1955, **20**, 333–346.

Fantz, R. L. Form preferences in newly hatched chicks. *J. comp. physiol. Psychol.,* 1957, **50**, 422–430.

Fatt, P. Skeletal neuromuscular transmission. *Handb. Neurophysiol.,* 1959, Sec. 1, **1**, 199–213.

Fearing, F. *Reflex action: a study in the history of physiological psychology.* Baltimore: Williams & Wilkins, 1930.

Feldberg, W., and J. H. Gaddum. The chemical transmitter at synapses in a sympathetic ganglion. *J. Physiol. (London),* 1934, **81**, 305–319.

————, and S. L. Sherwood. A permanent cannula for intraventricular injection in cats. *J. Physiol. (London),* 1953, **120**, 3P.

Ferster, C. B., and B. F. Skinner. *Sched-*

*ules of reinforcement.* New York: Appleton, 1957.

Fingerman, M. Tidal rhythmicity in marine organisms. *Cold Spring Harbor Sympos. quant. Biol.,* 1960, **25**, 481–489.

Fisher, A. E. Maternal and sexual behavior induced by intracranial chemical stimulation. *Science,* 1956, **124**, 228–229.

Fisher, C., W. R. Ingram, and S. W. Ranson. *Diabetes insipidus and the neurohormonal control of water balance.* Ann Arbor, Mich.: Edwards, 1938.

Flechsig, P. *Die Leitungsbahnen im Gehirn und Rückenmark des Menschen.* Leipzig: Engelmann, 1876.

Flickinger, R. A. Cell differentiation: some aspects of the problem. *Science,* 1963, **141**, 608–614.

Fluorens, P. *Recherches experimentales sur les propriétés et les fonctions du système nerveux dans les animaux vertébrés.* Paris: Crevot, 1824.

Foley, J. P. An experimental investigation of the effect of prolonged inversion of the visual field in the Rhesus monkey. *J. genet. Psychol.,* 1940, **56**, 21–51.

Fonberg, E., and J. M. R. Delgado. Avoidance and alimentary reactions during amygdala stimulation. *J. Neurophysiol.,* 1961, **24**, 651–664.

Ford, D. H., and W. C. Young. The role of progesterone in the production of cyclic vaginal changes in the female guinea pig. *Endocrinology,* 1951, **49**, 795–804.

Forgays, D. G., and J. W. Forgays. The nature of the effects of free-environmental experience on the rat. *J. comp. physiol. Psychol.,* 1952, **45**, 322–328.

Forgus, R. H. The effect of early perceptual learning on the behavioral organization of adult rats. *J. comp. physiol. Psychol.,* 1954, **47**, 331–336.

————. Advantage of early over late perceptual experience in improving form discrimination. *Canad. J. Psychol.,* 1956, **10**, 147–155.

Forman, D., and J. W. Ward. Responses to electrical stimulation of caudate nucleus in cats in chronic experiments. *J. Neurophysiol.,* 1957, **20**, 230–244.

Frank, A. H., and R. M. Fraps. Induction of estrus in the ovariectomized golden hamster. *Endocrinology,* 1945, **37**, 357–361.

Franzisket, L. Die Bildung einer bedingten Hemmung bei Rückenmarkfröschen. *Z. vergl. Physiol.,* 1955, **37**, 161–168.

Fredericson, E., A. W. Story, N. L. Gurney, and K. Butterworth. The relationship between heredity, sex, and aggression in two inbred mouse strains. *J. genet. Psychol.*, 1955, 87, 121–130.

French, J. D., R. Hernández-Peón, and R. B. Livingston. Projections from cortex to cephalic brain stem (reticular formation) in monkey. *J. Neurophysiol.*, 1955, 18, 74–95.

French, J. W. Trial and error learning in *Paramecium*. *J. exp. Psychol.*, 1940, 26, 609–613.

Frings, H., and M. Frings. The production of stocks of albino mice with predictable susceptibilities to audiogenic seizures. *Behaviour*, 1953, 5, 305–319.

Frisch, K. von. Über einen Schreckstoff der Fischhaut und seine biologische Bedeutung. *Z. vergl. Physiol.*, 1941, 29, 46.

———. Die Sonne als Kompass im Leben der Bienen. *Experientia*, 1950, 6, 210.

Fritsch, G., and E. Hitzig. Über die elektrische Erregbarkeit des Grosshirns. *Arch. Anat. Physiol., Leipzig*, 1870, 37, 300–332.

Frolov, J. P. Bedingte Reflexe bei Fischen. *Pflüg. Arch. ges. Physiol.*, 1928, 220, 339–349.

Galambos, R. Suppression of auditory nerve activity by stimulation of efferent fibers to cochlea. *J. Neurophysiol.*, 1956, 19, 424–437.

———. A glia-neural theory of brain function. *Proc. Nat. Acad. Sci. U.S.*, 1961, 47, 129–136.

———, and H. Davis. The response of single auditory nerve fibers to acoustic stimulation. *J. Neurophysiol.*, 1943, 6, 39–57.

———, R. E. Myers, and G. C. Sheatz. Extralemniscal activation of auditory cortex in cats. *Amer. J. Physiol.*, 1961, 200, 23–28.

———, G. Sheatz, and V. G. Vernier. Electrophysiological correlates of a conditioned response in cats. *Science*, 1956, 123, 376–377.

Gasser, H. S. Classification of nerve fibers. *Ohio J. Sci.*, 1941, 41, 145–159.

Gastaut, H. Corrélations entre le système nerveux végétatif et le système de la vie de relation dans le rhinencéphale. *J. Physiol. Path. gén.*, 1952, 44, 431–470.

———. The role of the reticular formation in establishing conditioned reactions. In H. H. Jasper et al. (Eds.), *Reticular formation of the brain*. Boston: Little, Brown, 1958. Pp. 561–579.

Gelber, B. Investigations of the behavior of *Paramecium aurelia*. *J. comp. physiol. Psychol.*, 1952, 45, 58–65.

———. Retention in *Paramecium aurelia*. *J. comp. physiol. Psychol.*, 1958, 51, 110–115.

Gellhorn, E. *Physiological foundations of neurology and psychiatry*. Minneapolis: University of Minnesota Press, 1953.

Gernandt, B. E. Vestibular mechanisms. *Handb. Physiol.*, 1959, Sec. 1, 1, 549–564.

Gesteland, R. C. Initial events of the electro-olfactogram. *Ann. N.Y. Acad. Sci.*, 1964, 116, 440–447.

———, J. Y. Lettvin, W. H. Pitts, and J. A. Rojas. Odor specificities of frog's olfactory receptors. In Y. Zotterman (Ed.), *Olfaction and taste*. New York: Pergamon Press, 1963. Pp. 19–44.

Ghiselli, E. E. The relationship between the superior colliculus and the striate area in brightness discrimination. *J. genet. Psychol.*, 1938, 52, 151–157.

Gibson, E. J., and R. D. Walk. The effect of prolonged exposure to visually presented patterns on learning to discriminate them. *J. comp. physiol. Psychol.*, 1956, 49, 239–242.

———, and ———. The "visual cliff." *Sci. Amer.*, 1960, 202, 64–71.

———, ———, H. L. Pick, and T. J. Tighe. The effect of prolonged exposure to visual patterns on learning to discriminate similar and different patterns. *J. comp. physiol. Psychol.*, 1958, 51, 584–587.

Ginsburg, B., and W. C. Allee. Some effects of conditioning on social dominance and subordination in inbred strains of mice. *Physiol. Zool.*, 1942, 15, 485–506.

Girden, E. The acoustic mechanism of the cerebral cortex. *Amer. J. Psychol.*, 1942, 55, 518–527.

———, F. A. Mettler, G. Finch, and E. Culler. Conditioned responses in a decorticate dog to acoustic, thermal and tactile stimulation. *J. comp. Psychol.*, 1936, 21, 367–385.

Giurgea, C. Die Dynamik der Ausarbeitung einer zeitlichen Beziehung durch direkte Reizung der Hirnrinde. *Ber. ges. Physiol.*, 1955, 175, 80.

Glanzer, M. Stimulus satiation: an explanation of spontaneous alternation and

Glanzer, M. (cont.)
related phenomena. Psychol. Rev., 1953,
60, 257–268.

Glees, P. Terminal degeneration within the
central nervous system as studied by a
new silver method. J. Neuropath. exp.
Neurol., 1946, 5, 54–59.

———, J. Cole, C. W. M. Whitty, and
H. W. B. Cairns. The effect of lesions in
the cingular gyrus and adjacent areas in
monkeys. J. Neurol. Psychiat., 1950, 13,
178–190.

Gloor, P. Amygdala. Handb. Neurophysiol., 1960, Sec. 1, 2, 1395–1420.

Goddard, G. V. Functions of the amygdala. Psychol. Bull., 1964, 62, 89–109.

Goldacre, R. J., and I. J. Lorch. Folding
and unfolding of protein molecules in relation to cytoplasmic streaming, amoe-
boid movement and osmotic work. Nature, 1950, 166, 497–500.

Goldstein, K. The organism. New York:
American Book, 1939.

Goltz, F. Der Hund ohne Grosshirn. Pflüg.
Arch. ges. Physiol., 1892, 51, 570–614.

Gould, E. Orientation in box turtles. Biol.
Bull., 1957, 112, 336–348.

Goy, W. R., and W. C. Young. Somatic
basis of sexual behavior patterns in
guinea pigs. Psychosom. Med., 1957a,
19, 144–151.

———, and ———. Strain differences in
the behavioral responses of female guinea
pigs to d-estradiol benzoate and progesterone. Behaviour, 1957b, 10, 340–354.

Granit, R. The spectral properties of the
visual receptors of the cat. Acta physiol.
scand., 1943, 5, 219–229.

———. Sensory mechanisms of the retina.
New York: Oxford, 1947.

———. Centrifugal and antidromic effects
on ganglion cells of retina. J. Neurophysiol., 1955a, 18, 388–411.

———. Receptors and sensory perception.
New Haven, Conn.: Yale University
Press, 1955b.

———. Neural activity in the retina.
Handb. Physiol., 1959, Sec. 1, 1, 693–
712.

———, and B. Kaada. Influence of stimulation of central nervous structures on
muscle spindles in cat. Acta physiol.
scand., 1952, 27, 130–160.

Grastyán, E. The hippocampus and higher
nervous activity. In M. A. B. Brazier
(Ed.), Central nervous system and behavior. Washington, D.C.: Josiah Macy
Foundation, 1959. Pp. 119–205.

Gray, J. Ciliary movement. London: Cambridge, 1928.

———. Studies in animal locomotion: V.
Resistance reflexes in the eel. J. exp.
Biol., 1936, 13, 181–191.

———. The role of peripheral sense organs
during locomotion in the vertebrates.
Sympos. Soc. exp. Biol., 1950, 4, 112–
125.

———, and H. W. Lissmann. The effect
of deafferentation upon the locomotory
activity of amphibian limbs. J. exp. Biol.,
1940, 17, 227–235.

———, and ———. The coordination of
limb movements in the amphibia. J. exp.
Biol., 1946, 23, 133–142.

Gray, J. A. B. Initiation of impulses at receptors. Handb. Physiol., 1959, Sec. 1,
1, 123–145.

———, and M. Sato. Properties of the
receptor potential in Pacinian corpuscles. J. Physiol. (London), 1953, 122,
610–636.

Green, J. D. Electrical activity in hypothalamus and hippocampus of conscious rabbits. Anat. Rec., 1954, 118, 304.

———. The hippocampus. Handb.
Physiol., 1960, Sec. 1, 2, 1373–1389.

———, C. D. Clemente, and J. De Groot.
Rhinencephalic lesions and behavior in
cats. J. comp. Neurol., 1957, 108, 505–
545.

Greenberg, B., and G. K. Noble. Social be-
havior of the American chameleon
(Anolis carolinensis Voigt). Physiol.
Zool., 1944, 17, 392–439.

Griffin, D. R. Listening in the dark. New
Haven, Conn.: Yale University Press,
1958.

Grohmann, J. Modifikation oder Funk-
tionsregung? Ein Beitrag zur Klärung der
wechselseitigen Beziehungen zwischen
Instinkthandlung und Erfahrung. Z.
Tierpsychol., 1938, 2, 132–144.

Groos, K. The play of animals. New York:
Appleton, 1915.

Grossman, S. P. Eating or drinking elicited
by direct adrenergic or cholinergic stimulation of hypothalamus. Science, 1960,
132, 301–302.

———. Effects of adrenergic and cholinergic blocking agents on hypothalamic
mechanisms. Amer. J. Physiol., 1962,
202, 1230–1236.

Grundfest, H. Synaptic and ephaptic transmission. Handb. Physiol., 1959, Sec. 1,
1, 147–197.

———, R. W. Sengstaken, and W. H.
Oettinger. Stainless steel microneedle

Grundfest, H., R. W. Sengstaken, and W. H. Oettinger (*cont.*) electrodes made by electrolytic pointing. *Rev. sci. Instrum.*, 1950, **21**, 360–361.

Grunt, J. A., and W. C. Young. Differential reactivity of individuals and the response of the male guinea pig to testosterone propionate. *Endocrinology*, 1952, **51**, 237–248.

————, and ————. Consistency of sexual behavior patterns in individual male guinea pigs following castration and androgen therapy. *J. comp. physiol. Psychol.*, 1953, **46**, 138–144.

Guhl, A. M. Social dominance and receptivity in the domestic fowl. *Physiol. Zool.*, 1950, **23**, 361–366.

————, N. E. Collias, and W. C. Allee. Mating behavior and the social hierarchy in small flocks of white leghorns. *Physiol. Zool.*, 1945, **18**, 365–390.

Guillemin, R., W. E. Dear, and R. A. Liebelt. Nychthermeral variations in plasma free corticosteroid levels of the rat. *Proc. Soc. exp. Biol. Med.*, 1959, **101**, 394–395.

Hagbarth, K-E. and D. I. B. Kerr. Central influences on spinal afferent conduction. *J. Neurophysiol.*, 1954, **17**, 295–307.

Hagen, E., H. Knoche, D. C. Sinclair, and G. Weddell. Role of specialized nerve terminals in cutaneous sensibility. *Proc. Roy. Soc. (London)*, 1953, **B 141**, 279–287.

Hain, A. M. The effect of (a) litter size on growth and (b) of estrone administered during lactation. *Quart. J. exp. Physiol.*, 1935, **25**, 303–313.

Halberg, F. Physiologic 24-hour periodicity in human beings and mice, the lighting regimen and daily routine. In R. B. Withrow (Ed.), *Photoperiodism and related phenomena in plants and animals.* Washington, D.C.: American Association for the Advancement of Science, 1959. Pp. 803–878.

————, H. A. Zander, M. W. Houglum, and H. R. Mühlemann. Daily variations in tissue mitoses, blood eosinophils and rectal temperatures of rats. *Amer. J. Physiol.*, 1954, **177**, 361–366.

Haldane, J. S. *The philosophy of a biologist.* London: Clarendon, 1935.

Hall, C. S. The inheritance of emotionality. *Amer. Scient.*, 1938, **26**, 17–27.

Hambrecht, F. T., P. D. Donahue, and R. Melzack. A multiple channel EEG telemetering system. *EEG clin. Neurophysiol.*, 1963, **15**, 323–326.

Hara, K. Visual defects resulting from prestriate cortical lesions in cats. *J. comp. physiol. Psychol.*, 1962, **55**, 293–298.

Haralson, J. V., and M. E. Bitterman. A lever-depression apparatus for the study of learning in fish. *Amer. J. Psychol.*, 1950, **63**, 250–256.

Harlow, H. F. Forward conditioning, backward conditioning and pseudo-conditioning in goldfish. *J. genet. Psychol.*, 1939, **55**, 49–58.

————. The formation of learning sets. *Psychol. Rev.*, 1949, **56**, 51–65.

————. Mice, monkeys, men and motives. *Psychol. Rev.*, 1953, **60**, 23–32.

————. Primary affectional patterns in primates. *Amer. J. Orthopsychiat.*, 1960, **30**, 676–684.

————. The heterosexual affectional system in monkeys. *Amer. Psychologist*, 1962a, **17**, 1–9.

————. Development of affection in primates. In E. L. Bliss (Ed.), *Roots of behavior.* New York: Harper, 1962b. Pp. 157–166.

————, N. C. Blazek, and G. E. McClearn. Manipulatory motivation in the infant rhesus monkey. *J. comp. physiol. Psychol.*, 1956, **49**, 444–448.

————, and J. Dagnon. Problem solution by monkeys following bilateral removal of the prefrontal areas. *J. exp. Psychol.*, 1943, **32**, 351–356.

————, R. T. Davis, P. H. Settlage, and D. R. Meyer. Analysis of frontal and posterior association syndromes in brain damaged monkeys. *J. comp. physiol. Psychol.*, 1952, **45**, 419–429.

————, M. K. Harlow, and D. R. Meyer. Learning motivated by a manipulation drive. *J. exp. Psychol.*, 1950, **40**, 228–234.

————, D. R. Meyer, and P. H. Settlage. The effects of large cortical lesions on the solution of oddity problems by monkeys. *J. comp. physiol. Psychol.*, 1951, **44**, 320–326.

Harriman, A. E., and R. B. MacLeod. Discriminative threshold of salt for normal and adrenalectomized rats. *Amer. J. Psychol.*, 1953, **66**, 465–471.

Harrington, N. R., and E. Learning. The reaction of Amoeba to light of different colors. *Amer. J. Physiol.*, 1900, **3**, 9–18.

Harris, G. W. Stimulation of the supra-optico-hypophysial tract in the con-

Harris, G. W. (cont.)
scious rabbit with currents of different wave form. *J. Physiol.* (*London*), 1948, **107**, 412–417.

———. *Neural control of the pituitary gland.* London: E. Arnold, 1955.

———, R. P. Michael, and P. P. Schott. Neurological site of action of stilboestrol in eliciting sexual behavior. In G. E. W. Wolstenholme and C. M. O'Connor (Eds.), *Neurological basis of behaviour.* London: Churchill, 1958.

Harris, L. J., J. Clay, F. J. Hargreaves, and A. Ward. Appetite and choice of diet. The ability of the vitamin-B deficient rat to discriminate between diets containing and lacking the vitamin. *Proc. Roy. Soc.* (*London*), 1933, **B 113**, 161–190.

Harris, S. C., A. C. Ivy, and L. M. Searle. The mechanism of amphetamine-induced loss of weight. *A.M.A. Journal*, 1947, **134**, 1468–1475.

Hartline, H. K. The discharge of impulses in the optic nerve of Pecten in response to illumination of the eye. *J. cell. comp. Physiol.*, 1938, **11**, 465–478.

Hartman, C. G. Some observations on the bonnet macaque. *J. Mammal.*, 1938, **19**, 468–474.

Hasler, A. D., R. M. Morrall, W. J. Wisby, and W. Braemer. Sun-orientation and homing in fishes. *Limnol. Oceanogr.*, 1958, **3**, 353–361.

———, and W. J. Wisby. Discrimination of stream odor by fishes and its relation to parent stream behavior. *Amer. Naturalist*, 1951, **85**, 223–238.

Head, H. *Studies in neurology.* New York: Oxford, 1920. 2 vols.

Heath, R. G., and R. Hodes. Induction of sleep by stimulation of the caudate nucleus in Macacus rhesus and man. *Trans. Amer. Neurol. Ass.*, 1952. Pp. 204–210.

———, and W. A. Mickle. Evaluation of seven years' experience with depth electrode studies in human patients. In E. R. Ramsey and D. S. O'Doherty (Eds.), *Electrical studies of the unanesthetized brain.* New York: Hoeber, 1960. Pp. 214–242.

Hebb, D. O. The innate organization of visual activity. I. Perception of figures by rats reared in total darkness. *J. genet. Psychol.*, 1937, **51**, 101–126.

———. *The organization of behavior.* New York: Wiley, 1949.

———, and K. Williams. A method of rating animal intelligence. *J. genet. Psychol.*, 1946, **34**, 59–65.

Hecht, S., S. Schlaer, and M. H. Pirenne. Energy, quanta and vision. *J. gen. Physiol.*, 1942, **25**, 819–840.

Heinroth, O. Beiträge zur Biologie, namentlich Ethologie und Physiologie der Anatiden. *Int. Orn. Congr.* V, 1910, 589–702.

Held, R., and S. J. Freedman. Plasticity in human sensorimotor control. *Science*, 1963, **142**, 455–462.

———, and A. Hein. Movement-produced stimulation in the development of visually guided behavior. *J. comp. physiol. Psychol.*, 1963, **56**, 872–876.

Helmholtz, H. von. *Handbuch der physiologischen Optik.* Leipzig: Voss, 1867.

Henderson, L. J. *The fitness of the environment.* New York: Macmillan, 1913.

Hendley, C. D., and R. Hodes. Effects of lesions on subcortically evoked movements in cat. *J. Neurophysiol.*, 1953, **16**, 587–594.

Henry, C. E., and K. H. Pribram. Effect of aluminum hydroxide cream implantation in cortex of monkey on EEG and behavior performance. *EEG clin. Neurophysiol.*, 1954, **6**, 693–694.

Herberg, L. J. Seminal ejaculation following positively reinforcing electrical stimulation of the rat hypothalamus. *J. comp. physiol. Psychol.*, 1963, **56**, 679–685.

Hernández-Peón, R. Reticular mechanisms of sensory control. In W. A. Rosenblith (Ed.), *Sensory communication.* New York: Wiley, 1961. Pp. 497–520.

———, and H. Brust-Carmona. Functional role of subcortical structures in habituation and conditioning. In J. F. Delafresnaye (Ed.), *Brain mechanisms and learning.* Springfield, Ill.: Charles C Thomas, 1961. Pp. 393–408.

———, and K.-E. Hagbarth. Interaction between afferent and cortically induced reticular responses. *J. Neurophysiol.*, 1955, **18**, 44–55.

———, and H. Scherrer. "Habituation" to acoustic stimuli in cochlear nucleus. *Federation Proc.*, 1955, **14**, 71.

———, ———, and M. Jouvet. Modification of electric activity in cochlear nucleus during "attention" in unanesthetized cats. *Science*, 1956, **123**, 331–332.

Herrick, C. J., and G. Bishop. A comparative survey of the spinal lemniscus system. In H. H. Jasper et al. (Eds.), *Reticular formation of the brain.* Boston: Little, Brown, 1958. Pp. 353–360.

Hersher, L., J. B. Richmond, and A. U. Moore. Maternal behavior in sheep and goats. In H. L. Rheingold (Ed.), *Maternal behavior in mammals*. New York: Wiley, 1963. Pp. 203–232.

Herter, K. Körpertemperatur und Aktivität beim Igel. *Z. vergl. Physiol.*, 1934, **20**, 511–544.

———. *Die Fischdressuren und ihre sinnesphysiologische Grundlagen*. Stuttgart: Thieme, 1953.

Hess, E. H. Space perception in the chick. *Sci. Amer.*, 1956, **195**, 71–80.

———. Effects of meprobamate on imprinting in waterfowl. *Ann. N.Y. Acad. Sci.*, 1957, **67**, 724–732.

———. Imprinting. *Science*, 1959, **130**, 133–141.

———. Imprinting in birds. *Science*, 1964, **146**, 1128–1139.

Hess, W. R. Stammganglien Reizversuche. *Ber. ges. Physiol.*, 1928, **42**, 554.

———. *Beiträge zur Physiologie des Hirnstammes*. Stuttgart: Thieme, 1932.

———. *The diencephalon, autonomic and extrapyramidal functions*. New York: Grune & Stratton, 1954.

———, and K. Akert. Experimental data on role of hypothalamus in mechanism of emotional behavior. *Arch. Neurol. Psychiat.*, 1955, **73**, 127–129.

Hetherington, A. W. The relation of various hypothalamic lesions to adiposity and other phenomena in the rat. *Amer. J. Physiol.*, 1941, **133**, 326–327.

Hill, W. F. Activity as an autonomous drive. *J. comp. physiol. Psychol.*, 1956, **49**, 15–19.

Hind, J. E. An electrophysiological determination of tonotopic organization in auditory cortex of cat. *J. Neurophysiol.*, 1953, **16**, 473–489.

Hines, M. Movements elicited from precentral gyrus of adult chimpanzees with sine wave currents. *J. Neurophysiol.*, 1940, **3**, 442–466.

———. Significance of precentral motor cortex. In P. C. Bucy (Ed.), *The precentral motor cortex*. Urbana: University of Illinois Press, 1944. Pp. 459–494.

———. The motor area. *Federation Proc.*, 1947, **6**, 441–447.

Hitchcock, F. A. The effect of low protein and protein-free diets and starvation on the voluntary activity of the albino rat. *Amer. J. Physiol.*, 1928, **84**, 410–416.

Hodes, R., S. M. Peacock, and R. G. Heath. Influence of the forebrain on somato-motor activity: I. Inhibition. *J. comp. Neurol.*, 1951, **94**, 381–408.

Hodgkin, A. L. A local electric response in crustacean nerve. *J. Physiol. (London)*, 1938, **91**, 5–7.

———. The ionic basis of nervous conduction. *Science*, 1964, **145**, 1148–1154.

———, and A. F. Huxley. Resting and action potentials in single nerve fibers. *J. Physiol. (London)*, 1945, **104**, 176–195.

Hoebel, B. G., and P. Teitelbaum. Hypothalamic control of feeding and self-stimulation. *Science*, 1962, **135**, 375–376.

Hoff, E. C. Cortico-spinal fibers arising in the premotor area of the monkey. *Arch. Neurol. Psychiat.*, 1935, **33**, 687–697.

Hoff, H. E., and C. G. Breckenridge. The medullary origin of respiratory periodicity in the dog. *Amer. J. Physiol.*, 1949, **158**, 157–172.

Hoffmann, K. Experimentelle Änderung des Richtungsfindens beim Star durch Beeinflussung der "inneren Uhr." *Naturwiss.*, 1953, **40**, 608–609.

———. Die Aktivitätsperiodik von in 18- und 36-Stunden-Tag erbrüteten Eidechsen. *Z. vergl. Physiol.*, 1959, **42**, 422–432.

———. Experimental manipulation of the orientational clock in birds. *Cold Spring Harbor Sympos. quant. Biol.*, 1960, **25**, 379–387.

Holst, E. von, and H. Mittelstaedt. Das Reafferenzprinzip. Wechselwirkungen zwischen Zentralnervensystem und Peripherie. *Naturwiss.*, 1950, **37**, 464–476.

———, and L. Schoen. Der Einfluss mechanisch veränderter Augenstellungen auf die Richtungslokalisation bei Fischen. *Z. vergl. Physiol.*, 1954, **36**, 433–442.

Holtfreter, J. A study of the mechanics of gastrulation. *J. exp. Zool.*, 1943, **94**, 261–318.

Honzik, C. H. Delayed reaction in rats. *Univer. Calif. Publ. Psychol.*, 1931, **4**, 307–318.

———. The sensory basis of maze learning. *Comp. Psychol. Monogr.*, 1936, **13**, 1–113.

Hoog, E. G. van't. On deep-localization in the cerebral cortex. *J. nerv. ment. Dis.*, 1920, **51**, 313–329.

Hoover, E. E. and H. F. Hubbard. Modification of the sexual cycle of trout by

Hoover, E. E., and H. F. Hubbard (*cont.*) control of light. *Copeia*, 1937, 4, 206–210.

Horsley, V., and R. H. Clarke. The structure and function of the cerebellum examined by a new method. *Brain*, 1908, 31, 45–124.

Hoskins, R. G. Studies on vigor: II. The effect of castration on voluntary activity. *Amer. J. Physiol.*, 1925, 72, 324–330.

Houston, A. H. Responses of juvenile chum, pink and coho salmon to sharp sea water gradients. *Canad. J. Zool.*, 1957, 35, 371–383.

Hubbard, S. J. A study of rapid mechanical events in a mechanoreceptor. *J. Physiol.* (*London*), 1958, 141, 198–218.

Hubel, D. H. Tungsten microelectrode for recording from single units. *Science*, 1957, 125, 549–550.

———. Single unit activity in striate cortex of unrestrained cats. *J. Physiol.* (*London*), 1959, 147, 226–238.

———, and T. N. Wiesel. Receptive fields of single neurones in the cat's striate cortex. *J. Physiol.* (*London*), 1959, 148, 574–591.

———, and ———. Integrative action in the cat's lateral geniculate body. *J. Physiol.* (*London*), 1961, 155, 385–398.

———, and ———. Receptive fields, binocular interaction and functional architecture in the cat's visual cortex. *J. Physiol.* (*London*), 1962, 160, 106–154.

Hüttel, R. Die chemische Untersuchung der Schreckstoffes aus Elritzenhaut. *Naturwiss.*, 1941, 29, 333–334.

Hull, C. L. *Principles of behavior.* New York: Appleton, 1943.

Humphrey, G. *The nature of learning in its relation to the living system.* London: Routledge, 1933.

Hunt, J. M. The effects of infant feeding frustration upon adult hoarding in the albino rat. *J. abnorm. soc. Psychol.*, 1941, 36, 338–360.

———, and H. Schlosberg. The influence of illumination upon general activity in normal, blinded, and castrated male white rats. *J. comp. Psychol.*, 1939, 28, 285–298.

———, ———, R. L. Solomon, and E. Stellar. Studies of infantile experience on adult behavior in rats: I. Effects of infantile feeding frustration on adult hoarding. *J. comp. physiol. Psychol.*, 1947, 40, 291–304.

Hunter, W. S. The delayed reaction in animals and children. *Behav. Monog.*, 1913, No. 6.

Hurvich, L. M., and D. Jameson. An opponent-process theory of color vision. *Psychol. Rev.*, 1957, 64, 384–404.

Huxley, H. E., and J. Hanson. The molecular basis of contraction in cross-striated muscles. In *The structure and function of muscle.* New York: Academic Press, 1960. Pp. 183–227.

Hydén, H. The neuron. In J. Brachet and A. E. Mirsky (Eds.), *The cell.* New York: Academic Press, 1960. Vol. 4, Pt. 1, Pp. 215–323.

———. Cytophysiological aspects of the nucleic acids and proteins of nervous tissue. In K. A. Elliott et al. (Eds.), *Neurochemistry.* (2d ed.) Springfield, Ill.: Charles C Thomas, 1962. Pp. 331–375.

———, and E. Egyházi. Nuclear RNA changes in nerve cells during a learning experiment in rats. *Proc. Nat. Acad. Sci. U.S.*, 1962, 48, 1366–1373.

———, and A. Pigón. A cytophysiological study of the functional relationship between oligodendroglial cells and nerve cells of Deiter's nucleus. *J. Neurochem.*, 1960, 6, 57–72.

Hyman, L. H. *The Invertebrates.* New York: McGraw-Hill, 1951. Vol. 2.

Hymovitch, B. The effects of experimental variations on problem solving in the rat. *J. comp. physiol. Psychol.*, 1952, 45, 313–321.

Imanishi, K. Social behavior in Japanese monkeys, *Macaca fuscata. Psychologia*, 1957, 1, 47–54.

Ingebritsen, O. C. Maze learning after lesion in the cervical cord. *J. comp. Psychol.*, 1932, 14, 279–294.

Ingram, W. R., R. W. Barris, and S. W. Ranson. Catalepsy: an experimental study. *Arch. Neurol. Psychiat.*, 1936, 35, 1175–1197.

Jackson, J. H. Remarks on evolution and dissolution of the nervous system. *J. ment. Sci.*, 1888, 33, 25–48.

Jacobsen, C. F. A study of cerebral function in learning. The frontal lobes. *J. comp. Neurol.*, 1931, 52, 271–340.

———. Functions of frontal association areas in primates. *Arch. Neurol. Psychiat.*, 1935, 33, 558–560.

———. Studies of cerebral function in primates: I. The functions of the frontal

Jacobsen, C. F. (*cont.*)
association areas in monkeys. *Comp. Psychol. Monogr.*, 1936, **13**, 1–60.
———, and G. M. Haselrud. Studies of cerebral function in primates: III. The effect of motor and premotor area lesions on delayed responses in monkeys. *Comp. Psychol. Monogr.*, 1936, **13**, 66–68.
———, and H. W. Nissen. Studies of cerebral function in primates: IV. The effects of frontal lobe lesions on the delayed alternation habit in monkeys. *J. comp. Psychol.*, 1937, **23**, 101–112.
———, J. B. Wolfe, and T. A. Jackson. An experimental analysis of the functions of the frontal association areas in primates. *J. nerv. ment. Dis.*, 1935, **82**, 1–14.

James, H. Flicker: an unconditioned stimulus for imprinting. *Canad. J. Psychol.*, 1959, **13**, 59–67.

Janis, I. L. Psychological effects of electric convulsive treatments. *J. nerv. ment. Dis.*, 1950, 111, 359–397; 469–489.

Janowitz, H. D., and M. I. Grossman. Some factors affecting the food intake of normal dogs with esophagostomy and gastric fistula. *Amer. J. Physiol.*, 1949, **159**, 143–148.
———, and ———. Effect of prefeeding, alcohol and bitters on food intake of dogs. *Amer. J. Physiol.*, 1951, **164**, 182–186.

Jasper, H. H. Functional properties of the thalamic reticular system. In J. F. Delafresnaye (Ed.), *Brain mechanisms and consciousness*. Springfield, Ill.: Charles C Thomas, 1954. Pp. 374–401.
———, and C. Ajmone-Marsan. *Stereotaxic atlas of the diencephalon of the cat*. Ottawa: National Research Council of Canada, 1954.
———, and C. Shagass. Conditioning occipital alpha rhythm in man. *J. exp. Psychol.*, 1941, **28**, 373–388.

Jaynes, J. Imprinting: The interaction of learned and innate behavior: II. The critical period. *J. comp. physiol. Psychol.*, 1957, **50**, 6–10.

Jenkins, T. N., L. H. Warner, and C. J. Warden. Standard apparatus for the study of animal motivation. *J. comp. Psychol.*, 1926, **6**, 361–382.

Jennings, H. S. *The behavior of lower organisms*. New York: Columbia University Press, 1906.

John, E. R., and K. F. Killam. Electrophysiological correlates of avoidance conditioning in the cat. *J. Pharmacol.*, 1959, **125**, 252–274.

Jung, R. Neuronal integration in the visual cortex and its significance for visual information. In W. A. Rosenblith (Ed.), *Sensory communication*. New York: Wiley, 1961. Pp. 627–674.
———, and R. Hassler. The extrapyramidal motor system. *Handb. Physiol.*, 1960, Sec. 1, **2**, 863–927.

Kaada, B. R. Somato-motor, autonomic and electrocorticographic responses to electrical stimulation of "rhinencephalic" and other structures in primates, cat and dog. *Acta physiol. scand.*, 1951, **24**, Suppl. 83, 1–285.
———. Cingulate, posterior orbital, anterior insular and temporal pole cortex. *Handb. Physiol.*, 1960, Sec. 1, **2**, 1345–1372.

Kalmus, H., D. B. Fry, and P. Denes. Effects of delayed visual control on writing, drawing and tracking. *Lang. Speech*, 1960, **3**, 96–108.

Kappers, C. U. A. *Vergleichende Anatomie des Nervensystems*. Haarlem: Bohn, 1920.
———. Principles of development of the nervous system (neurobiotaxis). In W. Penfield (Ed.), *Cytology and cellular pathology of the nervous system*. New York: Hoeber, 1932. Vol. 1, pp. 43–89.

Katz, B. Subthreshold potentials in medullated nerve. *J. Physiol. (London)*, 1947, **106**, 66–79.

Kawamura, S. The process of sub-culture propagation among Japanese macaques. In C. H. Southwick (Ed.), *Primate social behavior*. New York: Van Nostrand, 1963. Pp. 82–90.

Kayser, C. Essai d'analyse du mécanisme du sommeil hibernal. *Ann. Physiol. physicochim. Biol.*, 1940, **16**, 313–373.

Kellogg, W. N. Echo ranging in the porpoise. *Science*, 1958, **128**, 982–988.
———, J. Deese, and N. H. Pronko. On the behavior of the lumbospinal dog. *J. exp. Psychol.*, 1946, **36**, 503–511.
———, ———, and M. Feinberg. An attempt to condition the chronic spinal dog. *J. exp. Psychol.*, 1947, **37**, 99–117.

Kennard, M. A. Cortical representation of motor function. Studies on series of monkeys of various ages from infancy to maturity. *Arch. Neurol. Psychiat.*, 1942, **48**, 227–240.

Kennard, M. A. (*cont.*)
————. Effect of bilateral ablation of cingulate area on behavior of cats. *J. Neurophysiol.*, 1955, **18**, 159–169.

Kenshalo, D. R., J. P. Nafe, and W. W. Dawson. A new method for investigation of thermal sensitivity. *J. Psychol.*, 1960, **49**, 29–41.

Killam, E. F., and K. F. Killam. The influence of drugs on central afferent pathways. In W. S. Field (Ed.), *Brain mechanisms and drug action*. Springfield, Ill.: Charles C Thomas, 1957.

Kimble, G. A. *Hilgard and Marquis' conditioning and learning*. (2d. ed.) New York: Appleton, 1961.

Kimura, K., and L. M. Beidler. Microelectrode study of taste receptors of rat and hamster. *J. cell. comp. Physiol.*, 1961, **58**, 131–140.

Kinder, E. F. A study of the nest-building activity of the albino rat. *J. exp. Zool.*, 1927, **47**, 117–161.

Kislack, J. W., and F. A. Beach. Inhibition of aggressiveness by ovarian hormones. *Endocrinology*, 1955, **56**, 684–692.

Kleitman, N. *Sleep and wakefulness*. (Rev. ed.) Chicago: University of Chicago Press, 1963.

Klüver, H. *Behavior mechanisms in monkeys*. Chicago: University of Chicago Press, 1933.

————. Visual functions after removal of the occipital lobes. *J. Physiol.* (*London*), 1941, **11**, 23–45.

————, and P. C. Bucy. An analysis of certain effects of bilateral temporal lobectomy in the rhesus monkey. with special reference to "psychic blindness." *J. Psychol.*, 1938, **5**, 33–54.

Koehler, O., and A. Zagarus. Beiträge zum Brutverhalten des Halsbandregenpfeifers. *Beitr. Fortpfl. Vogel*, 1937, **13**, 1–9.

Köhler, W. *Gestalt psychology*. New York: Liveright, 1929.

Kohler, I. Über Aufbau und Wandlungen der Wahrnehmungswelt, insbesondere über 'bedingte Empfindungen.' *Sitzb. Oest. Akad. Wiss., phil-hist. Kl.*, 1951, **227**, Treatise 1.

Koikegami, H., T. Yamada, and K. Usui. Stimulation of amygdaloid nuclei and periamygdaloid cortex with special reference to its effect on uterine movements and ovulation. *Folia psychiat. neurol. jap.*, 1954, **8**, 7–31.

Koller, G. Hormonale und psychische

Steuerung beim Nestbau weisser Mäusse. *Zool. Anz., Suppl.*, 1956, **19**, 123–132.

Konishi, M. The role of auditory feedback in the vocal behavior of the domestic fowl. *Z. Tierpsychol.*, 1963, **20**, 349–367.

Konorski, J. The physiological approach to the problem of recent memory. In J. F. Delafresnaye (Ed.), *Brain mechanisms and learning*. Oxford: Blackwell, 1961. Pp. 115–132.

Kraft, M. S., W. Obrist, and K. H. Pribram. The effect of irritative lesions of the striate cortex on learning of visual discriminations in monkeys. *J. comp. physiol. Psychol.*, 1960, **53**, 17–22.

Kramer, G. Orientierte Zugaktivität gekäfigter Singvögel. *Naturwiss.*, 1950, **37**, 188.

————. Experiments on bird orientation. *Ibis*, 1952, **94**, 265–285.

Krech, D., M. R. Rosenzweig, and E. L. Bennett. Effects of environmental complexity and training on brain chemistry. *J. comp. physiol. Psychol.*, 1960, **53**, 509–519.

Krechevsky, I. "Hypotheses" in rats. *Psychol. Rev.*, 1932, **39**, 516–532 .

Kreidl, A. Weitere Beiträge zur Physiologie des Ohrlabyrinthes. *Sitzb. Oest. Akad. Wiss., phil-hist. Kl.*, 1893, **102**, 149.

Krieg, W. J. S. Accurate placement of minute lesions in the brain of the albino rat. *Quart. Bull. Northwestern Univer. Med. School*, 1946, **20**, 199–208.

Kruger, L., and P. Porter. A behavioral study of the functions of the rolandic cortex in the monkey. *J. comp. Neurol.*, 1958, **109**, 439–467.

Kryter, K. D., and H. W. Ades. Studies on the function of the higher acoustic nervous centers in the cat. *Amer. J. Psychol.*, 1943, **56**, 501–536.

Kuffler, S. W. Discharge patterns and functional organization of mammalian retina. *J. Neurophysiol.*, 1953, **16**, 37–68.

Kummer, H. Sociales Verhalten einer Mantelpaviangruppe. *Beih. Schweiz. Z. Psychol.*, 1957, 1–91.

Kuo, Z. Y. Ontogeny of embryonic behavior in Aves: IV. The influence of prenatal behavior on postnatal life. *J. comp. Psychol.*, 1932, **14**, 109–121.

Kuypers, H. G. J. M. Central cortical projections to motor and somatosensory cell groups. *Brain*, 1960, **83**, 161–184.

Kuypers, H. G. J. M. (*cont.*)
———. Corticospinal connections: postnatal development in the rhesus monkey. *Science*, 1962, **138**, 678–680.

Lack, D. *The life of the robin.* Baltimore: Penguin, 1953.
Lance, J. W., and R. L. Manning. Origin of the pyramidal tract in the cat. *J. Physiol.* (*London*), 1954, **124**, 385–399.
Langley, J. N. *The autonomic nervous system.* Cambridge: Heffer, 1921.
Larsson, S. On the hypothalamic organization of the nervous mechanism regulating food intake. *Acta physiol. scand.*, 1954, Suppl. 115, 7–40.
Lashley, K. S. Studies of cerebral function in learning. *Psychobiol.*, 1920, **2**, 55–135.
———. Studies of cerebral function in learning: IV. Vicarious function after destruction of the visual areas. *Amer. J. Physiol.*, 1922, **59**, 44–71.
———. *Brain mechanisms and intelligence.* Chicago: University of Chicago Press, 1929.
———. Integrative functions of the cerebral cortex. *Physiol. Rev.*, 1933, **13**, 1–42.
———. The mechanism of vision: XIII. Nervous structures concerned in the acquisition and retention of habits based on reactions to light. *Comp. Psychol. Monogr.*, 1935, **11**, 43–79.
———. An experimental analysis of instinctive behavior. *Psychol. Rev.*, 1938, **45**, 445–471.
———. The mechanism of vision: XVI. The functioning of small remnants of the visual cortex. *J. comp. Neurol.*, 1939, **70**, 45–67.
———. The mechanism of vision: XVII. Autonomy of the visual cortex. *J. genet. Psychol.*, 1942, **60**, 197–221.
———. Studies of cerebral function in learning: XII. Loss of the maze habit after occipital lesions in blind rats. *J. comp. Neurol.*, 1943, **79**, 431–462.
———. Studies of cerebral function in learning: XIII. Apparent absence of transcortical association in maze learning. *J. comp. Neurol.*, 1944, **80**, 257–281.
———. The mechanism of vision: XVIII. Effects of destroying the visual "associative areas" of the monkey. *Genet. Psychol. Monog.*, 1948, **37**, 107–166.

———. In search of the engram. *Symp. Soc. exp. Biol.*, 1950, **4**, 454–482.
———, and J. Ball. Spinal conduction and kinesthetic sensitivity in the maze habit. *J. comp. Psychol.*, 1929, **9**, 71–105.
———, and G. Clark. The cytoarchitecture of the cerebral cortex of Ateles: a critical examination of architectonic studies. *J. comp. Neurol.*, 1946, **85**, 223–306.
Lassek, A. M. *The pyramidal tract.* Springfield, Ill.: Charles C Thomas, 1954.
Lebidinskiaia, S. I., and J. S. Rosenthal. Reactions of a dog after removal of the cerebral hemispheres. *Brain*, 1935, **58**, 412–419.
Leblond, C. P. Extra-hormonal factors in maternal behavior. *Proc. Soc. exp. Biol.*, N.Y., 1938, **38**, 66–70.
Lee, B. S. Some effects of side-tone delay. *J. Acoust. Soc. Amer.*, 1950, **22**, 639–640.
Lehrman, D. S. Effect of female sex hormones on incubation behavior in the ring dove. *J. comp. physiol. Psychol.*, 1958, **51**, 142–145.
———. Hormonal regulation of parental behavior in birds and infrahuman mammals. In W. C. Young (Ed.), *Sex and internal secretions.* (3rd ed.) Baltimore: Williams & Wilkins, 1961. Vol. 2, pp. 1268–1382.
———, P. N. Brody, and R. P. Wortis. The presence of the mate and of nesting material as stimuli for the development of incubation behavior and for gonadotropin secretion in the ring dove. *Endocrinology*, 1961, **68**, 507–516.
Lele, P. P. Relationship between cutaneous thermal thresholds, skin temperature and cross-sectional area of the stimulus. *J. Physiol.* (*London*), 1954, **126**, 191–205.
Lende, R. A. Cerebral cortex: a sensorimotor amalgam in the Marsupialia. *Science*, 1963, **141**, 730–732.
Leopold, A. C. *Auxins and plant growth.* Berkeley: University of California Press, 1955.
Lettvin, J. Y., H. R. Maturana, W. S. McCulloch, and W. H. Pitts. What the frog's eye tells the frog's brain. *Proc. I.R.E.*, 1959, **47**, 1940–1951.
Levine, S. A further study of infantile handling and adult avoidance learning. *J. Pers.*, 1956, **25**, 70–80.
———. Psychophysiological effects of infantile stimulation. In E. L. Bliss (Ed.),

Levine, S. (cont.)
Roots of behavior. New York: Hoeber, 1962. Pp. 246–253.

———, J. A. Chevalier, and S. J. Korchin. The effects of early shock and handling on later avoidance conditioning. J. Pers., 1956. 24, 475–493.

———, and G. W. Lewis. The relative importance of experimenter contact in an effect produced by extra-stimulation in infancy. J. comp. physiol. Psychol., 1959, 52, 368–369.

———, and L. S. Otis. The effects of handling during pre- and postweaning on the resistance of the albino rat to deprivation in adulthood. Canad. J. Psychol., 1958, 12, 103–108.

Levy, D. M. Experiments in the sucking reflex and social behavior of dogs. Amer. J. Orthopsychiat., 1934, 4, 203–224.

Lewis, T. L. Pain. New York: Macmillan, 1942.

Liddell, E. G. T., and C. G. Phillips. Pyramidal section in the cat. Brain, 1943, 67, 1–9.

Liddell, H. S. The conditioned reflex. In F. A. Moss (Ed.), Comparative psychology. (2d ed.) Englewood Cliffs, N.J.: Prentice-Hall, 1942. Pp. 178–216.

Lim, R. K. S., C.-N. Liu, and R. L. Moffitt. A stereotaxic atlas of the dog's brain. Springfield, Ill.: Charles C Thomas, 1960.

Lindley, S. B. The maze-learning ability of anosmic and blind anosmic rats. J. gen. Psychol., 1930, 37, 245–267.

Lindsley, D. B., J. W. Bowden, and H. W. Magoun. Effect upon the EEG of acute injury to the brain stem activating system. EEG clin. Neurophysiol., 1949, 1, 475–486.

Lisk, R. D., and M. Newlon. Estradiol: evidence for its direct effect on hypothalamic neurons. Science, 1963, 139, 223–224.

Lissák, K., and E. Grastyán. The changes of hippocampal electrical activity during conditioning. EEG clin. Neurophysiol., Suppl. 13, 1960, 271–279.

Lissmann, H. W. The neurological basis of locomotory rhythms in the spinal dogfish (Scyllium canicula, Acanthias vulgaris): I. Reflex behaviour; II. The effect of deafferentation. J. exp. Biol., 1946, 23, 143–161, 162–176.

Lloyd, D. P. C. Principles of nervous activity. In J. F. Fulton (Ed.), Textbook of physiology. (17th ed.) Philadelphia: Saunders, 1955. Pp. 1–122.

———. Spinal mechanisms involved in somatic activities. Handb. Physiol., 1960, Sec. 1, 2, 929–949.

Lofts, B., and A. J. Marshall. The effects of prolactin administration on the internal rhythm of reproduction in male birds. J. Endocrin., 1956, 13, 101–106.

Lorente de Nó, R. Studies on the structure of the cerebral cortex: II. Continuation of the study of the ammonic system. J. Psychol. Neurol., Leipzig, 1934, 46, 113–177.

Lorenz, K. Der Kumpan in der Umwelt des Vögels. J. Orinth., 1935, 83, 137–214; 289–413.

———. Über den Begriff der Instinkthandlung. Folia biotheoretica, 1937, 2, 17–50.

———. The comparative method of studying innate behaviour patterns. Sympos. Soc. exp. Biol., 1950, 4, 221–268.

Loucks, R. B. The experimental delimitation of neural structures essential for learning: the attempt to condition striped muscle responses with faradization of the sigmoid gyri. J. Psychol., 1935, 1, 5–44.

———. Studies of neural structures essential for learning: II. The conditioning of salivary and striped muscle responses to faradization of cortical sensory elements and the action of sleep upon such mechanisms. J. comp. Psychol., 1938, 25, 315–332.

Lyman, C. P., and P. O. Chatfield. Physiology of hibernation in mammals. Physiol. Rev., 1955, 35, 403–425.

McAdam, D. W., J. R. Knott and W. R. Ingram. Changes in EEG evoked responses evoked by the conditioned stimulus during classical aversive conditioning in the cat. EEG clin. Neurophysiol., 1962, 14, 731–738.

McCleary, R. A., and C. T. Morgan. Food-hoarding in rats as a function of environmental temperature. J. comp. Psychol., 1946, 39, 371–378.

McClelland, W. J. Differential handling and weight gain in the albino rat. Canad. J. Psychol., 1956, 10, 19–22.

Macfarlane, D. A. The role of kinesthesis in maze learning. Calif. Univer. Publ. Psychol., 1930, 4, 277–305.

McGill T. E. Sexual behavior in three in-

McGill, T. E. (*cont.*)
bred strains of mice. *Behaviour*, 1962, 19, 341–350.

Machin, K. E. Electric receptors. *Sympos. Soc. exp. Biol.*, 1962, 16, 227–244.

Machne, X., and J. P. Segundo. Unitary responses to afferent volleys in amygdaloid complex. *J. Neurophysiol.*, 1956, 19, 232–240.

MacLean, P. D. Psychosomatic disease and the "visceral brain." Recent developments bearing on the Papez theory of emotion. *Psychosom. Med.*, 1949, 11, 338–353.

——, and J. M. R. Delgado. Electrical and chemical stimulation of frontotemporal portion of limbic system in the waking animal. *EEG clin. Neurophysiol.*, 1953, 5, 91–100.

——, R. H. Denniston, and S. Dua. Further studies on cerebral representation of penile erection: caudal thalamus, midbrain, and pons. *J. Neurophysiol.*, 1963, 26, 273–293.

——, S. Flanigan, J. P. Flynn, C. Kim, and J. R. Stevens. Hippocampal function: tentative correlations of conditioning, EEG, drug and radioautographic studies. *Yale J. Biol. Med.*, 1955, 28, 380–395.

——, and D. W. Ploog. Cerebral representation of penile erection. *J. Neurophysiol.*, 1962, 25, 29–55.

Magnes, J., G. Moruzzi, and O. Pompeiano. Electroencephalogram-synchronizing structures in the lower brain stem. In G. E. W. Wolstenholme and M. O'Connor (Eds.), *The nature of sleep.* Boston: Little, Brown, 1961. Pp. 57–85.

Magnus, R. *Körperstellung.* Berlin: Springer, 1924.

Magoun, H. W. Caudal and cephalic influences of the brain stem reticular formation. *Physiol. Rev.*, 1950, 30, 459–474.

——, F. Harrison, J. R. Brobeck, and S. W. Ranson. Activation of heat loss mechanisms by local heating of the brain. *J. Neurophysiol.*, 1938, 1, 101–114.

——, and R. Rhines. An inhibitory mechanism in the bulbar reticular formation. *J. Neurophysiol.*, 1946, 9, 165–171.

Maier, N. R. F., and T. C. Schneirla. *Principles of animal psychology.* New York: McGraw-Hill, 1935.

Malis, L. I., K. H. Pribram, and L. Kruger. Action potentials in "motor" cortex evoked by peripheral nerve stimulation. *J. Neurophysiol.*, 1953, 16, 161–167.

Malmo, R. B. Interference factors in delayed response in monkeys after removal of frontal lobes. *J. Neurophysiol.*, 1942, 5, 295–308.

Margules, D. L., and J. Olds. Identical "feeding" and "rewarding" systems in the lateral hypothalamus of rats. *Science*, 1962, 135, 374–375.

Marks, W. B., W. H. Dobelle, and E. F. MacNichol. Visual pigments of single primate cones. *Science*, 1964, 143, 1181–1182.

Marler, P. Studies of fighting in chaffinches: I. Behavior in relation to social hierarchy. *Brit. J. animal Behav.*, 1955, 3, 111–117.

Marquis, D. G. Effects of removal of the visual cortex in mammals, with observations on the retention of light discrimination in dogs. *Res. Publ. Ass. nerv. ment. Dis.*, 1934, 13, 558–592.

Marshall, A. J. Internal and environmental control of breeding. *Ibis*, 1959, 101, 456–478.

——, and C. J. F. Coombs. The interaction of environmental, internal and behavioural factors in the rook. *Proc. zool. Soc. (London)*, 1957, 128, 545–589.

——, and H. J. de S. Disney. Experimental induction of the breeding season in a xerophilous bird. *Nature*, 1957, 180, 647–649.

Marshall, N. B., R. J. Barrnett, and J. Mayer. Hypothalamic lesions in goldthioglucose injected mice. *Proc. Soc. exp. Biol. Med.*, 1955, 90, 240–244.

Marshall, W. H., C. N. Woolsey, and P. Bard. Representation of tactile sensibility in the monkey's cortex as indicated by cortical potentials. *Amer. J. Physiol.*, 1937, 119, 372–373.

Mason, W. A. The effects of environmental restriction on the social development of rhesus monkeys. In C. H. Southwick (Ed.), *Primate social behavior.* Princeton, N.J.: Van Nostrand, 1963. Pp. 161–173.

——, H. F. Harlow, and R. R. Rueping. The development of manipulatory responsiveness in the infant rhesus monkey. *J. comp. physiol. Psychol.*, 1959, 52, 555–558.

Masserman, J. H. Is the hypothalamus a center of emotion? *Psychosom. Med.*, 1941, 3, 3–25.

Massopust, L. C. Diencephalon of the rat. In D. E. Sheer (Ed.), *Electrical stimulation of the brain.* Austin: University of Texas Press, 1961. Pp. 182–202.

Matthews, G. V. T. Sun navigation in homing pigeons. *J. exp. Biol.*, 1953, **30**, 243–267.

——. *Bird Navigation.* London: Cambridge, 1955.

Matthews, L. H. Visual stimulation and ovulation in pigeons. *Proc. Roy. Soc., (London)*, 1939, **126B**, 557–560.

Mayer, J., R. G. French, C. F. Zighera, and R. J. Barrnett. Hypothalamic obesity in the mouse: production, description and metabolic characteristics. *Amer. J. Physiol.*, 1955, **182**, 75–82.

Mehler, W. R. The mammalian "pain tract" phylogeny. *Anat. Rec.*, 1957, **127**, 332.

Meikle, T. H., and J. Seichzer. Interocular transfer of brightness discrimination in "split-brain" cats. *Science*, 1960, **132**, 734–735.

Meites, J. Recent studies on the mechanisms controlling the initiation of lactation. *Rev. Canad. Biol.*, 1954, **13**, 359–370.

Menzel, R., and R. Menzel. Einiges aus der Pflegewelt der Mutterhündin. *Behaviour*, 1953, **5**, 289–304.

Merrillees, N. C. R., S. Sunderland, and W. Hayhow. Neuromuscular spindles in the extraocular muscles in man. *Anat. Rec.*, 1950, **108**, 23–30.

Mettler, F. A., and C. C. Mettler. The effects of striatal injury. *Brain*, 1942, **65**, 242–255.

Meyer, D. R., H. F. Harlow, and H. W. Ades. Retention of delayed responses and proficiency in oddity problems by monkeys with preoccipital ablations. *Amer. J. Psychol.*, 1951, **64**, 391–396.

——, and C. N. Woolsey. Effects of localized cortical destruction on auditory discriminative conditioning in cat. *J. Neurophysiol.*, 1952, **15**, 149–162.

Michael, R. P. Estrogen-sensitive neurons and sexual behavior in female cats. *Science*, 1961, **136**, 322–323.

Mickle, W. A. and H. W. Ades. A composite sensory projection area in the cerebral cortex of the cat. *Amer. J. Physiol.*, 1952, **170**, 682–689.

——, and ——. Rostral projection pathway of the vestibular system. *Amer. J. Physiol.*, 1954, **176**, 243–246.

Migeon, C. J., A. B. French, L. T. Samuels, and J. Z. Bowers. Plasma 17-hydroxycorticosteroid level and leucocyte values in the rhesus monkey, including normal variation and the effect of ACTH. *Amer. J. Physiol.*, 1955, **182**, 462–468.

Miller, M. R., H. J. Ralston, and M. Kasahara. The pattern of cutaneous innervation of the human hand, foot and breast. In W. Montagna (Ed.), *Cutaneous Innervation.* New York: Pergamon Press, 1960. Pp. 1–47.

Miller, N. E. Studies of fear as an acquirable drive. I. Fear as motivation and fear-reduction as reinforcement in the learning of new responses. *J. exp. Psychol.*, 1948, **38**, 89–101.

——. Learnable drives and rewards. In S. S. Stevens (Ed.), *Handbook of experimental psychology.* New York: Wiley, 1951. Pp. 435–472.

——. Experiments on motivation: studies combining psychological, physiological and pharmacological techniques. *Science*, 1957, **126**, 1271–1278.

Millott, N. J. Animal photosensitivity with special reference to eyeless forms. *Endeavour*, 1957, **16**, 19–28.

Minkowski, M. Experimentelle Untersuchungen über die Beziehungen der Grosshirnrinde und der Netzhaut zu den primären optischen Zentren besonders zum Corpus geniculatum externum. *Arb. hirnanat. Inst., Zürich*, 1913, 7, 255–362.

——. Étude sur les connexions anatomiques des circonvolutions rolandiques, pariétales et frontales. *Schweiz. Arch. Neurol. Psychiat.*, 1923, **12**, 71–104.

Mirsky, A. F. The influence of sex hormones on social behavior in monkeys. *J. comp. physiol. Psychol.*, 1955, **48**, 327–335.

——, H. E. Rosvold, and K. H. Pribram. Effects of cingulectomy on social behavior in monkeys. *J. Neurophysiol.*, 1957, **20**, 588–601.

Mishkin, M. Visual discrimination performance following ablations of the temporal lobe: II. Ventral surface vs. hippocampus. *J. comp. physiol. Psychol.*, 1954, **47**, 187–193.

——. Effects of small frontal lesions on delayed alternation in monkeys. *J. Neurophysiol.*, 1957, **20**, 615–622.

——, and K. H. Pribram. Visual discrimination performance following partial ablations of the temporal lobe: I.

Mishkin, M., and K. H. Pribram (cont.) Ventral vs. lateral. *J. comp. physiol. Psychol.*, 1954, 47, 14–20.

Mittelstaedt, H. Telotaxis and Optomotorik von Eristalsis bei Augeninversion. *Naturwiss.*, 1949, 36, 90–91.

Moltz, H. Imprinting: empirical basis and theoretical significance. *Psychol. Bull.*, 1960, 57, 291–314.

Moncrieff, R. W. *The chemical senses.* (2d ed.) London: Leonard Hill, 1951.

Montgomery, K. C. A test of two explanations of spontaneous alternation. *J. comp. physiol. Psychol.*, 1952, 45, 287–293.

———. Role of the exploratory drive in learning. *J. comp. physiol. Psychol.*, 1954, 47, 60–64.

Montgomery, M. F. The role of the salivary glands in the thirst mechanism. *Amer. J. Physiol.*, 1931, 96, 221–227.

Moore, C. R., and D. Price. Some effects of testosterone and testosterone-propionate in the rat. *Anat. Rec.*, 1938, 71, 59–78.

Morgan, C. T., and E. Stellar. *Physiological Psychology.* (2nd ed.) New York: McGraw-Hill, 1950.

———, ———, and O. Johnson. Food deprivation and hoarding in rats. *J. comp. Psychol.*, 1943, 35, 275–295.

Morrell, F. Lasting changes in synaptic organization produced by continuous neuronal bombardment. In J. F. Delafresnaye (Ed.), *Brain mechanisms and learning.* Oxford: Blackwell, 1961. Pp. 375–392.

———, and H. Jasper. Electroencephalographic studies of the formation of temporary connections in the brain. *EEG clin. Neurophysiol.*, 1956, 8, 201–215.

Morrison, R. S., and E. W. Dempsey. A study of thalamo-cortical relations. *Amer. J. Physiol.*, 1942, 135, 280–292.

Morrison, S. D., and J. Mayer. Adipsia and aphagia in rats after lateral subthalamic lesions. *Amer. J. Physiol.*, 1957, 191, 248–254.

Moruzzi, G., and H. W. Magoun. Brain stem reticular formation and activation of the EEG. *EEG clin. Neurophysiol.*, 1949, 1, 455–473.

Mosier, H. D. Comparative histological study of the adrenal cortex of the wild and domesticated Norway rat. *Endocrinology*, 1957, 60, 460–469.

Mott, F. W., and C. S. Sherrington. Experiments upon the influence of sensory nerves upon the movement and nutrition of the limbs. *Proc. Roy. Soc. (London)*, 1895, 57, 481–488.

Moulton, D. G., and D. Tucker. Electrophysiology of the olfactory system. *Ann. N.Y. Acad. Sci.*, 1964, 116, 380–428.

Mountcastle, V. B. Some functional properties of the somatic afferent system. In W. A. Rosenblith (Ed.), *Sensory communication.* New York: Wiley, 1961. Pp. 403–436.

Moynihan, M., and M. F. Hall. Hostile, sexual and other social behavior patterns of the spice finch (*Lonchura punctulata*) in capitivity. *Behaviour*, 1954, 7, 33–76.

Munk, H. *Über die Funktionen der Grosshirnrinde.* Berlin: Hirschwald, 1890.

Myers, R. E. Interocular transfer of pattern discrimination in cats following section of crossed optic fibers. *J. comp. physiol. Psychol.*, 1955, 48, 470–473.

———. Function of corpus callosum in interocular transfer. *Brain*, 1956, 79, 358–363.

———. Interhemispheric communication through corpus callosum: limitations under conditions of conflict. *J. comp. physiol. Psychol.*, 1959, 52, 6–9.

———. Corpus callosum and visual gnosis. In J. F. Delafresnaye (Ed.), *Brain mechanism and learning.* Oxford: Blackwell, 1961. Pp. 481–505.

Nalbandov, A. V., and L. E. Card. Endocrine identification of the broody genotype of cocks. *J. Hered.*, 1945, 36, 34–39.

Nauta, W. J. H. Hippocampal projections and related neural pathways to the midbrain in the cat. *Brain*, 1958, 81, 319–340.

———, and P. A. Gygax. Silver impregnation of degenerating axons in the central nervous system: a modified technique. *Stain Technol.*, 1954, 29, 91–93.

———, and H. G. J. M. Kuypers. Some ascending pathways in the brain stem reticular formation. In H. Jasper et al. (Eds.), *Reticular formation of the brain.* Boston: Little, Brown, 1958. Pp. 2–30.

Needham, J. *Biochemistry and morphogenesis.* London: Cambridge, 1942.

Nice, M. M. Studies of the life history of the song sparrow: II. The behavior of the song sparrow and other passerines. *Trans. Linn. Soc., N.Y.*, 1943, 6, 1–328.

Nicolai, J. Zur Biologie und Ethologie des Gimpels (*Pyrrhula pyrrhula* L.). *Z. Tierpsychol.*, 1956, **31**, 93–132.

Nicoll, C. S., and J. Meites. Prolongation of lactation in the rat by litter replacement. *Proc. Soc. exp. Biol. Med.*, 1959, **101**, 81–82.

Nieder, P. C., and W. D. Neff. Auditory information from subcortical electrical stimulation in cats. *Science*, 1961, **133**, 1010–1011.

Nissen, W. H. The effects of gonadectomy, vasotomy, and injection of placental and orchic extracts on the sex behavior of the white rat. *Genet. Psychol. Monog.*, 1929, **5**, 451–547.

————. A study of exploratory behavior in the white rat by means of the obstruction method. *J. genet. Psychol.*, 1930, **37**, 361–376.

————. Phylogenetic comparison. In S. S. Stevens (Ed.), *Handbook of experimental psychology*. New York: Wiley, 1951. Pp. 347–386.

————, K. L. Chow, and J. Semmes. Effects of restricted opportunity for tactual, kinesthetic and manipulative experience on the behavior of a chimpanzee. *Amer. J. Psychol.*, 1951, **64**, 485–507.

Noble, G. K. *The biology of the amphibia*. New York: McGraw-Hill, 1931.

————. Experimenting with the courtship of lizards. *Nat. Hist.*, 1934, **34**, 1–15.

————, and R. Borne. The effect of sex hormones on the social hierarchy of *Xiphophorus helleri*. *Anat. Rec.*, 1940, **78**, 147.

————, and H. T. Bradley. The relation of the thyroid and the hypophysis to the moulting process in the lizard, *Hemidactylus brookii*. *Biol. Bull.*, 1933, **64**, 289–298.

————, and B. Curtis. The social behavior of the jewelfish, *Hemichromis bimaculatus* Gill. *Bull. Amer. Mus. Nat. Hist.*, 1939, **76**, 1–48.

————, and B. Greenberg. Effects of seasons, castration and crystalline sex hormones upon the urogenital system and sexual behavior of the lizard (*Anolis carolinensis*): I. The adult female. *J. exp. Zool.*, 1941, **88**, 451–479.

————, and A. Zitrin. Induction of mating behavior in male and female chicks following injection of sex hormones. *Endocrinology*, 1942, **30**, 327–334.

Novikoff, A. B. The concept of integrative levels and biology. *Science*, 1945, **101**, 209–215.

Oberholzer, R. J. H., and W. O. Tofani. The neural control of respiration. *Handb. Physiol.*, 1960, Sec. 1, **2**, 1111–1129.

Oehlert, W., B. Schultze, and W. Maurer. Autoradiographische Untersuchung der Grösse der Eiweisstoffwechsels der verschiedenen Zellen des Zentralnervensystems. *Beitr. pathol. Anat.*, 1958, **119**, 343–376.

O'Kelly, L. I., and J. L. Falk. Water regulation in the rat: II. The effects of preloads of water and sodium chloride on the bar-pressing performance of thirsty rats. *J. comp. physiol. Psychol.*, 1958, **51**, 22–25.

Olds, J. Physiological mechanisms in reward. In M. R. Jones (Ed.), *Nebraska symposium on motivation*. Lincoln: University of Nebraska Press, 1955.

————. A preliminary mapping of electrical reinforcing effects in the rat brain. *J. comp. physiol. Psychol.*, 1956, **49**, 281–285.

————. Adaptive functions of paleocortical and related structures. In H. F. Harlow and C. N. Woolsey (Eds.), *Biological and biochemical bases of behavior*. Madison: University of Wisconsin Press, 1958. Pp. 237–262.

————. Differential effects of drives and drugs on self-stimulation at different brain sites. In D. E. Sheer (Ed.), *Electrical stimulation of the brain*. Austin: University of Texas Press, 1961. Pp. 350–366.

————, and P. M. Milner. Positive reinforcement produced by electrical stimulation of septal area and other regions of rat brain. *J. comp. physiol. Psychol.*, 1954, **47**, 419–427.

Orbach, J., and K. L. Chow. Differential effects of resections of somatic areas I and II in monkeys. *J. Neurophysiol.*, 1959, **22**, 195–203.

————, and R. L. Fantz. Differential effects of temporal neo-cortical resections on overtrained and non-overtrained visual habits in monkeys. *J. comp. physiol. Psychol.*, 1958, **51**, 126–129.

————, and G. Fischer. Factors influencing delayed response and discrimination performance in monkeys with bilateral resections of frontal granular cortex. *Arch. Neurol.*, 1959, **1**, 78–86.

Ottoson, D. Analysis of the electrical activity of the olfactory epithelium. *Acta physiol. scand.*, Suppl. **122**, 1956, 1–83.

Ottoson, D. (cont.)
———. Generation and transmission of signals in the olfactory system. In Y. Zotterman (Ed.), Olfaction and taste. New York: Pergamon, 1963. Pp. 35–44.

Paillard, J. The patterning of skilled movements. Handb. Physiol., 1960, Sec. 1, 3, 1679–1708.

Paintal, A. S. A study of right and left atrial receptors. J. Physiol. (London), 1953, 120, 596–610.

Palay, S. L., and G. E. Palade. The fine structure of neurons. J. biophys. biochem. Cytol., 1955, 1, 69–88.

Pantin, C. F. A. Behaviour patterns in lower invertebrates. Sympos. Soc. exp. Biol., 1950, 4, 175–195.

———. The elementary nervous system. Proc. Roy. Soc. (London), 1952, B140, 147–168.

Papez, J. W. A proposed mechanism of emotion. Arch. Neurol. Psychiat., 1937, 38, 725–743.

Parker, G. H. The elementary nervous system. Philadelphia: Lippincott, 1919.

———. Smell, taste and allied senses in the vertebrates. Philadelphia: Lippincott, 1922.

Pasik, P., T. Pasik, W. S. Battersby, and M. B. Bender. Visual and tactual discrinations by macaques with serial temporal and parietal lesions. J. comp. physiol. Psychol., 1958, 51, 427–436.

Pasik, T., P. Pasik, ———, and ———. Factors influencing visual behavior of monkeys with bilateral temporal lobe lesions. J. comp. Neurol., 1960, 115, 89–102.

Patton, H. D., and V. E. Amassian. Cortical projection zone of chorda tympani. J. Neurophysiol., 1952, 15, 243–250.

———, and ———. The pyramidal tract: its excitation and functions. Handb. Physiol., 1960, Sec. 1, 2, 837–861.

———, T. C. Ruch, and J. F. Fulton. The relation of the foot of the pre- and post-central gyrus to taste in the monkey and chimpanzee. Federation Proc., 1946, 5, 79.

Pavlov, I. P. Conditioned reflexes. London: Oxford, 1927.

Peacock, S. M., and R. Hodes. Influence of the forebrain on somato-motor activity: II. Facilitation. J. comp. Neurol., 1951, 94, 409–426.

Penfield, W. The excitable cortex of conscious man. Springfield, Ill.: Charles C Thomas, 1958.

Pengelley, E. T., and K. C. Fisher. Onset and cessation of hibernation under constant temperatures and light in the golden-mantled ground squirrel (Citellus lateralis). Nature, 1957, 180, 1371–1372.

Perdeck, A. C. Two types of orientation in migrating starlings, Sturnus vulgaris L., and chaffinches, Fringilla coelebs L., as revealed by displacement experiments. Ardea (Leiden), 1958, 46, 1–37.

Peters, R. W. The effect of changes in side-tone delay and level upon rate of oral reading of normal speakers. J. Speech Hearing Dis., 1954, 19, 483–490.

Pfaff, D. W. Cerebral implantation and autoradiographic studies of sex hormones. In J. Money (Ed.), Sex research. New York: Holt, Rinehart and Winston, 1965.

Pfaffmann, C. The sense of taste. Handb. Physiol., 1959, Sec. 1, 1, 507–533.

———. Taste and smell. In S. S. Stevens (Ed.), Handbook of experimental psychology. New York: Wiley, 1951. Pp. 1143–1171.

———, and J. K. Bare. Gustatory nerve discharges in normal and adrenalectomized rats. J. comp. physiol. Psychol., 1950, 43, 320–324.

Pfister, H. Über das Verhalten der Hühner beim Tragen von Prismen. Unpublished dissertation, University of Innsbruck, 1955.

Phillips, C. G. Cortical motor threshold and the thresholds and distribution of excited Betz cells in the rat. Quart. J. exp. Physiol., 1956, 41, 70–84.

Pilgrim, F. J., and R. A. Patton. Patterns of self-selection of purified dietary components by the rat. J. comp. physiol. Psychol., 1947, 40, 343–348.

Pinto, T., and R. B. Bromiley. A search for "spinal conditioning" and for evidence that it can become a reflex. J. exp. Psychol., 1950, 40, 121–130.

Pitt, F. The intelligence of animals: studies in comparative psychology. London: G. Allen, 1931.

Pittendrigh, C. S. Circadian rhythms and the circadian organization of living systems. Cold Spring Harbor Sympos. quant. Biol., 1960, 25, 159–184.

Poltyrew, S. S., and G. P. Zeliony. Grosshirnrinde und Assoziationsfunktion. Z. Biol., 1930, 90, 157–160.

Polyak, S. L. *The vertebrate visual system.* Chicago: University of Chicago Press, 1957.

Pomerat, C. M. Pulsatile activity of cells from the human brain in tissue culture. *J. nerv. ment. Dis.,* 1951, **114,** 430–449.

Porter, R. J. Antidromic conduction of volleys in pyramidal tract. *J. Neurophysiol.,* 1955, **18,** 138–150.

Porter, R. W., E. B. Cavanaugh, B. V. Critchlow, and C. H. Sawyer. Localized changes in electrical activity of the hypothalamus in estrous cats following vaginal stimulation. *Amer. J. Physiol.,* 1957, **189,** 145–151.

Powell, T. P. S., and W. M. Cowan. Centrifugal fibers in the lateral olfactory tract. *Nature,* 1963, **199,** 1296–1297.

Preston, J. B. Effects of chlorpromazine on the central nervous system of the cat: a possible neural basis for action. *J. Pharmacol. exp. Therap.,* 1956, **118,** 100–115.

Pribram, K. H., and M. Bagshaw. Further analysis of the temporal lobe syndrome utilizing fronto-temporal ablations. *J. comp. Neurol.,* 1953, **99,** 347–375.

———, and J. Barry. Further behavioral analysis of the parieto-temporal-preoccipital cortex. *J. Neurophysiol.,* 1956, **19,** 99–106.

———, and J. F. Fulton. An experimental critique of the effects of anterior cingulate ablations in monkey. *Brain,* 1954, **77,** 34–44.

———, and L. Kruger. Functions of the "olfactory brain." *Ann. N.Y. Acad. Sci.,* 1954, **58,** 109–138.

———, and M. Mishkin. Simultaneous and successive visual discrimination by monkeys with inferotemporal lesions. *J. comp. physiol. Psychol.,* 1955, **48,** 198–202.

———, ———, H. E. Rosvold, and S. J. Kaplan. Effects on delayed response performance of lesions of dorsolateral and ventromedial frontal cortex of baboons. *J. comp. physiol. Psychol.,* 1952, **45,** 565–575.

Prosser, C. L., and F. A. Brown. *Comparative animal physiology.* (2d ed.) Philadelphia: Saunders, 1961.

———, and W. S. Hunter. The extinction of startle responses and spinal reflexes in the white rat. *Amer. J. Physiol.,* 1936, **117,** 609–618.

Rabaud, E. L'instinct maternel chez les mammifères. *Bull. Soc. zool. fr.,* 1921a, **46,** 73–81.

———. L'instinct maternal chez les mammifères. *J. Psychol. norm. path.,* 1921b, **18,** 487–495.

Ramsey, A. O. Familial recognition in domestic birds. *Auk,* 1951, **68,** 1–16.

Ranson, S. W. Somnolence caused by hypothalamic lesions in the monkey. *Arch. Neurol. Psychiat.,* 1939, **41,** 1–23.

———. Regulation of body temperature. *Res. Publ. Ass. Res. nerv. ment. Dis.,* 1940, **20,** 342–399.

———, and H. W. Magoun. The hypothalamus. *Ergebn. Physiol.,* 1939, **41,** 56–163.

Rasch, E., H. Swift, A. H. Riesen, and K. L. Chow. Altered structure and composition of retinal cells in dark-reared mammals. *Exp. Cell Res.,* 1961, **25,** 348–363.

Rasmussen, G. L. The olivary peduncle and other fiber projections of the superior olivary complex. *J. comp. Neurol.,* 1946, **84,** 141–219.

———. Recurrent or "feed-back" connections of the auditory system of the cat. *Amer. J. Physiol.,* 1955, **183,** 653.

Rawson, K. S. Experimental modification of mammalian endogenous activity rhythms. In R. B. Withrow (Ed.), *Photoperiodism and related phenomena in plants and animals.* Washington, D.C.: American Association for the Advancement of Science, 1959. Pp. 791–800.

Reece, R. P., and C. W. Turner. Effect of stimulus of suckling upon galactin content of the rat pituitary. *Proc. Soc. exp. Biol. Med.,* 1937, **35,** 621–622.

Reeves, C. D. Discrimination of light of different wavelengths by fish. *Behav. Monogr.,* 1919, **4,** 1–106.

Rich, W. H., and H. B. Holmes. Experiments in marking young Chinook salmon on the Columbia River. *Bull. U.S. Bur. Fish,* 1928, **44,** 215–264.

Richter, C. P. A behavioristic study of the activity of the rat. *Comp. Psychol. Monogr.,* 1922, **1,** 1–55.

———. Animal behavior and internal drives. *Quart. Rev. Biol.,* 1927, **2,** 307–343.

———. Salt taste thresholds of normal and adrenalectomized rats. *Endocrinology,* 1939, **24,** 367–371.

Richter, C. P. (cont.)
———. Total self-regulatory functions in animals and human beings. Harvey Lect., 1942, 38, 63–103.
———, and B. Barelare. Nutritional requirements of pregnant and lactating rats studied by the self-selection method. Endocrinology, 1938, 23, 15–24.
———, and J. F. Eckert. Behavior changes produced in the rat by hypophysectomy. Proc. Assoc. Rev. nerv. Dis., 1936, 17, 561–571.
———, L. E. Holt, and B. Barelare. Vitamin B₁ craving in rats. Science, 1937, 86, 354–355.
Richter, D. The turnover of proteins and lipids in vivo in the brain. In K. A. C. Elliott et al. (Eds.), Neurochemistry. Springfield, Ill.: Charles C Thomas, 1962. Pp. 276–287.
Riddle, O. Physiological responses to prolactin. Cold Spring Harbor. Sympos. quant. Biol., 1937, 5, 218–228.
———, E. L. Lahr, and R. W. Bates. Effectiveness and specificity of prolactin in the induction of the maternal instinct in virgin rats. Amer. J. Physiol., 1935a, 113, 109.
———, ———, ———. Prolactin-induced activities which express maternal behavior in virgin rats. Amer. J. Physiol., 1935b, 113, 110.
———, ———, ———. The role of hormones in the initiation of maternal behavior in rats. Amer. J. Physiol., 1942, 137, 299–317.
Riesen, A. H. Plasticity of behavior: psychological aspects. In H. F. Harlow and C. N. Woolsey (Eds.), Biological and biochemical bases of behavior. Madison: University of Wisconsin Press, 1958. Pp. 425–450.
———. Effects of stimulus deprivation on the development and atrophy of the visual sensory system. Amer. J. Orthopsychiat., 1960, 30, 23–36.
———. Studying perceptual development using the technique of sensory deprivation. J. nerv. ment. Dis., 1961, 132, 21–25.
———, and L. Aarons. Visual movement and intensity discrimination in cats after early deprivation of pattern vision. J. comp. physiol. Psychol., 1959, 52, 142–149.
Riess, B. F. The isolation of factors of learning and native behavior in field and laboratory studies. Ann. N.Y. Acad. Sci., 1950, 51, 1093–1102.

Riopelle, A. J., R. G. Alper, P. N. Strong, and H. W. Ades. Multiple discrimination and patterned string performance of normal and temporal-lobectomized monkeys. J. comp. physiol. Psychol., 1953, 46, 145–149.
———, H. F. Harlow, P. H. Settlage, and H. W. Ades. Performance of normal and operated monkeys on visual learning tests. J. comp. physiol. Psychol., 1951, 44, 283–289.
Robertson, J. D. The ultrastructure of a reptilian myoneural junction. J. biophys. biochem. Cytol., 1956, 2, 381–394.
Robinson, E. A. and E. F. Adolph. Pattern of normal water drinking in dogs. Amer. J. Physiol., 1943, 139, 39–44.
Robson, J. M. Induction of oestrous changes in the monkey and bitch by triphenyl ethylene. Proc. Soc. exp. Biol. Med., 1938, 38, 153–157.
Rose, J. E. The cortical connections of the reticular complex of the thalamus. Res. Publ. Ass. nerv. ment. Dis., 1952, 30, 454–479.
———, R. Galambos, and J. R. Hughes. Microelectrode studies of the cochlear nuclei of the cat. Bull. Johns Hopkins Hosp., 1959, 104, 211–251.
———, and V. Mountcastle. Touch and kinesthesis. Handb. Physiol., 1959, Sec. 1, 1, 387–429.
———, and C. N. Woolsey. The relations of thalamic connections, cellular structure and evokable electrical activity in the auditory region of the cat. J. comp. Neurol., 1949, 91, 441–466.
Rosenblatt, J. S., and L. R. Aronson. The decline of sexual behavior in male cats after castration with special reference to the role of prior sexual experience. Behaviour, 1958a, 12, 285–338.
———, ———. The influence of experience on the behavioural effects of androgen in prepubertally castrated male cats. Animal Behav., 1958b, 6, 171–182.
Rosenzweig, M. R., D. Krech, E. L. Bennett, and M. C. Diamond. Effects of environmental complexity and training on brain chemistry and anatomy: a replication and extension. J. comp. physiol. Psychol., 1962a, 55, 429–437.
———, ———, ———, and J. F. Zolman. Variation in environmental complexity and brain measures. J. comp. physiol. Psychol., 1962b, 55, 1092–1095.
Ross, S. Sucking frustration in neonate

Ross, S. (*cont.*)
puppies. *J. abnorm. soc. Psychol.*, 1950, 46, 142–149.
———, V. H. Denenberg, P. B. Sawin, and P. Meyer. Changes in nest building behaviour in multiparous rabbits. *Brit. J. animal Behav.*, 1956, 4, 69–74.
Rossi, G. F. and A. Brodal. Corticofugal fibers to the brain-stem reticular formation: an experimental study in the cat. *J. Anat. (London)*, 1956, 90, 42–62.
Rosvold, H. E., and J. M. R. Delgado. The effect on delayed-alternation test performance of stimulating or destroying electrically structures within the frontal lobes of the monkey's brain. *J. comp. physiol. Psychol.*, 1956, 49, 365–372.
———, A. F. Mirsky, and K. H. Pribram. Influence of amygdalectomy on social interaction in a monkey group. *J. comp. physiol. Psychol.*, 1954, 47, 173–178.
———, and M. Mishkin. Non-sensory effects of frontal lesions on discrimination learning and performance. In J. F. Delafresnaye (Ed.), *Brain mechanisms and learning*. Oxford: Blackwell. 1961. Pp. 555–576.
———, M. K. Szwarcbart, A. F. Mirsky, and M. Mishkin. The effect of frontal-lobe damage on delayed-response performance in chimpanzees. *J. comp. physiol. Psychol.*, 1961, 54, 368–374.
Rothballer, A. B. Studies on the adrenaline-sensitive component of the reticular activating system. *EEG clin. Neurophysiol.*, 1956, 8, 603–621.
Rowan, W. Relation of light to bird migration and developmental changes. *Nature*, 1925, 115, 494–495.
———. Light and seasonal reproduction in animals. *Biol. Rev.*, 1938, 13, 374–402.
Rowell, T. E. On the retrieving of young and other behaviour in lactating golden hamsters. *Proc. Zool. Soc., London*, 1960, 135, 265–282.
Ruch, T. C. Somatic sensation. In T. C. Ruch and J. F. Fulton (Eds.), *Medical physiology and biophysics*. (18th ed.) Philadelphia: Saunders, 1960. Pp. 300–322.
———, and H. D. Patton. The relation of the deep opercular cortex to taste. *Federation Proc.*, 1946, 5, 89–90.
Ruegamer, W. R., L. Bernstein, and J. D. Benjamin. Growth, food utilization and thyroid activity in the albino rat as a function of extra handling. *Science*, 1954, 120, 184.

Rushmer, R. F. Control of cardiac output. In T. C. Ruch and J. F. Fulton (Eds.), *Medical physiology and biophysics*. Philadelphia: Saunders, 1960. Pp. 708–723.
Russell, E. S. Detour experiments with sticklebacks (*Gasterosteus aculeatus*). *J. exp. Biol.*, 1931, 8, 393–410.
———. *Directiveness of organic activities*. London: Cambridge, 1945.
Russell, G. V. Interrelationships within the limbic and centrencephalic systems. In D. E. Sheer (Ed.), *Electrical stimulation of the brain*. Austin: University of Texas Press, 1961. Pp. 167–181.
Russell, I. S., and S. Ochs. Localization of a memory trace in one cortical hemisphere and transfer to the other hemisphere. *Brain*, 1963, 86, 37–54.
Russell, W. R., and P. W. Nathan. Traumatic amnesia. *Brain*, 1946, 69, 280–300.

Saeki, Y., and Y. Tanabe. Changes in prolactin content of fowl pituitary during broody periods and some experiments on the induction of broodiness. *Poultry Sci.*, 1955, 34, 909–919.
Samaan, A. Le fréquence cardiaque du chien en différentes conditions expérimentales d'activité et de repos. *C. R. Soc. Biol., Paris*, 1934, 115, 1383–1388.
Sanders, F. K. Second order olfactory and visual learning in optic tectum of goldfish. *J. exp. Biol.*, 1940, 17, 416–434.
Sauer, E. G. F., and E. M. Sauer. Zur Frage der nächtlichen Zugorientierung von Grasmücken. *Rev. suisse Zool.*, 1955, 62, 250–259.
———, and ———. Star navigation of nocturnal migrating birds: the 1958 planetarium experiments. *Cold Spring Harbor Sympos. quant. Biol.*, 1960, 25, 463–473.
Sawin, P. B., V. H. Denenberg, S. Ross, E. Hafter, and M. X. Zarrow. Maternal behavior in the rabbit: hair loosening during gestation. *Amer. J. Physiol.*, 1960, 198, 1099–1102.
Sawyer, C. H., and B. Robinson. Separate hypothalamic areas controlling pituitary gonadotrophic function and mating behavior in female cats and rabbits. *J. clin. Endocrinol.*, 1956, 16, 914.
Schaeffer, A. *Ameboid movement*. Princeton, N.J.: Princeton University Press, 1920.

Scharrer, E., and B. Scharrer. Hormones produced by neurosecretory cells. *Recent Progr. Hormone Res.*, 1954, **10**, 183–232.

Scheibel, M. E., and A. B. Scheibel. Some structuro-functional correlates of development in young cats. *EEG clin. Neurophysiol.*, 1963, Suppl. 24, 235–246.

——, ——, A. Mollica, and G. Moruzzi. Convergence and interaction of afferent impulses on single units of reticular formation. *J. Neurophysiol.*, 1955, **18**, 309–331.

Scherrer, H., and R. Hernández-Peón. Inhibitory influence of reticular formation upon synaptic transmission in gracilis nucleus. *Federation Proc.*, 1955, **14**, 132.

Schjelderup-Ebbe, T. Social behavior in birds. In C. Murchison (Ed.), *Handbook of social psychology*. Worcester, Mass.: Clark University Press, 1935.

Schmid, B. Vorläufiges Versuchergebnis über das hundliche Orientierungsproblem. *Z. Hundeforsch*, 1932, **2**, 133–156.

Schmidt-Koenig, K. Internal clocks and homing. *Cold Spring Harbor Sympos. quant. Biol.*, 1960, **25**, 389–393.

Schreiner, L., and A. Kling. Behavioral changes following rhinencephalic injury in cat. *J. Neurophysiol.*, 1953, **16**, 643–659.

——, and ——. Effects of castration on hypersexual behavior induced by rhinencephalic injury in cat. *Arch. Neurol. Psychiat.*, 1954, **72**, 180–186.

——, and ——. Rhinencephalon and behavior. *Amer. J. Physiol.*, 1956, **184**, 486–490.

Schwartz, M., and F. A. Beach. Effects of adrenalectomy upon mating behavior in castrated male dogs. Abstract. *Amer. Psychol.*, 1954, **9**, 467.

Scott, E. M. Self selection of diet: I. Selection of purified components. *J. Nutri.*, 1946, **31**, 397–406.

Scott, J. P. Genetic difference in the social behavior of inbred strains of mice. *J. Hered.*, 1942, **33**, 11–15.

——. Social behavior organization and leadership in a small flock of domestic sheep. *Comp. Psychol. Monogr.*, 1945, **18**, 1–29.

——. Dominance and the frustration-aggression hypothesis. *Physiol. Zool.*, 1948, **21**, 31–39.

——. Critical periods in behavioral development. *Science*, 1962, **138**, 949–958.

Scoville, W. B. Localisation fonctionelle au niveau des lobes frontaux et temporaux. *Rev. Neurol.*, 1959, **98**, 762–766.

Searles, L. V. The organization of hereditary maze brightness and maze dullness. *Genet. Psychol. Monogr.*, 1949, **39**, 279–375.

Segundo, J. P., R. Naquet, and P. Buser. Effects of cortical stimulation on electrocortical activity in monkeys. *J. Neurophysiol.*, 1955, **18**, 236–245.

Selye, H. On the nervous control of lactation. *Amer. J. Physiol.*, 1934, **107**, 535–538.

Semmes, J. Agnosia in animal and man. *Psychol. Rev.*, 1953, **60**, 140–147.

Serota, H. M. Temperature changes in the cortex and hypothalamus during sleep. *J. Neurophysiol.*, 1939, **2**, 42–47.

Seton, E. T. *Lives of game animals*. Boston: Branford, 1953. Vol. 3.

Settlage, P., M. Zable, and H. F. Harlow. Problem solution by monkeys following bilateral removal of the prefrontal areas: VI. Performance on tests requiring contradictory reactions to similar and to identical stimuli. *J. exp. Psychol.*, 1948, **38**, 50–65.

Shapiro, H. A. The biological basis of sexual behavior in amphibia. *J. exp. Biol.*, 1937a, **14**, 38–47.

——. Effect of testosterone propionate on mating. *Nature*, 1937b, **139**, 588–589.

Shapovalov, L. The homing instinct of trout and salmon. *Proc. 6th Pacific Sci. Congr.*, 1940, **3**, 317–322.

Sharma, K. N., B. K. Anand, S. Dua, and B. Singh. Role of stomach in regulation of activities of hypothalamic feeding centers. *Amer. J. Physiol.*, 1961, **201**, 593–598.

Sharpless, S., and H. Jasper. Habituation of the arousal reaction. *Brain*, 1956, **79**, 655–680.

Shaw, E. The development of schooling behavior in fishes. *Physiol. Zool.*, 1960, **33**, 79–86.

——. Environmental conditions and the appearance of sexual behavior in the Platyfish. In E. L. Bliss (Ed.), *Roots of behavior*. New York: Hoeber, 1962. Pp. 123–141.

Sheffield, F. D., and T. B. Roby. Reward value of a non-nutritive sweet taste. *J. comp. Physiol. Psychol.*, 1950, **43**, 471–481.

Sheffield, F. D. and T. B. Roby (cont.)
———, J. J. Wulff, and R. Backer. Reward value of copulation without sex drive reduction. *J. comp. Physiol. Psychol.*, 1951, **44**, 3–8.

Shepard, J. F. More about the floor cue. *Psychol. Bull.*, 1935, **32**, 696.

Sherrington, C. S. Experiments on the value of vascular and visceral factors for the genesis of emotion. *Proc. Roy. Soc. (London)*, 1900, **66**, 390–403.

———. *The integrative action of the nervous system.* New Haven, Conn.: Yale University Press, 1906.

Shoemaker, H. H. Effects of testosterone propionate on behavior of the female canary. *Proc. Soc. exp. Biol. Med.*, 1939, **41**, 299–302.

Shore, L. E. A contribution to our knowledge of taste sensations. *J. Physiol. (London)*, 1892, **13**, 191–217.

Shurrager, P. S., and E. Culler. Conditioning in the spinal dog. *J. exp. Psychol.*, 1940, **26**, 133–159.

Sigg, E. B., and J. A. Schneider. Mechanisms involved in the interaction of various central stimulants and reserpine. *EEG clin. Neurophysiol.*, 1957, **9**, 419–426.

Sinclair, D. C., G. Weddell, and E. Zander. The relationship of cutaneous sensibility to neurohistology in the human pinna. *J. Anat. (London)*, 1952, **86**, 402–411.

Sjöstrand, F. S. The ultrastructure of the outer segments of the rods and cones of the eye as revealed by the electron microscope. *J. cell. comp. Physiol.*, 1953, **42**, 15–70.

Skinner, B. F. *The behavior of organisms.* New York: Appleton, 1938.

Skinner, W. A., R. D. Mathews, and R. M. Parkhurst. Alarm reaction of the top smelt, *Atherinops affini* (Ayres). *Science*, 1962, **138**, 681–682.

Sloan, N., and H. Jasper. Studies of the regulatory functions of the anterior limbic cortex. *EEG clin. Neurophysiol.*, 1950, **2**, 317–327.

Slonaker, J. R. The effect of the excision of different sexual organs on the development, growth and longevity of the albino rat. *Amer. J. Physiol.*, 1930, **93**, 307–317.

Small, W. S. An experimental study of the mental processes of the rat. *Amer. J. Psychol.*, 1899, **11**, 133–165.

Smith, J. E. Some observations on the nervous mechanisms underlying the behaviour of starfishes. *Sympos. Soc. exp. Biol.*, 1950, **4**, 196–220.

Smith, K. U., and W. M. Smith. *Perception and motion.* Philadelphia: Saunders, 1962.

Smith, M., and G. C. Kinney. Sugar as a reward for hungry and non-hungry rats. *J. exp. Psychol.*, 1956, **51**, 348–352.

Smith, P. E. Hypophysectomy and a replacement therapy in the rat. *Amer. J. Anat.*, 1930, **45**, 205–273.

Smith, S. Limits of educability in Paramecium. *J. comp. Neurol. Psychol.*, 1908, **18**, 499–510.

Smith, W. K. The results of ablation of cingular region of the cerebral cortex. *Federation Proc.*, 1944, **3**, 42.

———. Non-olfactory functions of the pyriform-amygdaloid-hippocampal complex. *Federation Proc.*, 1950, **9**, 118.

Snider, R., and J. C. Lee. A *stereotaxic atlas of the monkey brain.* Chicago: University of Chicago Press, 1961.

———, and W. T. Niemer. A *stereotaxic atlas of the cat brain.* Chicago: University of Chicago Press, 1961.

Snygg, D. The relative difficulty of mechanically equivalent tasks: II. Animal learning. *J. genet. Psychol.*, 1935, **47**, 321–336.

Sokolov, Y. N. *Perception and the conditioned reflex.* New York: Pergamon, 1963.

Sollenberger, R. T., and J. B. Hamilton. The effect of testosterone propionate upon the sexual behavior of castrated male guinea pigs. *J. comp. Psychol.*, 1939, **28**, 81–92.

Spaet, T., and H. F. Harlow. Problem solution by monkeys following bilateral removal of the prefrontal areas: II. Delayed reaction problems involving use of the matching-from-sample method. *J. exp. Psychol.*, 1943, **32**, 424–434.

Spalding, D. Instinct, with original observations in young animals. (Reprint.) *Brit. J. Animal Behav.* (1873), 1954, **2**, 2–11.

Spemann, H. *Embryonic development and induction.* New Haven, Conn.: Yale University Press, 1938.

Spence, K. W. *Behavior theory and conditioning.* New Haven, Conn.: Yale University Press, 1956.

Sperry, R. W. Visuomotor coordination in the newt (*Triturus viridescens*) after regeneration of the optic nerve. *J. comp. Neurol.*, 1943, **79**, 33–55.

Sperry, R. W. (*cont.*)
———. Optic nerve regeneration with return of vision in anurans. *J. Neurophysiol.*, 1944, 7, 57–70.

———. Cerebral regulation of motor coordination in monkeys following multiple transection of sensorimotor cortex. *J. Neurophysiol.*, 1947, **10**, 275–294.

———. Mechanisms of neural maturation. In S. S. Stevens (Ed.), *Handbook of experimental psychology*. New York: Wiley, 1951. Pp. 236–280.

———, N. Miner, and R. E. Myers. Visual pattern perception following subpial slicing and tantalum wire implantation in the visual cortex. *J. comp. physiol. Psychol.*, 1955, **48**, 50–58.

———, J. S. Stamm, and N. Miner. Relearning tests for interocular transfer following division of the optic chiasma and corpus callosum in cats. *J. comp. physiol. Psychol.*, 1956, **49**, 529–533.

Spiegel, A. Auftreten von Adensmen der Nebennierenrinde mit vermännlicher Wirkung bei Frühkastrierten Meerschweinchenmännchen. *Klin. Wschr.*, 1939, **18**, 1068–1069.

Stamm, J. S. Genetics of hoarding: I. Hoarding differences between homozygous strains of rats. *J. comp. physiol. Psychol.*, 1954, **47**, 157–161.

———, and K. H. Pribram. Effects of epileptogenic lesions in frontal cortex on learning and retention in monkeys. *J. Neurophysiol.*, 1960, **23**, 552–563.

———, and ———. Effects of epileptogenic lesions of inferotemporal cortex on learning and retention in monkeys. *J. comp. physiol. Psychol.*, 1961, **54**, 614–618.

———, and A. Warren. Learning and retention by monkeys with epileptogenic implants in posterior parietal cortex. *Epilepsia*, 1961, **2**, 229–242.

Stanley, W. C., and J. Jaynes. The function of the frontal cortex. *Psych. Rev.*, 1949, **56**, 18–32.

Steinhausen, W. Ueber die Beobachtung der Cupula in den Bogengangsampullen des Labyrinthes des lebenden Hechts. *Pflüg. Arch. ges. Physiol.*, 1933, **232**, 500–512.

Stellar, E., R. Hyman, and S. Samet. Gastric factors controlling water- and salt-solution drinking. *J. comp. physiol. Psychol.*, 1954, **47**, 220–226.

Stone, C. P. The congenital sexual behavior of the young male albino rat. *J. comp. Psychol.*, 1922, **2**, 95–153.

———. The retention of copulatory ability in male rats following castration. *J. comp. Psychol.*, 1927, 7, 369–387.

———. Copulatory activity in adult male rats following castration and injections of testosterone propionate. *Endocrinology*, 1939, **24**, 165–174.

———, and L. W. Ferguson. Temporal relationships in the copulatory acts of adult male rats. *J. comp. Psychol.*, 1940, **30**, 419–433.

Stonor, C. R. *Courtship and display among birds*. London: Country Life, Ltd., 1940.

Stratton, G. M. Vision without inversion of the retinal image. *Psychol. Rev.*, 1897, **4**, 341–360, 463–481.

Stroer, W. F. Zur vergleichenden Anatomie des primären optischen Systems bei Wirbeltieren. *Z. Anat. Entwgesch.*, 1939, **110**, 301–321.

Strong, T. N. Activity in the white rat as a function of apparatus and hunger. *J. comp. physiol. Psychol.*, 1957, **50**, 596–600.

Strumwasser, F. Regulatory mechanisms, brain activity and behavior during deep hibernation in the squirrel, *Citellus beecheyi*. *Amer. J. Physiol.*, 1959, **196**, 23–30.

Swann, H. G. The function of the brain in olfaction: II. The results of destruction of olfactory and other nervous structures upon the discrimination of odors. *J. comp. Neurol.*, 1934, **59**, 175–201.

———. The function of the brain in olfaction. *Amer. J. Physiol.*, 1935, **111**, 257–262.

Sweet, W. H. Pain. *Handb. Physiol.*, 1959, Sec. 1, 1, 459–506.

Symmes, D. Effect of cortical ablations on visual exploration by monkeys. *J. comp. physiol. Psychol.*, 1963, **56**, 757–763.

Szent-Györgyi, A. *Chemistry of muscular contraction*. (2d ed.) New York: Academic Press, 1951.

Szymanski, J. S. Aktivität und Ruhe bei Tieren und Menschen. *Z. allg. Physiol.*, 1919, **18**, 105–162.

Talbot, S. A., and W. H. Marshall. Physiological studies on neural mechanisms of visual localization and discrimination. *Amer. J. Ophthal.*, 1941, **24**, 1255–1264.

Tang, P.-C., and T. C. Ruch. Localization of brain stem and diencephalic areas controlling the micturition reflex. *J. comp. Neurol.*, 1956, **106**, 213–245.

Tasaki, I. Nerve impulses in individual auditory nerve fibers of guinea pig. *J. Neurophysiol.*, 1954, **17**, 97–122.

Tavolga, W. N. Effects of gonadectomy and hypophysectomy on prespawning behavior in males of gobiid fish. *Physiol. Zool.*, 1955, **28**, 218–233.

Teitelbaum, P., and A. N. Epstein. The lateral hypothalamic syndrome: recovery of feeding and drinking after lateral hypothalamic lesions. *Psychol. Rev.*, 1962, **69**, 74–90.

———, and E. Stellar. Recovery from the failure to eat produced by hypothalamic lesions. *Science*, 1954, **120**, 894–895.

Teuber, H.-L. Physiological psychology. *Ann. Rev. Psychol.*, 1955, **6**, 267–296.

Thiessen, D. D., and D. A. Rodgers. Population density and endocrine function. *Psychol. Bull.*, 1961, **58**, 441–451.

Thompson, R., and J. V. McConnell. Classical conditioning in the planarian, Dugesia dorotocephala. *J. comp. physiol. Psychol.*, 1955, **48**, 65–68.

Thompson, W. R., and L. M. Solomon. Spontaneous pattern discrimination in the rat. *J. comp. physiol. Psychol.*, 1954, **47**, 104–107.

Thorek, M. Experimental investigation of the role of the Leydig, seminiferous and Sertoli cells and effects of testiculear transplantation. *Endocrinology*, 1924, **8**, 61–90.

Thorndike, E. L. Animal intelligence: an experimental study of the associative process in animals. *Psychol. Monogr.*, Suppl. No. 8., 1898.

———. *Animal Intelligence.* New York: Macmillan, 1911.

Thorpe, W. H. *Learning and instinct in animals.* (2d ed.) Cambridge, Mass.: Harvard University Press, 1963.

Thudichum, J. L. W. *A treatise on the chemical constitution of the brain.* London: Baillière, 1884.

Tinbergen, N. Zur Soziologie der Silbermöwe. *Beitr. Fortpflanzungsbiol. Vögel*, 1936, **12**, 89–96.

———. *The study of instinct.* New York: Oxford, 1951.

———. *The herring gull's world.* Don Mills, Ont.: Collins, 1953a.

———. *Social behavior in animals.* London: Methuen, 1953b.

———. The evolution of signaling devices. In W. Etkin (Ed.), *Social behavior and organization among vertebrates.* Chicago: University of Chicago Press, 1963. Pp. 206–230.

———, and A. C. Perdeck. On the stimulus situation releasing the begging response in newly-hatched herring gull chick. *Behaviour*, 1950, **3**, 1–38.

Tolman, E. C. *Purposive behavior in animals and man.* New York: Appleton, 1932.

———. Cognitive maps in rats and men. *Psychol. Rev.*, 1948, **55**, 189–208.

———, B. F. Ritchie, and D. Kalish. Studies in spatial learning: I. Orientation and the short-cut. *J. exp. Psychol.*, 1946a, **36**, 13–24.

———, ———, and ———. Studies in spatial learning: II. Place learning versus response learning. *J. exp. Psychol.*, 1946b, **36**, 221–229.

Tower, S. S. Function and structure in the chronically isolated lumbo-sacral spinal cord of the dog. *J. comp. Neurol.*, 1937, **67**, 109–131.

———. Pyramidal lesion in the monkey. *Brain*, 1940, **63**, 36–90.

Treichler, F. R., and J. F. Hall. The relationship between deprivation, weight loss and several measures of activity. *J. comp. physiol. Psychol.*, 1962, **55**, 346–349.

Trevarthen, C. B. Double visual learning in split-brain monkeys. *Science*, 1962, **136**, 258–259.

Triplett, N. The educability of the perch. *Amer. J. Psychol.*, 1901, **12**, 354–360.

Tryon, R. C. Studies in individual difference in maze ability. *J. comp. Psychol.*, 1931, **12**, 1–22, 95–115, 303–345, 401–420.

Tsang, Y.-C. The function of the visual areas of the cortex of the rat in the learning and retention of the maze. *Comp. Psychol. Monogr.*, 1934, **10**, 1–56.

Tucker, D. Olfactory, vomeronasal and trigeminal receptor responses to odorants. In Y. Zotterman (Ed.), *Olfaction and taste.* New York: Pergamon Press, 1963. Pp. 45–69.

Tunturi, A. R. Further afferent connections of the acoustic cortex of the dog. *Amer. J. Physiol.*, 1945, **144**, 389–394.

Uricht, J. The social hierarchy in albino mice. *J. comp. Psychol.*, 1938, **25**, 373–413.

Uvnäs, B. Central cardiovascular control. *Handb. Physiol.*, 1960, Sec. 1, **2**, 1131–1162.

Valenstein, E. S., W. Riss, and W. C. Young. Sex drive in genetically heterogeneous and highly inbred strains of male guinea pigs. *J. comp. physiol. Psychol.*, 1954, 47, 162–165.

———, ———, and ———. Experiential and genetic factors in the organization of sexual behavior in male guinea pigs. *J. comp. physiol. Psychol.*, 1955, 48, 397–403.

Vaughan, E., and A. E. Fisher. Male sexual behavior induced by intracranial electrical stimulation. *Science*, 1962, 137, 758–760.

Vaugien, L. Ponte induite chez la peruche ondulée maintenue a l'obscurité et dans l'ambience des volières. *C. R. Acad. Sci.*, 1951, 232, 1706–1708.

Verhaart, W. J. C., and M. A. Kennard. Corticofugal degeneration following thermocoagulation of areas 4, 6 and 4 -s in *Macaca mulatta*. *J. Anat. (London)*, 1940, 74, 239–254.

Verney, E. B. The anti-diuretic hormone and the factors which determine its release. *Proc. Roy. Soc. (London)*, 1947, B135, 25–106.

Verworn, M. *Psycho-physiologische Protistenstudien*. Jena: Fischer, 1889.

Vogt, M. The concentration of sympathin in different parts of the central nervous system under normal condition and after the administration of drugs. *J. Physiol. (London)*, 1954, 123, 451–481.

Waelsch, H. Amino acid and protein metabolism. In K. A. C. Elliott et al. (Eds.), *Neurochemistry*. Springfield, Ill.: Charles C Thomas, 1962. Pp. 288–320.

Walberg, F. Corticofugal fibers to the nuclei of the dorsal columns. An experimental study in the cat. *Brain*, 1957, 80, 273–287.

Wald, G. The photoreceptor process in vision. *Handb. Physiol.*, 1959, Sec. 1, 1, 671–692.

———, P. K. Brown, and I. R. Gibbons. Visual excitation: a chemoanatomical study. *Sympos. soc. exp. Biol.*, 1962, 16, 32–57.

Walk, R. D., and E. J. Gibson. A comparative and analytical study of visual depth perception. *Psychol. Monogr.*, 1961, 75 (15).

Walker, A. E. Afferent connections. In P. Bucy (Ed.), *The precentral motor cortex*. Urbana: University of Illinois Press, 1944. Pp. 111–132.

———, and J. F. Fulton. Hemidecortication in chimpanzee, baboon, macaque, potto, cat and coati: a study in encephalization. *J. nerv. ment. Dis.*, 1938, 87, 677–700.

———, A. F. Thomson, and J. D. McQueen. Behavior and the temporal rhinencephalon in the monkey. *Johns Hopkins Hosp. Bull.*, 1953, 93, 65–93.

Walls, G. L. *The vertebrate eye and its adaptive radiation*. Bloomfield Hills, Mich.: Cranbrook Institute of Science, 1942.

———. The lateral geniculate nucleus and visual histophysiology. *Univer. Calif. Publ. Physiol.*, 1953, 9, 1–100.

Walsh, R. R. Single cell spike activity in the olfactory bulb. *Amer. J. Physiol.*, 1956, 186, 255–257.

Walthall, W. J. The influence of different maze surroundings on learning. *J. comp. physiol. Psychol.*, 1948, 41, 438–449.

Walzl, E. M., and V. Mountcastle. Projection of vestibular nerve to cerebral cortex of the cat. *Amer. J. Physiol.*, 1949, 159, 595–603.

Wang, G. H. The relation between "spontaneous" activity and estrous cycle in the white rat. *Comp. Psychol. Monogr.*, 1923, 2, No. 6.

Wangensteen, O. H., and A. J. Carlson. Hunger sensations in a patient after total gastrectomy. *Proc. Soc. exp. Biol. Med.*, 1931, 28, 545–547.

Ward, A. A. The cingular gyrus: area 24. *J. Neurophysiol.*, 1948, 11, 13–23.

Warden, C. J. *Animal motivation: experimental studies on the albino rat*. New York: Columbia University Press, 1931.

———, H. A. Fjeld, and A. M. Koch. Imitative behavior in cebus and rhesus monkeys. *J. genet. Psychol.*, 1940, 46, 103–125.

———, and T. A. Jackson. Imitative behavior in the rhesus monkey. *J. genet. Psychol.*, 1935, 46, 103–125.

———, T. N. Jenkins, and L. H. Warner. *Comparative psychology*. New York: Ronald, 1936, 3 vols.

Warner, L. H. A study of sex behavior in the white rat by means of the obstruction method. *Comp. Psychol. Monogr.*, 1927, No. 22.

———. A study of hunger behavior in the white rat by means of the obstruction method. *J. comp. Psychol.*, 1928, 8, 273–299.

Warren, J. M., and M. M. Sinha. Effect of differential reinforcement on size pref-

Warren, J. M., and M. M. Sinha (*cont.*) erences in cats. *Percept. mot. Skills,* 1957, 7, 17–22.

———, H. B. Warren, and K. Akert. *Umweg* learning by cats with lesions in the prestriate cortex. *J. comp. physiol. Psychol.,* 1961, 54, 629–632.

Warren, R. P., and L. R. Aronson. Sexual behavior in adult male hamsters castrated-adrenalectomized prior to puberty. *J. comp. physiol. Psychol.,* 1957, 50, 475–480.

———, and R. A. Hinde. Roles of the male and the nest-cup in controlling the reproduction of female canaries. *Anim. Behav.,* 1960, 9, 64–67.

Washburn, S. L., and I. De Vore. The social life of baboons. *Sci. Amer.,* 1961, 204, 62–71.

Watson, J. B., Kinesthetic and organic sensations: their role in the reactions of the white rat to the maze. *Psychol. Monogr.* 1907, 8, 1–100.

———. *Psychology from the standpoint of a behaviorist.* Philadelphia: Lippincott, 1919.

Watson, J. D., and F. H. C. Crick. A structure for deoxyribose nucleic acids. *Nature,* 1953, 171, 737–738.

Weber, H. H. The link between metabolism and motility of cells and muscles. *Sympos. Soc. exp. Biol.,* 1955, 9, 271–281.

Weddell, G., E. Palmer, and W. Pallie. Nerve endings in mammalian skin. *Biol. Rev.,* 1955, 30, 159–195.

Weichert, C. K., and S. Kerrigan. Effects of estrogens upon the young injected lactating rats. *Endocrinology,* 1942, 30, 741–752.

Weiner, I. H., and E. Stellar. Salt preference of the rat determined by a single-stimulus method. *J. comp. physiol. Psychol.,* 1951, 44, 394–401.

Weininger, O. The effects of early experience on behavior and growth characteristics. *J. comp. physiol. Psychol.,* 1956, 49, 1–9.

———, W. J. McClelland, and R. K. Arima. Gentling and weight gain in the albino rat. *Canad. J. Psychol.,* 1954, 8, 147–151.

Weiskrantz, L. Behavioral changes associated with ablation of amygdaloid complex in monkeys. *J. comp. physiol. Psychol.,* 1956, 49, 381–391.

———. Sensory deprivation and the cat's optic nervous system. *Nature,* 1958, 181, 1047–1050.

———, L. Mihailović, and C. G. Gross. Effects of stimulation of frontal cortex and hippocampus on behavior in the monkey. *Brain,* 1962, 85, 487–504.

———, and M. Mishkin. Effects of temporal and frontal cortical lesions on auditory discrimination in monkeys. *Brain,* 1958, 81, 406–414.

Weiss, P. A. Selectivity controlling the central-peripheral relations in the nervous system. *Biol. Rev.,* 1936, 11, 494–531.

———. Nerve patterns: the mechanics of nerve growth. *Growth,* 1941, 5, 163–203.

———. Experimental analysis of coordination by the disarrangement of central-peripheral relations. *Sympos. Soc. exp. Biol.,* 1950, 4, 92–111.

———. Patterns of organization in the central nervous system. *Res. Publ. Ass. nerv. ment. Dis.,* 1952, 30, 3–23.

Welch, W. K., and M. A. Kennard. Relation of cerebral cortex to spasticity and flaccidity. *J. Neurophysiol.,* 1944, 7, 255–268.

Welker, W. L. Some determinants of play and exploration in chimpanzees. *J. comp. physiol. Psychol.,* 1956a, 49, 84–89.

———. Effects of age and experience on play and exploration of young chimpanzees. *J. comp. physiol. Psychol.,* 1956b, 49, 223–226.

———. An analysis of exploratory and play behavior in animals. In D. W. Fiske and S. R. Maddi (Eds.), *Functions of varied experience.* Homewood, Ill.: Dorsey Press, 1961. Pp. 175–226.

Wells, L. J. Seasonal sexual rhythm and its experimental modification in the male of the thirteen-lined ground squirrel. *Anat. Rec.,* 1935, 62, 409–444.

———. Prolongation of breeding capacity in males of annual breeding wild rodent (*Citellus tridecemlineatus*) by constant low temperature. *Anat. Rec.,* 1936, 64, 138.

Welty, J. C. Experiments on group behavior of fishes. *Physiol. Zool.,* 1934, 7, 85–127.

Westerman, R. A. Somatic inheritance of habituation of responses to light in planarians. *Science,* 1963, 140, 676–677.

Wever, E. G. *Theory of hearing.* New York: Wiley, 1949.

Wheatley, M. D. The hypothalamus and affective behavior. *Arch. Neurol. Psychiat.,* 1944, 52, 296–316.

Whitman, C. O. The behavior of pigeons. *Carnegie Inst. Publ.*, 1919, No. 257, 1–161.

Wichterman, R. *Biology of Paramecium.* New York: McGraw-Hill, 1953.

Widdicombe, J. G. Respiratory reflexes from the trachea and bronchi of the cat. *J. Physiol. (London),* 1954, 123, 55–70.

Wiener, N. *Cybernetics.* New York: Wiley, 1948.

Wiesner, P. B., and N. M. Sheard, *Maternal behavior in the rat.* Edinburgh: Oliver & Boyd, 1933.

Wilder, C. E. Selection of rachitic and anti-rachitic diets in the rat. *J. comp. Psychol.,* 1937, 24, 547–577.

Wilson, H. V. On some phenomena of coalescence and regeneration in sponges. *J. exp. Zool.,* 1907, 5, 245–288.

Wilson, J. G., and W. C. Young. Sensitivity to estrogen studied by means of experimentally induced mating responses in the female guinea pig and rat. *Endocrinology,* 1941, 29, 779–783.

Wilson, M. Effects of circumscribed cortical lesions upon somesthetic and visual discrimination in the monkey. *J. comp. physiol. Psychol.,* 1957, 50, 630–635.

Wilson, W. A., and M. Mishkin. Comparison of the effects of inferotemporal and lateral occipital lesions on visually guided behavior in monkeys. *J. comp. physiol. Psychol.,* 1959, 52, 10–17.

Winkelmann, R. K. Similarities in cutaneous nerve end organs. In W. Montagna (Ed.), *Cutaneous innervation.* New York: Pergamon Press, 1960. Pp. 48–62.

Witt, D. M., A. D. Keller, H. L. Batsel, and J. R. Lynch. Absence of thirst and resultant syndrome associated with anterior hypothalectomy in the dog. *Amer. J. Physiol.,* 1952, 171, 780.

Wolfe, J. B. An exploratory study of food-storing in rats. *J. comp. physiol. Psychol.,* 1939, 28, 97–108.

Wolfson, A. The role of the pituitary, fat deposition, and body weight in bird migration. *Condor,* 1945, 47, 95–127.

———. Ecologic and physiologic factors in the regulation of spring migration and reproductive cycles in birds. In A. Gorbman (Ed.), *Comparative endocrinology.* New York: Wiley, 1959. Pp. 38–70.

Wolken, J. J. Photoreceptors: comparative studies. In M. B. Allen (Ed.), *Comparative biochemistry of photoreactive systems.* New York: Academic Press, 1958. Pp. 145–167.

Woodward, E. E., and J. M. Condrin. Physiological studies on hibernation in the chipmunk. *Physiol. Zool.,* 1945, 18, 162–167.

Woodworth, R. S. *Dynamic psychology.* New York: Columbia University Press, 1918.

———, and C. S. Sherrington. A pseudo-affective reflex and its spinal path. *J. Physiol. (London),* 1904, 31, 234–243.

Woolsey, C. N. "Second" somatic receiving areas in the cerebral cortex of cat, dog and monkey. *Federation Proc.,* 1943, 2, 55–56.

———. Patterns of sensory representation in the cerebral cortex. *Federation Proc.,* 1947, 6, 437–441.

———. Organization of somatic sensory and motor areas of the cerebral cortex. In H. F. Harlow and C. N. Woolsey (Eds.), *Biological and biochemical bases of behavior.* Madison: University of Wisconsin Press, 1958. Pp. 63–81.

———. Organization of cortical auditory system. In W. A. Rosenblith (Ed.), *Sensory communication.* New York: Wiley, 1961. Pp. 235–257.

———, and H.-T. Chang. Activation of the cerebral cortex by antidromic volleys in the pyramidal tract. *Res. Publ. Ass. nerv. ment. Dis.,* 1948, 27, 146–161.

———, ———, and P. Bard. Distribution of cortical potentials evoked by electrical stimulation of dorsal roots in *Macaca mulatta. Federation Proc.,* 1947, 6, 230.

———, and E. M. Walzl. Topical projection of nerve fibers from local regions of the cochlea to the cerebral cortex of the cat. *Bull. Johns Hopkins Hosp.,* 1942, 71, 315–344.

Worden, F. C., J. T. Marsh. Amplitude changes of auditory potentials evoked at cochlear nucleus during acoustic habituation. *EEG clin. Neurophysiol.,* 1963, 15, 866–881.

Wortis, J. *Recent advances in biological psychiatry.* New York: Plenum Press, 1960. Vol. 4.

Yerkes, R. M. The intelligence of earthworms. *J. animal Behav.,* 1912, 2, 332–352.

———, and J. H. Elder. The sexual and reproductive cycles of chimpanzees. *Proc. Nat. Acad. Sci. U.S.,* 1936, 22, 276–283.

Yoshii, N., and W. J. Hockaday. Conditioning of frequency-characteristic repetitive electroencephalographic response with intermittent photic stimulation. *EEG clin. Neurophysiol.*, 1959, **10**, 487–502.

Young, A. C. Neural control of respiration. In T. C. Ruch and J. F. Fulton (Eds.), *Medical physiology and biophysics*. Philadelphia: Saunders, 1960. Pp. 813–841.

Young, P. T. *Motivation and emotion*. New York: Wiley, 1961.

———, and J. P. Chaplin. Studies of food preference, appetite and dietary habit: III. Palatability and appetite in relation to bodily need. *Comp. Psychol. Monogr.*, 1945, **18**, 1–45.

Young, W. C., and W. R. Fish. The ovarian hormones and spontaneous running activity in the female rat. *Endocrinology*, 1945, **36**, 181–189.

Zacks, S. I. *The motor end plate*. Philadelphia: Saunders, 1964.

Zarrow, M. X., P. B. Sawin, S. Ross, and V. Denenberg. Maternal behavior and its endocrine basis in the rabbit. In E. L. Bliss (Ed.), *Roots of behavior*. New York: Harper, 1962. Pp. 187–197.

Zener, K. The significance of behavior accompanying conditioned salivary secretion for theories of the conditioned reflex. *Amer. J. Psychol.*, 1937, **50**, 384–403.

Zimbardo, P. G. The effects of early avoidance training and rearing conditions upon the sexual behavior of the male rat. *J. comp. physiol. Psychol.*, 1958, **52**, 764–769.

Zippelius, H.-M., and W. M. Schleidt. Ultraschall-Laute bei Mäusen. *Naturwiss.*, 1956, **43**, 502.

Zotterman, Y. Thermal sensations. *Handb. Physiol.*, 1959, Sec. 1, **1**, 431–458.

———. Studies in the neural mechanism of taste. In W. A. Rosenblith (Ed.), *Sensory Communication*. New York: Wiley, 1961. Pp. 205–216.

———. (Ed.). *Olfaction and taste*. New York: Pergamon, 1963.

Zubek, J. P. Studies in somesthesis: I. Role of the somesthetic cortex in roughness discrimination in the rat. *J. comp. physiol. Psychol.*, 1951, **44**, 339–353.

———. Studies in somesthesis: II. Role of somatic sensory areas I and II in roughness discrimination. *J. Neurophysiol.*, 1952a, **15**, 401–408.

———. Studies in somesthesis: III. Role of somatic areas I and II in the acquisition of roughness discrimination in the rat. *Canad. J. Psychol.*, 1952b, **6**, 183–193.

Zuckerman, S. *The social life of monkeys and apes*. London: Routledge, Ltd., 1932.

Zunini, G. Esperimenti del giro con pesci scerebrati. *Arch. Psicol. Neurol. Psychiat.*, 1941, **2**, 169–210.

# Author Index

# Subject Index